****

Dear Reader

Your reports are vital to the well-being of the *Good Hotel Guide*. Do please write to us when you have visited a hotel. Even the briefest of endorsements is useful, but lengthier reports are of greater value as they enable us to add new life to the entries. You may use the report forms at the back of the book, but this is not essential. Each year we award a bottle of champagne and a free copy of the *Guide* to 12 correspondents, for the literary style or the generous number of their reports, or both.

How to contact the *Good Hotel Guide*
By mail: From anywhere in the UK write to Freepost PAM 2931, London W11 4BR (no stamp is needed)
From outside the UK: Good Hotel Guide, 50 Addison Avenue, London W11 4QP, England
By telephone or fax:
(020) 7602 4182
By e-mail: Goodhotel@aol.com
Via the Internet: www.uk.aol.com/channels/travel/GHG

ADAM AND CAROLINE RAPHAEL

****

The Good Hotel Guide 2001

Great Britain and Ireland

Editors:
Adam and Caroline Raphael

Consulting Editor:
Hilary Rubinstein

Contributors:
John Ardagh, Richard Hayden, David Mabey,
Sarah Mitchell, Tamara Moluch, Annabel Randall,
Emily Read, Richard Stirling

EBURY PRESS
LONDON

Please send reports on hotels to
The Good Hotel Guide
50 Addison Avenue, London W11 4QP
or (posted in UK only)
Freepost PAM 2931, London W11 4BR
Tel/fax: (020) 7602 4182
E-mail: Goodhotel@aol.com

This edition first published in 2000 by Ebury Press,
Random House, 20 Vauxhall Bridge Road,
London SW1V 2SA

The Random House Group Limited Reg. No. 954009

www.randomhouse.co.uk

1 3 5 7 9 10 8 6 4 2

Text editor: Allison McKechnie
Managing editor for Ebury Press: Alison Wormleighton
Editorial assistants: Katinka Ardagh, Emma Hart

A CIP catalogue record for this book may be found in the British Library.

ISBN 0 09 187170 0

Typeset from author's disks by
SX Composing DTP, Rayleigh, Essex
Printed and bound in Great Britain by
Cox & Wyman Ltd, Reading, Berkshire

Contents

A note for new readers

The best way to find a good hotel is by personal recommendation. This guide is just that. It has fairly been described as word-of-mouth in print. Every hotel has been recommended to us by correspondents who have spent at least one night there, and have taken the trouble to write to us about it. Our entries are updated each year, using fresh reports from readers. We depend on your generous support. We verify and collate the reports, making an anonymous overnight inspection where necessary, and select those hotels which we consider make the grade. Hotels are dropped if critical reports outweigh those in favour, or if we have had no reports for some time. They are also dropped following a change of ownership, unless we are sure that standards have been maintained.

The *Guide*, which is revised and updated annually, is completely independent. Contributors are not paid for writing to us; hotels do not pay for their entry; the editors and their staff accept no free hospitality and no payments from anyone.

There are two volumes – the volume covering Continental Europe will be published early in 2001. Both volumes cover inns, guest houses and B&Bs that are of unusual character and quality, usually owner-managed. There are three types of entry. The full entries describe hotels that we feel confident about; italicised entries are provisional, due to mixed or ambivalent reports, inadequate information or lack of recent feedback. The Shortlist recommends hotels which, while we are unable positively to recommend them, help to plug gaps, particularly in cities; we must emphasise, however, that these are not necessarily true *Guide* entries, though some might eventually receive an italicised or full entry.

We do not attempt to be comprehensive, because we feel that would involve lowering our standards. As a result, there are many blank areas on our maps. We are particularly glad to receive nominations for hotels in a city, a town or a region that is poorly represented. Most of our entries, especially in rural areas, are for small establishments (though never with fewer than three rooms) in the hands of resident owners. We don't object in principle to large hotels and those run by managers, but in our experience they often fail to provide the welcome and care for guests' comfort that can be found in the best of the small, individually owned hotels. And this is particularly evident in the case of hotels owned by a chain, which explains why there are so few chain hotels in these pages.

The entries in this book cover a wide range. People want different things from a hotel, depending on whether they are making a single-night stop or spending a holiday in one place, whether they have young children with them, whether they are visiting a city or staying in the remote countryside, and also on their age and means. Despite the *Guide*'s title, many establishments included in it are distinctly unhotel-like. You should not expect of a simple B&B or pub the same type of facilities that are offered by a larger, more expensive hotel, and when staying in a restaurant-with-rooms, you will not necessarily find lounges and gardens. We try hard to convey the flavour of each place – our aim is that the descriptions will help you to find somewhere that suits your tastes, needs and purse.

Both positive and negative reports are vital to us. An entry is often dropped unless we get positive feedback, so do please write to us. If possible, use one of the report forms at the back of the book. This is not essential, however – any scrap of paper will do, or a fax or e-mail. The book's aim is to reflect the discriminating taste of its readers. We appreciate even the briefest endorsement or comment; but it is of course the stylish, witty, perceptive reports that help to give the *Guide* its special character. If an entry has misled you, please tell us, so that we can do better next time. We are always grateful, too, for suggestions as to how we can improve the *Guide*.

We should emphasise that this is a thoroughly personal work. The *Guide* was started 24 years ago by Hilary Rubinstein because he wanted a book that would tell readers honestly what to expect when making a reservation. His definition of a good hotel is: "Where the guest comes first." Brochures help, but they are often deceptive. Travel agents can be useful if they specialise in a particular locality, but they tend to know only a fraction of the hotels on their books, and usually only recommend hotels which pay them commission.

Inevitably, the book is full of personal prejudices and preferences, including the editors'. We loathe big, anonymous hotels where we might as well be in Los Angeles or Lisbon as in London. We try to avoid boring establishments which lack individuality in their decor and warmth in their welcome. We care about good food, but dislike pretentious menus. We cherish the dedicated hotelier who has a vocation for his work. It is to such rare people that this guide is dedicated.

Introduction

This guide is a celebration of independent hotels in the UK and Ireland. It has an eclectic audience, including parents with young children, young married couples, older visitors making the most of their retirement, and travellers on business who want something more personal than an anonymous chain hotel. The selected hotels vary greatly, but they have one thing in common – they care about their guests.

Once again this year, we have many attractive new entries, particularly in the countryside and in small towns. "Where hotels are owner-managed," writes George Goring, the owner of the much-admired *Goring Hotel*, London, "I believe they are better in this country than almost anywhere else in the world." We agree. But writing in *Caterer & Hotelkeeper*, Mr Goring paints a depressing picture of the London hotel scene. He maintains that independent hotels are a dying breed. In the past 40 years, he says, every major London hotel has been sold at least once: "In hotels like these, shareholders' interests are paramount, and the customer comes last." He contrasts this with his own privately owned hotel. "No one can sack me, I grow when I can afford it, I can make instant decisions from the top. I am answerable to no shareholders other than my family." Mr Goring fears that "where London leads, the rest of the country will surely follow". We hope he is wrong.

"Designer" or "boutique" hotels have proliferated in the cities, particularly in London, opening with a flourish and charging high prices. They are a welcome change to large, impersonal chain hotels. But few of them are owner-managed, and we wonder how many of them are offering what the traveller wants. The answer, judging by our postbag, is: "Not many." They may provide all manner of exotic "extras" – a goldfish bowl, and cans of oxygen in the mini-bar are fashionable this year, while a CD-player, fax connections and links to the Internet are standard. But report after report tells of the lack of a personal touch. "Who is doing whom a favour?" one reader wondered. What most people prize, in our experience, is not expensive trimmings, but what costs nothing: a helpful telephone manner, a friendly but not over-familiar welcome, a proprietorial or managerial presence, "being treated like a name, not a room number".

Here is what inspectors wrote of a stay in one smart new city hotel: "The welcome, which was neither warm nor sincere, amounted to a request (more of a command) that we sign a form. We were left holding our luggage. We discovered that reserving a room (at up to £300 a night) gave us no guarantee of a table in the restaurant; if we showed our room key, we were told, we would be given the next available table. When we checked out, nobody asked if we wanted help with luggage, if we had enjoyed our visit, if everything had been all right."

Thank heavens, there are some exceptions to this breed. We have two splendid new owner-managed city hotels this year: *Morgans*, Nottingham, a *César* winner, and *Eleven Didsbury Park*, Manchester.

Other gripes

Frustrated tales of lost deposits came again in 2000. Many hotels nowadays deduct some or all of the cost of the room the moment a credit card number is given to guarantee a reservation. But some do not make their cancellation policy clear. One reader was surprised to get a letter from a hotel saying that in the event of a cancellation, his non-refundable deposit of £50 would be held against a future booking. Another experienced far worse: having guaranteed a booking of a £250 room with a credit card, she had to cancel at the last minute because of illness. She was shocked when the whole amount was taken from her credit card account. The hotel was within its rights – when you make a booking, you enter into a contract – but such a couldn't-care-less attitude will hardly tempt her (or us) to try that hotel again. You should always make sure you know what the hotel's policy is, and insist that it confirms the booking in writing. Take out an insurance policy if you think you might have to cancel. And remember that the contract is not one-sided: the hotel has promised to provide you with hospitality. When reserving a room you should make a point of discussing your needs in detail. Visitors often tell us that they were given insufficient information at the time of booking. Accommodation is often inadequately described. "We were not warned that the allocated room was at the top of the house, reached by a narrow flight of steps," is a frequent complaint. VAT, breakfast and service often turn out to be additional to the price quoted. If a service charge is added to the bill and you feel it is not deserved, do not pay it.

Dinners

One reader this year accused us of attaching too much importance to food. But for many travellers it is of prime importance. We think there is nothing more depressing than staying in a hotel where much is right but the cooking is dire. We will forgive a lot in the bedrooms if we retire to them after an excellent meal. All of our *César* winners this year include good cooking among their many qualities.

Again, many correspondents objected to the tyranny of the set menu. One wrote: "We only wanted a course or two. Why should we pay £26 for a five-course meal? After one night of this, we took ourselves off to the local pub." Another reporter was amazed to have been charged the full price of a set lunch (£17), having had only a bowl of soup. A third longed for a simple alternative to the "designer dishes" served in a hotel's *Michelin*-starred restaurant.

In this office, indigestion is often brought on by the pretentiousness of the menus that cross our desk. This year's prize-winner offers gambas royal sur un lit de chutney, sauce exotique, followed by flamb blond de foie de volaille et langoustines et son coulis. We think that if the chef can't get his French right, he should stick to English.

Our least favoured culinary word: "drizzled". It should be banned from the kitchen, and left to the weather forecasters.

Breakfasts

"Time and time again," writes a regular *Guide* correspondent, "we find that the more expensive hotels fall apart at breakfast time, having concentrated all their energies on lunch and dinner." Since last impressions are just as important as first, we are surprised that many hotels take so little trouble over it, and leave it in the hands of inexperienced staff.

Expensive places, where breakfast is often charged extra, are among the worst offenders. We stayed at one horrendously expensive country house hotel where the breakfast was so poor that it reminded us of the last days of British Rail. On top of the £17 basic charge, fresh orange juice was charged extra, and we had to place a special order for a pot of yogurt to cheer up the mingy buffet. And here is what our inspectors in the £300-a-night hotel endured. "A young waiter spilled the stewed Cona coffee over the tablecloth and into our saucers. No attempt was made to wipe it up. The orange juice was described on the menu as 'freshly squeezed'. It was – from packets into jugs. Scrambled egg was watery; a boiled egg was brought rolling about on a small butter dish; toast (of the commercial kind) came at the start of the meal, so it was cold when our eggs arrived. The waiter asked if we wanted brown or white, but when we asked for the former, he told us they had run out of brown bread."

Where breakfast is concerned, the small B&Bs and guest houses usually win hands down. Take *The Old Rectory,* Hopesay (a *César* winner this year), where the breakfast, included in the B&B rate of £37.50 and personally served by the owners, has home-baked bread and home-made yogurt and preserves among much else. Or the similarly priced *Haydon House*, Bath, where it ranges through pancakes with whisky and rum porridge to scrambled eggs with smoked salmon, and eggs Benedict.

In our ideal breakfast, freshly squeezed orange juice is "non-negotiable"; so are decent bread, food to please the non-cooked-breakfast eater as well as the devotee of eggs and bacon, freshly made coffee, leaf tea, no background music, nothing packaged. We were saddened when one hotel proudly wrote to us this year: "In the interests of hygiene, we now serve cereals, sugar and jams not in open bowls but in sealed portions." We loathe the clutter all this creates, and we subscribe to the Terence Conran school of hygiene: there is too much of it about.

Piped music

Many readers wrote this year to support our campaign against this "pollution". As the music-loving MP Robert Key said in a debate in the House of Commons, "Music is an intensely personal thing . . . Canned music is increasingly disliked and despised. All music is devalued if it is treated as acoustic wallpaper." Survey after survey supports this. Blind people, who rely on background sounds, find piped music upsetting; so do the hard of hearing. Musicians find it unendurable. And, of course, like all "extras" it does not come free. We do not understand why so many hoteliers inflict it on their guests without finding out their views. One hotel described its piped music as "non-offensive". We think this is a contradiction in terms. "Whatever happened to silence?" is a frequent theme in the letters we receive.

Mobile phones

Another menace. We sympathise with the many travellers who use them in their bedroom to avoid the scam of over-charging by hoteliers, but they should not be permitted to use them in public rooms.

Value for money

This is the hardest component of a hotel to judge, and obviously at the top end of the price range you are entitled to expect more than at the simpler place where the emphasis is on keeping prices down. The £300-a-night hotel could have offered just as good value for money as the modest guest house, and our *César* awards salute establishments at both ends of the price range. But one of the reasons that, despite our name, we include (in common with most hotel guides) a fair number of pubs, guest houses and B&Bs, is that many of these are found much better value than the large hotels, particularly by *Guide* readers who use the Continental Europe volume as well as this one. They constantly write to us exclaiming at the "amazing value" they have found, particularly in France, where £30 per person for half board in a "proper hotel" is not uncommon.

And finally

"Hoteliers vary greatly in the ways in which they respond to requests they can't fulfil," writes one *Guide* reader this year. "There are the triumphant, the apologetic, the ineffectually helpful and the wonderful. Arriving at *Ashwick House*, Dulverton, having been walking, we were served sandwiches and coffee with great good grace. Only after we'd paid the bill did they tell us that they normally don't provide such a service. At *The Horn of Plenty*, Gulworthy, the owner made seven phone calls to find us a room for the night, as they were full. Such acts of kindness make a terrific advertisement for a hotel, in contrast to those places where any out-of-the-way request produces a self-satisfied 'No'."

The founder of the *Guide*, Hilary Rubinstein, defined a good hotel as one where the guest comes first. We salute all the dedicated hoteliers who follow this obvious, but often ignored, precept. You will find many of them in the pages that follow. Please write to us about them and any more that you discover. You will help them, and us, to prosper.

ADAM AND CAROLINE RAPHAEL
JULY 2000

The 2001 César awards

For the past 15 years, as a way of celebrating different kinds of excellence among hotels in England, Wales, Scotland and Ireland, we have given annual awards called *Césars*, named after the most celebrated of all hoteliers, César Ritz. Hotels of the grandest sort, like the finest restaurants, rarely lack public attention, but there are also many more modest establishments that are supremely good at what they do. Their owners are dedicated and often work round the clock. Their contribution to innkeeping deserves to be honoured along with that of the professionals at the top of the ladder.

This year, as before, we have awarded ten laurel wreaths to a mixed selection of establishments, each of which we think outstanding in its own class. Previous *César* winners, provided that they are still in the same hands and as good as ever, are indicated in the text by the symbol of a small laurel wreath.

AWARD

WINNER

Family hotel of the year

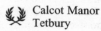 Calcot Manor
Tetbury

Richard Ball has turned this Cotswold farmstead into a flexibly run hotel with excellent facilities for families with children, as well as comforts for his child-free guests.

Country house hotel of the year

 Farlam Hall
Brampton

For many years the Quinion and Stevenson families have welcomed their guests with style and quality, but lack of pretension, in their Cumbrian country house, set in a landscaped Victorian garden.

Town house hotel of the year

 Morgans
Nottingham

Many town house hotels are smart but impersonal. With its thoughtful attention to every detail of her guests' comfort, Kathy Morgan's new venture is the opposite.

Guest house of the year

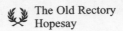
The Old Rectory
Hopesay

In their 17th-century house in a lovely
Shropshire garden, Roma and Michael
Villar offer a home-like atmosphere,
good food, quality wines and outstanding
value.

Scottish country house hotel
of the year

Dunain Park
Inverness

Much enjoyed by all generations this
year, Edward and Ann Nicoll's Italianate
mansion provides homely comforts,
excellent dinners and copious breakfasts
amid lovely Scottish scenery.

Inn of the year

The Nobody Inn
Doddiscombsleigh

An earlier host turned guests away by
pretending not to be in. Nick Borst-
Smith extends a welcome of the opposite
kind, and provides honest, unpretentious
food, well-priced wines, an amazing
selection of cheeses, simple bedrooms
and a wonderfully quirky atmosphere, all
at very reasonable prices.

Newcomer of the year

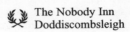
Three Chimneys Restaurant
and House Over-by
Colbost

A model of brilliant modern design in the
north-west corner of Skye: to their
award-winning restaurant, Eddie and
Shirley Spear have added chic bedrooms.
But all is run without pomp and
ceremony.

Restaurant-with-rooms of the year

The Summer House
Penzance

An engaging Anglo-Italian set-up in a
quintessentially English setting: Lynda
and Ciro Zaino offer good food, cheerful
service and good value in their quaint
corner house in the most westerly town
in Britain.

Spa guest house of the year

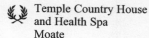

**Temple Country House
and Health Spa**
Moate

Bernadette and Declan Fagan provide
sustenance for both body and soul in
their superior guest house, where excellent meals and a tranquil setting complement all manner of soothing therapies.

Utterly enjoyable mild eccentricity

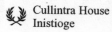

Cullintra House
Inistioge

Patricia Cantlon, supported by her six
cats, is the artistic hostess at this old
farmhouse, run in relaxed and lovably
eccentric style.

Special hotels

City hotels with luxury and/or grandeur

England
Bath Priory, Bath
Queensberry, Bath
Royal Crescent, Bath
42 The Calls, Leeds
Cadogan, London
Capital, London
Connaught, London
Goring, London
One Aldwych, London
22 Jermyn Street, London
Middlethorpe Hall, York

Scotland
One Devonshire Gardens, Glasgow

Northern Ireland
McCausland, Belfast

Republic of Ireland
Clarence, Dublin

Town and city hotels of character and/or value

England
Homelands, Barnard Castle
Bridge House, Beaminster
Du Vin, Bristol
White House, Charmouth
On the Park, Cheltenham
Casterbridge, Dorchester
Evesham, Evesham
Haley's, Leeds
D'Isney Place, Lincoln
Woolton Redbourne, Liverpool
Millers, London
Portobello, London
Eleven Didsbury Park, Manchester
Horton Grange, Newcastle upon Tyne
Morgans, Nottingham
Old Parsonage, Oxford

Mansion House, Poole
Burgoyne, Reeth
Rose and Crown, Romaldkirk
Jeake's House, Rye
George, Stamford
Caterham House, Stratford-upon-Avon
Castle, Taunton
Du Vin, Tunbridge Wells
Du Vin, Winchester
Wykeham Arms, Winchester
Mount Royale, York

Scotland
Gladstone House, Kirkcudbright
Clifton, Nairn

Northern Ireland
Ash-Rowan, Belfast

Republic of Ireland
Quay House, Clifden
Arbutus Lodge, Cork
Belcamp Hutchinson, Dublin
Simmonstown House, Dublin
Norman Villa, Galway

Rural charm and character in the luxury class

England
Farlam Hall, Brampton
Gidleigh Park, Chagford
Gravetye Manor, East Grinstead
Summer Lodge, Evershot
Manoir aux Quat'Saisons, Great Milton
Congham Hall, Grimston
Hambleton Hall, Hambleton
Hintlesham Hall, Hintlesham
Hunstrete House, Hunstrete
Chewton Glen, New Milton
Thornbury Castle, Thornbury
Sharrow Bay, Ullswater

Wales
Bodysgallen Hall, Llandudno

Scotland
Arisaig House, Arisaig
Kinnaird, Dunkeld
Inverlochy Castle, Fort William

Channel Islands
Château La Chaire, Rozel Bay
Longueville Manor, St Saviour

Republic of Ireland
Marlfield House, Gorey
Park, Kenmare

Rural charm and character at medium price

England
Rothay Manor, Ambleside
Wateredge, Ambleside
Amerdale House, Arncliffe
Callow Hall, Ashbourne
Little Barwick House, Barwick
Netherfield Place, Battle
Lindeth Fell, Bowness-on-Windermere
Linthwaite House, Bowness-on-Windermere
Woolley Grange, Bradford-on-Avon
Frogg Manor, Broxton
Aynsome Manor, Cartmel
Uplands, Cartmel
Castleman, Chettle
Tor Cottage, Chillaton
Ashwick House, Dulverton
Highfield House, Hawkshead
Bel Alp House, Haytor
At the Sign of the Angel, Lacock
Langar Hall, Langar
Bindon Country House, Langford Budville
Lewtrenchard Manor, Lewdown
Lea Hill, Membury
Morston Hall, Morston
Beetle and Wedge, Moulsford-on-Thames
Ees Wyke, Near Sawrey
Pear Tree, Purton
Stone House, Rushlake Green
Innsacre Farmhouse, Shipton Gorge
Plumber Manor, Sturminster

Newton
Trebrea Lodge, Tintagel
Priory, Wareham
Gilpin Lodge, Windermere

Wales
Ynyshir Hall, Eglwysfach
Tyddyn Llan, Llandrillo
Portmeirion, Portmeirion
Maes-y-Neuadd, Talsarnau

Scotland
Monachyle Mhor, Balquhidder
Dunain Park, Inverness
Knockie Lodge, Whitebridge

Republic of Ireland
Temple Country House, Ballymote
Cromleach Lodge, Castlebaldwin
Hilton Park, Clones
Assolas, Kanturk
Currarevagh House, Oughterard
Coopershill, Riverstown
Ballymaloe House, Shanagarry

Rural charm, simple style

England
Frog Street Farm, Beercrocombe
Blackmore Farm, Cannington
Nobody Inn, Doddiscombsleigh
Little Parmoor, Frieth
Bolebroke Mill, Hartfield
Hill Top Farmhouse, Haworth
Oak Tree Farm, Hopwas
Mizzards Farm, Rogate
Cadborough Farm, Rye
Innsacre Farmhouse, Shipton Gorge
Howtown, Ullswater

Scotland
Sheiling, Ullapool

Republic of Ireland
Kylenoe, Ballinderry

Hotels by the sea, luxury style

England
Burgh Island, Bigbury-on-Sea

St Martin's on the Isle, St
  Martin's
Island, Tresco

Scotland
Knockinaam Lodge, Portpatrick

Hotels by the sea, medium-priced or simple

England
Henley, Bigbury-on-Sea
Treglos, Constantine Bay
Tregildry, Gillan
Port Gaverne, Port Isaac
St Enodoc, Rock
Garrack, St Ives
Talland Bay, Talland-by-Looe
Trebrea Lodge, Tintagel
Nare, Veryan

Wales
Porth Tocyn, Abersoch
St Tudno, Llandudno

Scotland
Summer Isles, Achiltibuie

Channel Islands
White House, Herm

Republic of Ireland
Zetland House, Cashel Bay
Rosturk Woods, Mulranny

Walking and mountain hotels

England
Appletree Holme Farm, Blawith
Seatoller, Borrowdale
Mill, Mungrisdale
Hazel Bank, Rosthwaite
Wasdale Head, Wasdale Head

Wales
Pen-y-Gwryd, Nantgwynant

Scotland
Summer Isles, Achiltibuie

Hotels with a spa/good leisure facilities

England
Hartwell House, Aylesbury
Bath Priory, Bath

Budock Vean, Budock Vean
Highbullen, Chittlehamholt
Penmere Manor, Falmouth
Moonfleet Manor, Fleet
Hintlesham, Hintlesham
One Aldwych, London
Chewton Glen, New Milton
Garrack, St Ives
Vineyard, Stockcross
Cliveden, Taplow
Bishopstrow House, Warminster
Holbeck Ghyll, Windermere
Wallett's Court, West Cliffe
Middlethorpe Hall, York

Wales
Bodysgallen Hall, Llandudno

Scotland
Kinloch House, Blairgowrie
Isle of Eriska, Eriska
Green Hotel, Kinross

Republic of Ireland
Dunraven Arms, Adare
Knocklofty House, Clonmel
Sheen Falls Lodge, Kenmare
Temple Country House, Moate
Rathmullan House, Rathmullan
Mount Juliet, Thomastown

Fishing hotels

England
Callow Hall, Ashbourne
Holne Chase, Ashburton
Highbullen, Chittlehamholt
Combe House, Gittisham
Arundell Arms, Lifton
Black Swan, Ravenstonedale
Prince Hall, Two Bridges
Bishopstrow House, Warminster

Wales
Gliffaes, Crickhowell
Tyddyn Llan, Llandrillo
Lake, Llangammarch Wells
Llangoed Hall, Llyswen

Scotland
Muckrach Lodge, Dulnain
  Bridge
Kinnaird, Dunkeld
Forss House, Forss
Taychreggan, Kilchrenan

Kildrummy Castle, Kildrummy
Sheiling, Ullapool

Republic of Ireland
Mount Falcon Castle, Ballina
Caragh Lodge, Caragh Lake
Ballyvolane, Castlelyons
Enniscoe House, Crossmolina
Sheen Falls Lodge, Kenmare
Delphi Lodge, Leenane
Longueville House, Mallow
Newport House, Newport
Currarevagh House, Oughterard

Hotels for golfers

England
Budock Vean, Budock Vean
Highbullen, Chittlehamholt
Wind in the Willows, Glossop
Michael's Nook, Grasmere
Hintlesham Hall, Hintlesham
Lea Hill, Membury
Chewton Glen, New Milton
New Hall, Sutton Coldfield

Wales
Lake, Llangammarch Wells

Scotland
Greywalls, Gullane
Green Hotel, Kinross
Ladyburn, Maybole

Channel Islands
Atlantic, St Brelade

Republic of Ireland
Beaufort House, Beaufort
Hilton Park, Clones
Enniscoe House, Crossmolina
Currarevagh House, Oughterard
Mount Juliet, Thomastown

Hotels with tennis (T) and/or swimming (S)

England
Regent, Ambleside (S)
Eagle House, Bathford (T)
Lodge, Bathford (S)
Netherfield Place, Battle (T)
Park House, Bepton (T,S)
Burgh Island, Bigbury-on-Sea
  (T,S)

Mallory Court, Bishop's
  Tachbrook (T,S)
Blakeney, Blakeney (S)
Winterbourne, Bonchurch (S)
Lindeth Fell, Bowness-on-
  Windermere (T)
Woolley Grange, Bradford-on-
  Avon (T,S)
Frogg Manor, Broxton (T)
Budock Vean, Budock Vean
  (T,S)
Church Farm, Caxton (T)
Brockencote Hall, Chaddesley
  Corbett (T)
Gidleigh Park, Chagford (T)
Tor Cottage, Chillaton (S)
Highbullen, Chittlehamholt
  (T,S)
Treglos, Constantine Bay (S)
Corse Lawn House, Corse Lawn
  (T,S)
Cloth Hall Oast Cranbrook (S)
Delbury Hall, Diddlebury (T)
Evesham, Evesham (S)
Summer Lodge, Evershot (T,S)
Moonfleet Manor, Fleet (T,S)
Fowey Hall, Fowey (S)
Manoir aux Quat'Saisons, Great
  Milton (T)
Congham Hall, Grimston (T,S)
Hambleton Hall, Hambleton
  (T,S)
Mill at Harvington, Harvington
  (T,S)
Hassop Hall, Hassop (T)
Pheasant, Helmsley (S)
Homewood Park, Hinton
  Charterhouse (T,S)
Combe House, Holford (T,S)
Oak Tree Farm, Hopwas (S)
Hunstrete, Hunstrete (S)
Bindon Country House,
  Langford Budville (T,S)
Mizzards Farm, Rogate (S)
Ravenwood Hall, Rougham
  (T,S)
Boscundle Manor, St Austell
  (S)
Nanscawen House, St Blazey
  (S)
Ennys, St Hilary (T,S)

St Martin's on the Isle, St Martin's (S)
Star Castle, St Mary's (S)
Priory Bay, Seaview (T,S)
Charlton House, Shepton Mallet (T)
Soar Mill Cove, Soar Mill Cove (T)
Gabriel Court, Stoke Gabriel (T,S)
Plumber Manor, Sturminster Newton (T)
New Hall, Sutton Coldfield (T)
Hermitage, Swinburne (T)
Talland Bay, Talland-by-Looe (S)
Calcot Manor, Tetbury (T,S)
Island, Tresco (T,S)
Nare, Veryan (T,S)
Winstone Glebe, Winstone (T)
Watersmeet, Woolacombe (T,S)
Mount Royale, York (S)

Wales
Porth Tocyn, Abersoch (T,S)
Penpont, Brecon (T)
Gliffaes, Crickhowell (T)
Bodysgallen Hall, Llandudno (S,T)
Lake, Llangammarch Wells (T)
Llangoed Hall, Llyswen (T)
Portmeirion, Portmeirion (T,S)
Conrah Country House, Rhydgaled (S)

Scotland
Old Mansion House, Auchterhouse (T,S)
Todhall House, Dairsie (S)
Mackeanston House, Doune (T)
Kinnaird, Dunkeld (T)
Isle of Eriska, Eriska (T)
Inverlochy Castle, Fort William (T)
Greywalls, Gullane (T)
Culloden House, Inverness (T)
Dunain Park, Inverness (S)
Ardanaiseig, Kilchrenan (T)
Skirling House, Skirling (T)
Baile-na-Cille, Timsgarry (T)

Channel Islands
White House, Herm (T,S)

Atlantic, St Brelade (T,S)
Longueville Manor, St Saviour (T,S)

Northern Ireland
Beech Hill House, Derry (T)

Republic of Ireland
Dunraven Arms, Adare (S)
Caragh Lodge, Caragh Lake (T)
Zetland House, Cashel Bay (T)
Rock Glen, Clifden (T)
Castle Leslie, Glaslough (T)
Glin Castle, Glin (T)
Marlfield House, Gorey (T)
Assolas Country House, Kanturk (T)
Park Kenmare, Kenmare (T)
Sheen Falls Lodge, Kenmare (T)
Glenview House, Midleton (T)
Rosturk Woods, Mulranny
Rathmullan House, Rathmullan
Tinakilly House, Rathnew (T)
Coopershill, Riverstown (T)
Ballymaloe House, Shanagarry (T,S)
Mount Juliet, Thomastown (T)

Friendly informality/run like a private house

England
Frog Street Farm, Beercrocombe
Appletree Holme Farm, Blawith
Chilvester Hill House, Calne
Coach House at Crookham, Crookham
Nonsuch House, Dartmouth
Delbury Hall, Diddlebury
Old Rectory, Hopesay
Grey Cottage, Leonard Stanley
Hazelwood House, Loddiswell
Stone House, Rushlake Green
Strattons, Swaffham

Wales
Old Rectory, Bettws Gwerfyl Goch
Tŷ Isaf, Llanfachreth
Old Rectory, Llansanffraid Glan Conwy

Scotland
Todhall House, Dairsie
Apple Lodge, Lochranza
Viewfield House, Portree
Skirling House, Skirling
Talisker House, Talisker

Republic of Ireland
Kylenoe, Ballinderry
Temple House, Ballymote
Beaufort House, Beaufort
Hilton Park, Clones
Castle Leslie, Glaslough
Cullintra House, Inistioge
Delphi Lodge, Leenane
Roundwood House,
   Mountrath
Coopershill, Riverstown

Hotels that welcome children

England
Rothay Manor, Ambleside
Cavendish, Baslow
Harington's, Bath
Royal Crescent, Bath
Eagle House, Bathford
Blakeney, Blakeney
Woolley Grange, Bradford-on-
   Avon
Old Rectory, Campsea Ashe
Greyfriars, Canterbury
Gidleigh Park, Chagford
Corse Lawn, Corse Lawn
Kemps, East Stoke
Evesham, Evesham
Moonfleet Manor, Fleet
Fowey Hall, Fowey
Manoir aux Quat'Saisons, Great
   Milton
Hambleton Hall, Hambleton
Holdsworth House, Halifax
Highfield House, Hawkshead
Homewood Park, Hinton
   Charterhouse
Tollgate, Kingham
Bindon Country House,
   Langford Budville
Great House, Lavenham
42 The Calls, Leeds
Arundell Arms, Lifton

Holdfast Cottage, Little
   Malvern
Woolton Redbourne, Liverpool
Hazelwood House, Loddiswell
Basil Street, London
Connaught, London
22 Jermyn Street, London
Old Bell, Malmesbury
Meudon, Mawnan Smith
Morston Hall, Morston
Beetle and Wedge, Moulsford-
   on-Thames
Mill, Mungrisdale
Bank House, Oakamoor
Pen-y-Dyffryn, Rhydycroesau
St Enodoc, Rock
Biskra Beach, Ryde
Seaview, Seaview
Charlton House, Shepton Mallet
Soar Mill Cove, Soar Mill Cove
Cliveden, Taplow
Island, Tresco
Nare, Veryan
Wallett's Court, West Cliffe
Watersmeet, Woolacombe

Wales
Porth Tocyn, Abersoch
Garthmyl Hall, Garthmyl
Cawdor Arms, Llandeilo
St Tudno, Llandudno
Egerton Grey, Porthkerry
Three Cocks, Three Cocks

Scotland
Old Mansion House,
   Auchterhouse
Darroch Learg, Ballater
Kirkton House, Cardross
Enmore, Dunoon
Forss House, Forss
Inverlochy Castle, Fort William
The Duisdale, Isle Ornsay
Castle Venlaw, Peebles
Knockinaam Lodge, Portpatrick
Tigh an Eilean, Shieldaig
Old Pines, Spean Bridge
Baile-na-Cille, Timsgarry
Burrastow House, Walls

Channel Islands
St Brelade's Bay, St Brelade

Republic of Ireland

Hilton Park, Clones
Sheen Falls Lodge, Kenmare
Roundwood House, Mountrath
Coopershill, Riverstown
Ballymaloe House,
    Shanagarry
Inch House, Thurles
Lettercollum House,
    Timoleague

No-smoking hotels

England

Abbey House, Abbotsbury
Rowanfield, Ambleside
Shallowdale House, Ampleforth
Haydon House, Bath
Frog Street Farm,
    Beercrocombe
Henley, Bigbury-on-Sea
Appletree Holme Farm, Blawith
Old Bakery, Blockley
Old Rectory, Campsea Ashe
Blackmore Farm, Cannington
Avondale, Carlisle
Number Thirty One, Carlisle
Church Farm, Caxton
The White House, Charmouth
Tor Cottage, Chillaton
Brook House, Colwall
Manor Farm, Crackington
    Haven
Upton House, Cullompton
Stone Close, Dent
Little Parmoor, Frieth
Ashfield House, Grassington
Old Store, Halnaker
Grove House, Hamsterley
    Forest
Hatch, Hartest
Bolebroke Mill, Hartfield
Northleigh House, Hatton
Hill Top Farmhouse, Haworth
Underleigh, Hope
Old Rectory, Hopesay
Lower Bache House, Kimbolton
Penrhos Court, Kington
Lavenham Priory, Lavenham
Molesworth Manor, Little
    Petherick
Knightsbridge Green, London

New House Farm, Lorton
Winder Hall, Lorton
Number Twenty Eight, Ludlow
Swinside Lodge, Newlands
Bank House, Oakamoor
Cotswold House, Oxford
Tye Rock, Porthleven
Mizzards Farm, Rogate
Hazel Bank, Rosthwaite
Cadborough Farm, Rye
Old Vicarage, Rye
Nanscawen House, St Blazey
Lynch, Somerton
Strattons, Swaffham
Thomas Luny House,
    Teignmouth
Mulberry House, Torquay
Old Millfloor, Trebarwith
    Strand
Water Yeat, Water Yeat
Bales Mead, West Porlock
Old Parsonage, Westdean
Archway, Windermere

Wales

Old Rectory, Bettws Gwerfyl
    Goch
Old Rectory, Boduan
Tan-y-Foel, Capel Garmon
Isaf, Llanfachreth

Scotland

Todhall House, Dairsie
Mackeanston House, Doune
Drummond House, Edinburgh
Saxe Coburg House, Edinburgh
7 Danube Street, Edinburgh
Sibbet House, Edinburgh
24 Northumberland Street,
    Edinburgh
Ashburn House, Fort William
Crolinnhe, Fort William
Grange, Fort William
Gladstone House, Kirkcudbright
Albannach, Lochinver
Maridon House, Oban
Cuilcheanna House, Onich
Skirling House, Skirling
Old Pines, Spean Bridge
Talisker House, Talisker
Leachin House, Tarbert
Tiroran House, Tiroran

Altnaharrie, Ullapool
Sheiling, Ullapool

Republic of Ireland
Ballycormac House, Aglish
Anglesea Town House, Dublin
Simmonstown House, Dublin
Slaney Manor, Ferrycarrig
Old Presbytery, Kinsale

Hotels that welcome dogs

England
Holne Chase, Ashburton
Lodge, Bathford
Bibury Court, Bibury
Halmpstone Manor, Bishop's Tawton
Blakeney, Blakeney
Bracken House, Bratton Fleming
Greyfriars, Canterbury
Coach House at Crookham, Crookham
Ashelford, East Down
Glewstone Court, Glewstone
Holdsworth House, Halifax
Northleigh House, Hatton
Heddon's Gate, Heddon's Mouth
Tollgate, Kingham
22 Jermyn Street, London
Cottage in the Wood, Malvern Wells
Morston Hall, Morston
Mill, Mungrisdale
Hall, Newton-le-Willows
Beechwood, North Walsham
Port Gaverne, Port Isaac
Black Swan, Ravenstonedale
Arkleside, Reeth
Pen-y-Dyffryn, Rhydycroesau
Boar's Head, Ripley
Ravenwood Hall, Rougham
Innsacre, Shipton Gorge
Swan, Southwold
Strattons, Swaffham
Cliveden, Taplow
Prince Hall, Two Bridges
Nare, Veryan
Inn at Whitewell, Whitewell

Wales
Bear, Crickhowell
Cawdor Arms, Llandeilo
Lake, Llangammarch Wells

Scotland
Auchendean Lodge, Dulnain Bridge
Enmore, Dunoon
Ednam House, Kelso
Beechwood House, Moffat
Maridon House, Oban
Knockinaam Lodge, Portpatrick
Tigh an Eilean, Shieldaig
Creagan House, Strathyre
Baile-na-Cille, Timsgarry

Hotels for gourmets

England
Fischer's Baslow Hall, Baslow
Lettonie, Bath
Mallory Court, Bishop's Tachbrook
Waterside Inn, Bray
Gidleigh Park, Chagford
Gravetye Manor, East Grinstead
Michael's Nook, Grasmere
White Moss House, Grasmere
Manoir aux Quat'Saisons, Great Milton
Hambleton Hall, Hambleton
Northcote Manor, Langho
Capital, London
Connaught, London
Halkin, London
Mr Underhill's, Ludlow
Morston Hall, Morston
Beetle and Wedge, Moulsford-on-Thames
Chewton Glen, New Milton
Seafood Restaurant, Padstow
Yorke Arms, Ramsgill-in-Nidderdale
Sandgate, Sandgate
Charlton House, Shepton Mallet
McCoy's, Staddlebridge
Plumber Manor, Sturminster Newton
Castle, Taunton
Howard's House, Teffont Evias
Sharrow Bay, Ullswater

Old Beams, Waterhouses
White House, Williton
Winteringham Fields, Winteringham
Old Vicarage, Worfield

Wales
Old Rectory, Llansanffraid Glan Conwy
Carlton House, Llanwrtyd Wells
Plas Bodegroes, Pwllheli

Scotland
Summer Isles, Achiltibuie
Three Chimneys, Colbost
Inverlochy Castle, Fort William
Cross, Kingussie
Airds, Port Appin
Altnaharrie, Ullapool

Channel Islands
Longueville Manor, St Saviour

Republic of Ireland
Marlfield House, Gorey
Park, Kenmare
Sheen Falls Lodge, Kenmare
Rathmullan House, Rathmullan
Ballymaloe House, Shanagarry

Hotels with facilities for &

England
Rothay Manor, Ambleside
Hartwell House, Aylesbury
Park House, Bepton
Bibury Court, Bibury
Mallory Court, Bishop's Tachbrook
Blakeney, Blakeney
Leathes Head, Borrowdale
Millstream, Bosham
Lindeth Fell, Bowness-on-Windermere
Bracken House, Bratton Fleming
Blackmore Farm, Cannington
Brockencote Hall, Chaddesley Corbett
Coach House at Crookham, Crookham
Kemps, East Stoke
Evesham Hotel, Evesham

Horn of Plenty, Gulworthy
Holdsworth House, Halifax
Northcote Manor, Langho
42 The Calls, Leeds
Malmaison, Leeds
Cadogan, London
One Aldwych, London
Malmaison, Manchester
Meudon, Mawnan Smith
Malmaison, Newcastle upon Tyne
Beeches, Norwich
Black Swan, Ravenstonedale
Burgoyne, Reeth
Garrack, St Ives
Greenway, Shurdington
Stonor Arms, Stonor
Wellington Arms, Stratfield Turgis
New Hall, Sutton Coldfield
Leeming House, Watermillock
Grange, York

Wales
Milebrook House, Knighton

Scotland
Roman Camp, Callander
Kirkton House, Cardross
Muckrach Lodge, Dulnain Bridge
Forss House, Forss
Malmaison, Glasgow
Dunain Park, Inverness
Old Pines, Spean Bridge
Burrastow House, Walls

Northern Ireland
McCausland, Belfast
Narrows, Portaferry

Republic of Ireland
Mustard Seed at Echo Lodge, Ballingarry
Seaview House, Ballylickey
Clarence, Dublin
Hibernian, Dublin
Sheen Falls Lodge, Kenmare
Glenview House, Midleton
The Narrows, Portaferry
Rathmullan House, Rathmullan
Churchtown House, Tagoat
Aherne's, Youghal

Hotels with facilities for weddings

A civil wedding licence is necessary for hotels in England and Wales. In Scotland and Ireland it is not necessary. Please see the end of Facilities for hotels where you can get married.

Hotels that offer a Christmas package

So many hotels now offer a Christmas package that we no longer have the space to list them here. When a hotel tells us that it offers a package, we give that information under Terms.

How we choose our hotels

We are often asked how we select our entries. A fair question, since the hotels included in the *Guide* cater for a wide range of ages, incomes, tastes and prejudices. Moreover, they have been nominated by a miscellaneous collection of individuals of varying tastes. Though we have records going back nearly 25 years, we do not know the quality of judgment of everyone who writes to us. How then can there be any coherent standard behind our choices?

There is no single standard. Our own tastes are eclectic, and the only thing which all these hotels have in common is that the editors would be happy to stay in them. Nevertheless the process of selection is not arbitrary. Among the factors which assist us are the following:

• The consensus of recent reports on a hotel that already has an entry in the *Guide*, and the tone of the nominating letter in the case of a candidate for first-time selection. If someone whose judgment we know and trust tells us of an exciting new find or that a particular hotel does not deserve its entry, he or she obviously carries more weight than a nominator or complainant out of the blue.
• The hotel's brochure. Its pitch will usually reveal the kind of custom it is hoping to attract, and its photographs or drawings, while no doubt always aiming to beguile, may tell us instantly that this one is not for us.
• Menus. Very instructive in subtle as well as in obvious ways.
• Hoteliers' responses to our questionnaire. We invite them to expand on their answers by telling us what sort of custom they hope to attract. Not all take the trouble to do so; those who do are very helpful.
• Whether and how a hotel features in other guides.
• Inspections. In cases of doubt (due to unconvincing or ambivalent reports or lack of feedback), we carry out an anonymous inspection. We have a limited inspection budget, but a number of long-time readers have generously volunteered to do unreimbursed inspections for us.

No hotel is considered unless the nominator or inspector has spent a night in one of its rooms and had the opportunity to assess the sorts of thing that a tour with a clipboard will not reveal: noisy plumbing, thin walls; whether breakfast is as good as dinner; how effective the bedside lighting is; how comfortable the beds are; intangibles of atmosphere.

Of course, such a system is open to error, but the fact that we get far more endorsements than blackballs encourages us to think that we are on the right lines. No guide can afford to inspect hotels with the frequency needed to guarantee total reliability. But we are convinced that the way we operate, by reader recommendation backed up by independent inspection, is not only the most honest, but also the most reliable, method of selecting exceptional hotels.

One of the occupational hazards of our trade is the collusive or inspired report. A common practice is for hotels to give departing guests a report form and invite them to send us an "unsolicited" recommendation. Sometimes we receive a rash of fulsome reports on a particular establishment, all from people who have never written to us before. Some hotels photocopy our report forms, and, having prevailed on their guests to fill them in, post them to us in a batch. One hotel designed a special postcard for the purpose. Over the years, we have developed a sophisticated nose for this sort of try-on. So we would advise any hotel tempted to try it, not to waste their time or ours.

Hotels are dropped from the *Guide* when it is clear from our reports that there has been a fall in standards or – a tricky question this – when we feel that they are no longer offering value for money. We also omit a hotel after a change of ownership or management, if we do not have enough evidence that the new regime is maintaining previous standards. And hotels are dropped – sometimes unfairly – when we have had inadequate feedback. We are used to getting a spate of letters asking: "Why on earth have you left out — ?" If the case is well made, we reinstate the place in the next edition.

As we have said repeatedly over the years, we beg all those who find the *Guide* useful to make a habit of sending us reports after staying in a *Guide* hotel. We rely on the generosity and judgment of all our readers. So please do send us a few lines by post, fax, or e-mail, telling us about your likes and dislikes or even simply just saying we have got the place right (or wrong). Letters are the lifeblood of this guide. Who knows, you could even win one of the 24 bottles of champagne given annually to the writers of the best reports.

How to read the entries

The long and the short of it Entries vary greatly. A long entry does not necessarily imply an especially good hotel, nor a short one a marginal case. Sometimes it takes a lot of words to convey a place's special flavour, and sometimes we quote an amusing report at length. In general, city hotels get less space than country ones, because the surroundings matter less in a town, and because it is helpful, when a hotel is in a relatively remote area, for the entry to comment on the location.

Names At the end of each entry we give, in italics, the names or initials of people who have nominated that hotel or endorsed its entry in an earlier edition of the *Guide*. We don't give the names of writers who have chosen to remain anonymous, or of those who have written adverse reports, though their contributions are just as important as the laudatory ones. Nor do we give the names of our inspectors.

Maps and index These are at the end of the book. Each entry is listed under the name of the town or village. If you remember a hotel's name but not its exact location, you can consult the alphabetical list of hotels.

Nuts and bolts The factual material varies in length. Some hotels have lots of facilities, others few. We don't give detailed information about bedroom facilities. Most hotel bedrooms nowadays have telephone, TV and an *en suite* bathroom; many have tea-making facilities. If any of these is vital to your comfort, you should discuss it with the hotel at the time of booking. A "double room" may be double- or twin-bedded; you should mention which you prefer when booking. If you have strong pro- or anti-duvet feelings, this should also be discussed. We aim to provide accurate information about opening times, but hotels, particularly small ones, sometimes close on the spur of the moment. Similarly, hotels don't always give us reliable information about whether they take credit cards or, if they do, which ones; please check with the hotel if this is vital to you.

Italic entries These describe hotels which are worth considering but which we feel, for various reasons – inadequate information, lack of feedback, ambivalent reports – do not at the moment deserve a full entry.

Shortlist This is intended to plug gaps in the maps, particularly in large cities where we have few, or insufficient, entries. *We must emphasise that they do not necessarily meet our normal criteria.* We are particularly in need of comments on these hotels, and we welcome more suggestions.

Traveller's tales These tales of disaster are for the amusement of our readers and hardly any relate to hotels currently in the *Guide*. They have *no connection* with the entry immediately above.

Symbols We are against providing a lot of information in hiero-glyphic form. Days and months are abbreviated; "B&B" means bed and breakfast, "D,B&B" means dinner, bed and breakfast, and "alc" is *à la carte*. The "full alc" price is the hotel's estimate per person for a three-course meal and a reasonably priced half bottle of wine, including service and taxes; "alc" indicates the price excluding the wine. We say: "Unsuitable for disabled", when a hotel tells us that, and we list under "Special Hotels" places which claim to have full facilities for the disabled. But it is vital that you check details with the hotel. We have a "New" label for hotels making their debut in the *Guide* or being readmitted after an absence, and a "Budget" label for hotels which offer dinner, bed and breakfast at around £50 per person, or B&B for about £30 and dinner for about £20. *V* indicates hotels which have agreed to take part in our Voucher scheme.

Vouchers Once again we offer our readers an opportunity to obtain a discount at many *Guide* hotels. On the tear-out card in the centre of the book, you will find six vouchers which may be used at any hotel with *V* at the end of its entry. A voucher will entitle you to a discount of 25 per cent of the normal price for bed and breakfast (or the price of a room in the case of hotels that charge for breakfast separately). You can't use it if you are already on a bargain break or special deal, and you will be expected to pay the full price for all other services. The discount will apply whether you use the voucher for one night or for a longer visit, and it is for one room. You must produce two vouchers if you are booking two rooms. The vouchers remain valid till the publication of the 2002 edition in September 2001. *IMPORTANT: It is essential that you request a voucher booking at the time of reservation, and participating hotels may refuse a voucher reservation or accept the voucher for one night only if they expect to be fully booked at the full room price at that time.*

Tariffs Terms are unavoidably complicated. Some hotels have a standard rate for all rooms, regardless of season and length of stay, but many operate a complex system which varies from low season to high, and according to length of stay, what sort of facilities are offered, and whether the room is in single or double occupancy. To complicate matters further, most British hotels offer a variety of breaks. When figures are given without mention of a single or a double room they indicate the range of tariffs per person; otherwise we give a room rate. Lowest rates are what you pay for the simplest room, sharing a double, or out of season, or both; highest rates are for the "best" rooms, and for the high season if the hotel has one. Meal prices are per person. We must emphasise that the tariffs quoted are not totally reliable. We ask hotels, when they complete our question-naire in the spring of one year, to make an informed guess at their tariffs for the following year – not easy. Many hotels prefer to quote their current rates. Please *don't* rely on the figures printed. You should *always* check at the time of booking and not blame the hotel or the *Guide* if prices differ from those printed.

Special offers If you wish to spend two days or more at a hotel in the British Isles, it is worth asking about special offers. These can be amazing value, and may apply throughout the year. And the voucher scheme mentioned on the previous page should help you to find accommodation at cheaper rates.

As usual, we ask readers to tell us of any errors of omission or commission in both the descriptive and the informative parts of the *Guide*. The entries are written in good faith, but we can't guarantee that, after we have gone to press, a hotel won't close or change hands. We try to give accurate information under Location, especially with out-of-the-way places, and would like to know if you have found the directions inadequate. We know that it is an imposition to ask readers to write to us, but it is essential that people let us know their views if the *Guide* is to continue to meet the needs of travellers as well as it can.

A partisan view of rival guides and hotel groups

The *Good Hotel Guide*, unlike many of its competitors, takes no advertising, no hospitality and no payment of any kind. It pays the cost of all its inspections, always an overnight stay. Only by operating in this way can we preserve our reputation for independent judgment, built up over a quarter of a century.

In many bookshops and hotel bedrooms you will find lavishly illustrated publications masquerading as independent guides. Only when you read the small print do you find an acknowledgement that hotels pay "a contribution" or "a registration fee" to be included. The glossy Johansens guides, for example, charge hotels up to £2,500 for an entry. Not surprisingly, you will find not a word of criticism in these guides. He who pays the piper not only calls the tune but more often than not actually writes the words. The "paid-for" guides are, in fact, little more than advertising sheets, but it is dismaying how few ordinary readers, and even specialist travel book shops, know the difference between a genuinely independent guide and one that is not.

We prize independence not only for ourselves but also in the hotels we report on. Almost all the establishments in the *Good Hotel Guide* are independently owned and run. There are a few exceptions: some large hotels, and some in cities, are in the hands of managers. Others belong to groups that developed from a single hotel, eg, the Alternative Hotel Company which now has a *Hotel du Vin* in Bristol, in addition to those in Winchester and Tunbridge Wells, and Luxury Family Hotels, the child-friendly group which started with *Woolley Grange*, Bradford-on-Avon, and is now a small group, with three other hotels on the same lines, and an altogether different one, *The Kandinsky*, in Cheltenham.

Our experience is that chain hotels do not normally provide the personal style that our readers seek, so they rarely qualify for these pages. But this year we include three: *New Hall*, Sutton Coldfield, and *Shelley's*, Lewes (both Thistle hotels), and Granada's *Leeming House*, at Watermillock, in the Lake District, where an exemplary manager, who was dismissed at the time of the merger with Forte, has now been reinstated.

Many *Guide* hotels belong to a consortium for marketing purposes. The most famous, and by far the most expensive, is Relais & Châteaux, French-owned but worldwide. All Relais establishments, be they grand castles, lush country houses or gourmet restaurants, are privately owned. But so strong is the Relais brand image that they are sometimes mistaken for a chain. Some travellers in search of luxury use the Relais booklet extensively or exclusively. Others steer clear, not caring for the swank – and sometimes the snootiness – which they detect in these posh places. The present Relais contingent in the

UK are, in general, an impressive lot, more dependable in our view than their associates across the Channel and in the United States. But it is said that fewer British hotels are now joining, due to the high cost, and the fact that it is regarded as something of an old boys' network, out of tune with the more flexible approach to food, children, dress codes, etc, of the younger hoteliers. Because the style is so distinctive, we always mention a hotel's membership in its *Guide* entry.

We also mention hotels' membership of Pride of Britain, a small, upmarket, exclusively British consortium. Not all of its establishments are an independent entity – they include a Hebridean cruise company and the Royal Scotsman. About two-thirds of its members have an entry in the *Guide*.

The Best Western group, worldwide, and now merged with Consort, is an association of about 400 independent hotels, but its membership is less homogeneous than that of the groups mentioned above. In the US, Best Westerns are often motels; in the UK many are what in the old AA parlance would be called two- or three-star establishments. There are some Best Westerns in the *Guide*, but fewer this year than last, as some of the old Best Western members have pulled out of the new group, not happy with the changes it is introducing.

The self-explanatory Relais du Silence, long established on the Continent, has some members in the UK, a few of which are in these pages. Consortia of cheaper hotels include Minotel, with 250 members in the UK.

Many of our readers nowadays choose to stay in guest houses and B&Bs operated in private homes, because they are on the whole much cheaper than hotels. They vary in sophistication. Some function alone, others belong to various groups. A leading group is Wolsey Lodges, a non-profit-making consortium, which was launched in 1981. It is named for Henry VIII's cardinal, who toured the country expecting to be entertained in style. Its members are defined as "an Englishman's home where you are welcome to stay as a guest for a night or more". Today it has more than 200 members scattered throughout the UK, as well as a few on the Continent. They cater for travellers who like to socialise with their hosts, and enjoy the lottery of eating in dinner party style with fellow guests. There are some splendid examples of the species scattered through these pages. The Hidden Ireland association operates on the same principles and provides some of our most popular Irish entries. Many of our other Irish entries belong to *Ireland's Blue Book*, an association of upmarket country house hotels and restaurants.

Other UK groups include Bed and Breakfast for Garden Lovers, which lists about 80 properties that have a particularly attractive garden. Members of the Definitely Different group offer accommodation in old mills, a lighthouse, an old railway carriage and a number of former industrial buildings. There is also an association of narrowboat hotels operating on the canals of England and Wales. The National Trust has 70 tenants, mostly on working farms, who offer B&B at low prices. Information on two of the B&B groups which operate in London is given on page 516.

Each of the three national tourist boards – English, Welsh and Scottish – produces its own listing of hotels and guest houses, charging establishments a registration fee for inclusion. You won't get a warts-and-all description of a hotel which has had to pay a registration fee. The English Tourist Board has now harmonised its gradings with those of the AA and the RAC (which also charge for inclusion in their guides), but the Welsh and Scottish ones have been unable to come to an agreement with the motoring organisations. They argue, rightly in our view, that quality, rather than facilities, should be emphasised – otherwise there is a danger of imposing conformity of style. One *Guide* hotelier was bemused when the local tourist board inspector offered to advise him where to buy frilly cloths to cover his beautifully hand-crafted tables, and coordinated themed pictures, made in India, to deck his elegantly bare walls.

The AA guide also includes paid advertisements from some of its hotels, which might further confuse readers. Its standards are not necessarily those prized in these pages. We once watched a TV programme in which an AA inspector berated a hotelier for not having "captive coat hangers". These are an abomination as far as *Guide* readers are concerned: "Do they think we are thieves?" one correspondent wrote. One *Guide* hotelier wrote this year to tell us that she was so unhappy with the demeanour of the AA inspectors that she had pulled out of their guide.

As usual, if a hotel or a restaurant-with-rooms has a *Michelin* star, or a *Bib Gourmand* (for a good meal at a moderate price), we mention this in the text. When we list an inn that also has an entry in our sibling publication, the *Good Pub Guide*, we mention that fact.

England

The Old Rectory, Hopesay

ABBOTSBURY Dorset

Map 1

Abbey House   BUDGET
Church Street
Abbotsbury DT3 4JJ

Tel (01305) 871330
Fax (01305) 871088
E-mail info@theabbeyhouse.co.uk
Website www.theabbeyhouse.co.uk

A springtime inspection sets the scene: "On a warm sunny March day, this is a place of enchantment. The long low building is set in a large and lovely garden, and the views towards the huge golden-stoned tithe barn, abbey ruins, roofs liberally sprinkled with white doves, are quite stupendous." The core of this "comfortable, unassuming place" was once an infirmary serving the nearby Benedictine abbey; extensions were added during the 17th and 18th centuries. Inside are old flag-stoned floors, wide panelled doors, authentic windows and "not a trace of PVC". Bedrooms, "not grand or smart", vary in size and style. "Ours was spacious, looking over the lovely view; it had chintzy armchairs, lacy cloths on round tables, impressionist-style paintings. The faint shabbiness added to a feeling of relaxation and pleasure." Another visitor had a "very romantic" attic room, with its bathroom across a hall. The owners, Jonathan and Maureen Cooke, "obviously happy in what they are doing", are "most welcoming". Breakfast is "a feast", with everything from home-made muesli to smoked haddock on offer. Light lunches and cream teas are served on the lawn in fine weather. Evening meals are available only for house parties, but there are several pubs in the village: *The Ilchester Arms* (a long-standing main entry in the *Good Pub Guide*) is a sound bet. Abbotsbury is renowned for its subtropical gardens and its ancient swannery (established by the monks over 600 years ago). The panoramic expanses of Chesil Bank are 15 minutes' walk away, and the monument to Admiral Hardy – Nelson's flag captain at the battle of Trafalgar – is also worth viewing. (*Cathy Robinson, IGC Farman, and others*)

Open All year. Restaurant closed at night, except for house parties (by arrangement).
Rooms 1 family suite, 4 double. No telephone.
Facilities Lounge, breakfast room, tea room. No background music. 1½-acre grounds: stage for plays/classical concerts. Sea 15 mins' walk. Unsuitable for &.
Location Abbotsbury is on B3157 halfway between Weymouth and Bridport. Turn left at sign to Swannery; after 100 yds left through abbey arch; *Abbey House* on right. Train: Dorchester/Weymouth; then taxi.
Restrictions No smoking. No dogs.
Credit cards None accepted.
Terms B&B £30-£32.50. Child accommodated in parents' room: under 13, 50% of adult rate. Christmas package. 1-night bookings sometimes refused in high season.

ALDEBURGH Suffolk   Map 2

The Wentworth   *Tel* (01728) 452312
Wentworth Road   *Fax* (01728) 454343
Aldeburgh IP15 5BD
                       E-mail wentworth.hotel@anglianet.co.uk
                       Website www.smoothhound.co.uk/hotels/wentworth

Visitors this year, including a self-confessed "couple of old fusspots", continue to praise this traditional hotel which overlooks fishing huts and boats on Aldeburgh's shingle beach. The owner, Michael Pritt (whose grandfather came here in 1920), is "very much involved in looking after guests", he tells us, and visitors enjoy socialising in the public rooms with their log fires, antiques, books, plants, fresh flowers and Russell Flint prints. The staff are "polite, willing and cheerful", say *Guide* readers, even if they sometimes "lack a little experience". The "honest, no-nonsense" food continues to be enjoyed, particularly the fish dishes. The buffet choice at breakfast is appreciated, and so is the "delicious Finnan haddock with poached egg". Light lunches are served, on the garden terrace in fine weather. Some bedrooms in the main house are small, and some are on the second floor (no lift). Large, well-appointed no-smoking bedrooms, furnished in French country style, are in the annexe, *Darfield House*. Each room has a copy of the book *Orlando the Marmalade Cat* by the late Kathleen Hale (her "Owlbarrow" is Aldeburgh), and sea-facing rooms have binoculars. Aldeburgh is renowned for its connection with Benjamin Britten and his festival, which has brought many famous musicians and actors to stay at *The Wentworth*. (*R Liggins, Heather Sharland, Philip and Eileen Hall; also Sheelagh Innes*)

Open 5 Jan–27 Dec.
Rooms 31 double, 6 single. 7 in annexe, *Darfield House*. 5 on ground floor.
Facilities Ramps. 2 lounges, bar, restaurant, private dining room, conference room. No background music. Small garden. Shingle beach 200 yds.
Location On seafront, 5 mins' walk from centre. Parking. Train: Saxmundham (8 miles).
Restrictions No smoking: restaurant, bedrooms, 1 lounge. No dogs in restaurant.
Credit cards All major cards accepted.
Terms B&B £48–£71; D,B&B £61.50–£77. Reduced rates for child accommodated in parents' room. Set lunch £12.85, dinner £14.85. Weekend, midweek breaks; special events. Christmas package. 1-night bookings refused Sat.

ALSTON Cumbria   **Map 4**

Lovelady Shield   *Tel* (01434) 381203
Nenthead Road   *Fax* (01434) 381515
nr Alston CA9 3LF
       E-mail enquiries@lovelady.co.uk
       Website www.lovelady.co.uk

"The situation is quite superb, and the welcome was first class," says a visitor in 2000 to this handsome white 19th-century house. It is remotely set in the High Pennines, not far from England's highest market town, and "the surrounding countryside, including the small River Nent, is stunning". Other visitors wrote of the "unfussy service", the "family atmosphere", and the "truly hospitable" owners, Peter and Marie Haynes ("he has a gentle sense of humour, much appreciated when we arrived late and harassed, having lost our way on the fells in deep mist"). The chef, Barrie Garton, serves "classical English dishes, with a continental influence", eg, scrambled eggs with woodland mushrooms; roasted organic suckling pig with sage, honey and almonds; poached pear in elderflower syrup, stuffed with soft caramel. Portions are generous, with good ingredients. Vegetarians are catered for, with advance notice. A winter guest on his own was pleased to be served dinner by a fire in the lounge. "The service was excellent, and the meal was good, if not sparkling, washed down by a decent New Zealand sauvignon blanc." At breakfast there is freshly squeezed orange juice, and cooked dishes such as kedgeree (ordered in advance) and Cumberland sausages. The well-equipped bedrooms have "a homely feel" (two are quite small). "The dawn chorus was unforgettable." A good base for exploring Hadrian's Wall and the border country. (*John Townsend, and others*)

Open All year.
Rooms 11 double, 1 single.
Facilities Ramps to restaurant. 2 lounges, cocktail bar, restaurant. No background music. 3-acre grounds: river, fishing, croquet. Golf, riding nearby. Unsuitable for &. Civil wedding licence.

Location 2½ miles E of Alston. Take A689 to Nenthead. Hotel 2 miles on left, at junction with B6294.
Restrictions Smoking banned in restaurant, 1 lounge, "actively discouraged" in bedrooms. No dogs in public rooms.
Credit cards Amex, MasterCard, Visa.
Terms B&B from £67.50; D,B&B £87.50. Set Sun lunch £19.50; dinner £29.50. Child accommodated in parents' room: under 2, free; 2–16, £20. 3-night breaks. Christmas package. *V*

AMBERLEY West Sussex   Map 2

Amberley Castle   *Tel* (01798) 831992
Amberley   *Fax* (01798) 831998
nr Arundel BN18 9ND   *E-mail* info@amberleycastle.co.uk
                                       Website www.amberleycastle.co.uk

Surrounded by a 60-foot wall and a dry moat, Joy and Martin Cummings' Norman castle (Pride of Britain) stands on a bend of the River Arun. From the battlements there are wide views of the surrounding countryside. The portcullis is lowered at midnight, so it can be difficult to gain entrance thereafter, but the new suites in the stone-built Bishopric, in the moat, have their own entrance. Other luxurious bedrooms are distributed between the castle, a manor house and some barns. Their decor is "splendidly OTT", with heavy drapes and much panelling; many have a four-poster, and one of the suites has a double spa bath. The public rooms have antique furniture and suits of armour, and one visitor remarked on "the owners' propensity to decorate every room possible with cuddly toys". The restaurant is quite formal (men must wear a jacket and tie in the evening), and ambitious, with staff who have come from two *Michelin*-rosetted establishments (both are in the *Guide*). Its manager, Patrick Floret Miguel, was formerly at *Chewton Glen*, New Milton; the chef, Brian (Billy) Butcher, worked at *Gravetye Manor*, East Grinstead. He calls his cooking "eclectic English". A keynote starter is tian of marinated salmon topped with Sevruga caviar, with avocado and tomato mousse. Main courses include pan-fried fillet of Angus beef; roast codling topped with tapenade; roast monkfish with globe artichokes. In the large grounds, white peacocks stalk the lovely gardens, two lakes are home to black swans and ducks, there is a pond with Koi carp; also two goats, three alpacas and two miniature Shetland ponies in a paddock. A colony of jackdaws has nested in the castle for ten centuries. Family pets include two Pyrenean mountain dogs, a Persian chinchilla and Sam the parrot, who now has a new mate, Buca. There is also a farm with cattle, pigs and sheep. Conferences, functions and weddings are often held, and guests can arrive by helicopter. Nearby are water meadows full of flora and fauna, and the South Downs Way (good walking); also Arundel Castle; Petworth, Parham and Goodwood houses, and the Sussex coast.

Open All year.
Rooms 5 suites (in dry moat), 15 double.
Facilities Hall, 2 lounges, library, restaurant; function facilities. 15-acre grounds: gardens, croquet, dry moat, ponds, wildlife. Beach 10 miles. Unsuitable for &. Civil wedding licence.

Location SW of village 4 miles N of Arundel. Train to Amberley.
Restrictions No smoking: restaurant, bedrooms. No children under 12. No dogs.
Credit cards All major cards accepted.
Terms [2000] B&B: single/double £145–£300, suite £275–£300. Set lunch £12.50, dinner £35; full alc £50. Min. 2-night booking weekends. Castle breaks. Christmas package.

AMBLESIDE Cumbria   Map 4

Regent Hotel   *Tel* (015394) 32254
Waterhead Bay   *Fax* (015394) 31474
Ambleside LA22 0ES   *E-mail* lit@regentlakes.co.uk
                                Website www.regentlakes.co.uk

Standing opposite the slipway at Waterhead Bay on Lake Windermere, this traditional hotel is adorned in summer with hanging flower baskets. The Hewitt family owners have presided for many years, and the nominator admired the "combination of good food, relaxed atmosphere, excellent location for walking, and good value for money". The lake is visible from Sail Loft, a top room with nautical decor and a private balcony; spacious suites, also with a private balcony, overlook the flowery courtyard. The newest rooms are in a building in the garden. Some rooms overlook the road (busy by day, but quiet at night). The menu is "modern English with a taste of Cumbria", eg, roasted fillet of Cumbrian beef, or Holker Hall venison steak, followed by such hearty desserts as brioche bread-and-butter pudding with an apricot glaze, or chocolate roulade. Wines are modestly priced. There is a very small indoor swimming pool. More reports, please.

Open All year, except Christmas.
Rooms 3 suites, 24 double, 3 single. 5 in garden. 7 on ground floor.
Facilities Ramp. Lounge, drawing room, cocktail bar, restaurant (classical background music; pianist twice weekly); small indoor swimming pool. Courtyard, ½-acre garden. Near Lake Windermere: sailing, water-skiing, fishing.
Location S of centre on A591 Kendal–Keswick, at Waterhead Bay. Garden-facing rooms quietest. Train: Windermere (5 miles); then taxi/bus.
Restrictions No smoking: dining rooms, some bedrooms, 1 lounge. No dogs in public rooms.
Credit cards MasterCard, Visa.
Terms B&B: single £39–£59, double £79–£99, suite £89–£109; D,B&B: single £55–£89, double £109–£129, suite £119–£139. Set lunch £15, dinner £27.50. Off-season breaks. *V*

Rothay Manor   *Tel* (015394) 33605
Rothay Bridge   *Fax* (015394) 33607
Ambleside LA22 0EH   *E-mail* hotel@rothaymanor.co.uk
                                Website www.rothaymanor.co.uk

♀ *César award in 1992*

This listed Georgian house was once the home of a prosperous Liverpool merchant. Many original architectural features have been retained, including an imposing first-floor veranda with cast iron railings that overlooks the immaculate gardens. Inside are smart lounges and "an atmosphere of calm", despite a busy one-way traffic system close by. The bedroom windows are double-glazed, and the quietest rooms are on the garden side. Most are spacious, with a country house decor, fruit, bottled water, etc; three were recently refurbished. The lounges have open fires, deep carpets, flowers, books and magazines, and "squashy chairs". The hotel is run by brothers Nigel and Stephen Dixon, with their wives. Colette Nixon and Jane Binn are in charge of the restaurant, which has had a *Good Food Guide* entry for many years, thanks to the quality of its traditional cooking: roast beef, braised mallard, chocolate truffle gâteau, apple mincemeat tart are regular dishes, and there is a separate vegetarian menu. A wine is recommended to accompany each dish – "Their advice is worth following," says one aficionado. Dinner is served by candlelight on polished wooden tables, with heavy glass and tableware. Portions are generous, but guests may take three courses rather than five, and pay less. A traditional Sunday lunch is served; during the week there is a light lunch menu or soup and sandwiches. Plenty of choice at breakfast; afternoon teas are lavish and "good value". The "efficient service" and the "kind staff" are regularly praised. So are such thoughtful touches as the display, each day, of the weather forecast in reception. Special meals are provided for children, as are free cots, highchairs and baby-listening. (*SP, and others*)

Open 9 Feb–3 Jan.
Rooms 3 suites (in annexe, 20 yds: 1 honeymoon; 2 family, 1 with ♿ access), 15 double, 2 single.
Facilities Ramp. 3 lounges, 2 restaurants; meeting/conference facilities. No background music. 1-acre garden: croquet. Free use of nearby leisure centre. Near River Rothay and Lake Windermere: sailing, water-skiing, fishing, riding, golf.
Location On A593 to Coniston, ¼ mile SW of Ambleside. Garden-facing rooms quietest. Train: Windermere (5 miles); then taxi/bus.
Restrictions No smoking: restaurant, 1 lounge. No very young children in restaurant at night. No dogs.
Credit cards All major cards accepted.
Terms [2000] B&B: single £65–£75, double £110–£120, suite £150–£170; D,B&B: single £90–£100, double £150–£185, suite £200–£220. Set lunch £13.50, dinner (2 to 5 courses) £24–£30. Reductions for children. Winter rates. Off-season breaks. Christmas package. 1-night bookings sometimes refused Sat.

Rowanfield   *Tel* (015394) 33686
Kirkstone Road   *Fax* (015394) 31569
Ambleside LA22 9ET   *E-mail* email@rowanfield.com
                                        Website www.rowanfield.com

A small late-Regency farmhouse in a "gorgeous position" above Lake Windermere, on the road to Kirkstone Pass. It has panoramic views from "the hundreds" to "Coniston Old Man" and beyond. It is run as a guest house by the "very friendly" owners, Philip and Jane Butcher (he does the cooking). They have been redecorating, while maintaining the period feel. The lounge, now with much green, is equipped with a wood-burning stove, books, maps and games. The bedrooms are cheerful, with bright colours and patterned wallpaper; some have a sitting area, and the family room has a patio balcony; there are low-beamed or sloping ceilings in some; all have TV. The dining room has the original flagstone floor, a grandfather clock, an old pine dresser. An "excellent dinner", at 7, is sometimes available (when it is not, the Butchers can suggest local restaurants). Guests are asked to make their choice by 5 pm. A sample menu includes: poached pears with cottage cheese and tarragon vinaigrette; carrot and onion soup; chicken breast with honey and mustard glaze. There is always a hot or a cold pudding (eg, pear and pecan strudel or soft chocolate tart). Unlicensed; bring your own wine. At breakfast (8.15 to 9.30 am) there is freshly squeezed orange juice, home-made bread, American-style pancakes and a Cumberland spread. Stagshaw Gardens (National Trust) are nearby. (*KR*)

Open End Mar–end Nov, Christmas, New Year. Dinner not always available.
Rooms 3 superior, 5 double. No telephone.
Facilities 2 lounges, dining room (classical background music during dinner), drying room. ¾-acre garden. Lake Windermere, with water sports, 1½ miles. Unsuitable for &.
Location NE of Ambleside. Turn off A591 towards Kirkstone almost opposite *Bridge House*; *Rowanfield* ¾ mile on right. Train: Windermere; then taxi.
Restrictions No smoking. No children under 8. No dogs.
Credit cards MasterCard, Visa.
Terms [2000] B&B: single £52–£65, double £62–£90; D,B&B: single £83–£88, double £104–£136. Set dinner £23. Christmas package. 1-night bookings occasionally refused.

Wateredge Hotel
Borrans Road, Waterhead Bay
Ambleside LA22 0EP

Tel (015394) 32332
Fax (015394) 31878
E-mail ghg@wateredgehotel.co.uk
Website www.wateredgehotel.co.uk

♀ *César award in 1999*

"We feel at home the moment we arrive," says a regular visitor to this "real family-run hotel". "The welcome is warm, cases are carried, and the receptionist deserves an award for her helpfulness and charm." Derek and Pamela Cowap, their two sons, daughter and daughter-in-law, run this aptly named conversion of two 17th-century fishermen's cottages "with personal care for their guests". Everywhere is "sparkling clean"; the newer lounges are "bright, with lake views", the older ones, and the bar, are darker "but cosy"; some were redecorated this year. The bedrooms are priced according to size and position: some get noise from the nearby road (though it is hidden by thick hedges), in others "the only sound that disturbed us at night was an unusual bout of quacking by the ducks at the edge of the lake". Rooms in the old part are sometimes an odd shape; the newer ones are larger and more conventional. The honeymoon suite has a balcony overlooking the lake. The "good, plain sandwiches at lunch" were enjoyed this year, and dinners are generally thought "excellent – beautifully cooked, not too rich, and nicely but not fussily presented", with traditional dishes like potted shrimps; pea and mint soup; "succulent salmon; excellent Barbary

duck with a sauce of local damsons; refreshing lemon tart; an irresistible medley of exotic fruits". But some visitors would have liked a
few simpler options. Breakfast has freshly squeezed orange juice, "particularly good" muesli, and "grease-free bacon and eggs". But one
reporter thought the marmalade "rather insipid", another wrote of
"indifferent toast" and the Cowaps now write that, in the interest of
hygiene, open bowls of sugar, jam, etc, have been replaced by sealed
portions (anathema to many *Guide* readers). To while away the time,
you can sit in the open air and read, or watch the birds and the boats.
There is an "attractive gravel garden" on wasteland recently acquired
by the hotel. (*Mrs MH Box, and others*)

Open Early Jan–mid-Dec.
Rooms 6 suites (across small courtyard), 14 double, 3 single. 2 on ground
floor.
Facilities 3 lounges, TV room, bar, restaurant (background music at night). 1-
acre grounds: patio, lake frontage, private jetty, rowing boat, fishing, bathing.
Fishing permits for local rivers; complimentary use of nearby leisure club with
swimming pool, sauna, etc. Unsuitable for &.
Location 1 mile S of town; off A591 Kendal–Keswick at Waterhead (roadside
rooms double/triple-glazed). Train: Windermere; then taxi/bus.
Restrictions No smoking: restaurant, 2 lounges. No children under 7. No dogs
in public rooms.
Credit cards Amex, MasterCard, Visa.
Terms [2000] B&B £37–£78; D,B&B £57–£98. Set dinner £29.50. Off-
season breaks. 1-night bookings sometimes refused Sat. *V*

AMPLEFORTH North Yorkshire   Map 4

Shallowdale House   *Tel* (01439) 788325
West End, Ampleforth   *Fax* (01439) 788885
nr York, YO62 4DY

On a sheltered south-facing slope of the Hambleton Hills, this is the
home of Phillip Gill and Anton van der Horst. "They are charming and
kindly hosts," says a report this year. Set above green lawns, the house
was built in 1962. Every room has spectacular views of the surrounding unspoilt countryside, and "the wonderful setting is matched by the
comfort, food and hospitality". A maximum of six guests can be
accommodated at any time, as there are only three bedrooms, all
"charmingly decorated". Dinner, at 7.30, is by arrangement, and the
owners prepare "domestic-eclectic" food, with the emphasis on seasonal ingredients, eg, fennel and potato pancakes; pan-fried
Gressingham duck breasts; lemon meringue roulade. There is a modest wine list. Dinner is served by candlelight, at separate tables; coffee
is taken by a log fire in a lounge with antique furniture and floral fabrics. Breakfast "is excellent", and the bread, cakes and biscuits are
home made. Ampleforth, in the North York Moors National Park, is
famous for its Benedictine priory and public school. A good base for
visiting Castle Howard, Newby Hall, the ruins of Byland, Rievaulx
and Fountains abbeys, etc. Lawrence Sterne was curate in the delightful village of Coxwold, six miles away, where he wrote part of
Tristram Shandy.

Open All year, except Christmas, New Year.
Rooms 3 double (no telephone).
Facilities Drawing room, sitting room, dining room. No background music. 2½-acre grounds. Unsuitable for &.
Location 20 miles N of York. At W end of Ampleforth, on turning to Hambleton. Bus from York.
Restrictions No smoking. No children under 12. No dogs.
Credit cards MasterCard, Visa.
Terms B&B: single £32.50–£55, double £65–£80; D,B&B: single £52.50–£75, double £105–£120. Set dinner £21. Reductions for 3 nights or more. 1-night bookings refused bank holiday weekends. *V*

APPLETHWAITE Cumbria   Map 4

Underscar Manor   *Tel* (017687) 75000
Applethwaite   *Fax* (017687) 74904
nr Keswick CA12 4PH

"It's gorgeous, with wonderful atmosphere, stunning views, superb food," says a visitor in 2000 to this Italianate Victorian house. Its setting, in the Lake District National Park, with views across Derwentwater to the mountains beyond, is described as "one of the most breathtaking that I have ever seen" in *The Diary of a Victorian Country Gentlewoman* of 1860. Red squirrels and kites can be seen in the large wooded grounds; sheep graze a few yards from the terrace. Pauline and Derek Harrison (who also own *Moss Nook*, a reputable Manchester restaurant) and Gordon Evans, "run a slick professional operation, to which they give an air of lovable eccentricity", according to another visitor. Teddy bears are everywhere – one is seated at the disklavier grand piano in the hall, which tinkles away during dinner. "Crystal chandeliers and frilly cushions all add to the charm" (some find it OTT). The best bedrooms overlook the view, as does the ornate conservatory dining room, where smart dress is expected at dinner. Elaborate modern dishes are served by the chef, Robert Thornton, eg, hot-pot gâteau of lobster with a lobster-scented sauce; roast breast of chicken and roulade of leg meat and morille mushrooms, with a dauphinoise of carrot, celeriac and asparagus. Particularly liked was the "choice of seven little puddings on a plate – the mini-sticky toffee pudding was a taste of heaven". The wine list is "impressive, but lacks a selection of wines by the glass". Breakfast is "excellent, with fresh orange juice and hot dishes cooked to order". There are also 25 timeshare apartments in a building adjacent to the hotel, and a spa with an indoor swimming pool. (*Val Hennessy*)

Open All year, except possibly 2–4 Jan.
Rooms 11 double.
Facilities Hall (piano in evening), 2 lounges, restaurant; spa (indoor swimming pool). 40-acre grounds: gardens, woodland, stream; Derwentwater, fishing, water sports 1½ miles; golf nearby. Unsuitable for &.
Location Off A66, 1½ miles N of Keswick. Train: Penrith, then taxi.
Restrictions No smoking in restaurant. No children under 12. No dogs.
Credit cards Amex, MasterCard, Visa.

Terms D,B&B: double £170–£250. Set lunch £25, dinner £30; full alc £47. Special breaks by arrangement. Christmas package. 1-night bookings refused Sat.

ARNCLIFFE North Yorkshire   **Map 4**

Amerdale House   *Tel* (01756) 770250
Arncliffe, Littondale   *Fax* (01756) 770266
Skipton BD23 5QE

♀ *César award in 1995*

With access to "some of the most beautiful countryside in Britain", Paula and Nigel Crapper's Victorian manor house is in one of the quietest backwaters of the Yorkshire Dales. They have many devoted fans, drawn by the "peaceful ambience, superb food and genuine welcome". "I can't praise them highly enough," runs one tribute this year. Another guest writes: "The best part of the day is returning from a walk at 6 pm, to a wondrous kitchen aroma, and Paula's hand-written menu on the hall table. After a delicious dinner comes a malt whisky with home-made truffles by the fire, and then bed, with the moon shining through the window, and only the distant bleating of sheet to disturb the silence." At busy times the Crappers may be less in evidence and the atmosphere less personal, but their staff are "attentive and kindly". The hotel is "by no means luxurious", and the comfortable bedrooms vary in size; some are small; three are on the second floor (no lift). Much redecoration has taken place this year. The ingredients for the four-course dinner menu, cooked by Nigel Crapper, are sourced locally whenever possible, and he serves dishes like asparagus with melted butter and parmesan; casserole of seafood in a saffron sauce; roast rack of Dales lamb with a port and redcurrant jus; poached pear with panna cotta and chocolate sauce. No choice of main course; vegetarians should make their needs known in advance. Prices on the wine list range from £13.25 to £79 a bottle, with good selections from France and the New World. At breakfast there is black pudding and Cumberland sausage, as well as freshly squeezed orange juice and decent toast. The surrounding countryside of Littondale is excellent for walking and bird-watching – the hotel provides local maps, guidebooks, picnic lunches, even a boot box in the porch and help with drying clothes. Fountains Abbey, Harewood House and Skipton Castle are nearby; a spectacular 14-mile drive will take you to the start of the Settle–Carlisle Railway. (*JD Campbell, Trevor Lockwood, Martin Daly, and others*)

Open Mid-Mar–Mid-Nov. Restaurant closed midday.
Rooms 11 double. 1 in converted stables.
Facilities Lounge, library, bar, restaurant. No background music. 2-acre grounds. Unsuitable for &.
Location 17 miles NW of Skipton. Fork left off B6160 to Arncliffe. Bus every Wed.
Restrictions No smoking: restaurant. No dogs in hotel (annexe room only).
Credit cards MasterCard, Visa.
Terms [2000] D,B&B £69.50–£71.50. Single supplement £10. Set dinner £30. Special breaks: 4 nights for price of 3. 1-night bookings refused some weekends in high season.

ASHBOURNE Derbyshire | Map 3

Callow Hall
Mappleton
Ashbourne DE6 2AA

Tel (01335) 300900
Fax (01335) 300512
E-mail reservations@callowhall.co.uk
Website www.callowhall.co.uk

A Victorian mansion "of much charm", in an elevated position at the southern edge of the Peak District National Park. Set up a tree-lined drive in large grounds outside a pretty market town, it looks over rolling fells and dales, and the valley of the River Dove and its tributary, the Bentley Brook (with fishing rights for trout and grayling). "It is an oasis of peace, away from the nearby tourist bustle," says a visitor this year. Another wrote: "As a woman travelling alone, I look for somewhere I can feel at ease on my own. This is a beautiful place to stay." The owners, David, Dorothy and Anthony Spencer, hoteliers for many years, are "unpretentious, kind and welcoming". Mrs Spencer is usually at reception; her husband and son are the chefs. They do not offer flunkey-type service – you may have to carry your suitcases; bedrooms are not serviced at night. The interior has been described as "pleasingly simple, and mercifully free of OTT country house decor". With rugs on polished floors, stags' heads in the hall, bowls of flowers and pot-pourri, "it has the atmosphere of a loved and well-used family home". Some of the old furniture is heavily carved. The bedrooms, up a carved wooden staircase, are named after members of the family. Anthony is liked (it has a large, well-lit bathroom), but some rooms are small and have been considered expensive. Home-made biscuits, fresh fruit, mineral water, are replenished daily. The dining room is "dramatic with much red". Dinner is copious, if "a bit pricey", and the cooking is generally admired. Bread is home baked, sausages and salmon home-smoked. Main courses might include medallions of local venison, "full of flavour, with a gamey jus", sirloin of beef with duck liver pâté, oyster mushrooms and a red wine sauce; always a vegetarian option. Crisp vegetables come on a side plate. Puddings are a strong point, "especially the famous Callow Tart, a mixture of almonds, apricots and mincemeat". Service is "professionally friendly". "First-class breakfasts", in a light room, have freshly squeezed orange juice, real tea, "perfect poached eggs". Children are welcomed. Functions are sometimes held. The garden and woodland "are gradually returning to their former Victorian glory", say the Spencers. Holly, "an affectionate yet restrained" labrador, will accompany visitors on walks. Nearby are many stately homes, including Chatsworth, Kedleston, Hardwick Hall, Haddon Hall, and Calke Abbey; also Alton Towers. (*Mrs DE Garrad, JD Crosland, Sue Davies, and others*)

Open All year, except Christmas, possibly 1 week Feb.
Rooms 1 suite, 16 double. 2 on ground floor.
Facilities Lounge, bar, restaurant; function/conference facilities. No background music. 42-acre grounds: garden, woodland, farm, stables; river, fishing (tuition available).
Location ¾ mile from Ashbourne: A515 to Buxton; sharp left at top of 1st hill by *Bowling Green* pub, 1st right to Mappleton; cross bridge; drive on right. Train: Derby; then taxi.

Restrictions No smoking in restaurant. Dogs by arrangement; not in public rooms.
Credit cards All major cards accepted.
Terms [2000] B&B: single £85–£110, double £130–£190, suite £190. Set Sun lunch £20.50, dinner £38; full alc £41. Weekend, midweek breaks. 1-night bookings sometimes refused weekends. *V*

ASHBURTON Devon   **Map 1**

Holne Chase   *Tel* (01364) 631471
Ashburton   *Fax* (01364) 631453
nr Newton Abbot TQ13 7NS   *E-mail* info@holne-chase.co.uk
                                          Website www.holne-chase.co.uk

۞ *César award in 1999*

The "idyllic setting" of this former hunting lodge makes one "hanker back to an England almost lost", says a visitor this year. Owned by Sebastian and Philippa Hughes, it is on a huge estate in the Dartmoor National Park. The River Dart runs through the grounds; there is a pond with ducks and geese, and acres of woodland with wild flowers, animals and birds. It is famed for its dog-friendliness, with Batty the basset hound as hostess (she has her own website: www.batty-basset.co.uk). Dogs and their owners are accommodated in converted stables that open on to the drive and gardens (these rooms are said to have thin walls). Front bedrooms in the main house look across the lawn and tall trees to distant hills. Some rooms are quite small, with a small bathroom. The idiosyncratic style of the place does not suit everyone: we have had some reports of a cool welcome, and complaints unsympathetically handled, and it is not cheap. But the majority are favourable: "the staff are entirely professional"; "food, comfort and service all impeccable"; "a hospitable proprietor". And for one lucky man, *Holne Chase* was the scene of a successful Valentine's Day proposal, "with the complicity of the restaurant manager". Chef Ross Hadley is new this year: his "fresh and simplistic approach" to cooking has attracted praise: "We found ourselves in food heaven"; "highly imaginative meals with first-class service". The modern menus include, eg, beignets of lemon sole with basil oil; breast of guinea fowl wrapped in a wild mushroom mousse, with roast parsnips; vanilla crème brûlée with rhubarb syrup. There is now always a vegetarian main course. The wine list is "great but expensive", but there are some good house wines. Light lunches are available. The house has a "comfortable, slightly dated" feel: log fires burn in the public rooms, newspapers lie around in the bar. Many guests come for the fishing; the hotel has rights on a mile of the Dart, and will arrange tuition; riding and shooting on Dartmoor can be arranged. The Hugheses have expanded their empire with the acquisition of the *Little Admiral*, Dartmouth, which makes its *Guide* debut this year, and *St Olave's*, Exeter, currently on the Shortlist. (*John Grist, MH, Alexander Keeling, Sir John Hall, DC Rissik, and others*)

Open All year.
Rooms 6 suites, 11 double. 6 in stables 150 yds. 1 on ground floor.
Facilities Ramp. Lounge, library, bar, restaurant; private dining/meeting

room. No background music. 70-acre grounds in 300-acre estate: River Dart (fly fishing), croquet, putting. Golf nearby.

Location From N and E: M5 to Exeter, then A38 to 2nd Ashburton turn-off; pass Pear Tree garage on left; after 2 miles cross Holne bridge; hotel ¼ mile on right. From Plymouth: leave A38 at 1st Ashburton turn-off. Train: Newton Abbot; taxi or hotel may meet.

Restrictions No smoking in restaurant. No children under 10 in restaurant at night. No dogs in public rooms.

Credit cards Diners, MasterCard, Visa.

Terms B&B: single from £95, double £125–£145, suite £165; D,B&B (2 nights min.): double £150–£175, suite £190–£205. Set lunch £20–£25, dinner £32.50. Special breaks. Christmas, New Year, cookery, painting, shooting packages; fly-fishing courses; garden tours. 3-centre packages (Ashburton, Dartmouth, Exeter). 1-night bookings sometimes refused. *V*

ASHFORD Kent *See SHORTLIST*   Map 2

ASHWATER Devon   Map 1

Blagdon Manor   *Tel* (01409) 211224
Ashwater EX21 5DF   *Fax* (01409) 211634
                                    E-mail stay@blagdon.com
                                    Website www.blagdon.com

A Grade II listed 17th-century country house "in the middle of nowhere", on the Devon/Cornwall border. Set in large grounds, and carefully restored and furnished by the "delightful owners", Tim and Gill Casey, it has oak beams, slate flagstones and a snooker table in the bar, chintzy fabrics, fresh flowers, an open fire in winter. A "delicious home-cooked dinner" is served at 8 pm in house-party style round one long table. No choice until dessert; a sample menu includes wild mushroom soup; fillet of lamb with a herb crust; chocolate crème brûlée with a raspberry sorbet. "It is *so quiet,*" said the nominator. "No sound of traffic, only birds and cows. A gorgeous library, superb sitting room, lovely grounds." You can see Dartmoor in one direction, in the other the Cornish coast, ten miles away. Local attractions include Rosemoor and other gardens, and sundry National Trust properties. (*VH*)

Open All year, except Christmas.

Rooms 7 double.

Facilities Lounge, library, games room, bar/snooker room, dining room; 2 meeting rooms. No background music. 8-acre grounds: gardens, golf practice, croquet, helipad. Shooting, riding, fishing nearby. Unsuitable for &.

Location 6 miles NE of Launceston. A388 towards Holworthy. Past Chapman's Well and 1st sign to Ashwater. Right at 2nd sign; first right (signposted Blagdon/Viza). House on right.

Restrictions Smoking in bar/snooker room only. No children under 16. Dogs by arrangement; not in public rooms.

Credit cards Amex, MasterCard, Visa.

Terms B&B: single £60–£70, double £95–£110. Set dinner £21.21.

If you find details of a hotel's location inadequate, please tell us.

ATHERSTONE Warwickshire   Map 3

Chapel House   *Tel* (01827) 718949
Friar's Gate   *Fax* (01827) 717702
Atherstone CV9 1EY

In the square (a conservation area) of an old market town and next
door to St Mary's church, whose bells chime hourly, stands David
Arnold's 18th-century white-painted dower house. Many original features have been maintained. Now a small restaurant-with-rooms, it is
surrounded by a walled garden with fishpond and fountain. Bedrooms
are small (some have a sloping ceiling), and some bathrooms may be
"a little cramped". Quietest rooms overlook the garden, as do most
public rooms. The restaurant holds special events on many Fridays:
eg, a pre-Burns night supper ("Haggis, neeps, and a wee dram");
Befores and Afters (for those who prefer to omit a main course); the
Chapel House Pudding Club ("last time, someone managed 12; can
you?"). Dishes on the varied menus include, eg, risotto of south coast
crab; grilled fillet of Scotch beef; rich chocolate tart. There is always
a dish of the day. "The owner is charm personified," and, "All the staff
were nice; our French waiter was delightful," are recent comments.
Birmingham and the National Exhibition Centre are within easy reach,
and the A5 is two miles away. Local attractions include Tamworth
Castle, Bosworth battlefield, Lichfield and Coventry cathedrals.
(*Diana and Jonathan Oxley*)

Open All year, except Christmas. Restaurant closed bank holiday Mons.
Rooms 9 double, 5 single.
Facilities Lounge, 2 dining rooms; 2 conference rooms. No background
music. ¼-acre garden. Unsuitable for &.
Location In market square, by church. From S bear right at Nationwide
Building Society, then right at T-junction. First left into Friar's Gate. Parking
directly outside.
Restrictions No smoking in restaurant. No children under 10 in restaurant.
No dogs.
Credit cards All major cards accepted.
Terms [2000] B&B: single £52.50–£60, double £70–£85. Set lunch £15; full
alc £34–£37.50. *V*

AYLESBURY Buckinghamshire   Map 2

Hartwell House   *Tel* (01296) 747444
Oxford Road   *Fax* (01296) 747450
nr Aylesbury HP17 8NL   *E-mail* info@hartwell-house.com
                                              Website www.hartwell-house.com

"The combination of an architecturally distinguished building and a
fine setting must make this one of the most attractive hotels in the
UK," says a report this year on this magnificent honey-coloured mansion near Aylesbury. Other visitors "spent a weekend and loved it". It
stands in a huge park with a little chapel, a trout lake, statuary, cows
behind a ha-ha. The exiled king of France, Louis XVIII, held court at
Hartwell House in the early 19th century, and today, in its tenth year

as a hotel (Relais & Châteaux), it is much visited by the rich and famous (Bill Clinton and the Emperor of Japan have both stayed), and often used for corporate events. The interior is grand: an 18th-century Baroque great hall, a Jacobean central staircase, fine paintings and plasterwork, chandeliers and a maze of corridors. The huge best bedrooms have large windows, panelling and tapestries. "The King's Room, with its double aspect, yellow curtains and four-poster bed, was ideal for a golden wedding – at a price (£350)," one couple wrote. Newer rooms (some are duplexes) are in *Hartwell Court*, a converted stable block. This also houses a spa with a swimming pool, a small gym and a buttery that serves light lunches. The dining room is formal (men are required to wear a jacket and tie), and the dishes on "Bill of Fare" are elaborate, eg, trio of foie gras with a millefeuille of spiced apples; seabass stuffed with a morel mousse; milk chocolate bavarois on a coffee bean sauce. We would be grateful for reports on the work of Daniel Richardson, formerly *sous-chef*, who has taken over the kitchen. The cooking has been thought "good, but not outstanding" in the past, and breakfasts may be "only adequate". But the courteous manager, Jonathan Thompson, and his staff are regularly praised. Nearby Aylesbury has suffered at the hands of developers, though some attractive old houses round the church survive, and the award-winning Buckinghamshire County Museum is worth a visit. *Hartwell House*'s summer breaks include free entry into one of various local stately homes. (*Sir Timothy Harford, and others*)

Open All year.
Rooms 13 suites, 32 double, 1 single. Some in stable block. Some on ground floor. 1 equipped for &.
Facilities Lift, ramp. 4 drawing rooms, bar, 4 dining rooms; conference facilities; spa: indoor swimming pool, whirlpool, sauna, beauty salon, bar/buttery. No background music. Pianist in vestibule, Fri/Sat evening. 94-acre grounds: tennis, croquet, lake (fishing), woodlands.
Location 2 miles S of Aylesbury on A418 towards Oxford; hotel on right. Train: Aylesbury; then taxi.
Restrictions No smoking: dining rooms, morning room, some bedrooms. No children under 8. No dogs in public rooms, main house bedrooms.
Credit cards MasterCard, Visa.
Terms [2000] Room: single £135, double £215, suite £325–£660. Breakfast: continental £11.50, English £16.90. D,B&B £160–£215 per person. Set lunch £22.00, dinner £45. Winter, spring champagne breaks; summer breaks, spa breaks. Christmas, New Year house parties.

BAMPTON Devon   **Map 1**

Bark House   NEW   *Tel* (01398) 351236
Oakfordbridge   *Website* www.lineone.net/~bark.house.hotel
Nr Bampton EX16 9HZ

Long, low and wisteria-covered, this old stone house in the Exe valley was once a barn used to store bark chips for the local tannery, hence its name. Now it is run by owner/chef Alistair Kameen, with Justine Hill, as a reasonably priced small hotel. The nominator, from New Zealand, found it "very appealing . . . Our bedroom was large, with five windows ranging from stone-mullioned to bay, an arched oak door to the garden, and quality furnishings. The owner is into food. The excellent three-course dinner, preceded by canapés in the lounge, ended with coffee and truffles." Two choices of each course on the menu, eg, pear and parsnip soup, or salmon and dill flan; local cod with a tomato sauce, or beef casserole; chocolate tart or butterscotch ice-cream. Breakfast is "equally good and substantial". Morning tea can be brought to the room or DIY; children of "considerate parents" are welcomed. Guests can take tea and drinks in the lovingly tended terraced garden. *Bark House* does its best to welcome guests with a mobility problem, but due to its age, it has no facilities for wheelchairs. It is on a road that is sometimes busy by day, but quiet at night. Good walking nearby, and the north and south Devon Coast Paths are about 40 minutes away by car. (*Craig Fletcher*)

Open April–Oct, Christmas, New Year. Restricted service Nov–Mar.
Rooms 5 double. Also one 2-bedroomed self-catering cottage.
Facilities Lounge, restaurant (light classical background music at night). 1¼-acre garden.
Location Hamlet 3 miles W of Bampton. On A396, 9 miles N of Tiverton. Train: Tiverton Parkway.
Restrictions No smoking: restaurant, bedrooms. No dogs in public rooms.
Credit cards None accepted.
Terms [2000] B&B £32.50–£45; D,B&B £54–£65.50. Set dinner £22.50. 2-day special break: D,B&B from £51 per person. Christmas, New Year packages.

BARNARD CASTLE Co. Durham   **Map 4**

Homelands   BUDGET   *Tel* (01833) 638757
85 Galgate
Barnard Castle DL12 8ES

The ruins of a 12th-century castle, built for Barnard Balliol (a cohort of William the Conqueror), give the name to this market town on the River Tees. Charles Dickens is one of many famous visitors to be commemorated with a blue plaque, and the famous Bowes Museum is housed in a French Renaissance-style mansion on the town's outskirts. This "marvellous place" makes a good base for visiting all these attractions, say *Guide* readers. Run by the "svelte, dynamic" owner, Irene Williamson, it is the "epitome of an excellent guest house". The restaurant, open to the public and attracting diners from nearby hotels, looks over "an immaculate cottage garden" at the rear. The food, on a short, weekly-changing menu, is admired too: "leek and cheese tartlet with wonderfully light pastry; succulent pork fillet; tender, rare beef. Chocolate biscuit feuilleté with fresh fruit was crisp, and delightfully presented." Mr Williamson "knows about wine and serves it properly"; several good options are available by the glass. The house is filled with antiques ("there to be used, not just looked at") and pictures. The bedrooms have been redecorated this year. Front ones overlook a road that is busy by day but quiet at night. All have double glazing, a colour-coordinated decor, TV, etc, and thoughtful extras. Some are "compact" with a small shower room. "Close to perfection in the small town hotel bracket," says an inspector. "Exceptional quality at a budget price." Very cheap; very small (five bedrooms), very popular. Book well ahead. (*Mrs B Durkin, and others*)

Open All year, except Christmas, New Year.
Rooms 3 double, 2 single.
Facilities Lounge, restaurant (light classical background music at night). Small garden. Unsuitable for &.
Location Central (rooms double-glazed). Bus stop 50 metres.
Restrictions No smoking: restaurant, bedrooms. No children under 6. No dogs.
Credit cards None accepted.
Terms B&B: single £25–£30, double £42–£50. Set dinner £13.95.

BARNSTAPLE Devon   **Map 1**

Lynwood House   *Tel* (01271) 343695
Bishop's Tawton Road   *Fax* (01271) 379340
Barnstaple EX32 9EF   *E-mail* info@thelynwood.freeserve.co.uk
                              Website www.thelynwood.freeserve.co.uk

A yellow brick Victorian restaurant-with-rooms, on the edge of an old market town on the Taw estuary. It has been run for 31 years by the Roberts family. John Roberts is front-of-house; his wife and son, Ruth and Matthew, are the chefs. The building, fronted by a gravel parking area, is hardly a thing of beauty, and it is on a road, but inside it is "warm, and personally run", with an "unpretentious, lived-in feel", and "the owners are extremely professional hoteliers". The restaurant, popular with locals, is attractively decorated, with round tables, candles and plants. Mrs Roberts "seeks out the best ingredients, and grows herbs and vegetables". The fish dishes were considered the most successful by our inspector, especially the "delicious chunky fish soup", but she thought the prices, about £15.50 for a main course, high for the area. The five bedrooms "are first rate". Colour schemes may not be particularly harmonious, but each room is well equipped, with a cafetière, fresh milk, biscuits, fruit, etc, and "the showers really are high powered". Breakfast, in a small, pleasant upstairs room, includes freshly squeezed orange juice, creamy scrambled eggs with smoked salmon ("the best I've eaten"), and home-made marmalade. Light lunches are served in the bar. "Two adorable springer spaniels add just the right homely touch." Beaches and the Royal North Devon Golf Club (the oldest in England) are nearby.

Open All year; restaurant closed Sun to non-residents.
Rooms 5 double.
Facilities Lounge, bar, breakfast room, restaurant. No background music. Beaches, golf nearby. Unsuitable for &.
Location 1 mile SE of centre. Carpark. Regular buses, courtesy car, from station.
Restrictions No smoking: restaurant, 2 bedrooms. Dogs in bedrooms by arrangement.
Credit cards Amex, MasterCard, Visa.
Terms B&B: single £47.50, double £67.50. Full alc £31. 2-day break: D,B&B (double) £220. *V*

BARWICK Somerset   Map 2

Little Barwick House   *Tel* (01935) 423902
Barwick, nr Yeovil BA22 9TD   *Fax* (01935) 420908

For many years a *Guide* favourite under the ownership of Christopher
and Veronica Colley, this "charming Georgian house" in an interesting village near Yeovil was taken over this year by Tim and Emma
Ford, who are running it with an emphasis on the restaurant. "They are
a nice young couple, with plenty of experience behind them," said a
visitor soon after the takeover. "The food was wonderful, with good
choice, and there is a comprehensive wine list – most bottles are under
the £20 mark." The public rooms have been redecorated: the lounge is
"bright and comfortable"; there is a "cosy bar". Tim Ford has worked
in some distinguished hotel restaurants, including *Sharrow Bay*,
Ullswater, *Mallory Court*, Bishop's Tachbrook, and *Summer Lodge*,
Evershot (*qqv*). His cooking is praised for its "lack of fuss". Duck liver
parfait, grilled Dover sole, roast Dorset lamb, dark chocolate cheesecake are some of the specialities served in the smart dining room. The
bedrooms are being "freshened up". Some shower rooms are small.
Breakfast includes generous glassfuls of fresh orange juice and "wonderful scrambled eggs". Winter breaks are good value. Barwick is
noted chiefly for the 18th-century follies – pillars, towers and arches –
on the edge of its park. There are plenty of houses and gardens to visit
nearby. (*Heather Sharland*)

Open All year. Restaurant closed to non-residents Sun evening/Mon.
Rooms 6 double.
Facilities Lounge, bar, restaurant. No background music. 3½-acre garden.
Unsuitable for ♻.
Location Left off A37 Yeovil–Dorchester at 1st roundabout. Hotel ¼ mile on
left. Train: Yeovil (1 mile).
Restrictions No smoking: restaurant, bedrooms. No dogs in public rooms.
Credit cards Amex, MasterCard, Visa.
Terms [2000] B&B £42–£46.50; D,B&B £60–£66.50. Set lunch £11.95, din-
ner £27.95. Reductions for 2 nights or more. 1-night bookings sometimes
refused. *V*

BASLOW Derbyshire   Map 3

The Cavendish   *Tel* (01246) 582311
Baslow DE45 1SP   *Fax* (01246) 582312
                   E-mail info@cavendish-hotel.net
                  Website www.cavendish-hotel.net

"Comfortable and well run. The situation is glorious." "Not cheap, but
the staff were delightful without exception. We liked the informal, yet
efficient style." "Civilised, low-key and unpretentious." This year and
last, there has been praise for this hotel owned by the Duke and
Duchess of Devonshire, which Eric Marsh has run since 1975. It
stands on the northern edge of the family estate in the Peak District
National Park, beside a busy road, but the bedrooms overlook
Chatsworth Park, with its ancient trees, river and garden; guests can

reach it by walking through a field. The hotel is child-friendly, and the winter offer is good value: book for Friday and Saturday nights and stay free on Sunday night, paying only for meals. The public rooms may be "a bit dated", but they are furnished with antiques (many are from Chatsworth), and they have impressive flower arrangements, and log fires in winter. Eric Marsh has assembled an interesting collection of paintings, "ranging from Victorian fine art to 20th-century graffiti", and a bronze figure on the lawn was commissioned to commemorate the millennium. "It is a joy," one guest wrote. The bedrooms in the Mitford wing are named after members of the duchess's famous family; older rooms are in what was once an inn. Most have been found comfortable; some have "a generous sitting area", though bathrooms may be "a bit old-fashioned", and lighting "romantic, but hell to read by". The suite, with a separate entrance, is generally let by the month. In the restaurant the food is thought good, if sometimes "over-ambitious", with dishes like lamb and apricot sausage on a galette of potatoes with a sauce of sweetbreads, kidneys and wild mushrooms; ragout of monkfish and cockles in a white Burgundy and saffron sauce with saffron wine parcels. For an extra charge you can dine at a table in the kitchen, watching the chef, Nick Buckingham, at work. The simpler meals, served in the Garden Room, were particularly enjoyed this year: "Poached salmon, cooked to perfection; robust Irish stew with really good gravy." Breakfast, served all morning, has "really good home-made marmalade", freshly squeezed orange juice, a wide variety of cooked dishes, and it can include Bucks Fizz. *The Cavendish*'s new brother, *The George*, Hathersage (*qv*), makes its *Guide* debut this year. (*Sir Timothy Harford, Padi Howard; also Tessa Stuart*)

Open All year.
Rooms 1 suite, 23 double.
Facilities Lounge with bar, 2 restaurants; private dining room, conference room. No background music. 1-acre ground on edge of park: putting green. River, fishing nearby. Unsuitable for &.
Location On A619 in Chatsworth grounds. M1 exit 29. Train: Chesterfield; then bus/taxi.
Restrictions No smoking: restaurant, some bedrooms. No dogs.
Credit cards All major cards accepted.
Terms Room: single £95–£115, double £125–£145, suite £195. Breakfast £6.50–£10.60 or alc. Light meals in Garden Room. Restaurant: set lunch £30.50, dinner £38.75. Winter bonus weekends; Romantic breaks; Christmas package. 1-night bookings sometimes refused in summer.

Fischer's Baslow Hall   *Tel* (01246) 583259
Calver Road   *Fax* (01246) 583818
Baslow DE45 1RR

♀ *César award in 1998*

"An impeccable welcome, top-class hospitality and superlative food," say regular *Guide* correspondents this year. "If only more hoteliers were like Max and Susan Fischer." Other visitors, too, admired the "professional, rather than exuberantly jolly, style" of this Edwardian stone manor house. It stands up a winding chestnut tree-lined drive on

the edge of the Chatsworth estate. Also liked is the decor, with its
enthusiastically collected antiques and country pine furniture, set off
by bold colours, good fabrics, fresh flowers and bowls of pot-pourri.
The Fischers run both a *Michelin*-starred restaurant and a bistro
(*Michelin* red "Meals") in their two front rooms, using "fresher than
fresh ingredients" and "with a striking use of herbs that enhance and
complement the flavour of the main ingredients". The modern
European specialities include, eg, chargrilled duck sausage on can-
nellini bean panache; pig's trotter stuffed with chicken and morel
mushrooms. The fresh fruit Pavlova "is exquisite". Even the brasserie
dishes are "quite elaborate, with rich sauces". There is an extensive
and fairly priced wine list. Residents must reserve a dinner table. The
bedrooms match the rest: "We were upgraded to a suite; it had
antiques, interesting pictures and ornaments, free sherry and mineral
water, and a basket of interesting fruit. The bathroom had generous
goodies and a huge bath." Other visitors liked Haddon, a room with
high ceilings, and tall windows overlooking the front garden. But
another wrote that some rooms are very small. "Impeccable breakfasts" have freshly squeezed orange juice, home-baked bread and
croissants. Haddon Hall is four miles distant; Chatsworth, Hardwick
and Kedleston halls are a comfortable drive away; a good base for
walking and climbing. (*Francine and Ian Walsh, Rosemary Wright,
DW, and others*)

Open All year, except 25/26 Dec. Restaurant closed Sun evening; café closed
Sat evening/Sun (informal supper served to residents).
Rooms 1 suite, 5 double.
Facilities Reception, lounge/bar, breakfast room, restaurant, café (light back-
ground music). Function facilities. 5-acre grounds. Fishing 3 miles, golf
nearby. Unsuitable for &. Civil wedding licence.
Location Take A623 Baslow–Stockport. Last entrance on right within village
boundary. Train: Chesterfield, 12 miles; then taxi.
Restrictions No smoking: restaurant, bedrooms. No children under 12 in
restaurant after 7 pm. No dogs.
Credit cards All major cards accepted.
Terms B&B: single £80–£95, double £95–£130. English breakfast £8.50.
Restaurant: set lunch (2 to 3 courses) £20–£24, dinner £45; café: full alc
£31.50. Child accommodated in parents' room: B&B £15. Winter 2-night
packages; weekend breaks. 1-night bookings sometimes refused bank holidays, New Year.

BASSENTHWAITE LAKE Cumbria   Map 4

The Pheasant   NEW   *Tel* (017687) 76234
Bassenthwaite Lake   *Fax* (017687) 76002
nr Cockermouth   *E-mail* pheasant@easynet.co.uk
CA13 9YE   *Website* www.the-pheasant.co.uk

*Set back from the lake among trees: 400-year-old inn, warmly recom-
mended this year for "combination of atmosphere and comfort".
Owned by a trust; much improved since major refurbishment and
arrival, in 1999, of new manager, Matthew Wylie. 3 lounges (1 no-
smoking), oak-panelled bar. Antiques, beams, log fires. Traditional*

cooking in smoke-free restaurant (popular for Sunday lunch). No background music. 20-acre grounds. No children under 8. No dogs in bedrooms. Closed Christmas Day. MasterCard, Visa accepted. 16 bedrooms. B&B £45–£80; D,B&B (min. 2 nights) £58.50–£98.50. Set lunch £15.50, dinner £22.95. 1-night bookings refused weekends. More reports, please. *V*

BATH Somerset   **Map 2**

Apsley House   *Tel* (01225) 336966
141 Newbridge Hill   *Fax* (01225) 425462
Bath BA1 3PT
                                              E-mail info@apsley-house.co.uk
                                              Website www.apsley-house.co.uk

David and Annie Lanz's "upmarket B&B", a mile from the centre, was built as a country house. It is now in a built-up area but inside, said its nominator, it seems unchanged, with period features, and antiques and original oil paintings appropriate to its date. Breakfast (it includes smoked salmon, strawberries and melon, large pots of preserves, "even Marmite") is served at separate tables in a "lovely room" that overlooks the garden. Vegetarians are catered for. The drawing room is "lovely too", and a bedroom at the top was admired: "Large and pretty, without being too chintzy, it had a big cast iron bath and a shower cubicle." Another room, lower down, is "huge, with an immense bathroom, a fireplace, and French windows opening on to the garden" (where tables and chairs stand on the lawn). There are fresh flowers and fruit in the bedrooms, and the hosts are "warmly welcoming". No evening meals, but Bath has one of the highest con-centrations of reputable eating places outside London. (*DP*)

Open All year, except Christmas.
Rooms 9 double.
Facilities Drawing room, bar, breakfast room: background radio/CDs all day. ¼-acre garden. Unsuitable for ♿.
Location 1 mile W of centre. A4 (Upper Bristol Rd, Newbridge Rd); left into Apsley Rd. Carpark. Bus/taxi from centre.
Restrictions No smoking: breakfast, drawing room, some bedrooms. No children under 5. No dogs.
Credit cards All major cards accepted.
Terms [2000] B&B: single £60–£75, double £75–£125, family £75–£130. 2-night breaks; off-season breaks.

The Bath Priory   *Tel* (01225) 331922
Weston Road   *Fax* (01225) 448276
Bath BA1 2XT
                                              E-mail bathprioryhotel@compuserve.com
                                              Website www.slh.com/theprior

A "magnificent hotel" in a Grade II listed Georgian Gothic-style building in large grounds on the edge of the city. The centre is reached by a short bus ride or a walk through Victoria Park. Owned by Andrew Brownsword, who also owns Bath Rugby Club, and managed by Tim Pettifer, it is liked for the "cosy opulence" of the public rooms, with their large paintings (many are portraits), antiques, chandeliers, flower arrangements and log fires. For many guests, the highlight is the "wonderful food", served in the Gothic Room (with antiques and fine paintings), in a garden room or in an orangery. The chef, Robert Clayton, well deserves his *Michelin* star, says a visitor this year. "The flavours are wonderful, and looking over the immaculate garden is a joy. The staff are unfailingly welcoming." The hotel's vegetable, herb and fruit garden supplies the kitchens, and Mr Clayton's philosophy is: "When properly prepared, the simplest of foods can have the most exquisite taste." The three-course menu changes daily, and includes, eg, ravioli of smoked haddock with a shellfish sauce; roast venison with braised red cabbage; coconut millefeuille with hazelnut cream. The wine list is wide ranging. The bedrooms seem to be variable, however: one couple reported a hot one over the boiler room, and another with poor maintenance. The best are spacious and "thoughtfully furnished"; "one of the best we've had in Britain", says a visitor this year. Those that overlook the gardens are peaceful; others can get traffic noise. There is an open-air swimming pool, and a spa with an indoor pool (in the style of a Roman bath) and a gym. (*Adrian Turner, BW*)

Open All year.
Rooms 27 double, 1 single. Some on ground floor.
Facilities.Drawing room, library, restaurant (classical background music at dinner); conference facilities. 4-acre grounds: swimming pool, croquet. Spa: indoor swimming pool, gym, sauna, etc.
Location 1 mile W of centre, off A4 to Bristol. From E take London Rd to the Paragon; right into Lansdown Rd, 3rd left into Julian Rd; continue along Crescent La, Weston Rd (park on left, golf course on right). Hotel 300 yds on left, after mini-roundabout at junction with Park Lane.
Restrictions No smoking in restaurant. Guide dogs only.
Credit cards All major cards accepted.
Terms [2000] B&B: single £140, double £210–£310; D,B&B: single £160, double £250–£340. Set lunch £25, dinner £45. Weekend breaks. Christmas package.

Harington's Hotel   *Tel* (01225) 461728
8–10 Queen Street   *Fax* (01225) 444804
Bath BA1 1HE   *E-mail* post@haringtonshotel.co.uk
     Website www.haringtonshotel.co.uk

A small hotel, which consists of a group of 18th-century houses on a cobbled street in the middle of town. It is liked for its "agreeably informal style" and the warmth of the owner/managers, Susan and Desmond Pow, "who have a knack for making guests feel at home". Their staff "are unfailingly attentive and friendly". The bedrooms, recently refurbished by Mr Pow, have pastel colours and cable TV, and they are "surprisingly quiet, considering the hotel's position in the centre of Bath". Some are up a steep spiral staircase (no lift; this is a listed building). Breakfast "is served with a smile"; "very good coffee" is on tap all day. The pleasant little café, open to the public, serves reasonably priced light meals – pasta, salads, etc, until 8 pm, and drinks until midnight. Many other eating places are nearby. Parking is awkward: after unloading on the pavement outside, you must drive to the long-term carpark, five minutes' walk away. The

hotel's great advantage is that it is close to the city's main attractions
– the Roman Baths, the Abbey, the Assembly Rooms and the Theatre
Royal. (*AE*)

Open All year, except Christmas.
Rooms 13 double.
Facilities Coffee lounge, bar, restaurant; tiny courtyard. Mixed background
music all day. Unsuitable for &.
Location Central; in small street near Queen Sq. From George St, turn into
Milsom St. Right after *Jolly's* into Quiet St; 1st left into Queen St. Long-term
carpark in Charlotte St, 200 metres (£5 for 24 hours).
Restrictions Smoking in bar only. No dogs.
Credit cards All major cards accepted.
Terms B&B: single £60–£88, double £78–£115. Full alc £21. 1-night book-
ings often refused Sat.

Haydon House   *Tel* (01225) 444919
9 Bloomfield Park   *Fax* (01225) 427351
Bath BA2 2BY   *E-mail* stay@haydonhouse.co.uk
                                   Website www.haydonhouse.co.uk

With a dovecote in front and a colourful rear garden (with statues), this
B&B is in a semi-detached Edwardian house, in a quiet residential
area above the city. No parking problems; it is an easy walk down to
the centre, a steepish walk back (or you can take a bus). Gordon and
Magdalene Ashman-Marr, with two golden retrievers, Cloud and
Cobweb, create a homely feel. The house is crammed with photos of
family and friends, china ornaments, plants and dried flowers. The
bedrooms, decorated in bold colours and packed with ornaments, have
home-made shortbread, a decanter of sherry, a hot-water bottle, and a
bath or a power shower. One has a four-poster; a large one at the top,
with a sitting area, is suitable for a family. The "extremely helpful"
owners are regularly praised by *Guide* readers. The host – "he must
have been vaccinated with a phonograph needle", one American visitor wrote – keeps up a flow of conversation while serving the communal breakfast. Plenty of choice: pancakes with maple syrup, whisky or
rum porridge, scrambled eggs with smoked salmon, eggs Benedict,
and home-made mango-and-orange marmalade, all served with good
china, silver and crystal. Vegetarian and vegan options can be
arranged, and a continental breakfast can be taken in the bedroom.
"The gracious Magdalene keeps everything running smoothly." Help
is offered with theatre and dinner reservations. In low season, guests
who book for two nights may stay free for a third, except Friday,
Saturday. (*Warmly endorsed this year by John and Pat Woodliffe*)

Open All year.
Rooms 5 double.
Facilities Sitting room, study, breakfast room (soft classical background
music); sun terrace. ½-acre garden. Sports/leisure centre nearby. "Not really
suitable for &, but they are welcome by prior arrangement."
Location From centre take A367 (to Exeter) *c.* ½ mile up Wells Rd. Right into
shopping area (Bear pub on right). At end of short dual carriageway fork right
into Bloomfield Rd; Bloomfield Pk 2nd right. Street parking. Bus 14 from
centre.
Restrictions No smoking. Children by arrangement. No dogs.

Credit cards Amex, MasterCard, Visa.
Terms B&B: single £50–£65, double £70–£97. 3 nights for price of 2 (except Fri/Sat, bank holidays) Nov–Mar. 1-night bookings occasionally refused weekends. *V*

Lettonie
35 Kelston Road
Bath BA1 3QH

Tel (01225) 446676
Fax (01225) 447541
Website www.bath.co.uk/lettonie

Martin Blunos, "a brilliant chef" (*Michelin* two stars), and his Welsh wife, Siân (front-of-house), preside over this restaurant-with-rooms in a large Georgian house on a hillside on the edge of Bath. With antique furniture, large rooms, high ceilings, verandas and balconies, it is quite imposing, but it is also a family home. The Blunoses live here with their sons, Leon and Mark, and the "unstuffy atmosphere" was liked again this year. Visitors praised the "caring and enthusiastic" owners and their young French staff. There are plenty of reminders of Mr Blunos's homeland: "Lettonie" is French for Latvia; paintings of Latvian country scenes, by Mr Blunos's uncle from Riga, decorate the pretty restaurant, and the signature dish is a spectacular affair of scrambled duck egg with Sevruga caviar, served aflame with blinis and a glass of vodka, for which £5 is added to the price of the *prix-fixe* menu (£47.50). Other dishes include baked cod with a cream sauce, garnished with winkles; braised stuffed pig's trotter with a rich port sauce. The two dining rooms have well-spaced antique tables, comfortable, high-backed chairs, smart place-settings. The bar was recently redecorated to make it more comfortable – "lots of sofas and chairs". The four bedrooms are reserved for restaurant guests. Recent visitors had one that was large and light, with a wooden chandelier on its high ceiling, Edwardian furnishings, a gas coal fire, and an adequate bathroom. "It looked across parkland, the fringes of the city, and hills across a valley; though there is a main road and a railway line among the trees we heard no noise, and the sunset was wonderful. Personal touches were everywhere: a bowl of fruit, mineral water, interesting pictures, magazines, etc." A continental breakfast, with freshly squeezed orange juice, is brought to the room. There is a steeply sloping garden with a pond. More reports, please.

Open All year, except 2 weeks Jan, 2 weeks Aug, Sun, Mon.
Rooms 4 double (for restaurant guests).
Facilities Reception, bar, restaurant, private dining room; classical background music. 1-acre garden.
Location 2 miles NW of Bath on A431 to Kelston, Bristol.
Restrictions No smoking: restaurant, bedrooms. No dogs.
Credit cards All major cards accepted.
Terms [2000] B&B: single £95, double £150. Set lunch £25, dinner £47.50.

The length of an entry need not reflect the merit of a hotel. The more interesting the report, or the more unusual or controversial the hotel, the longer the entry.

The Queensberry   *Tel* (01225) 447928
Russel Street   *Fax* (01225) 446065
Bath BA1 2QF   *E-mail* enquiries@bathqueensberry.com
                                       Website www.bathqueensbury.com

🏆 *César award in 2000*

Again this year there is almost unanimous praise for Stephen and Penny Ross's upmarket small hotel, composed of adjoining town houses in a residential street near the Assembly Rooms. "After 25 years on the road, I think this is my perfect hotel," one visitor wrote. "Everything is criminally comfortable; you eat like a king." Other visitors called it "a gem", praised the "most obliging" staff, and thought its restaurant, *The Olive Tree*, "one of the best in Bath", and good value. "No wedding parties, discos, etc, to spoil the peace." The finely proportioned houses were designed by John Wood for the Marquis of Queensberry in 1772. Flower baskets hang in front in summer. Some bedrooms and the small bar open on to courtyard gardens at the rear. 18th-century stucco ceilings, cornices and panelling set off a contemporary decor and modern watercolours. There is a "particularly pretty drawing room in rust and yellow", where teas are served (some find its lighting "a bit dim"). The stairways are elegant with a dark blue carpet and cream paintwork. On the first floor, bedrooms are large ("ours was tasteful and uncluttered, decorated in primrose and dark blue"); higher up, they are smaller and cheaper. All have a smart marble bathroom. Light meals and a continental breakfast can be brought to the bedrooms. A cooked breakfast is served in the basement restaurant, which is light and cheerful, with pink walls and a tiled floor with rugs. At night, candles burn and modern British/Mediterranean dishes, cooked by Mathew Prowse, include mussels steamed with leek and saffron; duck breast with parsnip purée; rhubarb and orange jelly with Grand Marnier ice-cream. The wines "are reasonably priced". Parking can be difficult. (*Peter Wilson, DW, and others*)

Open All year, except Christmas. Restaurant closed midday on bank holiday Mon.
Rooms 29 double. Some on ground floor.
Facilities Lift. Drawing room, bar, restaurant (background jazz at lunch, dinner); meeting room. 3 courtyard gardens.
Location 100 yds from Assembly Rooms. Take Bennett St left off Lansdown Rd, then 1st right. Street parking.
Restrictions No smoking in restaurant. Guide dogs only.
Credit cards MasterCard, Visa.
Terms [2000] B&B: single £90–£110, double £90–£210. English breakfast £9.50. Set lunch £15.50, dinner £25; full alc £40. Winter breaks. 1-night bookings sometimes refused.

Royal Crescent Hotel   *Tel* (01225) 823333
16 Royal Crescent   *Fax* (01225) 339401
Bath BA1 2LS   *E-mail* reservations@royalcrescent.co.uk
                                       Website www.royalcrescent.co.uk

"For views, setting and friendly service, this is one of the best," says a visitor this year to this "landmark hotel". It stands in all its Georgian splendour in the middle of John Wood's glorious crescent, looking down across the city. No hotel sign; guests are greeted by "impeccably mannered doormen in tails". Owned by Cliveden Ltd (see also Taplow), and managed by Laurence Beere, it is composed of two adjoining Georgian houses and the Palladian villas in the peaceful gardens behind. Chandeliers, antiques and fine paintings fill the grand public rooms. The suites are grand, too, and lavishly equipped, and most doubles are large, with a "tastefully restrained" decor, TV concealed in a cabinet, decanters with drinks, "a pleasing variety of toiletries" in the bathroom. Two restaurants: *Pimpernel's*, in the main house, serves an eclectic choice of dishes including, eg, spiced foie gras Szechuan style; turbot baked with aromates; banana soufflé with caramel ice-cream; vegetarian dishes like spinach and lemongrass soup, or truffle and mushroom risotto. The less formal *Brasserie Bar*, in the dower house in the garden, has "murals involving cypress trees", polite waiters, and Mediterranean-style cooking. Meals are sometimes served to a piano accompaniment. There is a plunge pool in the garden, a Bath House for soothing Japanese-style treatments, a launch for cruising on the Kennet and Avon Canal, a hot-air balloon for aerial sightseeing. Children are welcomed (baby-sitting can be arranged), and so are dogs. Not cheap, with lots of extras on the bill. Weddings and all manner of other functions are catered for. (*DH, A and CR*)

Open All year. Restaurants closed to non-residents over Christmas.
Rooms 16 suites, 29 double. In 5 buildings. Some on ground floor. 24-hour room service.
Facilities Lift. 3 drawing rooms, bar, 2 restaurants (piano sometimes at night); function facilities. 1-acre garden: Bath House, croquet. River launch, hot-air balloon trips, theatre tickets arranged. Civil wedding licence.
Location ½ mile from centre. (No hotel sign; entrance to left of magnolia.) Hotel will send directions. Valet parking.
Restrictions No smoking: restaurants, 9 bedrooms. No dogs in public rooms.
Credit cards Diners, MasterCard, Visa.
Terms [2000] Room: single £195, double £195–£395, suite £465–£750. Breakfast: continental £14.50, English £17.50. Set lunch £15–£22; full alc dinner £50. Christmas package. 1-night bookings often refused weekends.

BATHFORD Somerset   **Map 2**

Eagle House   `BUDGET`   *Tel* (01225) 859946
Church Street   *Fax* (01225) 859430
Bathford BA1 7RS   *E-mail* jonap@eagleho.demon.co.uk
                            Website www.eaglehouse.co.uk

An informal B&B in a conservation village three miles east of Bath (a frequent local bus service runs between the two). Surrounded by a large garden, it is on a quiet road off Bathford's steep hill. The listed Georgian building, by John Wood the Elder, is grand; its owners, John and Rosamund Napier, are not. The decor is informal rather than *soigné*: "old furniture (good, but not too smart) and family possessions are scattered everywhere". The Napiers welcome families with small children and dogs. High chairs, baby-listening and children's suppers are available; the large, wildish garden has a treehouse, a sandpit, a Tarzan swing and a grass tennis court. The two-bedroomed cottage, with its own walled garden and kitchen, is particularly good for a family. In the main house, each bedroom is named after a tree: Pear is large, "pretty and sprigged", with pine furniture, a garden view and a pristine bathroom. The handsome drawing room has a fine marble fireplace and moulded ceiling; a curving staircase leads up from the hall. Breakfast, served until 10 am on weekdays, 10.30 on Sunday, is plentiful. In winter, guests with a bird's name for a surname, eg, gosling, finch, wren, get a discount (size of discount relative to size of bird). More reports, please.

Open 2 Jan–20 Dec.
Rooms 1 suite, 6 double, 1 single. 2 in cottage with sitting room, kitchen, walled garden.
Facilities Drawing room, breakfast room. No background music. 2½-acre garden: tennis, croquet, sandpit, treehouse, swings. Golf, hot-air ballooning, riding, boating, etc, nearby. Unsuitable for &.
Location Up Bathford Hill past *Crown* pub. 1st right (Church St), house is 200 yds on right behind high stone wall and wrought iron gates (conservation area; no sign permitted). Do not go to Eagle Lodge. Ample parking. 3 buses an hour from Bath.
Restrictions No smoking in bedrooms. Dogs not allowed in public rooms if other guests object.
Credit cards MasterCard, Visa.
Terms B&B: single £38–£52, double £46–£76, suite £75–£98. Cooked breakfast £3.40. Child accommodated in parents' room free. Winter breaks 1 Nov–Easter. 1-night bookings sometimes refused Sat, bank holidays. *V*

The Lodge	*Tel* (01225) 858467
Bathford Hill	*Fax* (01225) 858172
Bathford, Bath BA1 7SL	*E-mail* lodgethe@aol.com
	Website www.lodgehotelbath.co.uk

"A splendid room and a still more splendid bathroom. Very helpful owners." Keith and Mary Johnson's B&B, a listed Georgian house, is on Bathford's steep hill, trafficky by day but quiet at night. It is set in a large landscaped garden (with a swimming pool), and it makes a "restful base" from which to tour Bath and the West Country. With dogs and cats, it has a "family atmosphere", and visitors' dogs are kindly received. Tea is served free of charge to arriving guests. Breakfast includes a buffet with exotic fruits, cereals, yogurt, "and a huge and varied cooked plateful". Some rooms were recently redecorated. One couple were put out that the "double bed" they had requested turned out to be "twin beds latched together and separately made up", but they liked the complimentary sherry. Another guest wrote: "The most important 'extra' is the care and concern given by Mary; I can't praise her enough for this home-from-home approach." The Johnsons own a narrowboat on the Kennet and Avon Canal, which guests may hire by the day. They specialise in house parties, and are knowledgeable about local attractions, eating places, etc. (*RAP, Maureen Brimble, and others*)

Open All year.
Rooms 1 suite, 5 double. 1 on ground floor.

Facilities Lounge, breakfast room. No background music. 3-acre garden: swimming pool (heated May–Oct). River, canal ¼ mile: fishing, boating; golf nearby.
Location M4 exit 18; A46 towards Bath to roundabout at end of dual carriageway; under railway bridge; 1st left, then straight up hill; house on right, 100 yds after *Crown* inn. Ample secure parking. Train: Bath; then bus/taxi, or they will meet.
Restrictions No smoking in breakfast room. No dogs in public rooms.
Credit card MasterCard.
Terms B&B: single £55–£65, double £65–£110, suite £110. Child accommodated in parents' room: under 5, free. Breaks "negotiable". 1-night bookings sometimes refused weekends. *V*

BATTLE East Sussex   Map 2

Netherfield Place   *Tel* (01424) 774455
Battle TN33 9PP   *Fax* (01424) 774024
                            E-mail reservations@netherfieldplace.co.uk
                            Website www.netherfieldplace.co.uk

"A hotel of quality and character. Lovely grounds with many amenities; a keen and accommodating young staff. We had an enjoyable visit," say visitors this year to Michael and Helen Collier's 1920s Georgian-style country house (Pride of Britain). Set up a long drive, it stands in large gardens, planted to be colourful round the year, and surrounded by a park. It is good for a family holiday: plenty of action is available, eg, fishing, clay-pigeon shooting, archery and putting; horse riding can be arranged. The decor is traditional: chandeliers, big sofas, potted plants and magazines in the public rooms; floral fabrics in the bedrooms (each one is named for a knight who fought at the battle of Hastings). The small, dormer-windowed rooms at the top of the house are "cosy"; those on the first floor are spacious. Old-fashioned carpeted bathrooms have capacious towels and bathrobes and good toiletries. The panelled restaurant serves modern English cooking, using ingredients from the kitchen garden, in large portions; roast local lamb comes with parsnip purée and braised Puy lentils; venison is served with steamed spinach and a blackcurrant sauce. Dishes are "too exuberantly garnished" for some, and one couple this year thought dinner "a bit disappointing", but simpler presentation can be requested. Light lunches include "delicious soups and sandwiches". Home-made afternoon teas are served. "Superb home-made bread and good coffee at breakfast." The coast is eight miles away. Ashford railway station for the Channel Tunnel is less than an hour's drive. Bodiam Castle, Batemans, Sissinghurst and Great Dixter are among local attractions. (*John and Sandy Chute, and others*)

Open All year, except last 2 weeks Dec, 1st 2 weeks Jan.
Rooms 10 double, 4 single.
Facilities Lounge, bar, restaurant (classical background music during lunch and dinner); 2 small conference/function rooms. 30-acre grounds: gardens, tennis, putting, croquet, clay-pigeon shooting, woodland walks. Golf, fishing, riding nearby. Sea 8 miles. Unsuitable for &. Civil wedding licence.
Location 3 miles NW of Battle. Turn left towards Netherfield off A2100; hotel 1½ miles on. Train: Battle; then taxi.

Restrictions Smoking discouraged in restaurant. Dogs by arrangement; not in public rooms.
Credit cards All major cards accepted.
Terms B&B: single £55–£70, double £100–£130; D,B&B: single £80–£95, double £165–£175. Set lunch £18.50, dinner £29; full alc £38.50. 2-night breaks. 1-night bookings refused Sat in summer, bank holidays. *V*

BEAMINSTER Dorset   Map 1

The Bridge House   *Tel* (01308) 862200
Prout Bridge   *Fax* (01308) 863700
Beaminster DT8 3AY

E-mail enquiries@bridge-house.co.uk
Website www.bridge-house.co.uk

"Our room was beautiful; the welcome was friendly; we received most efficient attention." Praise again this year for Peter Pinkster's small hotel, parts of which date from the 13th century. An earlier visitor thought it "delightful", with "clean and crisp" bedrooms, "excellent breakfasts and dinners . . . the staff could not have been more helpful". Once a priest's house, it has thick walls, mullioned windows, old beams and inglenook fireplaces. The public rooms have been refurbished this year. The restaurant does a busy local trade. Linda Paget, deputy head chef for four years, is now in charge. Using fresh local produce and home-grown herbs when possible, she continues the English/international style of cooking, eg, pan-fried scallops with smoked bacon and garlic; sautéed pigeon breasts with mushroom and port wine sauce; orange and brandy pancakes. The wine list is "extensive and well provided with wines at a modest price". Light lunches are served in a conservatory with green plastic furniture, or outdoors in summer; tea is taken by a fire on winter afternoons. Breakfast includes freshly squeezed orange juice and a variety of uncooked and cooked items. The bedrooms are spread throughout the main house, converted stables and a new wing; those by the road get some traffic noise; rear ones are quiet. "Views vary: lovely garden on one side, light industry on the other." Beaminster, pronounced Bemminster, is a pretty, if busy, town in the middle of Hardy country (it is Emminster in *Tess of the D'Urbervilles*). Parnham House, the stone manor in formal gardens which is now the John Makepeace Furniture Workshops, is three-quarters of a mile to the south; many stately homes and gardens are within easy reach; and the coast is six miles away. (*VH, and others*)

Open All year.
Rooms 13 double, 1 single. 5 in coach house. 4 on ground floor.
Facilities Sitting room, lounge/bar, sunroom, conservatory, restaurant; patio. No background music. ⅓-acre walled garden.
Location 2 mins' walk from centre (front rooms double-glazed). Private carpark. Train: Crewkerne, 8 miles; then taxi.
Restrictions No smoking: restaurant, bedrooms. No dogs in public rooms, unattended in bedrooms.
Credit cards All major cards accepted.
Terms B&B: single £58–£88, double £94–£124; D,B&B (min. 2 days): single £91–£110, double £141–£170. Set lunch £9.75–£13.50, dinner £24.50–£27.50. Winter breaks; Christmas package. 1-night bookings sometimes refused weekends. *V*

BEAULIEU Hampshire   Map 2

Master Builder's House   `NEW`   *Tel* (01590) 616253
Buckler's Hard   *Fax* (01590) 616297
Beaulieu SO42 7XB   *E-mail* res@themasterbuilders.co.uk
                                     Website www.themasterbuilders.co.uk

*In charming New Forest setting, in time-warp village on the Beaulieu
River: old hotel (Best Western), recently refurbished by owners of* The
George, *Yarmouth (qv). "Charming reception; outstanding staff,
pretty restaurant (food mostly good)," says inspector this year. No
background music. 25 bedrooms: "gorgeous" ones in main building;
small, less attractive ones in annexe block. Lounge, public bar;
pleasant patio with views of water and boats; sloping garden. Unsuitable for* &. *All major credit cards accepted. No dogs. B&B: single
£110, double £145–£195; D,B&B: single £132.50, double £190–£240.
Set lunch/ dinner £22.50; Full alc £43 [2000]. More reports, please.*

BEERCROCOMBE Somerset   Map 1

Frog Street Farm   `BUDGET`   *Tel/Fax* (01823) 480430
Beercrocombe, Taunton TA3 6AF
Q *César award in 1988*

"We wholeheartedly endorse the *Guide*'s description," say visitors
this year to Henry and Veronica Cole's listed 15th-century farmhouse,
which never accommodates more than six guests at one time. It is one
of our most popular small guest houses, loved for the exuberant charm
of the hostess, and its deep rural setting on a large Somerset working
farm, with fields and woods on one side, orchards on the other. Earlier
accolades: "Here small is truly beautiful." "A welcoming, comfortable
home. Guests leave as friends." "Very friendly and most peaceful."
"There can't be many places of this quality where two people can stay
and be fed for less than £100 a day." Dinner, by arrangement, at 7 pm,
is generally served at separate tables, but guests may eat together if
they prefer. Mrs Cole's country cooking is much admired: "succulent
fillet steak and mouth-watering lemon meringue pie"; "excellent wild
salmon". No licence; bring your own wine. Breakfast includes "perfectly cooked bacon and eggs". There is a large lounge, with beams
and a wood stove. Henry Cole is a racehorse trainer and the horses in
the fields around are "worth studying, even if you are not a betting
type". Plenty of National Trust properties in the area: Barrington
Court, Montacute, Brampton D'Evercy and Tintinhull; the busy market town of Ilminster is nearby; the north and south coasts are about
21 miles away. (*Mr and Mrs G Turner*)

Open Apr–Oct.
Rooms 1 suite, 2 double. No telephone/TV.
Facilities 2 lounges, dining room. No background music. 130-acre working
farm: garden, trout stream. Unsuitable for &.
Location 7 miles SE of Taunton. M5 exit 25. Take A358 past the *Blackbrook
Tavern* to Ilminster. In Hatch Beauchamp, at *Hatch Inn*, take Station Rd; left
down no through road. Signposted.

Restrictions No smoking. Children by arrangement; not under 11. No dogs.
Credit cards None accepted.
Terms B&B: single £30–£35, double £54–£60. Set dinner £18. Weekly rates.
1-night bookings sometimes refused weekends.

BEPTON West Sussex   Map 2

Park House
Bepton, nr Midhurst
GU29 0JB

Tel (01730) 812880
Fax (01730) 815643
E-mail parkhousebepton@talk21.com

In an area of outstanding natural beauty at the foot of the South
Downs, this rambling, red-roofed and gabled hotel has been run by the
O'Brien family for over 50 years. It is liked for its "lovely country
house atmosphere, with overtones of the Raj", its caring owners and
staff, and "delightful grounds". Behind a "rather suburban" exterior is
an elegant drawing room with "an unusually good selection of books"
and a fire in cold weather. Photographs of famous visitors are displayed in the bar. The pretty bedrooms are well kept; most are
spacious; some are in a nearby cottage and an annexe. One large group
reported that there was insufficient hot water to cope with all their
after-golf bathing. The short, unwritten menu offers traditional home
cooking, eg, rack of lamb with a redcurrant and rosemary jus; steak-
and-kidney pie; French apple flan and apple or rhubarb crumble. An
early or late supper is willingly provided for theatre- and concert-
goers. The hotel has a wisteria-covered terrace, a small converted barn
for conferences and functions, two grass tennis courts, a nine-hole
par three pitch-and-putt golf course and a heated outdoor swimming
pool. Cowdray Park polo, Goodwood racecourse, Chichester, Parham
and Petworth houses and the Sussex coast are within easy reach.
(*E Brice, KW, and others*)

Open All year.
Rooms 13 double, 1 single. 2 in annexe, 2 in cottage. 1 adapted for &.
Facilities Lounge, bar, dining room. No background music. 9-acre grounds:
tennis, croquet, swimming pool, pitch-and-putt golf; golf nearby.
Location SW of Midhurst. A286 through town; left on to B2226; hotel on left
after 2 miles.
Restrictions No smoking: dining room, some bedrooms. Dogs in some bed-
rooms; not in public rooms.
Credit cards Amex, MasterCard, Visa.
Terms B&B: single £60–£85, double £100–£150. Set lunch £15–£20, dinner
£18–£26. Winter breaks.

BIBURY Gloucestershire   Map 3

Bibury Court
Bibury
nr Cirencester GL7 5NT

Tel (01285) 740337
Fax (01285) 740660
E-mail reservations@biburycourt.co.uk

Charles Dickens is said to have based events in *Bleak House* on long-
running legal disputes over the ownership of this Tudor manor house.
But a regular *Guide* correspondent tells us that there is nothing bleak

about the welcome by the present owners, Andrew and Anne Johnston and Jane Collier, who aim "to provide good food and wine in informal and comfortable surroundings". "It is a long-established, popular hotel. The general manager, Simon Gould, who bears more than a passing resemblance to Groucho Marx, is most efficient, and the staff, many of whom have been there for years, are friendly." Many bedrooms have a four-poster bed; some other beds are "a bit narrow". Lighting can be poor, and housekeeping may not always be impeccable, but bathrooms are well equipped; hot water is plentiful, and one bath "is big enough to swim in". The panelled lounge has a flagstone floor, large chairs and sofas. There is a conservatory for summer dining. The gardens stretch down to the river, where the hotel has fishing rights. Tom Bridgeman, the chef, prepares elaborate dishes, eg, pigeon salad with avocado, black pudding and balsamic syrup; veal with celeriac purée, sun-dried tomatoes and prunes; brandy snap basket with lemon and ginger sorbet and poached mango. Light

lunches and afternoon teas are served. Breakfast is continental, full English, vegetarian or Jacobean (with cold meats and pickled walnut chutney). Functions are often held, and outside lunchers and diners are catered for. William Morris's house at Kelmscott is nearby. (*JH*)

Open All year.
Rooms 1 suite, 16 double, 1 single. 1 on ground floor with &. access.
Facilities Drawing room, bar, restaurant, conservatory, TV/billiard room. No background music. 7-acre grounds: "secret garden", orchard; on River Coln, fishing.
Location Village centre, behind church.
Restriction No smoking: restaurant, conservatory. No dogs in restaurant.
Credit cards All major cards accepted.
Terms [2000] B&B £52.50–£95. D,B&B £77.50–£125. English breakfast £4.50–£6.95. Set dinner £27.50. 2-day breaks. Christmas package. 1-night bookings sometimes refused Sat.

BIGBURY-ON-SEA Devon   **Map 1**

Burgh Island Hotel   NEW   *Tel* (01548) 810514
Burgh Island   *Fax* (01548) 810243
Bigbury-on-Sea TQ7 4BG   *E-mail* reception@burghisland.com
                                     Website www.burghisland.com

♥ *César award in 1993*

A lovingly restored Art Deco extravaganza, "a fantasy world of the 1920s", on a private island in Bigbury Bay. In its heyday it was visited by Edward, Prince of Wales, with Mrs Simpson, and by Agatha Christie. At low tide you walk across a causeway; at high water it is "romantically cut off", and guests are carried across on a sea tractor. Two years ago the owners, Tony and Beatrice Porter, put the hotel up for sale so it was dropped from the *Guide*. But no suitable buyer appeared; it has been taken off the market and given a major refurbishment. Accommodation is in suites with one or two bedrooms; most have a balcony and a sea view. There is also a two-roomed cottage on the beach. The furniture and fittings are in period style, down to the last milk jug, and it is all "fabulous" and great fun; "you are pampered from the moment you arrive". Paul, the barman, "whips up astonishing cocktails" in the peacock-domed palm court. Tea is taken in a glassed-in sun lounge and dinner is served in a 1920s ballroom; in deference to its splendour, guests are asked to dress formally. "On Saturday you can capture that Fred 'n' Ginger mood when a light tenor croons dance songs of the period. Chef Matthew Read's GM-free menu draws on superb local produce, cooked with flair" (eg, cream of mushroom soup with truffle oil; seabass with squid ink linguine and fennel; lemon tart with orange syrup and clotted cream). There is a natural swimming pool in the rocks below the hotel, and a private beach with water sports. (*Siân James, Lynn Wildgoose, Sue Baynton-Power*)

Open All year, except Jan, and Sun–Thurs in Feb.
Rooms 15 suites. Also 2-bedroomed house on beach.
Facilities Lift. Sun lounge, palm court/cocktail bar, restaurant, ballroom; 1930s original recordings played; live music/dinner-dance Sat. On 26-acre private island: natural sea swimming pool; beach, water sports; tennis; 14th-century inn; helipad. Golf, sailing, fishing nearby. Unsuitable for &. Civil wedding licence.
Location Leave A38 at Modbury exit. Hotel arranges transfer. Lockup garage on mainland.
Restrictions No smoking at breakfast. No children under 7 in restaurant at night. No dogs.
Credit cards All major cards accepted.
Terms [Until Easter 2001; 5% increase thereafter] D,B&B (2- to 4-night stay) £110–£172. Full alc lunch £28; set dinner £38–£45.

The Henley	*Tel* (01548) 810240
Folly Hill	*Fax* (01548) 810020
Bigbury-on-Sea TQ7 4AR	

With "stunning views, charming service and good, unpretentious food", this inexpensive small hotel has delighted many visitors this year. "An idyllic few days," wrote one couple, who also praised the "delightful welcome" and the "charming dining room". Set in a small, pretty terraced garden above the Avon estuary, it looks across to Burgh Island and beyond. A private path leads down the cliff to a sandy beach. The owner, Martyn Scarterfield, has been renovating the former Edwardian holiday cottage since he bought it in a derelict state some years ago, and the exterior is now much smarter. A new veranda-style dining room makes the most of the view. The rest "is delightful" too: dark red walls and nice old furniture, well polished, in the hall; a pleasant small sitting room with games, books, magazines, etc; Lloyd Loom chairs. Binoculars are provided. The bedrooms are simple, light and well equipped, and most have the view. The host is a self-taught chef; in the morning you discuss the evening's dinner. "Everything is

fresh, straightforward and delicious." Tomato and basil soup; roast
rack of lamb with a large dish of "perfectly cooked vegetables"; cherry
and almond tart, are among the dishes on the short menu. "An excellent breakfast too, with local bacon." "We make no extravagant
claims," says the brochure. "Our aim is to make guests feel at home in
relaxing surroundings." There is limited family accommodation. Dogs
are welcomed. (*Brian and Eve Webb, CR, HS*)

Open Mar–Nov.
Rooms 6 double.
Facilities 2 lounges, bar, veranda dining room; classical music/jazz back-
ground music at night; garden; steps to beach. Golf, sailing, fishing, Coast Path
nearby. Unsuitable for &.
Location 5 miles S of Modbury. Through Bigbury; past golf course. Hotel on
left as road slopes down to sea.
Restrictions No smoking. No dogs in public rooms.
Credit cards Amex, MasterCard, Visa.
Terms [2000] B&B £35–£45; D,B&B £51–£61. Set dinner £17. 5% off-
season reduction.

BIGGIN-BY-HARTINGTON Derbyshire   Map 3

Biggin Hall   `BUDGET`   *Tel* (01298) 84451
Biggin-by-Hartington   *Fax* (01298) 84681
Buxton SK17 0DH   *E-mail* 100610.1573@compuserve.com
                                     Website www.bigginhall.co.uk

Informally run by its "courteous owner", James Moffett, this 17th-
century house has a tranquil setting in the Peak District National
Park. Its chief glory is the position: you can walk directly out on to
the Tissington Trail and over the fields to the dales. With its stone
walls, mullioned windows, beams and old furniture, it is an unpretentious place. The library has a "more enlightened selection of books
than the usual offerings". Most bedrooms are spacious, with old
beams and chintz, TV and a well-appointed bathroom. Direct-dial
telephones with a modem socket were installed this year. Two small
singles form a "suite" good for two people travelling together, but not
wishing to share or pay a single supplement. Some accommodation is
in the *Bothy*, which once housed itinerant workers, and an 18th-
century stone building 30 yards from the main house. Many of these
rooms were recently refurbished. A traditional dinner is served at 7,
in a room with a picture window. "The atmosphere is pleasant. Talk
takes place between guests, and there is a good view across the fields,
if you get the right table." Two choices (one vegetarian) of main
course, perhaps pork with a creamy grain mustard sauce or ratatouille
with saffron rice. With improved cooking facilities, Mr Moffett tells
us, the vegetables are much better this year. Desserts include sticky
toffee pudding and sherry and brandy trifle; there is a good cheeseboard. The continental breakfast has a wide selection of cereals, dried
fruits and home-made croissants; guests not on a special break pay a
small supplement for the cooked one. Cream teas are available.
The "Icebreaker Special" winter break includes mulled wine by the
fire at night, porridge for breakfast, and a picnic lunch. Groups of

doctors are often entertained. Convenient for visiting the market towns of Ashbourne, Buxton and Bakewell; stately homes such as Chatsworth and Haddon Hall; and Alton Towers (16 miles away). More reports, please.

Open All year.
Rooms 17 double, 2 single. 10 (4 on ground floor) in annexes.
Facilities Sitting room, library, dining room; meeting room. No background music. 7-acre grounds. River Dove 1½ miles. Not really suitable for &.
Location.½ mile W of A515. 8 miles N of Ashbourne. 4 buses daily.
Restrictions No smoking: dining room, library, some bedrooms. No children under 12. No dogs in main house.
Credit cards Amex, MasterCard, Visa.
Terms B&B: single £40–£60, double £50–£95; D,B&B £35–£70 per person. English breakfast £3.50. Packed lunches from £2.50. Set dinner £15.50. Winter breaks, Christmas package. 1-night bookings sometimes refused. *V*

BIRMINGHAM West Midlands *See SHORTLIST*   Map 3

BISHOP'S TACHBROOK Warwickshire   Map 3

Mallory Court   *Tel* (01926) 330214
Harbury Lane   *Fax* (01926) 451714
Bishop's Tachbrook   *E-mail* reception@mallory.co.uk
nr Leamington Spa CV33 9QB   *Website* www.mallory.co.uk

"Cares of the day slip away and one cannot help but relax and luxuriate." This is how one couple described their stay in this recently extended and refurbished 1920s mansion (Relais & Châteaux). The new suites "are superb", the atmosphere "is lovely", the enlarged terrace is ideal for taking lunch or tea under sunshades, and "the splendid new kitchen produces excellent results". "It is as if it has been there for ages," one guest wrote of the refurbishment; another admired the "comfortable Englishness, which is quite unique". Only caveat: "We weren't too sure about the automatic machine which keeps the keys of the grand piano in the lounge tinkling away during dinner." The bedrooms are immaculate and lavishly decorated; many beds "are Olympic". The smallest rooms face the carpark; upgrades are common at quiet times. The owners, Jeremy Mort and Allan Holland (the chef), head a "well-trained young foreign staff". The traditional English/ French cuisine, served in the oak-panelled dining room, "is always interesting", eg, main courses of calf's liver with Italian bacon, or saddle of young rabbit stuffed with langoustines; desserts such as Sauternes custard with Armagnac prunes, or glazed lemon tart. The wine list offers both Old and New World wines. Breakfast is "equally good". Light lunches (soups, sandwiches, salads, etc) and lavish afternoon teas are served; there is room service from 7 am to 11.30 pm. The grounds are magnificent, with statuary, a herb garden, flowers, an orchard, a lily pond, and the original (unheated) swimming pool. A small air-conditioned conference centre is in a converted stable block. Birmingham, Warwick and Stratford-upon-Avon are nearby. Other local attractions include Charlecote Park, Packwood House, Snowshill

Manor; the Cotswolds are within 40 minutes' drive. (*Francine and Ian Walsh, Pat and Jeremy Temple*)

Open All year.
Rooms 8 suites, 10 double. 1 suitable for &.
Facilities Ramp. 3 lounges (automatic piano plays some evenings), conservatory, restaurant, private dining room; conference/function facilities. 10-acre gardens: unheated swimming pool, tennis, squash, croquet. Hot-air balloon trips, riding, fishing, shooting, golf nearby. Civil wedding licence applied for.
Location 2 miles S of Leamington Spa. M40 exit 13 (from S), 14 (from N). Hotel off B4087 to Harbury. Train: Leamington Spa; then taxi.
Restrictions No smoking in restaurant. No children under 9 (except babies with own cot). No dogs in public rooms, owners must provide basket in bedroom.
Credit cards All major cards accepted.
Terms B&B: single £165, double £175–£275. English breakfast £10. Bar lunches. Set lunch £25, dinner £37.50; full alc £65. 2/3-day winter breaks. Christmas package.

BISHOP'S TAWTON Devon   Map 1

Halmpstone Manor   *Tel* (01271) 830321
Bishop's Tawton   *Fax* (01271) 830826
nr Barnstaple EX32 0EA
       E-mail charles@halmpstonemanor.co.uk
       Website www.halmpstonemanor.co.uk

The family home of Charles and Jane Stanbury is on a working farm in the rolling hills of north Devon. The restful atmosphere of the old house is liked, and so is the professional management, though it is run more like a private home than a hotel. "No false intimacy; we were called 'Sir' and 'Madam' throughout our visit, which we like," was one comment. Help with luggage, and complimentary tea with cake in the lovely sitting room, are also appreciated. "Fresh flowers everywhere, a lovely dining room (no piped music), only five tables, elegantly set with old-fashioned chunky cutlery, crisp table napkins." The four-course dinners (with choice) are admired too. Roast local duckling and beef feature on the menus, along with "delectable home-grown vegetables". Breakfast includes fresh orange juice and home-made preserves. Most bedrooms are spacious, and they are supplied with sherry, biscuits and other extras; two have a four-poster. There are family photos, knick-knacks and a log fire in the sitting room, and a patio with views of the moors. Plenty to visit nearby, including Lydford Gorge, Lynton and Lynmouth, Rosemoor and Marwood gardens – you need a car.

Open All year, except Nov, Christmas/New Year, Jan. Lunch by arrangement.
Rooms 5 double.
Facilities Lounge, bar, restaurant. No background music. ½-acre garden. Unsuitable for &.
Location 4 miles SE of Barnstaple. A39 to Bideford for 300 yds. A377 to Exeter/Crediton. Through Bishop's Tawton; opposite petrol station turn left on to minor road; follow signs for 2 miles. Train: Barnstaple; then taxi.
Restrictions No smoking: restaurant, some bedrooms. No children under 12. No dogs in public rooms.
Credit cards All major cards accepted.

Terms [2000] B&B: single £70, double £100–£140. D,B&B: single £95, double £150–£190. Set dinner £25 (£30 to non-residents). *V*

BLACKPOOL Lancashire *See SHORTLIST*   **Map 4**

BLAKENEY Norfolk   **Map 2**

The Blakeney Hotel   *Tel* (01263) 740797
Blakeney   *Fax* (01263) 740795
nr Holt NR25 7NE

No longer an East Anglian port, Blakeney is now a yachting centre and holiday destination, and this long-established hotel on the quayside caters for guests young and old throughout the year. Families with young children have all they need, from high chairs and baby-sitting to early evening meals (but one parent was taken aback by the list of dos and don'ts for children that accompanied the confirmation of her reservation). The "very attractive" indoor swimming pool, and the "lovely walks" along the estuary, particularly at low tide, are great attractions. Two lounges – one upstairs – have fine views over the estuary towards Blakeney Point; log fires in winter "enhance the friendly atmosphere". Many bedrooms have a sea view; some rooms in the modern Granary annexe have use of a patio overlooking the garden. Plenty of off-peak breaks are available. Staff are "cheerful" (many have been here for years); the long-serving restaurant manager is "eagle-eyed", but sightings of owner or management are said to be rare. The food is firmly traditional (one visitor this year found it disappointing): at dinner there is a choice between a daily *table d'hôte* or a seasonal *carte*. Typical dishes include local mussels with white wine, garlic and parsley; pan-fried veal in breadcrumbs on a tarragon and whisky sauce; desserts from the trolley. Light lunches are served on weekdays; on Sunday a choice of roasts forms the centrepiece of the menu. Some visitors thought the food of a high standard this year, but one regular reported some disappointing meals during a recent stay. There is good birdwatching at the National Trust's Blakeney Point nature reserve; boat trips to see the seals can be arranged. Blickling Hall, Holkham Hall, and the North Norfolk steam railway at Sheringham are nearby. (*JH Bell, Sheelagh Innes, Moira Jarrett, John Knott; also Susan Hoeksema, and others*)

Open All year.
Rooms 51 double, 8 single. 10 in annexe across drive. 1, on ground floor, with access for &.
Facilities Lift, ramps. Lounge, sun lounge, cocktail bar, restaurant; function facilities; indoor swimming pool, spa bath, sauna and mini gym; games room. ¼-acre garden: table-tennis, swings. Sailing, fishing, water sports, golf, tennis, nearby.
Location On quay. Off A149 coast road, 8 miles W of Sheringham. Train: Sheringham; then taxi.
Restrictions No smoking in restaurant. Only guide dogs in public rooms.
Credit cards All major cards accepted.
Terms [2000] B&B single £58–£97; D,B&B (min. 2 nights) £64–£106. Light

lunches Mon–Sat; set Sun lunch £14, dinner £20; full alc £35. 2- to 7-day breaks; midweek breaks for senior citizens. Christmas, New Year packages. 1-night bookings usually refused Fri/Sat.

BLAWITH Cumbria   Map 4

Appletree Holme Farm   *Tel* (01229) 885618
Blawith
nr Ulverston LA12 8EL

"We needed comfort, good food, a peaceful location, good walking country, ample space to read in front of a fire. We found them all, and more, at this rather special place," says a visitor this year to this old stone farmhouse in a remote corner of the south-western part of the Lake District. "The welcome was warm; we were impressed by the care for guests' comfort, and the high standards." The fellside setting is idyllic, amid carefully tended gardens and orchards, and the immediate surroundings are a designated site of special interest, where flora and fauna are protected. Pheasants strut on the lawns. "Foxes, rabbits, deer, and as many as 46 varieties of birds have been counted in a single day," write the owners, Roy and Shirley Carlsen. They do not offer hotel-style facilities: there is no reception; visitors are asked not to arrive between 2 and 5 pm without prior arrangement. The homely lounge has a log fire, brasses, silver and paintings, and there is a well-stocked library. The bedrooms are not luxurious, but all have a fell view and private facilities. One bathroom is across a corridor; two have a double bath. The suite, on two floors, has a private patio and a separate entrance. The kind hosts "strike the balance between formality and informality", and the home-cooked food is enjoyed: "It lacks fashionable 'fusion' elements; it is ample, varied, of high quality and well cooked." No choice on the four-course menu, which might consist of Galia melon with damson coulis and sorbet; braised pork loin with mustard cream sauce; chocolate meringue roulade with strawberries; English cheeses. Preferences are discussed in advance. The wine list is "splendid and reasonably priced". Breakfast, ordered the night before, includes porridge, goat's milk yogurt, oak-smoked kippers, Cumberland sausages, eggs done in many ways, and home-made marmalade. Coniston Water is three miles away; many other sporting activities are available (see below); and there are stately homes, art galleries and market towns to visit. (*Sir Robin McLaren*)

Open All year. Dining room closed midday (picnics/light lunches available).
Rooms 1 suite (adjacent to main building), 3 double.
Facilities Sitting room, library, dining room. No background music. 2½-acre grounds: gardens, orchards. Lake, tarn, swimming, fishing, boating, golf, pony-trekking nearby. Coniston Water 3 miles. Unsuitable for &.
Location M6 exit 36; A590 to Greenodd; A5084 to Blawith church; up lane opposite church; right after farm; left 1 mile, at sign. Train/coach: Ulverston; hosts will meet.
Restrictions No smoking. Children by arrangement. No dogs in house.
Credit cards MasterCard, Visa.
Terms [2000] D,B&B £65.50–£82.50. Set dinner £23.50. £3 reduction for 2 nights or more (except bank holidays).

BLOCKLEY Gloucestershire   Map 3

The Old Bakery   *Tel/Fax* (01386) 700408
High Street, Blockley
nr Moreton-in-Marsh GL56 9EU

"Beautifully converted" from a row of four cottages built around
1800, this small guest house is "modelled on a French restaurant-with-
rooms", according to Linda Helme. Sadly, her co-owner, John
Benson, died at the beginning of 2000, but she continues to run the
place as before. "Hands-on hospitality" is her style. The "great atmosphere" and "immaculate bedrooms" are praised, and the house is furnished with antiques, "interesting pictures, lots of books and
comfortable chairs". The handsome dining room looks through French
windows on to the small, "beautifully kept" garden. Ms Helme (who
earlier worked in publishing) "spends much of the day preparing the
evening meal", say one couple who singled out "the best salmon we'd
ever eaten, and an inspired duck dish which brought back memories of
taste not experienced since childhood". Dinner is a set four-course
menu based, when possible, on local and organic ingredients; and Ms
Helme "takes great pains to find out about guests' likes and dislikes in
advance". There is a choice of "superb wines at low prices". Breakfast
is "delicious too", with freshly squeezed orange, and "scrambled eggs
to die for". A cottage across a lane is let for self-catering (its residents
can dine at *The Old Bakery*). Blockley, said to be one of the most
unspoiled villages in the Cotswolds, is well placed for excursions:
Stratford-upon-Avon is 14 miles away, Cheltenham 15, Oxford 35.
Hidcote, Sudeley Castle and many other attractions are nearby.
(*Christine Neagle and David Young, RM*)

Open Feb–Nov. Closed 2 weeks in June. Dining room closed to non-residents.
Rooms 1 suite, 2 double. No telephone. Also self-catering cottage across lane.
Facilities Sitting room, study/bar, dining room. No background music.
Garden: courtyard, patio. Unsuitable for &.
Location Corner of High Street and School Lane. Towards Broadway, turn
right off A44 at Bourton-on-the-Hill. Follow signs to Blockley village centre.
Parking.
Restrictions No smoking. No children under 12. No dogs.
Credit cards Amex, MasterCard, Visa (all with 2% surcharge).
Terms [2000] D,B&B £60–£100. 1-night bookings occasionally refused
weekends.

BONCHURCH Isle of Wight   Map 2

Winterbourne   BUDGET   *Tel* (01983) 852535
Bonchurch   *Fax* (01983) 853056
nr Ventnor PO38 1RQ

"The prettiest place I ever saw in my life, at home or abroad," wrote
Charles Dickens when he stayed at *Winterbourne* (then a private
house) during the summer of 1849, while writing *David Copperfield*.
He enjoyed "great games of rounders on the shore every afternoon,
with all Bonchurch looking on". Now run as a hotel by Mr and Mrs

O'Connor, the place is thought "charmingly quaint", and liked for its setting overlooking the sea amid lawns, terraced gardens, streams and waterfalls. The manager, Mr Maddox, "is a treasure: he is reception-ist/bellboy/headwaiter/*sommelier*/gardener/swimming pool operator/plumber". There is a new chef this year, Matthew Lordan, and we'd be grateful for reports on his "English/French cooking", served in the red-walled dining room. The fixed-priced menus, with lots of choice, include dishes like pan-fried Cajun salmon with anchovy mayonnaise, or avocado, tomato and mozzarella salad; chicken in a cloud-ear mushroom and celery velouté, or rack of lamb with rosemary and white wine. There is always a vegetarian option and a dish of the day. While staying here, you could climb to the top of St Boniface Down, as Dickens did, or explore the network of local footpaths. Ventnor's botanic garden is also worth a visit. More reports, please.

Open All year.
Rooms 2 family (in annexe), 9 double, 3 single.
Facilities Lounge, bar, restaurant (classical background music at night). 4-acre grounds: gardens, unheated swimming pool, stream, waterfalls, access to beach. Riding, fishing, golf, tennis, bowls, etc, nearby. Unsuitable for &.
Location 1 mile NE of Ventnor. Local small bus.
Restrictions No smoking in restaurant. No dogs in public rooms.
Credit cards Amex, MasterCard, Visa.
Terms [2000] D,B&B: single £49–£59, double £96–£155, suite £116–£136. Light lunch available; set dinner £17.95. Reductions for 4 nights or more. *V*

BORROWDALE Cumbria   Map 4

The Leathes Head   BUDGET   *Tel* (017687) 77247
Borrowdale   *Fax* (017687) 77363
Keswick CA12 5UY   *E-mail* enq@leatheshead.co.uk

A gabled Lakeland stone Edwardian house in a "great location", high up in wooded grounds outside Borrowdale. Set well back from the road to Keswick, it has extensive views of the spectacular surrounding countryside. It was taken over in late 1999 by Roy and Janice Smith. No significant changes have been made, though they are considering becoming completely smoke-free in 2001. Visitors soon after the take-over reported that all was still well. Popular with serious walkers and climbers, the house is furnished in keeping with its age, and original features – stained glass, old fireplaces and plasterwork – have been retained. In a sunroom overlooking the garden and furnished with wicker armchairs, tea and drinks are served. Books, local guidebooks and games are scattered around. The chef, David Jackson, who has stayed on from the previous regime, recently won a Les Routiers food award. His menus change daily and include, eg, confit of duck, liver and ham; baked salmon in a herb crust; chocolate truffle cake. There is always a vegetarian dish and, for an extra charge, venison and pheasant are available in season. Guests have access, for a small fee, to a nearby leisure club. Children are welcomed: there are family rooms, and high tea for the very young (but no baby-listening service). (*Robert Calvert, FG Miller*)

Open Mid-Feb–Dec (closed midweek Nov, Dec except Christmas).
Rooms 11 double. 2 on ground floor, 1 with some facilities for &.
Facilities Ramp. Lounge, bar lounge, restaurant. Light classical background music in bar, restaurant in evening. 2½-acre grounds: garden, children's play area, woodland. Bicycle/boat hire; lake, water sports nearby. Temporary membership of local leisure club.
Location 3½ miles S of Keswick on B5289. Train: Penrith; then bus.
Restrictions Smoking in bar only. No children under 7 in restaurant at night. No dogs.
Credit cards MasterCard, Visa.
Terms B&B £36–£54.50; D,B&B £49.50–£69.50. Set dinner £21.50. Christmas, New Year packages; spring, summer, autumn breaks. 1-night bookings sometimes refused. ***V*** (half board only)

Seatoller House   NEW/BUDGET   *Tel* (017687) 77218
Borrowdale   *Fax* (017687) 77189
Keswick CA12 5XN
                        E-mail seatollerhouse@btconnect.com
                        Website www.seatollerhouse.co.uk

In a beautiful setting at the head of the Borrowdale valley (much of which is owned by the National Trust), this 350-year-old house, owned by Lake Hunts Ltd, has been an unpretentious guest house for more than a century. Much loved by walkers and climbers for its "homely atmosphere", it was one of the *Guide*'s most popular budget entries for many years, until a change of management led to its being dropped. But new managers, Jay and Morven Anson, have brought it back to a high standard, we are told: "A warm welcome, attention to detail, very good cooking." "A quiet and happy environment. A constant reminder of the natural beauty that Cumbria has to offer." Meals are served at two long oak tables. Dinner, announced by a gong, is at 7 pm. No choice on the menu: tomato and lentil soup with home-made bread, and baked ham with Cumberland sauce were enjoyed this year. There is a short, well-chosen wine list. Breakfast, at 8.30, is a hearty affair; fruit has now been added to the menu. "Marvellous walks from the door; a nice garden." (*June Wilmers, Dr JB Kershaw, RL Galloway, and others*)

Open Feb–Dec. Dining room closed Tues.
Rooms 9 double. 2 on ground floor. 1 in garden annexe. No telephone/TV.
Facilities Lounge, library, tea room, restaurant, drying room. No background music. 2-acre grounds: pond.
Location 8 miles S of Keswick on B5289. Train: Penrith; regular buses.
Restrictions Smoking in lounge only. No dogs in public rooms.
Credit cards MasterCard, Visa.
Terms D,B&B £40.50–£42.50. Set dinner £11. Packed lunches available. Weekly rates.

Hotels often book you into their most expensive rooms or suites unless you specify otherwise. Even if all room prices are the same, hotels may give you a less good room in the hope of selling their better rooms to late customers. It always pays to discuss accommodation in detail when making a reservation, and to ask for a free upgrade on arrival if the hotel isn't full.

BOSHAM West Sussex   Map 2

The Millstream   *Tel* (01243) 573234
Bosham Lane   *Fax* (01243) 573459
Bosham, nr Chichester PO18 8HL   *E-mail* info@millstream-hotel.co.uk.
                                            Website www.millstream-hotel.co.uk.

A "good but not snooty" hotel, 25 years old this year. The manager,
Antony Wallace, leads a "very friendly staff", says a visitor this
year. "We were probably a bit of a nuisance – I was singing all week
in a choir at Chichester Cathedral with some awkward timings, and
my wife had brought her word processor to work on a book, but all
this was treated as quite normal." Others called the service
"attentive, but not pushy". Composed of a small manor house and an
18th-century malt house cottage, the hotel is set in tranquil gardens
by a stream with ducks. The public rooms and bedrooms are pretty,
with pale colours, antique and period furniture, potted plants and
unexceptional pictures. But the all-day piped music in the public
rooms might not suit all tastes. The chef, Bev Boakes, has presided
over the kitchens for 25 years. Dinner is a fixed-price traditional
affair with plenty of choice, eg, tuna en croûte with lemon, lime and
yogurt dressing, or chicken-liver parfait; pan-fried breast of duck
with cranberry sauce, or roast beef carved from a trolley. A vegetarian menu is also available. Much redecoration took place recently,
and a thatched waterside cottage in the corner of the garden has been
turned into two suites. Bosham, pronounced Bozzum, is full of
history: its church was visited by King Harold before he set off to
visit Duke William of Normandy in 1064 (this is depicted in the
Bayeux Tapestry), and the incident of King Canute and the tide is
said to have occurred here. The hotel is well placed for Chichester
and its artistic events (theatre-goers can order a late supper);
Goodwood, Petworth, and Arundel Castle are within striking
distance. (*Richard Neale*)

Open All year.
Rooms 3 suites (2 in cottage in garden), 27 double, 5 single. 7 on ground floor,
1 equipped for &.
Facilities Lounge (pianist Fri, Sat), bar, restaurant; classical background
music 10.30 am to 10.30 pm in public rooms; conference room. 1-acre garden,
stream. Civil wedding licence.
Location In village 3½ miles W of Chichester. Follow signs to hotel. Carpark.
Station/bus-stop in village.
Restrictions No smoking: restaurant, 60% of bedrooms. No dogs in public
rooms.
Credit cards All major cards accepted.
Terms [2000] B&B: single £72–£75, double £115–£120, suite £145–£160;
D,B&B (min. 2 nights) £55–£100 per person. Set lunch £15, dinner £22.50.
Midweek rates. Bridge, Christmas, New Year packages. 1-night bookings
refused Sat.

BOURNEMOUTH Dorset *See SHORTLIST*   Map 2

BOWNESS-ON-WINDERMERE Cumbria   **Map 4**

Fayrer Garden House   *Tel* (015394) 88195
Lyth Valley Road   *Fax* (015394) 45986
Bowness-on-Windermere   *E-mail* lakescene@fayrergarden.com
LA23 3JP   *Website* www.fayrergarden.com

Iain and Jackie Garside's Victorian house, half a mile above the lake, has its devotees who come back year after year. The attractions are its beautiful large grounds (with azaleas, rhodendrons, deer, rabbits and badgers), good food, and friendly staff. The best bedrooms have a distant lake view; some are large, and many have a spa bath; some also have a four-poster. Ground-floor rooms have a French window opening on to a terrace. A major refurbishment recently took place and our inpectors had a room with much blue, heavy swagging and drapes – "all rather funereal". The restaurant is popular with outside diners – "not many places can boast being full, with visitors dressed up, on a Sunday night in March". Edward Wilkinson's modern British cooking was enjoyed: "a miniature pineapple filled with fresh fruit; sirloin of beef, tender and pink; banana ice-cream in a brandy snap basket, prettily presented". The moderately priced wine list has a choice of six house wines at £12.50, and plenty of half bottles. "The cheerful Australian staff made the place; they were laid back, but in a pleasant way." But reception (no help with luggage) was thought cool, and our inspector felt that a more hands-on proprietorial presence would have helped. Breakfast was "a let-down": a buffet with packaged orange juice, fresh fruit salad, prunes and apricot compote; but poor cooked dishes. Bowness is a busy tourist centre on Lake Windermere – many lake boats set out from here, and the roads can become congested in season. Mr Garside's brother, Charles, owns *Miller Howe*, Windermere.

Open All year, except Jan.
Rooms 17 double, 1 single. 5 on ground floor.
Facilities 2 lounges, bar, restaurant (CDs or piano at night). 5-acre grounds. Lake ½ mile: fishing, boating, etc; free use of local leisure centre; golf nearby.
Location 1 mile S of Bowness on A5074.
Restrictions No smoking: restaurant, 1 lounge, some bedrooms. No children under 5 in restaurant at night. No dogs in public rooms.
Credit cards Amex, MasterCard, Visa.
Terms B&B £32.50–£45; D,B&B £45–£99. Set lunch £14.95, dinner £29.95. Christmas package. 1-night bookings sometimes refused Sat. ***V***

Lindeth Fell   *Tel* (015394) 43286
Lyth Valley Road   *Fax* (015394) 47455
Bowness-on-Windermere LA23 3JP   *E-mail* kennedy@lindethfell.co.uk
                    Website www.lindethfell.co.uk

"You feel like a guest in someone's house," is one recent accolade for Pat and Diana Kennedy's early 19th-century house, set at the end of a tree-lined drive well above the bustle of Windermere. It offers good value, too, and "there are no nasty surprises when you settle the bill". The gardens, with their small lake and banks of rhododendrons, are especially good in spring and early summer, when they are open to the public (many other fine gardens are nearby). Many outdoor activities may be enjoyed in the large grounds (see below). On warm days, tea and drinks are served on a terrace. The house itself is spacious, with "good places for sitting around in". The lounges (one was redecorated this year) have family photographs, bric-à-brac, watercolours, books and magazines, a log fire. One has a fine plaster ceiling and large windows looking over the treetops towards distant Windermere. A new dining room with lake views has been created, where Stephen Marsden's five-course dinners are served: cheese and herb roulade filled with spinach; chargrilled tuna steak on a bed of celery; prune and Armagnac tart, all feature on his extensive menus. There is always a vegetarian main course. Bedrooms vary in size and are priced accordingly. The best ones have a lake view; top ones are quite small, with a sloping ceiling. Some recent praise: "The considerate hosts are ever-available; the staff make the guest feel truly cared for." "Lovely views, comfy bed, enveloping towels." The hotel has a good return trade: one satisfied customer has been here every October for over a decade. More reports, please.

Open Mid-Feb–Jan.
Rooms 12 double, 2 single. 1 on ground floor, adapted for &.
Facilities Ramp. Hall, 2 lounges, dispense bar, 3 dining rooms. No background music. 7-acre grounds: gardens, tennis, croquet, putting, bowls, small lake. Lake Windermere 1 mile: free fishing; golf nearby. Civil wedding licence applied for.
Location 1 mile S of Bowness on A5074. Train/bus to Windermere.
Restrictions No smoking: dining rooms, 1 lounge. No children under 7 in dining rooms at night. No dogs in house.
Credit cards MasterCard, Visa.
Terms B&B: single £30–£52, double £60–£138; D,B&B: single £52–£69, double £130–£172. Light lunch/picnic £6. Set lunch £13.50, set dinner £23. Off-season rates. Christmas package. 1-night bookings sometimes refused weekends. *V*

BRADFORD West Yorkshire *See SHORTLIST*   **Map 4**

BRADFORD-ON-AVON Wiltshire   **Map 2**

Woolley Grange	*Tel* (01225) 864705
Woolley Green	*Fax* (01225) 864059
Bradford-on-Avon BA15 1TX	*E-mail* info@woolleygrange.com
	Website www.woolleygrange.com

Q *Cesar award in 1992*

Set on the edge of a lovely Wiltshire town, this Jacobean manor house was the first in a quartet of Luxury Family Hotels, set up by Nigel and Heather Chapman. Others in the group now include *The Old Bell*, Malmesbury, *Moonfleet Manor*, Fleet and *Fowey Hall*, Fowey (*qqv*). All aim to offer a child-friendly environment, combined with civilised comforts for adults. "Pleasant bedrooms", with beams and windows in odd places, have been fitted into the original structure; some are spacious, others small but cleverly designed; some have a gas log fire; some can be arranged to form an inter-connecting suite. Parents pay by the room, squeezing in as many children as they can tolerate. From 10 am to 6 pm a nanny presides over a playroom for small children, where their meals are served; baby-sitting is available in the evening. A huge Victorian hen house is equipped for older children with table-tennis, pool and videos, and there are plenty of attractions outdoors (see below). Informal antiques and amusing primitive paintings (some specially commissioned) adorn the public areas. When small children are settled in bed, parents sit down to a candlelit dinner with dishes such as spiced veal sweetbreads with cranberry compote and oyster mushrooms; seabass with roast celeriac and a white bean and organic vegetable broth; spiced poached pear with caramelised rice pudding and ginger ice-cream. The kitchen is supplied by a new organic garden. Light meals are served in the conservatory. The extensive wine list was this year thought "average for a country house hotel, with high mark-ups". There is a panelled hall with newspapers, magazines, comics for children, and a lounge with a "slightly threadbare air". The attractive building and "happy atmosphere" have long been admired, but staying here is not cheap, and this year there are also some criticisms. One three-generation family had "an enjoyable week", and praised the staff: "They are polite, friendly, and disposed to be helpful." But they thought that the food varied "from very good to rather poor" and reported long waits between courses in the restaurant: "The whole set-up is willing but amateur." For guests without children there are honeymoon packages and local activity holidays. Longleat is nearby. More reports, please.

Open All year.
Rooms 3 suites, 19 double, 1 single. 9 in courtyard or coach house. 1 on ground floor.
Facilities Ramp. 3 lounges, restaurant, conservatory; children's nursery, games rooms. No background music. 14-acre grounds: gardens, swimming pool, tennis, badminton, croquet, children's play area. Cycling, riding, golf, fishing, hot-air ballooning nearby.
Location 1 mile NE of Bradford-on-Avon on B3105. Train: Bath/Bradford-on-Avon/Chippenham.
Restrictions No smoking in restaurant. No dogs in restaurant.
Credit cards All major cards accepted.
Terms [2000] B&B: single £90, double £165–£185, suite £170–£250. Light meals available; set lunch £20, dinner £34.50; full alc £40. Child accommodated free in parents' room. Christmas, New Year, winter, 7-night packages (ask for details). 1-night bookings refused weekends.

BRAMPTON Cumbria   Map 4

 Farlam Hall   *Tel* (016977) 46234
Brampton CA8 2NG   *Fax* (016977) 46683
                                                         E-mail farlamhall@dial.pipex.com
                                                         Website www.farlamhall.co.uk

César award: Country house hotel of the year

"Absolutely marvellous." "Exceptional." Two comments this year on this "delightful hotel" (Relais & Châteaux), owned and run by the

Quinion and Stevenson families. The "pampering atmosphere", "lack of pretension", and "very comfortable bedrooms" are also appreciated. Set in a landscaped Victorian garden with tall trees, a stream and a pond with a fountain, the house is approached up a sweeping drive past a small lake with black swans. The public rooms are ornately Victorian, with dark wallpaper, heavy furniture, trimmings and ornaments. Traditional bedrooms have a mixture of stripes and floral designs, and they are priced according to size (best ones have a whirlpool bath). All have high-quality linen, good lighting, sweets, fresh fruit, books and magazines. Those on the road hear traffic, but windows are double-glazed; in other rooms you might hear "the soothing sounds of the countryside through an open window". Drinks are served in the lounge (no bar). Dinner, cooked by Barry Quinion, is "classic country house, a friendly though formal affair" (men are asked to wear a tie; waitresses wear long dresses). The four-course menu changes daily. "A wonderful lobster mousse was followed by a supremely tender cut of beef." Wines by the glass are available at reasonable prices, and the evening can end with "a warming Armagnac by the fire". Brampton village was founded by Augustinian monks in 1166; it has an old church, mostly 13th-century, and an ancient border fortress, Naworth Castle. A good base for many country activities (walking, birdwatching, riding, garden-visiting, etc), and for sightseeing: Hadrian's Wall and associated archaeological digs are within easy reach. (*Lesley Chapman and Robert Purdy, Margaret Watson, Jillian Battersby, and others*)

Open All year, except 25–30 Dec. Restaurant closed midday (light lunch for residents by arrangement).
Rooms 12 double. 1 in converted stable block. 2 on ground floor.
Facilities Ramps. 2 lounges, restaurant. No background music. 12-acre grounds. Golf, riding, birdwatching nearby. Unsuitable for &.
Location On A689, 2½ miles SE of Brampton (*not* in Farlam village). Rooms double-glazed. Train: Carlisle.
Restriction No smoking in some bedrooms. No children under 5.
Credit cards MasterCard, Visa.
Terms [2000] D,B&B: single £120–£135, double £220–£250. Light/packed lunches by arrangement. Set dinner £30 (£31 on Sat). Special breaks.

BRATTON FLEMING Devon   **Map 1**

Bracken House   BUDGET   *Tel* (01598) 710320
Bratton Fleming
nr Barnstaple EX31 4TG

Prue and Lawrie Scott are the "unpretentious owners" of this Victorian ex-rectory; they are also wildlife enthusiasts, who enjoy sharing this interest with their guests. They look after injured owls, and Mr Scott often gives a talk about owls. The decor is in keeping, with owl ornaments and plenty of taxidermy. *Guide* readers appreciate the informal ambience, the "genuinely warm welcome", with free tea and cakes, and the "glorious setting" in rolling country high on the western edge of Exmoor, with views to the distant Taw estuary and Hartland Point. In the grounds are woodland and paddocks, animals and birds, a small lake generally inhabited by mallards, and hens on the lawn for fresh eggs. The library is well supplied with local information, and there is a small bar in the drawing room. The bedrooms, which vary greatly in size, have a simple decor, with melamine matching furniture of good quality; bathrooms have a power shower. After a substantial English breakfast (fresh orange juice, all manner of cooked dishes), guests make their choice from the dinner menu (always with a vegetarian course). The Aga-cooked meal, served between 7 and 7.30 pm, might include asparagus soup; duck breast with plum sauce; white and dark chocolate cheesecake. Dogs are welcomed. Sunday-to-Sunday bookings are preferred. Nearby is much natural beauty; also fine beaches, the Rosemoor and Marwood Hill gardens, and two National Trust properties, Arlington Court and Knightshayes Court. (*J and MM*)

Open Apr–Oct. Dining room closed midday.
Rooms 8 double. 2 on ground floor; 1 suitable for &. No telephone. 1 self-catering cottage.
Facilities Ramps. Drawing room/bar, library, dining room; light classical background music early evening. 8½-acre grounds. Riding, boating nearby.
Location On edge of village 7 miles NE of Barnstaple. Bus from Barnstaple.
Restrictions No smoking: dining room, library. No children under 12.
Credit cards MasterCard, Visa.
Terms B&B £30–£58; D,B&B £47–£75. 1-night bookings sometimes refused.

BRAY Berkshire   Map 2

The Waterside Inn	*Tel* (01628) 620691

The Waterside Inn   *Tel* (01628) 620691
Ferry Road   *Fax* (01628) 784710
Bray SL6 2AT
                                        E-mail waterinn@aol.com
                                 Website www.waterside-inn.co.uk

Now Britain's only *Michelin* three-starred restaurant, Michel Roux's "truly exceptional establishment" (Relais & Châteaux) "should be visited by every food lover at least once", says a report this year. Other *Guide* readers wrote of an "outstanding restaurant, with formal but approachable service, the best food we'd ever eaten; sauces rich but sublime in their intensity, cheeses outstanding in their range, presentation and quality. The wine list was impressive and not intolerably priced, which tempted us to trade up, and added pleasure to the meal." But eyebrows were raised because only one member of the party of four was given a menu with prices. At meals, "smart casual clothing is expected", and dishes might include spiced foie gras terrine with poached figs; grilled rabbit fillets with glazed chestnuts; dome of white and dark chocolate with raspberries, or a plate crowded with a selection of six desserts. The "idyllic riverside setting" and the "friendly welcome from the carefully trained young French staff" are regularly praised. Drinks are served in a summer house by the water, or on an electric launch. The suite and the two best bedrooms overlook the river. "Our room was small but extremely pleasant, decorated in warm tones of orange and honey, with a wrought iron four-poster bed. Its bathroom was exquisite." Breakfast, served in the bedroom, "is just right after the indulgence of the night before: a large wooden tray with orange juice, yogurt, coffee or tea, croissants, jam, petits pains au chocolat, all excellent". Corporate visitors can sometimes adversely affect the atmosphere at mealtimes, but all this year's reporters loved the place, and are planning a return visit "as soon as we have saved the money". Bray is the village immortalised in the song about the adaptable vicar of its large old church. Windsor Castle is five miles away; Heathrow airport is a 20-minute drive. (*Paul Hingston, P and SB*)

Open All year, except 26 Dec–28 Jan, 3 days early Apr. Restaurant closed Mon, Tues midday, and Sun evening 1 Oct–30 Mar.
Rooms 1 suite (in cottage, 30 yds), 8 double.
Facilities Restaurant; private dining room; launch for drinks/coffee. No background music. Unsuitable for ♿. Civil wedding licence.
Location On Thames, just SE of Maidenhead. M4 exit 8/9 towards Maidenhead Central. At 2nd roundabout turn towards Windsor/Bray. Left after ½ mile on to B3028. In Bray 2nd right into Ferry Rd; hotel on left. Train: Maidenhead; then taxi.
Restrictions No children under 12. No dogs.
Credit cards All major cards accepted.
Terms [2000] B&B: single/double £145–£170, suite £260. Set 3-course lunch: Wed–Sat £30, Sun £46; 5-course *menu exceptionnel* (lunch/dinner) £69.50; alc £90.

BRIGHTON East Sussex   Map 2

Topps NEW   *Tel* (01273) 729334
17 Regency Square   *Fax* (01273) 203679
Brighton BN1 2FG

In quiet square near sea and conference centre: Regency building, carefully restored, immaculate throughout. Managed by Bernard Houssin. 15 bedrooms, most with gas-coal fire, 3 no-smoking, 2 with balcony, some on ground floor. Full English breakfast in no-smoking room. "Thoughtful management; attentive service," says recent visitor. No dogs in public rooms. NCP carpark close by. All major credit cards accepted. B&B: single £49–£69, double from £84.

See also SHORTLIST

BRISTOL   Map 1

Hotel du Vin & Bistro NEW   *Tel* (0117) 925 5577
The Sugar House   *Fax* (0117) 925 1199
Narrow Lewins Mead   *E-mail* admin@bristol.hotelduvin.co.uk
Bristol BS1 2NU   *Website* www.hotelduvin.com

An "inspired renovation" of a Grade II listed 18th-century sugar refinery and warehouse in the city centre. It is the third member of the Alternative Hotel Company, set up by Gerald Basset and Robin Hutson (see also Winchester and Tunbridge Wells). As before, they aim to provide bistro-style meals, serious wines (the cellar here has a strong Iberian accent), an informal atmosphere, and uncluttered bed-rooms (each sponsored by a wine house), with a modern bathroom, a CD-player, a large bed with Egyptian cotton sheets. A sweeping stair-case leads up to a maze of dark corridors at various levels, illuminated by alcoves where wine bottles are displayed. The largest bedrooms are double height, with a sitting area. "Ours," say inspectors, "was spacious, with a huge bathroom, a minimalist decor, low beds with a wide wooden frame. In the busy Georgian dining room, tables are packed, the waiting staff are predominantly French, apart from the manageress, a charming beauty. Dinner was very satisfactory, partic-ularly the main courses: rare, tender roast pigeon with creamed cab-bage and truffle mash; outstanding bream with cucumber, aubergine and fresh ravioli. Service was competent and friendly throughout." (*Sue Davies, and others*)

Open All year.
Rooms 5 suites, 35 double.
Facilities Lift. Lounge, billiard room, bar, bistro. No background music.
Location City centre (front rooms get traffic noise). From motorways and A4, follow signs to centre. Pass Bentalls department store on left. After *c.* 400 yds hotel is visible on opposite side of carriageway. Follow road to traffic lights (keep in right-hand lane). Right at war memorial (doubling back). Hotel is on small side road after 200 yds.
Restriction No dogs.
Credit cards All major cards accepted.
Terms Room: single £99, double £99–£125, suite £150–£195. Breakfast: con-tinental £7.50, English £9.50. Full alc £35. Christmas package.

See also SHORTLIST

BROADWAY Worcestershire   **Map 3**

Collin House   *Tel* (01386) 858354
Collin Lane   *Fax* (01386) 858697
Broadway WR12 7PB
                                  E-mail collin.house@virgin.net
                          Website www.broadway-cotswolds.co.uk/collin

Set amid orchards and gardens outside the picture-postcard town, this 15th-century Cotswold stone manor house was built by a prosperous wool merchant. It is now a "civilised and well run" small hotel and restaurant, owned by Tricia and Keith Ferguson. The interior has "the feel of a country house": mullioned windows, flagstones, beams, inter-esting pictures, good antiques. The bedrooms are cosy, with sloping beams, matching fabrics and home-made shortbread; some have a four-poster. Some rooms, particularly the single, are small. Dinner is taken in the candlelit dining room, with silver and white damask. The food is traditional English, served in generous helpings. The long menu includes main courses such as Aga-baked halibut steak; roast rack of lamb; wild boar steak with wild mushrooms and local duck. The puddings are home made, including the ice-creams. Morning coffee; bar meals (except Saturday supper) and teas are served, and there is a traditional Sunday lunch. Breakfast has "rather good coarse marmalade", porridge and grilled kippers, but one couple this year didn't think much of the toast. Some traffic noise from the A44 nearby. The north Cotswolds, Warwick and Sudeley castles and Blenheim Palace are all within easy distance. More reports, please.

Open All year, except Christmas.
Rooms 1 suite, 5 double. No telephone.
Facilities Ramp. Lounge, bar, restaurant. No background music. 2-acre grounds. Riding, golf nearby. Unsuitable for &.
Location 1 mile NW of Broadway on A44, 75 yds from roundabout. Turn right down Collin La. Train: Moreton-in-Marsh, 9 miles; Evesham, 6 miles; then bus/taxi.
Restrictions Smoking in lounge only. No children under 12 in restaurant. No dogs.
Credit cards MasterCard, Visa.
Terms [2000] B&B: single £69, double £92–£102; D,B&B: double £121. Set lunch £16.95; full alc dinner £35. Bar meals. 2-night breaks. 1-night bookings refused Sat in summer. ***V***

BROXTON Cheshire   **Map 3**

Frogg Manor   *Tel* (01829) 782629
Nantwich Road   *Fax* (01829) 782459
Broxton, Chester CH3 9JH

Ω *César award in 1997*

"We were totally enamoured of this rural idyll." "A unique blend of home comforts, friendly atmosphere and culinary delights." Two visitors this year pay tribute to this white Georgian house, in a well-heeled area near Chester, over which the "flamboyant and delightfully eccentric" John Sykes presides. He is manager, chef and self-styled "chief frog", dedicated to 1930s/1940s music (of which there is an "inexhaustible collection") and to frogs – several hundred (ceramic, straw, brass, etc) are scattered around the house. The bedrooms are plush and themed: a lavishly draped four-poster is the centrepiece of the Wellington suite, and the Churchill suite has an "amazing bathroom". All rooms are stocked with shoe-cleaning kit, toothbrushes, dressing gowns, tea, coffee, biscuits and hangover cures. Cotton sheets are standard; Irish linen ones are supplied on request. Public rooms are "sumptuously comfortable and elegantly decorated", and service is "the best": one guest this year requested Dandelion & Burdock at midnight; a suitably chilled can was immediately provided. The large, eclectic menus offer a "delicious choice", ranging from Beef Wellington and Poona king prawns to escalopes de veau Normande, and including vegan and vegetarian dishes. Everything is cooked to order. Dinner is announced by a bugle call and served between 7 and 10 pm, but you should make clear at what time you want to eat. A light supper can be arranged for late-comers. Breakfast *à la carte* (remember to order toast) is served round the clock from Monday to Saturday, and between 9 and 10.30 am on Sunday. The garden is romantically floodlit at night, and it has views across Cheshire to the Welsh mountains. (*Capt. NDV Robertson, Brian Thompson*)

Open All year.
Rooms 1 suite, 5 double.
Facilities Lounge, bar lounge, restaurant (1930s/40s background music); private dining room; conference facilities. 9-acre grounds: tennis. Unsuitable for &. Civil wedding licence.
Location 15 miles SE of Chester. From A41, take A534 to Nantwich. Hotel on right.
Restriction Dogs by arrangement. In 1 bedroom only; not in public rooms.
Credit cards All major cards accepted.
Terms [2000] Room: single £50–£110, double £70–£140. Alc breakfast *c.* £10. Set lunch £19.80, dinner £34.50. Full alc £40. Discounts for more than 1 night (except Christmas, New Year). *V*

BUDOCK VEAN Cornwall   Map 1

Budock Vean Hotel   *Tel* (01326) 252100
Budock Vean, nr Mawnan Smith   *Fax* (01326) 250892
Falmouth TR11 5LG   *E-mail* relax@budockvean.co.uk
                                         Website www.budockvean.co.uk

"Staying here is addictive," writes a fan of this resort-style hotel. Recently expensively refurbished, it stands in huge grounds with subtropical gardens and woodland, in a designated area of outstanding natural beauty. It is owned and managed by the Barlow family, who also own *Treglos*, Constantine Bay (*qv*); many of the staff are long-serving. It has a private waterfront on the Helford Passage ("super views"), and it offers golfing holidays with tuition – it has an "interesting" and well-maintained nine-hole golf course. The large swimming pool opens on to a terrace in summer; in winter it is enclosed, and has a log fire. The spa provides natural health and beauty treatments. Devotees find the hotel "welcoming, elegant and comfortable". There are "snooze-inducing" sofas, log fires in the lounge. The well-equipped bedrooms have a modern bathroom. Shoes are polished overnight, and early morning tea can be brought to the room. The cocktail bar serves "delicious pre-dinner appetisers". Formal dress is required at dinnertime in the main restaurant, but the same menu is served less formally in the Country Club restaurant. "Sublime lemon sole, and melt-in-the-mouth salmon" were enjoyed this year, and other dishes on the five-course dinner menu, with plenty of choice, might be smoked eel and fine leaf salad; roast loin of pork with sage and onion stuffing, or grilled haddock with prawns and capers. Puddings are "positively dangerous", and there is a "superb" board of West Country cheeses. Wines are reasonably priced. Breakfasts are "equally generous, and full of choice – delicious scrambled eggs, and the fried bread deserves a lifetime achievement award". *Budock Vean* does not specifically promote itself as a hotel for young children (no playground or playroom), but families are welcomed, "provided the peace and relaxation of fellow guests is respected", and there is good accommodation for them in cottage suites. Famous gardens are nearby: Heligan, Glendurgan, Trebah, Trelissick. (*Mary Wood, Peter Lush, DJ*)

Open All year, except 3–18 Jan.
Rooms 4 suites, 46 double, 7 single.
Facilities Lift. 3 lounges, conservatory, cocktail bar (pianist at night), restaurant, snooker room. 65-acre grounds: garden, country club: bar, restaurant, natural health spa, 9-hole golf course, tennis, croquet, archery, river frontage, fishing, water sports, etc; riding nearby. Unsuitable for ♿. Civil wedding licence.
Location 5 miles S of Falmouth. A39 to Hillhead roundabout; right to Mawnan Smith. Follow brown signs to Trebah Gardens; hotel ½ mile after gardens.
Restrictions No smoking in dining room. No children under 7 in cocktail bar or main restaurant after 7 pm. No dogs in public rooms.
Credit cards MasterCard, Diners (*2% surcharge*), Visa.
Terms [2000] B&B: single £39–£87, double £78–£174; suite £183–£239; D,B&B from £49 per person. Bar lunches. Set dinner £25; full alc £38. Special breaks: golf, Valentine, etc. Christmas, Easter tariffs.

BURFORD Oxfordshire   Map 2

The Lamb   NEW   *Tel* (01993) 823155
Sheep Street   *Fax* (01993) 822228
Burford OX18 4LR

In a picture-postcard village, Richard de Wolf's "lovely old inn" makes a "marvellous base for exploring the Cotswolds", says a regular *Guide* correspondent. Full of 15th-century character, it has mullioned windows, polished oak floors, flagstones, Oriental rugs, antiques, polished brass and an open fire in its main lounge. In the restaurant, well-spaced tables stand on bare floorboards, and Pascal Clavaud serves quite ambitious dishes, eg, chicken liver and Armagnac parfait; tenderloin of pork on creamed tarragon sweet potato; caramelised pineapple pancake with a rum sabayon. "Service was excellent, and the food well cooked and presented. A most reasonably priced wine list." Behind the inn are a small paved courtyard and a walled garden, where neat lawns are surrounded by flowering shrubs and small trees. "A charming female receptionist insisted on carrying our heavy luggage. Our ground-floor room was comfortable, with a small bathroom. Early tea was brought in the morning; not DIY." The bar serves good snacks on weekdays and a formal Sunday lunch. Some bedrooms are up narrow steps. (*Anne Steel, Good Pub Guide*)

Open All year, except 25/26 Dec.
Rooms 15 double.
Facilities 3 lounges, bar, restaurant. No background music. Courtyard; ½-acre garden. River fishing ½ mile. Unsuitable for ♿.
Location 500 yds from centre. Parking. Bus from Oxford. Nearest station 8 miles.
Restriction No smoking in restaurant.
Credit cards MasterCard, Visa.
Terms [2000] B&B: single £65–£85, double £100–£120; D,B&B: single £85–£100, double £140–£160. Set lunch £20, dinner £25. Spring, summer, midweek, weekend breaks. 1-night bookings sometimes refused weekends.

Give the *Guide* positive support. Don't leave feedback to others.

BURNHAM MARKET Norfolk · Map 2

The Hoste Arms
The Green
Burnham Market PE31 8HD

Tel (01328) 738777
Fax (01328) 730103
E-mail thehostearms@compuserve.com
Website www.hostearms.co.uk

On the green of a lovely Norfolk village, this old inn is where Lord Nelson used to collect his dispatches. In the past it has served as court assizes, auction house and brothel. Under the current owners, Paul Whittome (who describes himself as a "passionate and dedicated hotelkeeper") and his wife Jeanne, it is a lively place, with upmarket bedrooms, a bar with real ales, a large shell collection and a small art gallery. The cooking of the Australian chef, Andrew McPherson, keeps the restaurant (it has wooden floors and panels, tables close together) very busy, with guests being fed in relays. The eclectic brasserie-style menu includes dishes like mussels steamed in white wine; Szechuan chilli chicken with crispy vegetables; steak and chips. "Plain, well-cooked" Dover sole was enjoyed by an inspector this year, but she was not so keen on the chocolate mousse that followed. In the walled garden, heaters enable guests to dine alfresco in summer. Even at breakfast the place can be buzzing ("it is not a place for relaxing"). Many of the staff are young, and service can be "amateurish"; there is also a report of a cool reception. The bedrooms vary: a "lovely, large one overlooking the green" was liked this year, though its bedside lighting was "much too dim"; rooms in an extension look through French windows on to the garden, where there are "chairs for summer drinkers, and children running around". The rooms "are of reasonable size, well fitted out", and have Designers Guild fabrics. Our inspectors' "small and dark" bathroom had a shower attachment only, "but very good towels". The annexe (formerly the town's station), a short walk away, has "small but adequate" bedrooms; a car will take its residents to the inn for meals. In his brochure, Mr Whittome writes of his "aversion to rules" and he adds: "Please speak up! I am very deaf, and this is sometimes mistaken for rudeness." The village is surrounded by a designated area of natural beauty, with nature reserves, historic buildings, golf courses, etc. (*Philip and Eileen Hall, and others*)

Open All year.
Rooms 6 junior suites, 17 double, 5 single. 6 in annexe.
Facilities Lounge, conservatory, 4 dining rooms; conference facilities; pianist Fri evenings Oct–Mar, occasional jazz concerts. Walled garden. Sea, bird sanctuaries, golf nearby. Unsuitable for &.
Location Central. Large carpark. Train: Norwich/Kings Lynn; then hotel car (small charge).
Restrictions No smoking in 2 dining rooms. "Not suitable for noisy or badly behaved children, but charming ones are warmly welcomed."
Credit cards MasterCard, Visa.
Terms B&B £43–£95; D,B&B (min. 2 nights) £75–£145. Bar meals. Full alc £25–£30. Child accommodated in parents' room: under 14, £15. Christmas package.

Report forms (Freepost in UK) are at the end of the *Guide*.

BURPHAM West Sussex   Map 2

The Burpham   *Tel* (01903) 882160
Burpham, nr Arundel BN18 9RJ   *Fax* (01903) 884627

The 18th-century shooting lodge of the Dukes of Norfolk is now a small country hotel run by George and Marianne Walker. He is "great fun"; she "solicitous"; their staff are "obviously happy in their work". "The location, at the end of the longest cul-de-sac in Sussex, ensures peace and quiet," says a regular *Guide* correspondent this year. "The house is comfortable, warm, well aired, and stocked with flowers, even in February." The bedrooms, with lots of velour, are well equipped, but there is one report of dim lighting, and some bathrooms may be "claustrophobic". The English/French/Swiss food (influenced by the Swiss origins of Mrs Walker) is considered "quite wonderful"; "outstandingly good". "Luscious fresh scallops in a delicious sauce" are singled out for praise. Main courses are "generously served". One visitor commented that he had "never before been presented at breakfast with such superb bacon, sausages and tomatoes". The new conservatory has views across the croquet lawn and the South Downs, and allows guests to breakfast and dine in a "blaze of sunshine". Burpham (pronounced Ber'-fum) has a Norman church and a cricket pitch on which WG Grace once played; Arundel Castle and Peter Scott's Wildfowl Trust are close by; Chichester and Goodwood are within easy reach. There is good walking all around. (*B and P Orman, Dr FP Woodford, DG Clarke, Joy and Raymond Goldman, Dr GA Fothergill*)

Open All year, except Christmas Day, last week Jan, first week Feb. Restaurant closed midday, Mon evening.
Rooms 9 double (1 on ground floor), 1 single.
Facilities Hall (occasional classical background music at night), lounge, bar, restaurant, conservatory; small conference room. ¾-acre garden: croquet. Coast 6 miles: sand/shingle beaches, safe bathing.
Location NE of Arundel. Left off A27 Arundel–Worthing towards Warningcamp/Burpham just after railway bridge. Hotel on right after 2½ miles (look for sign on A27).
Restrictions No smoking: restaurant, some bedrooms. No children under 12. No dogs.
Credit cards Amex, MasterCard, Visa.
Terms B&B £42.50–£55; D,B&B £67–£78.50. Set dinner £23.50. Special breaks; Stress Remedy breaks. *V*

BURRINGTON Devon   Map 1

Northcote Manor NEW   *Tel* (01769) 560501
Burrington, nr South Molton   *Fax* (01769) 560770
EX37 9LZ   *E-mail* rest@northcotemanor.co.uk
    Website www.northcotemanor.co.uk

Up meandering drive through 20-acre wooded grounds: wisteria-clad 18th-century manor house overlooking sweeping lawns. Pride of Britain member, refurbished by new owner, David Boddy, in 1999. Managed by Karen Dawson; her husband, Chris, formerly of Ynyshir

Hall, *Eglwysfach, Wales* (qv), *is chef. Elaborate cooking and personal attention in smoke-free restaurant with large medieval-style murals, light classical music, wine list specialising in New Zealand vintages. Civil wedding licence. 18-hole golf course adjacent; fishing in River Taw. Closed 1st week Jan. Unsuitable for &. No children under 10. No dogs in public rooms. All major credit cards accepted. 11 bedrooms. B&B £60–£125. Set lunch £21.50, dinner £34.50.* *V**

BURY ST EDMUNDS Suffolk   Map 2

Ounce House   *Tel* (01284) 761779
Northgate Street   *Fax* (01284) 768315
Bury St Edmunds IP33 1HP   *E-mail* pott@globalnet.co.uk

A civilised B&B in a Victorian merchant's house, which the owners, Simon and Jenny Pott, have decorated in keeping with its age. Good fabrics, antiques, pictures and prints, and inviting colour schemes abound. Guests have the use of a bay-windowed drawing room with a large fireplace, and a library with TV, an upright piano and an honesty bar. There is a useful parking area in front of the house, which is on a busy road; the quietest of the three bedrooms overlooks the walled garden. Breakfasts are "perfectly cooked and presented". Dinner can be served if numbers are sufficient. It is taken communally, and traditional: four courses, eg, carrot and coriander soup; pheasant casserole; raspberry brûlée; cheese. The "warm and helpful" Mrs Pott is an excellent source of information on local history, and the ruined abbey is close by – Bury St Edmunds, named for King Edmund the Martyr, who was murdered by Danes in the 9th century, was an important centre of pilgrimage. The town has many handsome buildings, including the Theatre Royal, the second oldest working theatre in the country. Ickworth House (National Trust) is nearby. More reports, please.

Open All year.
Rooms 3 double.
Facilities Drawing room, snug, bar/library, dining room. No background music. ¾-acre walled garden. Unsuitable for &.
Location Central (rear bedroom quietest). Leave A14 (formerly A45) at 2nd Bury exit. Left at 1st roundabout into Northgate St; house at top of hill. Private parking. Collection can be arranged from railway station.
Restrictions Smoking in bar/library only, "provided that you light a candle". No dogs.
Credit cards All major cards accepted.
Terms [2000] B&B: single £58–£65, double £80–£90. Set dinner (by arrangement, for 4 or more) £24–£26. Weekend rates; reductions for 3 or more nights.

See also SHORTLIST

Important: terms printed in the *Guide* are only a rough indication of the size of the bill to be expected at the end of your stay. It is vital that you check the tariffs when booking.

CALNE Wiltshire   **Map 2**

Chilvester Hill House   *Tel* (01249) 813981 and 815785
Calne SN11 0LP   *Fax* (01249) 814217
                                   E-mail gill.dilley@talk21.com

♺ *Cesar award in 1992*

Built in 1888 for the land agent of Lord Lansdowne, the owner of
nearby Bowood estate, this Victorian house (a Wolsey Lodge member) has long been a *Guide* favourite. In keeping with the house's setting, the owners, Gill and John Dilley, recently redecorated its
exterior, replacing the weathered woodwork with Bowood oak,
which has been carved and moulded by local craftsmen in true
Victorian style. The Dilleys, who are known and loved for their
"charm and slight eccentricity", also breed beef cattle, which graze in
the fields around the large garden. Indoors, there are antiques and
mementos of many years in the Middle East. No brochure – prospective visitors are sent an informative letter discussing facilities and
food likes and dislikes. Dinner (a four-course meal including home-
grown and local vegetables) is served round one large table, with
couples separated to encourage conversation; the Dilleys often join
their guests for pre-dinner drinks or afterwards for coffee. There is no
obligation to eat in, and help is given with reservations for local
eating places. "The rooms cannot be faulted," writes a devotee (they
are generously equipped, with a hot drinks tray, good biscuits and so
on), "and in the style of a visit to a country house, the beds are turned
down during dinner." *En suite* bathrooms have a hand-held shower
only, but a large shower room is available (bathrobes are provided).
The Dilleys write that "breakfast is 'what you like when you like it',
although most guests settle for something between 8 and 9 am". On
offer are freshly shelled grapefruit, a choice of eight cereals, locally
produced chipolatas and bacon, locally oak-smoked kippers as well
as kidneys, tomatoes and mushrooms and eggs any way, plus
home-made jams and preserves. Dr Dilley has encyclopaedic local
knowledge: sights include the Neolithic stone circle at Avebury,
the National Trust village of Lacock, the Slimbridge Wildfowl
Trust. (*Chris Kay*)

Open All year, except possibly 1 week autumn and/or spring.
Rooms 3 double. No telephone.
Facilities Drawing room, sitting room with TV, dining room. No background
music. 2½-acre grounds (also 5 acres used for cattle). Golf, riding locally.
Unsuitable for &.
Location From Calne, A4 towards Chippenham. Right after ½ mile to
Bremhill; drive immediately on right (gateposts with stone lions).
Restrictions No smoking in dining room. Generally no children under 12,
except babes in arms. No dogs in house.
Credit cards All major cards accepted.
Terms B&B: single £45–£55, double £75–£85. Packed/snack lunches. Set
dinner £18–£25. 10% discount for B&B if 1 week or more.

CAMBRIDGE Cambridgeshire *See SHORTLIST*   **Map 2**

CAMPSEA ASHE Suffolk   **Map 2**

The Old Rectory `BUDGET`   *Tel/Fax* (01728) 746524
Campsea Ashe
nr Woodbridge IP13 0PU

♀ *César award in 1995*

"Warm hospitality, excellent cooking. Thoroughly deserves its place
in the *Guide*." One of this year's reports on a creeper-covered
Georgian house, both a restaurant-with-rooms and a Wolsey Lodge,
which stands in a large garden with statuary, by the church in a village
not far from Aldeburgh. It is informally run by owner/chef Stewart
Bassett, with long-time manager Tina Morford. Visitors value its
"relaxed atmosphere", "old-world comfort" and eccentric charm, and
above all the reasonably priced food and "amazing wine list". Dinner
is served by candlelight at 7.30 in the old-style dining rooms, or in the
conservatory, at well-spaced bare wooden tables with big rattan
chairs. The three-course, no-choice menu might consist of pan-fried
halibut on a bed of spinach with butter sauce; braised spiced lamb with
roasted almonds; chocolate brandy cake. Breakfast includes an extensive buffet. In the large drawing room, high ceilings and grand
antiques are set off by rich terracotta walls, and there is an honesty bar.
Accommodation ranges from a large four-poster room overlooking
the churchyard to a small double above the garden; the one above the
kitchen can be noisy. Budget B&B accommodation is offered in a cottage in the village, good for a family. Children are warmly welcomed,
though there are no special facilities for them; high tea must be booked
in advance. Guests should not arrive between 2 and 4 pm. Plant propagation courses for gardeners are held. The RSPB reserve at Minsmere
is nearby. (*Dr K Langford, Mrs J Wensley; also JN, and others*)

Open All year, except Christmas, 3 weeks Mar. Restaurant closed midday,
Sun evening; bedrooms sometimes closed Sun.
Rooms 6 double, 1 single. No telephone/TV (pay-phone in hall).
Facilities Drawing room, honesty bar, restaurant; function facilities. No back-
ground music. 4-acre garden: croquet. Riding, golf nearby; sea at Aldeburgh,
10 mins' drive. Unsuitable for &.
Location In village 1½ miles E of A12 on B1078. Next to church. Train:
Wickham Market, via Ipswich.
Restrictions No smoking. No dogs in public rooms.
Credit cards All major cards accepted.
Terms [2000] B&B: single £45, double £60–£72. D,B&B (obligatory Sat):
single £63, double £96–£108. Set dinner £18.50. Child accommodated in par-
ents' room: under 3, free; 3–10, B&B £10. Plant propagation courses.

****

Hotel in Scotland. You are expected to make your dinner selection over breakfast, and to choose next day's breakfast over
dinner. When one visitor asked for an extra egg, the host said
this should have been ordered the previous evening. One day,
my cooked breakfast was placed on the table, without a cover,
before I had finished my first course.

****

CANNINGTON Somerset   Map 1

Blackmore Farm   BUDGET   *Tel* (01278) 653442
Cannington   *Fax* (01278) 653427
nr Bridgwater TA5 2NE   *E-mail* dyerfarm@aol.com
                                        Website www.dyerfarm.co.uk

"It is a truly wonderful building; the prices are ridiculously reason-able," say inspectors this year of this pink-washed medieval manor house, Grade I listed, with a "lovely little chapel" attached. Set down a quiet lane on a large working farm not far from the M5, it is the family home of the owners, Ann and Ian Dyer, who offer "traditional farmhouse bed and breakfast". They run it in generous style: "No charge for tea and delicious home-made sponge cake offered on arrival; the hospitality tray in the bedroom had every conceivable kind of drink, bowls of fruit, chocolate, shortbread; the bathroom was just as lavishly equipped." The old house has retained many original fea-tures: heavy latched doors, stone archways, mullioned windows, a spi-ral stone staircase, garderobes and oak beams; old pewter pots, hay forks and "nasty looking man-traps" are scattered about. "You feel you have stepped back into the past." Only four bedrooms, simply fur-nished "in quiet good taste"; they look over fields or the farmyard. The West Room has Gothic arches and an oak four-poster bed. The Gallery has oak panelling and beams, and a sitting room down a flight of steps. The Solar has three single beds and a shower. A room in a converted barn is adapted for disabled visitors. At breakfast, in the Great Hall, guests eat together at a long refectory table by a massive sandstone fireplace. "It was very good, with fruit, yogurt, scrambled egg with smoked haddock, and a vegetarian option." There are plenty of restau-rants nearby. You can watch the cows being milked from a gallery, play croquet in the garden, and visit a cottage nearby where Coleridge once lived. A good base for exploring the Quantocks, the west Somerset coast and Exmoor.

Open All year.
Rooms 1 suite, 3 double. 1, on ground floor, adapted for ♿. No telephone.
Facilities Lounge/TV room, breakfast room. No background music. 1½-acre garden in 750-acre farm: croquet, children's play area. Coarse fishing, riding, golf, cycling nearby.
Location From Bridgwater: A39 to Minehead; after 3 miles left at Tincknells into Blackmore La. Farm ¾ mile on left, after *Maltshovel* pub. Train: Bridgwater, 4 miles; irregular bus service.
Restrictions No smoking. No dogs.
Credit cards MasterCard, Visa.
Terms B&B: single £30–£38, double £42–£50; suite £50–£58.

Readers with mobility problems might like to know of the *Smooth Ride Guides,* which publish information about many hotels with facilities for the disabled. *Tel* (01279) 77966, *fax* (01279) 777995, *e-mail* july.ramsey@virgin.net

CANTERBURY Kent   Map 2

The Canterbury Hotel   *Tel* (01227) 450551
71 New Dover Road   *Fax* (01227) 780145
Canterbury CT1 3DZ   *E-mail* canterbury.hotel@btinternet.com

A Victorian red brick house that differs from the neighbouring small
hotels on the Dover road by virtue of its Gallic atmosphere. Managed
by M. Boizot, it has a young French staff and an ambitious restaurant
hung with Renoir prints and called *La Bonne Cuisine*. The chef,
Raphael Rollé, is new this year, so we'd be grateful for reports on his
cooking. His menus include, eg, foie gras de canard; pot au feu de la
mer en symphonie; pigeon rôti à l'ail. But breakfast is an English affair.
The decor is attractive, with lots of blue and yellow. Redecoration of
the bedrooms (they are on three floors; some are spacious) has been
proceeding. They have bright colours and a small but gleaming bathroom; "boiling hot water, even at midnight", was appreciated by our
inspector. Three self-catering apartments are new this year. Drinks and
bar snacks are served in the lounge or on a patio. There are drawbacks:
the road is busy, and there is background music most of the time. But
the hotel has much to recommend it, too, not least its carpark and its
location: the sights of Canterbury are ten minutes' walk away.

Open All year.
Rooms 3 self-catering apartments, 20 double, 3 single.
Facilities Lift. Lounge, bar, restaurant; jazz/"easy listening"/classical back-
ground music all day; small conference facilities. Small garden.
Location On A2, ½ mile S of centre. Carpark. Train to Canterbury East.
Restrictions No smoking in restaurant. No children under 6 in restaurant at
night. No dogs in public rooms.
Credit cards All major cards accepted.
Terms [2000] B&B: single £55–£80, double £75–£105. Set lunch from £14,
dinner from £17; full alc £40. Half board rates available (min. 2 nights).
Christmas package.

Greyfriars   `BUDGET`   *Tel* (01227) 456255
6 Stour Street   *Fax* (01227) 455233
Canterbury CT1 2NR   *E-mail* christine@greyfriars-house.co.uk
                            Website www.greyfriars-house.co.uk

*Keith and Christine Chapman's 9-bedroomed guest house (former
gate house of Franciscan monastery). In quiet cul-de-sac between
main pedestrian street and River Stour, behind* County Hotel.
*Riverside garden. Simple comforts, good value. Children welcomed.
English, continental or vegetarian breakfast. Free secure parking. No
background music. No dogs. Visa accepted. B&B: single £20–£35,
double £40–£55, family £55–£75 [2000]. More reports, please.*

See also SHORTLIST

We are particularly keen to have reports on italicised entries.

CARLISLE Cumbria   Map 4

Avondale   `BUDGET`   *Tel/Fax* (01228) 523012
3 St Aidan's Road   *E-mail* beeanbee@hotmail.com
Carlisle CA1 1LT

"One of the most comfortable guest houses I have used," says a visitor in 2000 to this large Edwardian house. It retains many original features – fireplaces, stained glass, elaborate ceilings, door handles, etc, and has a decor to match. It is on a quiet road in a residential area, ten minutes' walk from the centre. The owners, Michael and Angela Hayes, have recently redecorated, and all three bedrooms now have a private bathroom as well as TV. The largest room overlooks the garden. The "civilised atmosphere" is liked, and so are the breakfasts, with "expertly cooked fresh eggs". A simple evening meal is available by arrangement. It is "traditional, wholesome and uncomplicated", say the owners, eg, leek, onion and potato soup; chicken casserole; fresh fruit salad. Portions are generous. Unlicensed; bring your own wine. No brochure, but Mr Hayes will write a description if asked. (*Murray Elkington*)

Open All year, except Christmas.
Rooms 3 double, 1 with bathroom *en suite*. No telephone.
Facilities Sitting room, dining room. No background music. Small front and rear gardens. Unsuitable for &.
Location From M6 exit 43 go into Carlisle. Turn right just past church on right after 4th traffic lights. Parking. Train/bus stations nearby.
Restrictions No smoking. No dogs.
Credit cards None accepted.
Terms (*Not VAT-rated*) B&B £20–£22. Evening meal £9.

Number Thirty One   *Tel/Fax* (01228) 597080
31 Howard Place   *E-mail* bestpep@aol.com
Carlisle CA1 1HR   *Website* www.number31.freeservers.com

Philip and Judith Parker's guest house is "something special", says a visitor from Australia this year. Other guests praise the "relaxing environment", the "excellent breakfast" and the "kind hosts". Their Victorian terraced house is on a tree-lined street in the town centre. Its lounge is crammed with knick-knacks and souvenirs of travel; there is a small patio garden. Only three bedrooms: the Blue Room, at the rear, is the largest; the Green Room has an Oriental-style decor; from the Yellow Room in front, the owners claim, you can see the Pennines on a fine day. A three-course, no-choice evening meal is served by arrangement, at separate tables, and the food is thought "well presented, and good value". Philip Parker says he cooks "in the Floyd manner, with glass in hand (normally nothing stronger than sparkling water)", and he adds: "Virtually everything is home made; ingredients are bought each day; we avoid produce with additives; trout and salmon are smoked on the premises when I catch them; breakfast sausages are made to a Cumbrian recipe." Each dish is described at length on the menu: main courses include, eg, breast of chicken cooked with vermouth; salmon marinated in vodka and lime. The

Parkers regularly transport their guests to and from the railway station; they have a stock of books on tape for the blind. (*Peter and Hilary Ray, Jean Moore Warrick*)

Open 1 Mar–1 Nov.
Rooms 3 double. No telephone.
Facilities Lounge, dining room/library (background music). Small patio. Salmon/trout fishing on River Eden, nearby. Unsuitable for &.
Location From M6 exit 43 take Warwick Rd towards Carlisle. Howard Pl is 1st right after 5th traffic lights. Free guest parking with permit. Hotel will meet train/bus (10 mins' walk).
Restrictions No smoking. No children under 16. No dogs.
Credit cards Amex, MasterCard, Visa.
Terms B&B: single £55, double £75–£95. Set dinner £25.

CARLTON-IN-COVERDALE North Yorkshire   Map 4

The Foresters Arms   NEW   *Tel* (01969) 640272
Carlton-in-Coverdale
nr Leyburn DL8 4BB

A "charming inn", says the *Good Pub Guide*. "It cleverly manages to offer delicious, imaginative food, while retaining the atmosphere of a village local." "It makes a great base for a walking holiday," adds a correspondent this year who enjoyed the "very comfortable" bedrooms (there are only three) and the good cooking of the owner/chef, Barrie Higginbotham. Seafood is a speciality: grilled Dover sole, fillet of sea bream and haddock all feature on the menu, as well as local game and a good choice of vegetarian dishes. Log fires, flagstone floors and real ales are other pleasures on offer. Carlton, in the Yorkshire Dales National Park, is a picturesque old stone-built village. Middleham, Bolton Castle and Aysgarth Falls are nearby; also good cycling, climbing and fishing. (*Peter Wilson*)

Open Feb–end Dec. Closed Sun night/Mon, Tues midday.
Rooms 3 double.
Facilities Bar, restaurant; mixed background music. Unsuitable for &.
Location Off A684, 5 miles SW of Leyburn.
Restrictions No children at lunch in bar; no under-12s in restaurant. Dogs in 1 room only; not in restaurant.
Credit cards MasterCard, Visa.
Terms B&B: single £40, double £75. Full alc (excluding VAT) £26.

CARTMEL Cumbria   Map 4

Aynsome Manor   BUDGET   *Tel* (015395) 36653
Cartmel   *Fax* (015395) 36016
nr Grange-over-Sands   *E-mail* info@aynsomemanorhotel.co.uk
LA11 6HH   *Website* www.aynsomemanorhotel.co.uk

♋ *César award in 1998*

"The Varley family know how to run a good hotel. The service and staff seem never to change. The food is excellent in both quality and variety." A returning visitor's tribute to this traditional hotel, run by two generations of Varleys: Tony and Margaret ("now taking things a bit quieter"), and their son Chris and his wife Andrea. It is a handsome 16th-century house in a picturesque village on the edge of the Lake District. One of its great attributes is "the perfect silence of the surrounding countryside, particularly at night". Many visitors are regulars. The decor is cheerful and traditional. There are two "very pleasant" lounges, spacious and well lit; one has a fine old marble fireplace. The bedrooms vary in size; some are suitable for a family; one, on the top floor, is heavily beamed with sloping ceilings; two are in a cottage with a sitting room, across the cobbled courtyard. Two visitors this year thought their bathroom in need of refurbishment, but they were forgiving, in view of "the excellent value offered". In the oak-panelled restaurant, with its large bay windows, moulded plaster ceiling and oil paintings, dinner (at 7 pm) is quite formal: jacket and tie are expected of male diners. The English country house cooking is mostly thought "consistent and interesting" (it has an entry in the *Good Food Guide 2000*). Dishes include fishcakes of salmon and lemon sole in a white wine sauce; roast breast of pheasant with a sherry and ginger sauce. A dessert trolley to end, with pies and gâteaux. On Sunday there is a traditional lunch, and a supper with soup and a cold buffet. We get the occasional complaint of residents being rushed through their meal at the weekend to make way for outside diners, and one visitor this year would have liked a few simpler dishes on the menu, and regretted the lack of a no-smoking lounge. Cartmel's ruined 12th-century priory is close by. Local attractions include Holker Hall, Levens Hall and Sizergh Castle. (*Joan H Coleman, David Reed; also Dr Walsh, Elizabeth Sandham*)

Open All year, except 2–26 Jan. Lunch served Sun only.
Rooms 12 double. 2 in cottage (with private lounge) across courtyard.
Facilities 2 lounges, cocktail bar, dining room. No background music. ¼-acre gardens. Lake Windermere 4 miles: water sports; golf nearby. Unsuitable for &.
Location 12 miles from M6 exit 36. Leave A590 at Cartmel sign. Hotel on right, ½ mile before village. Train: Grange-over-Sands, 2½ miles; then taxi.
Restrictions Smoking banned in restaurant, discouraged in bedrooms. No children under 5 in restaurant at night. No dogs in public rooms, unattended in bedrooms.
Credit cards Amex, MasterCard, Visa.
Terms D,B&B £48–£69. Set Sun lunch £12.75, dinner from £17. Weekend, midweek, Christmas breaks; bonus breaks for returning guests. Child accommodated in parents' room: under 5, £6; 5–12, £25 (half board). 1-night bookings occasionally refused. ***V***

Uplands   *Tel* (015395) 36248
Haggs Lane, Cartmel   *Fax* (015395) 36848
nr Grange-over-Sands LA11 6HD   *E-mail* uplands@kencomp.net

Tom and Di Peter are the owners of this small cream pebbledash house decorated in contemporary style. It is a peaceful place on a hillside, with views across a patchwork of fields, with stone walls and sheep, to Morecambe Bay. Deer, squirrels, pheasants and badgers are sometimes seen in its large garden; there is a resident pair of "gorgeous marmalade cats". The entrance, in a tiny courtyard with plants in pots and tubs, small statues and clematis over an archway, resembles an Italian walled garden. In the public rooms, ivory walls are set off by pale yellow and green carpets. A highlight of a stay here is the food cooked by Tom Peter, described this year as "ambitious, mostly superb, pricey but good value". The tureen of soup at each table, accompanied by a small loaf of home-baked bread, is enjoyed. Main courses, each accompanied by five vegetables, might include baked fillet of turbot with champagne sauce, or medallions of venison with a blackcurrant and juniper sauce. "Standards are high," say regular visitors, and the "good-humoured service" is praised. Mrs Peter, who often wears a caftan, is "very cheery". At breakfast, a toaster is provided at each table. The bedrooms are on the small side, but pretty; three have a small shower room, the others a bathroom; two enjoy the view. Uplands is a mile from Cartmel village, with its 12th-century priory and racecourse, and two miles from Grange-on-the-Sands, the Victorian resort on the shores of Morecambe Bay. The local stately home, Holker Hall, with an award-winning garden, is two miles away; Levens Hall is eight miles distant. One guest tried the golf course at Cartmel: "It is flat but interesting." (*SB, and others*)

Open 1 Mar–1 Jan. Restaurant open for lunch Thurs–Sun, for dinner daily, except Mon.
Rooms 5 double.
Facilities Lounge, restaurant. No background music. 2-acre garden. Golf nearby; Lake Windermere 6 miles. Unsuitable for &.
Location In Cartmel, opposite *Pig & Whistle*, take road to Grange-over-Sands for 1 mile; hotel on left. Private parking. Train: Grange-over-Sands; then taxi.
Restrictions No smoking in restaurant. No children under 8. No dogs in public rooms.
Credit cards Amex, MasterCard, Visa.
Terms D,B&B £56–£86. Set lunch £15.50, dinner £28. Reductions (£10–£20) for 2 nights or more Nov–Apr. Christmas package. 1-night bookings occasionally refused Sat. ***V***

CASTLE COMBE Wiltshire   Map 2

The Castle Inn   NEW   *Tel* (01249) 783030
Castle Combe SN14 7HN   *Fax* (01249) 782315
                                           E-mail res@castle-inn.co.uk
                                           Website www.castle-inn.co.uk

In a famous, ultra-picturesque Cotswold village in a wooded valley, this "delightful, well-managed place" belongs to the same small group as the much-admired *Château la Chaire*, Rozel Bay, in the Channel Islands (*qv*). Run by Marc Gibbons, it is warmly recommended by a regular visitor: "The 12th-century building has been carefully and sympathetically restored, and the only concession to modernity is the pleasant conservatory restaurant, which gives on to a terrace where one can drink or breakfast while enjoying views of the 14th-century church and delightful cottages. The bedrooms, all different, all with original beams, are outstanding" (they are supplied with sweets, mineral water, etc; bathrooms have plastic ducks, bathrobes, five have a spa bath).

Standards of housekeeping "are high", and the staff are "efficient throughout and very friendly". There are "excellent bar meals", and the restaurant serves "good and sensible food" from a menu which changes every few weeks: lots of choice, with main courses like lamb shank with baby onions, garlic and rosemary; sausage on shredded cabbage and potato with Wiltshire gammon; always a vegetarian dish. Desserts include pears steeped in sloe gin in a brandy snap with pear ice-cream; sticky chocolate pudding with marinated vanilla orange. "The wine list is too unambitious for buffs, but most will find it adequate and fairly priced." "In support of the British food industry, we are avoiding the use of French produce," writes the chef, Jamie Gemmell. Only snag: parking in the village is restricted, so spring and autumn might be the best times to visit. (*CC Schofield*)

Open All year.
Rooms 11 double.
Facilities Lounge, bar, restaurant; classical background music; conference room. Garden. Unsuitable for &.
Location Centre of village 5 miles NW of Chippenham.
Restrictions No smoking: restaurant, some bedrooms. No dogs.
Credit cards All major cards accepted.
Terms B&B: single £67.50–£80, double £90–£105; D,B&B: single £92.50–£107.50, double £115–£130. Full alc £27.95. 1-night bookings refused Sat Apr–Sept. Special breaks. Christmas, New Year packages. ***V***

CAXTON Cambridgeshire   Map 2

Church Farm   BUDGET   *Tel* (01954) 719543
Gransden Road   *Fax* (01954) 718999
Caxton, Cambridge CB3 8PL   *E-mail* churchfarm@aol.com

A Wolsey Lodge member, this converted 17th-century farmhouse, owned by Peter and Maggie Scott, offers "traditional hospitality in an Englishman's house". Mr Scott "has an amazing memory for names", introducing guests to each other as they arrive for the communal breakfast, where everything is "freshly cooked and efficiently served, with relays of hot toast". The home-cooked dinner, by arrangement, is also communal. "All is efficiently run and well maintained," wrote inspectors. "Perfect quiet at night; beds are made with proper bedding rather than duvets, but reading lights are a bit dim." Photographs of Mrs Scott in her former role of mayor of nearby St Ives (not the Cornish one) are prominently displayed. Nice views of the church from the well-maintained garden (with carp pond and tennis court). Residential courses on art, history and architecture are held. Handy for Cambridge, eight miles away, where the *Guide* currently does not have a single full entry. More reports, please.

Open All year, except alternate Christmas, New Year. Dinner sometimes not served.
Rooms 1 suite (30 yds from main house), 3 double. 2 on ground floor. No telephone. Also self-catering cottage.
Facilities Lounge, dining room. Occasional classical/choral background music evenings. 3-acre grounds: tennis, croquet.
Location Off A1198, 11 miles NW of Royston, 10 miles S of Huntingdon. At

S end of Caxton, by War Memorial, take side road W to Gransdens. Farm is
½ mile on, just past church, on right behind red brick wall.
Restrictions No smoking. No children under 8. No dogs.
Credit cards MasterCard, Visa.
Terms B&B £30–£40. Set dinner £13.50–£19.50. Residential courses: history, art, architecture.

CHADDESLEY CORBETT Worcestershire   Map 3

Brockencote Hall
Chaddesley Corbett
nr Kidderminster DY10 4PY

Tel (01562) 777876
Fax (01562) 777872
E-mail info@brockencotehall.com
Website www.brockencotehall.com

"The rooms are excellent and the service good," says a regular visitor
this year to this late-Victorian mansion. Its setting is peaceful, in a
large park with an ornamental lake, a Tudor dovecote, and sheep
grazing in fields. For all its English looks, however, it has a strong
Gallic flavour. Alison and Joseph Petitjean have run it as a hotel since
1986 with an "impeccably polite" French staff; chef Didier Philipot
presides in the kitchen. His "French fusion" menus are based on
English produce: Hereford snails and frogs' legs are served with a
potato and garlic pancake; Devon cod comes with tapenade and
ratatouille; bitter chocolate blinis are accompanied by peanut brittle
ice-cream. There are some reasonably priced house wines. Coffee and
petits fours are included in the price of the meal. The restaurant is
popular with outside diners and visitors on business, and gourmet
nights are organised. But one visitor would have liked a few simpler
options. The spacious public rooms, some recently refurbished, are
formal, with honey-coloured panelling, open fires, potted plants. The
large bedrooms are "perfect for a woman on her own". They have
fresh flowers, fruit, sherry, up-to-date magazines and an impressive
bathroom – some have a spa bath. But there is one report of some
maintenance problems. One visitor thought breakfast "extremely
good", but "not for those in a hurry". Others wrote of "the smallest
kipper we had ever seen, and jams and marmalade that were indistinguishable". Weekend breaks include reflexology treatment.
Chaddesley Corbett village has a harmonious blend of 16th- to 19th-
century houses; its old church is part Norman. Nearby is Harvington
Hall, a moated 16th-century manor house. A good base for visiting
Warwick Castle, Cadbury World and West Midlands Safari Park. (*Sue
Davies, and others*)

Open All year.
Rooms 17 double. Some on ground floor; 1 adapted for &.
Facilities Stairlift, ramp. Hall, 3 lounges, conservatory, restaurant; function facilities. No background music. 70-acre grounds: gardens, lake, croquet, tennis. Golf nearby.
Location On A448 between Kidderminster and Bromsgrove. M42 exit 1; M5 exit 4. Train: Kidderminster; then taxi.
Restrictions No smoking in restaurant. Guide dogs only.
Credit cards All major cards accepted.
Terms B&B: single £110–£130, double £135–£170; D,B&B: single £137.50–£157.50, double £190–£225. Set lunch £22.50, dinner £27.50; full

alc £47.70. Child accommodated in parents' room: under 12, free. Short breaks; aromatherapy, shooting, golfing breaks. Christmas package. *V*

CHAGFORD Devon   **Map 1**

Gidleigh Park   *Tel* (01647) 432367
Chagford TQ13 8HH   *Fax* (01647) 432574
                                       E-mail gidleighpark@gidleigh.co.uk
                                       Website www.gidleigh.com

Q *César award in 1989*

A "quintessential country house hotel" on the edge of Dartmoor. Built in rather severe Tudor style, it was once the home of a shipping magnate. Now, it is a hotel of "unashamed luxury" (Relais & Châteaux) with a *Michelin* two-star restaurant. But it still "makes you feel as if you are staying with friends", says a regular visitor. This is thanks to the hands-on approach of the owners, Paul and Kay Henderson, the "perfect front-of-house team" managed by Catherine Endacott, and the housekeeper, Penny Watson, who "gives such a warm welcome, remembers names, etc". Wellington boots and fishing rods in the hall, ticking clocks and purring Siamese cats add a homely touch. In the lounges are wood fires, rich fabrics, antiques and watercolours of Dartmoor. "Our room was magnificent, with everything we wanted, and one of the best bathrooms we've found in Britain," says a report in 2000. The bedrooms are priced by size and view; some are small; courtyard-facing ones are cheapest. The chef, Michael Caines, "shows great confidence and balance" in his modern French cooking, served in the panelled dining room. Savoured this year were "Jerusalem artichoke and truffle soup, full of flavour and with the texture of velvet; pan-fried red mullet with olives, tomato, and fennel cream sauce, a marriage made in heaven". One guest advises: "No matter what else you skip, save room for such puddings as millefeuille of crème brûlée," but another thought the food "over fussy". The "Falstaffian wine list" is wide ranging, and fairly priced. "There is a superb choice of wines by the glass, and many half bottles." Light lunches are available. The Teign River runs through the "stunning grounds", where guests can admire peaceful croquet lawns, manicured herb gardens and a new lime walk. Hunting with Harris hawks or falcons is now possible. Children are welcomed. (*Padi Howard, AT, and others*)

Open All year.
Rooms 2 suites, 12 double. Also 3-room cottage, 350 yds.
Facilities Hall, lounge, bar, 2 dining rooms. No background music. 45-acre grounds: gardens, croquet, tennis, bowls, putting, walks. Fishing, riding nearby. Unsuitable for &.
Location Approach from Chagford, *not* Gidleigh. From main square, facing Webbers with Lloyds Bank on right, turn right into Mill St. After 150 yds fork right; downhill to Factory Crossroad; straight across into Holy St; follow lane 1½ miles to end. Train: Exeter, 20 miles; then taxi.
Restrictions No smoking in restaurant. No children under 7 in restaurant. No dogs in public rooms.
Credit cards Diners, MasterCard, Visa.
Terms D,B&B: single £265–£415, double £385–£460, suite £415–£475. Set

lunch £38, dinner £65. Winter discounts. Walking holidays, wine weekends, hunting, shooting and fishing organised. 1-night bookings sometimes refused.

CHARMOUTH Dorset   Map 1

The White House BUDGET   *Tel* (01297) 560411
2 Hillside, The Street   *Fax* (01297) 560702
Charmouth DT6 6PJ   *E-mail* white-house@lineone.net

Joel Kassirer and Chris Poole offer "great food, great service, great value", say visitors this year to their white-walled Regency house. Set back from the long main street that runs up the steep hill of this seaside resort, it has handsome windows, a fine staircase, rounded doors and original cornices. The bedrooms in the main house are "small, but nicely decorated"; larger ones are in a cottage annexe. A magnolia grows in the front courtyard. In the small rear landscaped garden there are tables, chairs and recliners. A fruit and vegetable garden supplies the kitchen with organically grown produce. The five-course dinner menu offers "traditional and modern" cooking, eg, salad of locally smoked trout; venison in an orange and redcurrant sauce; hazelnut and dark chocolate roulade. "Vegetarians are well catered for," says a report this year. The place is run "with friendly informality"; first names tend to be used; guests chat across the tables at dinner. Charmouth's beach is not particularly attractive, but spectacular National Trust coastal walks are close by. Local attractions include Montacute House, Forde Abbey and Abbotsbury's swannery and tropical gardens. A word of warning: "If you have a large car, careful negotiation is needed around the side of the building." (*Robert B Osborn, S and A Verschoor, and others*)

Open Mid-Feb–mid-Nov. Restaurant closed midday.
Rooms 9 double, 1 single. 3 in cottage annexe. 2 on ground floor.
Facilities Lounge, bar, restaurant (soft classical music during dinner). ½-acre garden. Beach 5 mins' walk.
Location Central. Private parking. Train: Axminster; hosts will meet.
Restrictions No smoking. No children under 14. Dogs in 1 room only; not in public rooms.
Credit cards Amex, MasterCard, Visa.
Terms B&B £35–£54.50; D,B&B £48–£68. Set dinner £19.50. Special short breaks. *V*

CHELTENHAM Gloucestershire   Map 3

Hotel on the Park   *Tel* (01242) 518898
Evesham Road   *Fax* (01242) 511526
Cheltenham GL52 2AH   *E-mail* stay@hotelonthepark.co.uk
                                    Website www.hotelonthepark.co.uk

"We loved it," says one American visitor this year to Darryl Gregory's Regency town house. "It is absolutely gorgeous, with fine antiques throughout. We felt welcome in spite of the formality of the surroundings, we enjoyed chatting with our hosts, and we appreciated their kind treatment of our children." The decor is in keeping with the age of the house, with antiques, swagged and tasselled curtains, mirrors and ticking clocks in the public rooms. The French windows of the drawing room and library look over the trim rear garden. Large bedrooms and bathrooms, as stylish as the rest, are reached up a curving staircase. The restaurant is run as a concession by Simon Holstone, who cooks contemporary British dishes on a short weekly-changing menu and a *carte*, eg, risotto of truffle, mascarpone and foie gras; brill poached in red wine; roast figs and pears with cinnamon sauce. But they are "very accommodating about children's mealtime needs". Pittville Park is opposite, across a busy tree-lined road; rear bedrooms are quietest. The hotel keeps a boat on the River Severn, six miles away. Once a fashionable spa, Cheltenham claims to be the most complete Regency town in Britain. It is home to Europe's largest boarding school for girls, a famous racecourse, and an annual literary festival. Sudeley Castle is close by. (*Katherine Galligan*)

Open All year.
Rooms 1 suite, 12 double.
Facilities Drawing room/bar, library, restaurant (classical background music). Small garden. Unsuitable for ♿.
Location 5 mins' walk from centre. On A435 towards Evesham (front rooms double-glazed). Carpark. Cheltenham station (2 miles); then taxi.
Restrictions Smoking banned in restaurant, library, discouraged in bedrooms. No children under 8. Small dogs only, by arrangement; not in public rooms.
Credit cards All major cards accepted.
Terms [2000] Room: single £78.50, double £96.50–£116.50, suite £126.50–£156.50. Breakfast: continental £6, English £8.25. Set lunch £14.50, dinner £22.50; full alc £35.50. Child accommodated in parents' room: £15. 2-day breaks. ***V***

The Wyastone　　NEW/BUDGET　　　　*Tel* (01242) 245549
Parabola Road　　　　　　　　　　　*Fax* (01242) 522659
Cheltenham GL50 3BG　　*E-mail* reservations@wyastonehotel.co.uk

This bay-windowed Victorian house, which featured in earlier editions of the *Guide*, returns, run as a guest house by new owners, Mr and Mrs Howard. It is set in a tree-lined avenue close to the centre of Cheltenham. A visitor on her own in 2000 wrote of a friendly welcome, with her cases carried for her. "I was addressed by name. My quiet bedroom at the back was very pleasant. Dinner was freshly cooked and efficiently served." The meal might include prawn cocktail; grilled salmon; hot chocolate pudding with custard. If you prefer to dine out, the Howards will help with reservations. There is a lounge, and in summer you can have a drink by the pond (with a fountain and Koi carp) in the secluded patio garden. (*Rosemary Viner*)

Open All year. Dining room closed lunchtime and Christmas.
Rooms 2 family, 7 double, 6 single.
Facilities Lounge, bar/TV room, dining room (light background music at mealtimes). Patio garden. Unsuitable for ♿.
Location Central. Parking. Cheltenham station; then taxi.
Restrictions No smoking: dining room, bedrooms. No dogs.
Credit cards Amex, MasterCard, Visa.
Terms B&B: single £53, double £75, family £95. Full alc dinner £20.

See also SHURDINGTON and SHORTLIST

CHESTER Cheshire *See SHORTLIST*   **Map 3**

CHETTLE Dorset   **Map 2**

Castleman   BUDGET   *Tel* (01258) 830096
Chettle   *Fax* (01258) 830051
nr Blandford Forum DT11 8DB   *E-mail* chettle@globalnet.co.uk

In a designated area of outstanding natural beauty on the edge of
Cranborne Chase, Chettle is one of the few remaining feudal villages
in England. It has been owned by the Bourke family for over
150 years. Its Queen Anne manor house, open to the public in summer, is, according to Pevsner, an outstanding specimen of English
Baroque. The dower house has been turned into this restaurant-with-
rooms, run in unfussy style by Edward Bourke and Barbara
Garnsworthy. She is chef; her brother, Brendan, is the manager. "We
have never tried to be a 'country house hotel' with manicured gardens, full room service, etc," they say. "We aim to offer good food,
wine and accommodation at sensible prices." The house, which was
remodelled in Victorian days, has been carefully converted while
preserving period features – a porticoed doorway, galleried hall,
carved staircase, plasterwork ceilings, a Jacobean fireplace; there are
some interesting 17th-century paintings. "With character in every
stone, it is comfortable in all ways," say enthusiasts this year. Other
visitors admired the peaceful location, the "plain but not sparse"
bedrooms, and the service, which is "attentive without pomp". The
place is thought "exceptional value" and the "excellent, relatively
simple" food is admired. The varied menus include, eg, goat's
cheese and black olive tartlet; braised rabbit with chorizo sausage;
plum frangipane tart with honey ice-cream. Vegetarians are well
catered for. No menu for breakfast, but you can have freshly
squeezed orange juice and more or less whatever you want ("very
good scrambled eggs"). Good country walks from the door.
Salisbury, and many historic houses, including Wilton, Kingston
Lacy, Stourhead and Longleat, are within easy reach; so is plenty of
action for the sportingly inclined (see below). (*John and Hazel
Williams, and others*)

Open All year, except Christmas, Feb.
Rooms 8 double.
Facilities 2 drawing rooms, bar, restaurant. No background music. 2-acre
grounds: stables for visiting horses/dogs. Golf, riding, fishing, shooting,
cycling nearby. Only restaurant suitable for &.
Location Village 1 mile off A354 Salisbury–Blandford; hotel signposted.
Train: Salisbury; then taxi/bus (stop 1 mile from hotel).
Restrictions No smoking: restaurant, 1 drawing room. No dogs.
Credit cards MasterCard, Visa.
Terms [2000] B&B: single £40, double £65–£75. Set Sun lunch £15; full alc
£25. 5% discount for 3 or more nights; 10% for 7 or more.

CHICHESTER West Sussex *See SHORTLIST* Map 2

CHILLATON Devon Map 1

Tor Cottage *Tel* (01822) 860248
Chillaton, nr Lifton *Fax* (01822) 860126
PL16 0JE *E-mail* info@torcottage.demon.co.uk
Website www.torcottage.demon.co.uk

"Everything is done in exquisite taste," say inspectors this year visiting this upmarket B&B in a secluded Devon valley. Filled with antiques, good fabrics, fresh flowers, ornaments and family photographs, it is set in large wooded grounds with a stream, Shetland ponies and wildlife. Bridleways lead from the grounds to Dartmoor and the Tamar valley. The hostess, Maureen Rowlatt ("a strong, warm person"), promises badgers, buzzards and butterflies as well as deer and pheasants, and wild flowers in spring and summer. She welcomes her guests with a trug filled with fresh fruit, a bottle of Cava, luxury chocolates. There is a swimming pool in the garden, available all day to visitors (after 11.30 am they might find themselves sharing it with Mrs Rowlatt or some of her friends). The suite is upstairs in the cottage; other bedrooms are in the garden; one is decorated in Art Deco style; it has a "beautiful black-and-white bathroom" and a private conservatory. All have a log fire, a CD player, a fridge and a private terrace; two have a kingsize bed. Breakfast is served in a "delightful conservatory" ("good kedgeree; super scrambled eggs with smoked salmon") or in the bedroom; in summer it can be taken alfresco. Vegetarians are catered for. The personal attention from the "most friendly hostess" is praised, and so is the tea with cakes served to arriving guests. Very popular with the garden-loving Japanese (one of whom wrote: "It is like we visit to aunt's house"). Dinner is no longer served, but reservations can be made in nearby restaurants (*Neil's*, in Tavistock, six miles away, was enjoyed this year).

Open 6 Jan–20 Dec.
Rooms 1 suite (in main building), 3 double (in garden). No telephone.
Facilities 2 sitting rooms, conservatory, breakfast room (background music according to guests' taste). 18-acre grounds: 2-acre garden, swimming pool (generally open May–Sept), stream, bridleway, walks. River, fishing ½ mile; boating, canoeing 6 miles. Unsuitable for &.
Location ½ mile S of Chillaton. At village square, with pub and shop on left, drive 300 metres up hill towards Tavistock. Take drive on right, marked: "Bridlepath. No Public Vehicular Access". Cottage gate at end of unmade road.
Restrictions No smoking. No children under 16. Guide dogs only.
Credit cards MasterCard, Visa.
Terms [2000] (Min. 2 nights) B&B £45–£76. Winter breaks: 3 nights for the price of 2.

Hotels are dropped if we lack positive feedback. If you can endorse an entry, please do so.

CHITTLEHAMHOLT Devon   **Map 1**

Highbullen Hotel
Chittlehamholt
Umberleigh EX37 9HD

Tel (01769) 540561
Fax (01769) 540492
E-mail info@highbullen.co.uk
Website www.highbullen.co.uk

♔ *César award in 1991*

"A splendid stay. The atmosphere is happy. We have been visiting for 20 years; some of the staff have been there since our first visit." An endorsement this year for Hugh and Pam Neil's Victorian Gothic mansion, high above the Mole and Taw valleys, which looks towards Exmoor and Dartmoor. Its many fans appreciate the sporting amenities – fishing, tennis, swimming, etc, which make it good for a family holiday, though the indoor pool is very small. A challenging 18-hole golf course, free to residents, surrounds the buildings, and the bar is often packed with golfing groups, which not everyone appreciates. But "golf widows are comfortable in the warm public rooms", and regular visitors appreciate the no-frills style and the "excellent value for money". Reception is informal; on arrival, you telephone for someone to greet you, and you won't necessarily be helped with luggage, which can be awkward, since most accommodation is in houses and cottages in the grounds. These rooms are simple, and sound insulation can be poor. The best bedrooms are in the main house; many have a "marvellous view". The restaurant, directed by the proprietors' daughter, Colette Potter, "continues to improve". There is plenty of choice on a daily-changing menu: eg, quail's eggs on a tossed salad with bacon; seabass with olive oil, garlic and herbs; guinea fowl with tarragon, white wine and cream; butterscotch pecan tart. The wine list is "a fascinating document". Breakfast, mainly self-service, has a generous buffet (it includes strawberries, figs and peaches in season); cooked dishes cost extra. Rosemoor Garden, Dartington Hall, and three National Trust properties – Arlington Court, Killerton House and Knightshayes – are within half an hour's drive. Colette Potter and her husband, Mike, also own *Stumbles*, a restaurant with ten bedrooms in South Molton, nearby. (*Brian and Eve Webb, and others*)

Open All year.
Rooms 38 double, 2 single. 28 in cottages/converted farm buildings. Some on ground floor.
Facilities Drawing room, conservatory and library; bar (background music in evening), billiard room, breakfast room, restaurant; indoor swimming pool, steam room, sunbed, exercise room, table-tennis, squash. 100-acre grounds: woodland, garden, croquet, putting, 2 swimming pools, 18-hole golf course, indoor tennis (golf/tennis tuition), 10 miles river fishing (ghillie available). Unsuitable for ♿.

Location M5 exit 27. A361 to South Molton. B3226 for 5 miles, up hill to Chittlehamholt; through village, ½ mile to hotel. Train: Tiverton Parkway, then taxi; Exeter St David's to connect with North Devon branch line to King's Nympton – hotel will meet, "but remember to ask the guard to stop the train".
Restrictions No smoking in restaurant. No children under 8. No dogs.
Credit cards MasterCard, Visa.
Terms D,B&B £60–£95. Bar lunches £12. Set dinner £25. Midweek reductions. Off-season breaks.

COLCHESTER Essex *See SHORTLIST*   **Map 2**

COLN ST ALDWYNS Gloucestershire   **Map 3**

The New Inn at Coln   *Tel* (01285) 750651
Coln St Aldwyns   *Fax* (01285) 750657
nr Cirencester GL7 5AN   *E-mail* stay@new-inn.co.uk
                                        Website www.new-inn.co.uk

A creeper-clad coaching inn, which has provided shelter for travellers since it was established in the reign of Elizabeth I. Today, visitors appreciate the welcoming atmosphere created by Brian and Sandra-Anne Evans and their young staff. "The front door opens into the cosy bar, where staff and regulars alike survey and/or salute in equal measure," one visitor wrote. The "delicious and innovative" cooking of chef Stephen Morey, the "first-class, well-priced" wine list, and the wide range of ales and malt whiskies earned the inn the title Gloucestershire Dining Pub of the Year in the *Good Pub Guide 2000*. Vegetarian dishes, as well as such traditional fare as fish and chips and steak-and-kidney pie, are served in the long bar with its inglenook fireplace; a more sophisticated modern British/Mediterranean menu is offered in the split-level restaurant which has open fires, low beams and Oriental rugs (you must book). There is a small residents' lounge and terraced garden. The bedrooms in the main house are small; one, by the bar, is noisy. Larger, quieter and more modern rooms are in a converted dovecote. The riverside walk to Bibury is recommended. Well placed for visiting Westonbirt and Bath, and William Morris's house at Kelmscott.

Open All year.
Rooms 13 double, 1 single. 6 in dovecote. 1 on ground floor.
Facilities Lounge, bar, breakfast room, restaurant; conference/function facilities; terrace. No background music. River 100 yds; golf nearby.
Location In village 8 miles E of Cirencester, between Bibury and Fairford.
Restrictions No smoking in restaurant. No children under 10 in restaurant or accommodation. Dogs in Dovecote rooms and bar only.
Credit cards Amex, MasterCard, Visa.
Terms [Until 31.3.01] B&B: single £68, double £96–£115; D,B&B £68.50–£91.50 per person. Bar meals. Set lunch: weekdays £22.50, Sun £16.75; dinner £26.50. Midweek breaks. Christmas package. 1-night bookings refused Sat.

The *Guide* takes no free hospitality and no advertisements.

COLWALL Worcestershire   Map 3

Brook House   NEW/BUDGET   *Tel/Fax* (01684) 540604
Walwyn Road
Colwall, nr Malvern WR13 6QX

Maggie Powell's "superior B&B", in 17th-century Grade II* listed house, gabled, half-timbered, recently refurbished. In 2½-acre grounds, with mini-arboretum, wide views of Malvern Hills. "The delightful hostess cannot do enough for you," says nominator. 3 bedrooms (Lemon, Peach and Green), with TV, en suite *bathroom. English or continental breakfast ("well cooked") in room overlooking stream and lovely landscaped gardens (highly rated by Royal Horticultural Society). Morning room with TV available to guests. Colwall station ½ mile. Closed Christmas, New Year. Unsuitable for &. No smoking. No dogs. Credit cards not accepted. B&B £27.50–£37.50.*

CONSTANTINE BAY Cornwall   Map 1

Treglos Hotel   *Tel* (01841) 520727
Constantine Bay   *Fax* (01841) 521163
Padstow PL28 8JH   *E-mail* enquiries@treglos-hotel.co.uk
Website www.treglos-hotel.co.uk

♥ *César award in 1994*

"Another year, another very satisfactory stay. The service is as good as ever, and we eat well at breakfast and dinner. The *Treglos* deserves praise for consistent quality and value for money." "Every bit as good as you say it is." Praise this year for this traditional hotel, which the Barlow family have owned for 35 years. Not luxurious, it is run in old-fashioned style, and it welcomes all generations, offering school holiday packages, and bridge holidays in low season. The position is wonderful, overlooking Constantine Bay and Trevose Head. There is a wide sandy beach ten minutes' walk away, and easy access to the coastal footpath. Other visitors have been less enthusiastic about the food, "but the fish course, not announced until the last minute, was different every night, and always interesting. Desserts were almost invariably rich." The buffet breakfast is liked, and so is the afternoon tea, served on a west-facing terrace. The decor – brick fireplaces, log fires, chintzy furniture, patterned carpets – is conventional. Bedrooms have light colour schemes and built-in white furniture. The single rooms are small, but "a lovely room, with large balcony" was enjoyed. The garden has secluded corners, "good for Tai Chi". There is a warm indoor swimming pool. Eight golf courses are within a 40-minute drive (one is two minutes away). Many National Trust properties are nearby, as well as good coastal walks. (*JH, and others*)

Open 10 Mar–5 Nov.
Rooms 4 suites, 34 double, 6 single. Some on ground floor. 4 self-catering flats, 1 bungalow, in grounds.
Facilities Lift, ramps. 2 lounges, bridge room, TV room, restaurant; children's

den, snooker room; indoor swimming pool, whirlpool. No background music. 1½-acre grounds: croquet, badminton, boathouse for children. Sandy beach, golf, tennis, riding, water sports nearby.

Location 3 miles W of Padstow. Avoid Bodmin, Wadebridge. From cross-roads at St Merryn take B3276. Turn right by Constantine Bay stores: hotel 50 yds on right. Train: Bodmin; then bus/taxi.

Restrictions No smoking: dining room, 1 lounge. No children under 7 in dining room after 7.30 pm. No dogs in public rooms.

Credit cards MasterCard, Visa.

Terms B&B £48–£93; D,B&B £63–£107. Bar lunches. Set lunch from £11.50, dinner £25; full alc £39. Child accommodated in parents' room during school holidays, half-term: £15–£25. Weekly rates; weekend, midweek breaks; bridge, golf packages. ***V***

CORSE LAWN Gloucestershire   Map 3

Corse Lawn House   *Tel* (01452) 780771
Corse Lawn GL19 4LZ   *Fax* (01452) 780840
E-mail hotel@corselawnhouse.u-net.com
Website www.corselawnhousehotel.co.uk

Owned and run as a hotel for 23 years by Denis and Baba Hine, of the brandy family, this Queen Anne Grade II listed building is set back from the green of a village near Tewkesbury. The ornamental pond in front, now inhabited by assorted wildfowl, began life as a coach wash into which a stagecoach with four horses could be driven and turned around. Though much extended, the place maintains a country house air, and the "understated decor" and "relaxed style" are admired. The bedrooms, all named for a brandy or a local village, are mostly large, with a high ceiling, king-size bed, good storage, home-made biscuits, real tea and coffee, and a smart bathroom. Denis Hine and his son, Giles, are front-of-house. Mrs Hine and Andrew Poole run the kitchen, which serves both the formal restaurant and the brightly upholstered bistro. The food is French/English, eg, chargrilled squid with rocket salad; pan-fried guinea fowl breasts; grilled seabass with wild mush-room sauce. A vegetarian menu is available. Bread is home baked. The wine list has "some first-class choices at a reasonable cost". The bistro has a good choice of snacks and light meals, which are also available from room service. Breakfast, served until 10 in the restaurant, 11 in the bedroom, includes freshly squeezed orange juice, mango with lime, home-made yogurt with kiwi as well as traditional eggs and bacon, etc, and kippers ("but not in the bedroom"). There are cots, high chairs and baby-listening for small children. In the grounds are a tennis court, a covered swimming pool and croquet, horses in a paddock, and the family's two dogs. Plenty to see nearby, including Tewkesbury's beautiful abbey, the Westonbirt Arboretum, and the Wildfowl Trust and Wetlands Centre at Slimbridge. More reports, please.

Open All year, except 25/26 Dec.

Rooms 2 suites, 16 double. 5 on ground floor.

Facilities 2 lounges, bar, bistro, restaurant; 2 private dining rooms. No back-ground music. 12-acre grounds: croquet, tennis, badminton, covered swim-ming pool. Golf, fishing, riding nearby. Civil wedding licence.

Location 5 miles SW of Tewkesbury on B4211.
Restrictions No smoking in restaurants. No dogs in restaurants.
Credit cards All major cards accepted.
Terms B&B: single £75, double £120, suite £150; D,B&B: single £90, double £155, suite £185. Set lunch £16.95, dinner £25; full alc £35. 2-day breaks. ***V***

COVENTRY West Midlands *See SHORTLIST*   **Map 2**

CRACKINGTON HAVEN Cornwall   **Map 1**

Manor Farm   BUDGET   *Tel* (01840) 230304
Crackington Haven EX23 0JW

A Domesday-old stone manor house in a small village on the rocky north Cornish coast, in a designated area of outstanding natural beauty. Surrounded by acres of farmland and "wonderfully quiet at night", it is run in house party style by the owners, Paul and Muriel Knight. "We offer our guests the best of the 'old world'," they write. "Our main appeal is to those who wish to escape the crowds." Recent visitors admired the "splendid house" and its "elegant atmosphere" (mullioned windows, old beams, log fires and antique furniture). "The decor is delightful; the gardens are immaculate." Guests tend to change in the evening. Drinks are at 6.30; the "delicious and attractively presented" dinner is at 7, served at one large table, using porcelain, silver, good glass. No choice; a sample four-course menu consists of fried brie with beetroot and horseradish salad; breast of duck with plum and rum sauce; blueberry and apple pie; cheese and biscuits. Wines are "well priced". Coffee and chocolates follow in the lounge. The music room is new this year. A farmhouse breakfast is served at 8.30 am. The South West Coast Path runs nearby. (*JA*)

Open All year, except Christmas. Dinner not served in Aug.
Rooms 4 double. No telephone/TV, etc.
Facilities Lounge, TV room, music room, bar, dining room. No background music. 2-acre garden in 25-acre farmland. Sea 1 mile. Unsuitable for &.
Location From Wainhouse Corner on A39 follow signs to Crackington Haven. At beach turn inland, ignoring Highcliff Rd; after 1 mile left into Church Park Rd, then 1st right.
Restrictions No smoking. No children. No dogs in house.
Credit cards None accepted.
Terms B&B £30–£35; D,B&B £48–£53. Set dinner £18.

CRANBROOK Kent   **Map 2**

Cloth Hall Oast   NEW   *Tel/Fax* (01580) 712220
Cranbrook TN17 3NR

New venture by Mrs Katherine Morgan, who ran the picturesque, part-Tudor Old Cloth Hall, SE of Cranbrook, for 18 years. She has moved, with her antiques, family portraits, travel souvenirs, four-poster bed, etc, into newly converted adjoining barn/oast house/ stables. 3 double rooms (no telephone; no smoking). 5-acre garden:

heated outdoor swimming pool. Unsuitable for &. Closed Christmas, New Year. Children by arrangement. No dogs. Credit cards not accepted. B&B only: double room £85. Visitors to the previous set-up admired the "warm welcome; splendid country breakfasts; tranquil setting". We'd like reports, please.

Kennel Holt
Goudhurst Road
Cranbrook TN17 2PT

Tel (01580) 712032
Fax (01580) 715495
E-mail hotel@kennelholt.demon.co.uk
Website www.kennelholt.co.uk

A romantic part Tudor, part Edwardian house, "both excellent and unusual", in a "wonderfully quiet setting" in the Weald of Kent. It stands in an "idyllic" garden, with a pond, topiaried yew hedges, a croquet lawn, and birdsong. It was mostly liked again this year: a returning guest found the "food and welcome as good as ever" this year, and praised the "very nice" owners, Neil and Sally Chalmers. "No large conference suites, no health and fitness centre; we want you to feel at home," they write (but small "upmarket" conferences and functions are catered for). The bedrooms have antiques, exposed timbers and mullioned windows; two have a four-poster. Guests have the use of a beamed lounge, "perfect for relaxing", and an oak-panelled library with an honesty bar, Edwardian books, a large collection of vinyl discs and CDs. Neil Chalmers, in charge of the kitchens, cooks modern dishes with a strong continental influence, eg, prawn, clam, oyster and mussel herb spaghettini; lasagne with wild mushrooms; roast cod with spring onion mash and red wine sauce. Some well-priced wines. Clovis, the schnauzer, is no longer around; "his successor, Clotty, is still under training; the public are yet to comment," say the Chalmerses. Twenty-eight houses and 37 gardens open to the public, notably Sissinghurst, are within easy reach. The Channel Tunnel is a 40-minute drive away. (*WK Wood, Richard Creed, and others*)

Open All year, except 2 weeks in Jan. Restaurant closed Mon, to non-residents Sun evening.
Rooms 8 double, 2 single. 1, with separate entrance, on ground floor.
Facilities Hall, sitting room, library (occasional classical background music), restaurant; private dining/meeting room. 5½-acre grounds. Golf, fishing, walking, cycling nearby. Unsuitable for &.
Location 1 mile NE of Cranbrook, off A262. Train: Staplehurst, 4 miles.
Restrictions No smoking in restaurant. No children under 10 in restaurant for dinner. No dogs.
Credit cards MasterCard, Visa.
Terms (*Excluding 10% "optional" service charge added to meal bills*) B&B: single £90, double £145–£175. Set lunch £17.50–£22.50, dinner £27.50–£32.50. 3-night breaks in low season. 1-night bookings refused some weekends May–Sept.

There are many expensive hotels in the *Guide*. We are keen to increase our coverage at the other end of the scale. If you know of a simple place giving simple satisfaction, do please write and tell us about it.

CROOKHAM Northumberland

Map 4

The Coach House at Crookham BUDGET *Tel* (01890) 820293
Crookham *Fax* (01890) 820284
Cornhill-on-Tweed *E-mail* thecoachhouse@englandmail.com
TD12 4TD *Website* www.secretkingdom.com/coach/house.htm

♧ *César award in 1997*

"Comfortable and welcoming", this cluster of old farm buildings, built around a courtyard, is set back from a road by a damson orchard, not far from the site of Flodden Field. It has been run in a very personal style for 24 years by the exuberant hostess, Lynne Andersen. "We don't pretend to offer hotel-type service or atmosphere," she says. "We aim to cater for guests as if for visiting friends." The decor may be nothing special, but there is no doubting the kindness of the owner and her staff, and the generous spirit of the place, eg, tea and home-made cakes are offered free of charge on arrival, dogs are looked after if their owners wish to spend a day in Edinburgh, an hour's drive away. The disabled are particularly well catered for – "everywhere accessible in a wheelchair; lovely terrace looking on to a field with sheep and a friendly goat", and they are looked after in an unobtrusive way. Visitors tend to socialise over pre-dinner drinks in the drawing room, formerly the coach house, which has a beamed ceiling and huge arched windows. Dinner, at 7.30 pm, is "very sound home cooking", served at antique tables in a former smithy, with good paintings and large fireplaces. Starters might include fresh crab mayonnaise, or tagliatelle with smoked mackerel and cream. No regular choice of main course (it might be roast pork or baked salmon), but individual needs are catered for: one visitor was delighted to be served a freshly caught trout as an alternative to a substantial meat dish. "Masses of vegetables, lovely puddings, an interesting selection of cheeses." Soups, ice-creams, preserves, etc, are home made; eggs are free-range; meat is locally reared. The library contains some "unusually interesting books". Bedrooms are "plainly but pleasantly furnished"; many are good-sized; they have white cotton bedlinen, fresh flowers and a large bathroom; some have a fridge; there are adjoining rooms, good for a family. Plenty of choice at breakfast, including kedgeree, devilled kidneys. Lots to see nearby: castles and stately homes; Northumberland's National Trust coastline. The Pennine Way passes close by. (*Anne and Robin Sharp, and others*)

Open Easter–end Oct.
Rooms 7 double, 2 single. Some adapted for &.
Facilities Lounge with honesty bar, TV lounge, 2 dining rooms; large terrace. 3-acre grounds. Golf, fishing, riding, hunting, gliding, birdwatching nearby.
Location On A697, 3½ miles N of Milfield. Bus from Berwick-on-Tweed.
Restrictions No smoking: dining room, main lounge. No dogs in public rooms, unattended in bedrooms.
Credit cards MasterCard, Visa (*4% surcharge*).
Terms B&B £25–£39; D,B&B £42.50–£56.50. Set dinner £17.50.

We need detailed fresh reports to keep our entries up to date.

CUCKFIELD West Sussex　　　　　　　　　　Map 2

Ockenden Manor　　　　　　　　*Tel* (01444) 416111
Ockenden Lane　　　　　　　　　　*Fax* (01444) 415549
Cuckfield　　　　　　　　*E-mail* ockenden@hshotels.co.uk
nr Haywards Heath RH17 5LD　　*Website* www.hshotels.co.uk

"A beautiful place", this 16th-century house, part stone, part half-timbered, is set in mature gardens that look over the downs. A Pride of Britain member, it is owned by Sandy and Anne Goodman, who own a small group of luxury hotels in Sussex. One of its strong points is its nearness to Gatwick airport (13 miles). And honeymooners wrote this year of the "charming" long-serving manager, Kerry Turner. "He greeted us with the warmth praised in previous editions of the *Guide*. The comfort of our room was matched by the brilliantly clean and well-appointed bathroom and the grounds, which, though well maintained, had a natural appearance. We were treated as guests rather than customers. The staff take pride in their work." Another guest wrote of "a very satisfying stay". The decor is luxurious: much panelling; antiques, flowers and an open fire in the drawing room; an inglenook fireplace in the bar; heraldic stained glass and an embossed ceiling in the dining room, which is candlelit at night. There is a new chef this year, Martin Hadden, formerly head chef of the *Halcyon Hotel*, London; his cooking is thought "good; in parts very good". Starters might include fresh herb risotto; ballotine of fresh salmon and herbs. Typical main courses: grilled red mullet with tapenade and fennel velouté; rump of lamb with Jerusalem artichokes and tomato and tarragon jus. There is a vegetarian menu, a "tasting menu", and an "excellent wine list". But the absence of a no-smoking sitting area is regretted. Some bedrooms (some have long, low beams) are in the old house; larger, if less characterful, ones are in a later wing. The Tudor village of Cuckfield makes a good base for visiting Brighton and Glyndebourne. Many famous houses and gardens (eg, Nymans and Leonardslee) are nearby, so is Mannings Heath golf club, and the Bluebell steam railway runs from Sheffield Park, 18 miles away. (*Oliver and Kate Longstaff, and others*)

Open All year.
Rooms 3 suites, 18 double, 1 single.
Facilities Bar, sitting room, dining room; function facilities. No background music. 9-acre grounds: croquet. Golf nearby. Unsuitable for &. Civil wedding licence.
Location In village 2 miles W of Haywards Heath. Take B2115 from A23. Follow road into village; hotel at end of Ockenden La. Train to Haywards Heath; taxi/bus.
Restrictions No smoking in restaurant. No dogs.
Credit cards All major cards accepted.
Terms B&B: single £105, double £130–£200, suite £245–£275. English breakfast £5. Set lunch £128.50, dinner £33–£45. 2-day breaks; Sunday rates. Christmas, New Year packages. 1-night bookings refused weekends.

All our inspections are carried out anonymously.

CULLOMPTON Devon   Map 1

Upton House   NEW/BUDGET   *Tel/Fax* (01884) 33097
Cullompton EX15 1RA

An upmarket B&B in a quiet country setting in the Culm valley, near Tiverton. "A wonderful place to stay," say the nominators. "The lovely old house has been painstakingly restored by the friendly owner, Fay Down. The lounge and dining room are of the quality of a smart hotel." The 17th-century house has old beams, an inglenook fireplace, antique furniture. Breakfast is served round one large table in a panelled room where an inscription by an 18th-century workman can be read. Plenty of eating places are within a radius of two miles – the *Merry Homes* restaurant was liked this year. Mrs Down's husband, Chris, an amateur jockey, and their son, Richard, breed racehorses on the 180-acre organic farm (lots of wildlife) that surrounds the house. The Exmoor National Park is not far. (*John and Ann Hearle*)

Open All year, except Christmas/New Year.
Rooms 3 double. No telephone.
Facilities Lounge, conservatory, breakfast room. No background music. Large garden. On 180-acre farm: lake, fishing, stabling. Walking, riding, golf nearby. Unsuitable for &.
Location SE of Tiverton. From M5, exit 28, go towards Cullompton. Left to Broadclyst; follow main street through town. Take left turn, Meadow Lane, signposted Sports Centre. Next T-junction turn right, cross motorway bridge. Next left, signposted Plymtree. *Upton* is next lane on left.
Restrictions No smoking. No children under 12. No dogs.
Credit cards None accepted.
Terms B&B £20–£25.

DARLINGTON Co. Durham *See SHORTLIST*   Map 4

DARTMOUTH Devon   Map 1

The Little Admiral   NEW   *Tel* (01803) 832572
27–29 Victoria Road   *Fax* (01803) 835815
Dartmouth TQ6 9RT   *E-mail* little-admiral.co.uk

Old hotel, taken over and extensively renovated in mid-1999 by Sebastian and Philippa Hughes of Holne Chase, *Ashburton (qv). In small side street back from waterfront. Managed by James and Magalie Garland. Liked for friendly reception, attractive lounges and wine bar, where light meals and tea are served. 10 small but pretty no-smoking bedrooms on 1st and 2nd floor (no lift). Limited parking (reserve in advance). Closed Sun/Mon Nov–Feb. MasterCard, Visa accepted. B&B: single £55–£60, double £70–£120. Inspectors in late 1999 had some reservations: hotel over-heated throughout; distracting "easy listening" background music in public rooms; tea made in cafetières; pressed service at breakfast. So we'd like more reports, please.*

Nonsuch House   *Tel* (01803) 752829
Church Hill, Kingswear   *Fax* (01803) 752357
Dartmouth TQ6 0BZ   *E-mail* enquiries@nonsuch-house.co.uk
                                   Website www.nonsuch-house.co.uk

♈ *César award in 2000*

"Excellent in every way. The setting is superb." "Fantastic." "A combination of high standards and enchanting views; visitors are made to feel part of the family. Great value." Praise continues for this small, upmarket guest house, reached by car or by a ferry from Dartmouth. It comprises two Edwardian villas on a hillside; every room overlooks the view across the river to Dartmouth harbour with fields beyond, and also out to sea. With his parents, Geoffrey and Patricia, Kit Noble "provides a blissful retreat from urban worries", promising "no piped music, no artificial flowers, no UHT milk cartons". "His genuinely friendly, but unfussy, style was mirrored in the quality of the dinner he cooked for us." "Delicious crab salad starter; supremely fresh John Dory in the lightest of sauces; melt-in-the-mouth Pavlova." No liquor licence; bring your own wine. The decor is one of "quiet elegance": original fireplaces, rugs, books and magazines in the sitting room. In summer, meals are served in a "lovely conservatory", with balconies looking over the garden and the view. In the bedrooms "everything is of quality – nice old furniture; good lights, fresh flowers, home-made biscuits, milk in a flask". Breakfast has "excellent coffee and proper bread"; also fresh orange juice, home-made muesli. For a change from the set dinner, you could try the many eating places in Dartmouth, including the famous *Carved Angel*, "but we can't imagine why anyone would go elsewhere". The booking procedure is liked too: "No deposit required; a hand-written letter of confirmation. No reception desk, just an airy hallway and the friendliest of welcomes." (*Jenny and Tony Dawe, David and Penny Stevens, Romney Bathurst*)

Open All year.
Rooms 3 double.
Facilities Lounge, dining room, conservatory. No background music. ½-acre garden: patio. Rock beach 200 yds; sailing nearby. Unsuitable for &.
Location 2 miles before Brixham, on A3022, take A379 Dartmouth/Kingswear. After mini-roundabout, fork left to A3205 downhill. Through woods, left up Higher Contour Road, down Ridley Hill to *Nonsuch* at hairpin bend ("look for the first available parking place"). Ferry to Dartmouth (5 mins' walk).
Restrictions No smoking: dining room, bedrooms. Unsuitable for young children. No dogs.
Credit cards None accepted.
Terms B&B: single £60–£65, double £75–£80. Set dinner £21.50. Off-season rates. Christmas, New Year, Easter house party; Valentine weekend. 1-night bookings sometimes refused weekends.

See also SHORTLIST

DEDHAM Essex   Map 2

Dedham Hall & Fountain Restaurant
Brook Street, Dedham
nr Colchester CO7 6AD

Tel (01206) 323027
Fax (01206) 323293
E-mail jimsarton@dedhamhall.demon.co.uk
Website www.dedhamhall.demon.co.uk

"We were very impressed," says a visitor this year to Wendy and Jim
Sarton's combined guest house, restaurant and art school (you should
reserve your table in the restaurant when booking accommodation).
"Beautifully situated, professionally run," writes an inspector, "with
excellent food and a pleasantly relaxed atmosphere." The setting in
Constable country (Flatford Mill is two miles away) could hardly be
more picturesque. A small 15th-century house, a larger 18th-century
one, and a barn (where painting courses are held) stand in "idyllic gardens" with chickens, white geese in a large pond, daffodils on lawns
in spring, and a view of Dedham's church tower. The artists are
accommodated in the former stables and piggeries. "Lovely paintings
hang in the book-filled lounge, where we were given tea in pretty cups
with wonderful gooey chocolate cake." The guests' bedrooms (no
keys are given) are dotted around. "Ours was large, old-fashioned,
slightly shabby, with William Morris wallpaper, books, a large bathroom, a power shower." Some rooms are approached through the
kitchen, where "a bank of Agas emits delicious smells". In the popular restaurant (with well-spaced tables, candles and flowers) the food
was found "very good, not exotic: home-made bread, properly cooked
lamb and beef came with a good selection of vegetables. The wine list
was good and moderately priced." Breakfast (in a room also used by
the students) has "toast out of this world", bowls of sliced fresh fruit,
and "wonderful bacon". Paintings by Sir Alfred Munnings may be
seen in his home, Castle House, nearby. Plenty of local interest:
Ickworth, Kentwell and Melford halls; Beth Chatto's garden,
Colchester (eight miles away). (*Mrs PM Glover, and others*)

Open All year, except Christmas, New Year.
Rooms 8 double, 8 single. Also 3 double, 7 single ground-floor rooms in
annexe, used for painting holidays. No telephone.
Facilities 2 lounges, 2 bars, dining room, restaurant; studio. Classical back-
ground music sometimes. 6-acre grounds.
Location Village centre; end of High St, on left. Train: Colchester or
Manningtree; then taxi.
Restrictions No smoking: restaurant, some bedrooms. No dogs.
Credit cards MasterCard, Visa.
Terms B&B: single £50, double £75; D,B&B: single £65, double £105. Set
dinner £21.50.

Maison Talbooth
Stratford Road, Dedham
nr Colchester CO7 6HN

Tel (01206) 322367
Fax (01206) 322752
E-mail mtreception@talbooth.co.uk
Website www.talbooth.com

A pink-washed Victorian house (Pride of Britain) on a bluff with wide
views of the Vale of Dedham. It provides luxurious accommodation for

the Milsom family's restaurant, *Le Talbooth, a* half-timbered former weaver's cottage by a bridge over the River Stour, ten minutes' walk away. For those who don't care to walk, there is a courtesy car that takes visitors to *Le Talbooth,* or to the Milsoms' other restaurant, *The Pier at Harwich,* Harwich (*qv*). *Le Talbooth* is near a busy road, but the setting is delightful, with a flowery terrace and swans gliding by, and *Maison Talbooth* is a peaceful place. Its bedrooms are named for poets. The most lavish is Shakespeare, an enormous suite with a large sunken bath in its opulent bathroom, and a terrace leading into the garden (mainly lawn, with loungers). Milton looks over the vale. Tennyson, Brooke and Kipling are smaller and cheaper. All have a sitting area, lavish fabrics and wallpaper, sherry, mineral water, fruit and reading matter. Snacks and drinks are generally available during the day, served in a beautifully proportioned drawing room with a gas fire, squashy chairs and settees. Breakfast, ordered the previous day, is served in the bedroom. The whole house can be taken over for a conference. *Le Talbooth,* founded 42 years ago, has a new head chef this year, Daniel Clarke. Terry Barber, after 40 years in the kitchen – he started at the age of 12 – has become a director. We'd like reports on the food, please. Dishes such as a warm spiced crab and gruyère tart; braised shank of lamb; banana and ginger soufflé are served, "but you can always ask for a plain grilled steak", says managing director Paul Milsom.

Open All year. Restaurant closed Sun evening Sept–May.
Rooms 1 suite, 9 double. 5 on ground floor.
Facilities Drawing room (classical background music evenings); function facilities. 3-acre grounds: croquet. Restaurant, bar, garden on banks of Stour, 10 mins' walk (courtesy car provided). Civil wedding licence.
Location 6 miles NE of Colchester, just E of A12 exit Stratford St Mary. Train: Colchester; then taxi.
Restrictions Smoking discouraged in restaurant during mealtimes. No dogs.
Credit cards All major cards accepted.
Terms (*Excluding 10% service charge on meals*) B&B: single £120–£150, double £155–£175, suite £195. Cooked breakfast £7.50. Set lunch £19, dinner £27; full alc £30. 2-night breaks. Christmas package. 1-night bookings refused Sat.

DENT Cumbria   **Map 4**

Stone Close   BUDGET   *Tel* (015396) 25231
Main Street   *Fax* (015396) 25181
Dent,   *E-mail* accommodation@stoneclose.co.uk
nr Sedbergh LA10 5QL   *Website* www.stoneclose.co.uk

Doubling as an information point for the Yorkshire Dales National Park, this whitewashed tea shop is also a "delightful B&B". Set in a picturesque old village (with narrow cobbled streets, old stone houses with small windows and window boxes), it comprises two listed 17th-century cottages. It has flagstone floors, exposed beams, cast iron ranges, pine furniture. "The atmosphere and the welcome from Kay and Peter Rushton are exceptional," says a devoted regular. Their "delicious home baking" is renowned. Teas and meals (home-made soups, salads, baked potatoes, etc, on blackboard menus) are served all day until early evening, and a "first-rate" three-course evening meal, accompanied by a small selection of wines, is available for residents by arrangement. Homity pie (cheese, onion and potato baked in a pastry case) comes with a salad; gammon, eggs and tomato with wholemeal bread and pickle. Apple pie, fruit crumbles, local ice-creams to finish. There are four simple, pretty bedrooms; one has facilities *en suite*, the others share a bathroom ("you can see down the lovely Dee valley while showering"). Breakfast is a well-presented wholefood affair with a vegetarian option. A lounge is now available for the exclusive use of residents. "People must realise that this is not a hotel (in fact it is something nicer)." "Amazing value – book early." The independent Dent Brewery, close by, produces "excellent beer" for the local pubs. (*DR*)

Open Feb–Dec. Tea shop closed midweek Nov–early Dec, Jan–mid-Mar.
Rooms 3 double, 1 single. 1 with bathroom. No telephone. 3-bedroom cottage adjacent (self-catering, or let for min. 7-day stay).
Facilities Residents' lounge, tea room/restaurant (classical background music all day). Small rear garden. River, fishing 300 yds. Unsuitable for &.
Location Centre of village 4 miles SE of Sedbergh. Carpark adjacent.
Restrictions No smoking. No dogs in public rooms.
Credit cards MasterCard, Visa.
Terms B&B: single £21.50, double £37–£52; D,B&B £28.50–£36 per person. Evening meal £14. 1 night B&B free in stay of 5 or more days. Special rates for exclusive use of all rooms. 1-night bookings refused Sat. *V*

DIDDLEBURY Shropshire   Map 3

Delbury Hall   *Tel* (01584) 841267
Diddlebury   *Fax* (01584) 841441
Craven Arms SY7 9DH   *E-mail* wrigley@delbury.com
                                          Website www.delbury.com

"Fantastic hosts; really welcoming, always around, yet somehow invisible. Lovely lounge; elegant dining room with excellent food, lovely china and silver, great wine list. Gorgeous grounds." "Better than a four-star hotel – much more relaxing." This year's reports on this Georgian red brick house, said to be one of the finest in Shropshire. Not a hotel, but the family home of Lucinda and Patrick Wrigley, it is in a hamlet near the old market town of Ludlow. It stands by a small lake with ornamental ducks, in a large estate amid lovely countryside. It has flowery gardens, a tennis court, a trout fishery with two stocked ponds, and a small farm and vegetable garden which supply the kitchen. "I have not tasted such home-churned butter for 50 years," wrote one visitor, who also appreciated "comforting tea with super cakes and buns". The house has an impressive interior: fine plasterwork, family portraits and an open-string oak staircase leading to a spectacular gallery, but the atmosphere is informal. In house-party style, guests help themselves to drinks in the large sitting room – "no spirit measures!" Dinner is communally served, by candlelight. Patrick Wrigley, a former amateur jockey, learned to cook at Leith's cookery school in London. No choice, but he likes to discuss the menu in advance. Regular dishes include seafood soup with mussels, prawns, cream and tomato; grilled duck breast with a raspberry vinegar sauce; crispy apple tart with ice-cream or custard. Home-grown ingredients are used where possible. The wine list is "first-class and well priced". Breakfasts are "exemplary." The bedrooms are large, with antique furniture; because the Wrigleys did not wish to damage their graceful proportions, only one has facilities *en suite*; the others are let with a private bathroom. You should not expect hotel-type facilities here: Patrick Wrigley writes: "I am hall porter and night porter, as well as proprietor and chef." Close by are Offa's Dyke, Much Wenlock, Wenlock Edge and Stokesay Castle. (*Joanne Hoddy, and others*)

Open All year, except Christmas. Lunch not served.
Rooms 4 double, all with *en suite* or private bathroom.
Facilities Drawing room, sitting room, dining room; children's playroom. No background music. 12-acre grounds in 80-acre parkland: tennis, lake, trout fishery, dovecote. Unsuitable for &. Civil wedding licence.
Location In village NE of Craven Arms. Follow signs to trout fishery, then *Delbury Hall*. Train: Ludlow 8 miles, Craven Arms 5 miles.
Restrictions No smoking: dining room, bedrooms. No small children in dining room at night. No dogs in house (kennels available).
Credit cards MasterCard, Visa.
Terms [2000] B&B £45–£55. Set dinner £30.

DODDISCOMBSLEIGH Devon   Map 1

 The Nobody Inn   BUDGET   *Tel* (01647) 252394
Doddiscombsleigh   *Fax* (01647) 252978
nr Exeter EX6 7PS   *E-mail* inn.nobody@virgin.net

César award: Inn of the year

With a remarkable list of 700 well-priced wines, a large choice of malt whiskies, a huge selection of Devon cheeses and "honest, upretentious food", this "lovely old inn", "wonderfully quirky", is reached up narrow Devon roads near Exeter. Its name derives from a tale of an unfriendly owner who locked the door against weary travellers. When they knocked and received no answer they continued their journey, assuming that nobody was in. Today, Nick Borst-Smith presides over a "marvellously unchanging" place, welcoming locals and overnight visitors and offering "amazing value". "I can't fault it," is one comment this year. The lounge bar has inglenook fireplaces, low beams, Windsor chairs, carriage lanterns, hunting prints, and a "civilised atmosphere, enhanced by the friendly enthusiasm of the service and the lack of piped music and fruit machines". It serves some quite unusual dishes, eg, Blue Vinny soup; chicken in a mustard cream sauce. Specialities of the restaurant, with its red carpet and red-fringed lamps, include spicy Nobody Soup; locally caught rainbow trout; pork tenderloin in white wine and cream; apricot and almond tart. Only seven bedrooms: some simply furnished ones are above the pub. Their lighting may be a bit dim, and towels rather small, but extras include a drinks tray with whisky, sherry and gin, and a hot-water bottle. The best rooms are in *Town Barton*, a Georgian manor house 150 yards away by the old parish church, which has "some of the best stained glass in the West Country". These rooms are large and well thought out, and they have a fridge containing the ingredients for a continental breakfast. But if you opt for this you miss a "splendid affair", served in the bar, with freshly squeezed orange juice, hot toast made to order, and "the best ever fry-up". (*Kevin Merchant, Good Pub Guide, and others*)

Open All year. Restaurant closed midday, Sun evening/Mon night.
Rooms 6 double, 1 single. 3 (1 on ground floor) in *Town Barton* 150 yds.
Facilities Bar, lounge bar, restaurant. 3-acre grounds; patio.
Location 6 miles SW of Exeter, off A38 at Haldon Hill. Local buses (sometimes) from Exeter.
Restrictions No smoking in restaurant. No children under 14. No dogs.
Credit cards Amex, MasterCard, Visa.
Terms [2000] B&B: single £23–£38, double £70. Full alc £20.

DORCHESTER Dorset   Map 1

Casterbridge Hotel
49 High East Street
Dorchester DT1 1HU

Tel (01305) 264043
Fax (01305) 260884
E-mail reception@casterbridgehotel.co.uk
Website www.casterbridgehotel.co.uk

"The owners were so hospitable," says a visitor this year to this unassuming B&B hotel. It has been owned for over 80 years by the Turner family who also own *The Priory*, Wareham (*qv*), and it is run by Rita and Stuart Turner. It is on the busy high street, which the smart little lounge overlooks, but the four front bedrooms are double-glazed, and the building rambles backwards to a quiet courtyard with a fountain. The staff are mostly thought "obliging". And everyone agrees: "Very good value for money." The attractive larger bedrooms have a big bed, and there is good family accommodation. Some rooms are tiny, with a low doorway. The "very English" breakfast, with cereals, muffins, all manner of fruits, and a good choice of cooked dishes, including kedgeree, is "good and generous" apart from "boring toast". No restaurant, but tea and coffee are available all day, guests may picnic in the conservatory, and there are plenty of eating places nearby. The *Mock Turtle*, up the hill, is warmly recommended. Loading and unloading a car can be tricky but the hotel offers help and advice. Outings, guided walks and chauffeur-driven tours of local sights are arranged for guests who arrive by train. The historic county town of Dorset (the model for Thomas Hardy's Casterbridge) has many 17th- and 18th-century houses and some Roman remains. (*Mrs J Blair, TM Farmiloe, and others*)

Open All year, except 25/26 Dec.
Rooms 10 double, 4 single. 6 in annexe across courtyard; 3 on ground floor, with access for ♿ (but no other facilities).

Facilities Ramps. Lounge, bar/library, breakfast room, conservatory. No background music. Small courtyard. Leisure centre 1 mile; sandy beach, bathing 8 miles.
Location Main street, 100 yds below town clock (front rooms double-glazed). 2 garages; free overnight parking in public carpark in adjacent street. Station 1 mile.
Restrictions No smoking: breakfast room, 11 bedrooms. No dogs.
Credit cards All major cards accepted.
Terms B&B: single £40–£52, double £68–£85. Discounts for extended stays; winter weekend breaks. *V*

DORCHESTER-ON-THAMES Oxfordshire   Map 2

The George   *Tel* (01865) 340404
25 High Street   *Fax* (01865) 341620
Dorchester-on-Thames OX10 7HH

Before it became a coaching inn in the 15th century, this timber and tile building was the brewhouse of the 12th-century Norman abbey opposite. Today, fronted by a gleaming yellow coach, it is a civilised place, liked for its "old-fashioned charm", black-and-white façade, uneven roofing, creaking floorboards, old oak furniture, rustic/horsy memorabilia and assorted prints. The lounge overlooks a water garden. Meals are served in the L-shaped bar, with its flagstone floor and huge fireplace, and in the beamed and stone-walled restaurant in a converted barn. The cooking of Simon Quarrie "is excellent as usual", reported one returning guest. He serves sophisticated dishes, eg, mussel and saffron chowder with rouille sauce; saddle of lamb on a casserole of borlotti beans; teardrop of iced chocolate and ginger parfait. The wine list is "quite exceptional as is the range of malt whiskies". The bedrooms vary greatly: two are large, with a four-poster, others low-ceilinged with oak beams; some are in converted stables round the old courtyard (cars are parked here, so there can be noise when diners depart). Those that overlook the village's main street hear the chimes of the abbey's clock sounding the quarter-hour. One family this year had rooms above the kitchen, which they found "unbearably hot" and imperfectly maintained. Another couple reported an alarm call that failed to materialise. Wittenham Clumps, with exhilarating views over the Thames valley, is within walking distance. A good base for Oxford, Blenheim, Henley, Garsington opera. During the week conferences and "team-building sessions" are held, but the "jovial manager", Michael Pinder, assures us that private visitors do not get short shrift. (*Good Pub Guide, WK Wood, PH, and others*)

Open All year.
Rooms 1 family, 15 double, 2 single. 9 in stable block. Some on ground floor.
Facilities Lounge, bar, restaurant ("easy listening" background music); function and conference rooms. 2½-acre grounds. River Thame 200 yds, Thames ¼ mile.
Location In village 8 miles SE of Oxford, opposite abbey. Parking.
Restrictions No smoking: restaurant, bedrooms. No dogs in eating areas during meal service.
Credit cards Amex, MasterCard, Visa.

Terms [2000] B&B: single £65–£75, double £85–£100. English breakfast
£3.50. Full alc £26. 2-day breaks.

DOVER Kent *See SHORTLIST* Map 2

DULVERTON Somerset Map 1

Ashwick House *Tel/Fax* (01398) 323868
Dulverton TA22 9QD *E-mail* ashwickhouse@talk21.com
  Website www.ashwickhouse.co.uk

 Q *César award in 1994*

"The situation is delightful, and the house is beautifully furnished and
maintained. Our bedroom was one of the most comfortable we have
come across. Tremendous attention to detail." Again this year, visitors
praise this "quirkily run, elegant" Edwardian house and the "outstanding dedication" of its owner/manager/chef Richard Sherwood.
"More like a private house than a hotel", it stands high above the Barle
valley, and the main change this year is that the trees which formerly
flanked the drive have been felled for safety reasons, and the resulting
stumps have been turned by a local woodcarver into "eerie depictions"
of extinct and endangered Exmoor animals. In the house, the baronial-
style galleried hall still has the original William Morris wallpaper and
huge stained-glass windows. In the lounge, a fire crackles, a grandfather clock ticks, and there are "inviting sofas". Everywhere are
informative hand-written notes. Spacious bedrooms are equipped with
fresh fruit, mineral water, Scrabble, binoculars, a CD-player and
speak-your-weight scales. At night, a cartoon-character hot-water
bottle warms your bed. At dinner, every menu, presented as a scroll,
has the diners' names. The meal (no choice of main course) might
include Somerset apple and coriander soup; smoked fish soufflé;
boned local quail with a sherry and almond sauce; chocolate rum torte.
There is a fairly priced wine list. The cooking was thought "uniformly
excellent" this year. Breakfast has freshly pressed apple juice, free-
range eggs, brown toast, and the day's weather forecast. In fine
weather, guests eat outdoors on the south-facing terrace. The dramatic
landscape of Exmoor is all around, and nearby places to visit include
Dunster Castle; Knightshayes, and Selworthy thatched village. (*Jenny
Dawe, Ann H Edwards, and others*)

Open All year.
Rooms 6 double.
Facilities 2 lounges, library, dining room; terrace. No background music.
6-acre grounds: water garden, croquet, woodland. Unsuitable for &.
Location 2½ miles NW of Dulverton. Take B3223 towards Lynton; up steep
hill, over 2 cattle grids; signpost on left. Train: Tiverton Parkway; then bus.
Restrictions No smoking: dining room, library, 2 bedrooms. No children
under 8. No dogs in house.
Credit cards None accepted.
Terms B&B £48–£64; D,B&B £63–£85. Set lunch £14.50, dinner £21.
2- to 5-day breaks. Christmas, New Year house parties. ***V***

DUNWICH Suffolk   Map 2

The Ship Inn NEW/BUDGET   *Tel* (01728) 648219
St James Street
Dunwich, nr Saxmundham IP17 3DT

Stephen and Ann Marshlain's "delightful old brick pub, with a good
bustling atmosphere", is in an old Suffolk seaside village (it was once
a thriving medieval port). The main bar is furnished with benches,
pews, captain's chairs and wooden tables on its tiled floor, a wood-
burning stove and lots of nautical memorabilia. There is a conservatory, a sunny rear terrace and a large garden. Meals are very simple
(eg, good fish fried with home-made chips; followed by "scrumptious
home-made puddings"). The few bedrooms, recently redecorated, are
pretty, with views of sea and marsh. "Plenty of books and board
games," says the nominator. "Breakfasts were wonderful, including
squeeze-your-own orange juice. The staff were pleasant and friendly."
The RSPB bird sanctuary at Minsmere is nearby. (*Good Pub Guide,
Cathy Robinson*)

Open All year, except Christmas.
Rooms 3 double. No telephone.
Facilities Conservatory, bar, breakfast room, restaurant. No background
music. Large garden. Beach 2 mins' walk. Unsuitable for &.
Location Centre of village, 4 miles SW of Southwold.
Restrictions No smoking in restaurant. No dogs in restaurant.
Credit cards MasterCard, Visa.
Terms B&B: single £40–£45, double £59. Full alc £20. 2-day breaks in win-
ter (except school holidays).

DURHAM Co. Durham *See SHORTLIST*   Map 4

DUXFORD Cambridgeshire *See SHORTLIST*   Map 2

EAST DOWN Devon   Map 1

Ashelford NEW   *Tel* (01271) 850469
East Down, nr Barnstaple   *Fax* (01270 850862
EX31 4LU   *E-mail* ashelford@ashelford.co.uk
                                      Website www.ashelford.co.uk

"Everything about it is fantastic," says the nominator of this upmarket
guest house, set in large grounds with pasture, woodland, and wide
views across the National Trust's Arlington Court to Exmoor. "The
peace and quiet is amazing, with Exmoor ponies in a paddock, lovely
walks." Three bedrooms are in the 17th-century farmhouse, and the
owners, Tom and Erica McClenaghan, have just converted a barn to
make a "superb suite", with a sitting room upstairs, a six-foot antique
bed, views of a lily pond and stream – "so romantic". One bathroom
has an extra-long antique bath. All rooms are provided with a fridge,
spare toothbrushes, hangover powders, etc; wellies and walking sticks

can be borrowed. Tea on arrival (no charge) comes with home-made cake. There are log fires and TV in the guests' sitting rooms, "and for booze, they do not charge rip-off prices". A home-cooked evening meal can be arranged – "portion control is unknown here". Local produce is cooked in "old-fashioned style", say the McClenaghans. No children, but dogs are welcome – there is an outside bath for them, and kennels are available.

Open All year. Lunch not served.
Rooms 1 suite, 4 double. 2 in barn. No telephone.
Facilities 2 lounges, snug, dining room; occasional background music "to suit guests". 70-acre grounds: garden, water garden, pasture, woodlands. 10 mins' drive from N Devon coast. Unsuitable for &.
Location 6 miles NE of Barnstaple. Turn off A39 just N of Shirwell.
Restrictions No smoking in dining room before 10 pm, or in bedrooms. No children under 16.
Credit cards MasterCard, Visa.
Terms B&B: double £94–£106, suite £130–£140. Set dinner (by arrangement) £30–£35.

EAST GRINSTEAD West Sussex   Map 2

Gravetye Manor   *Tel* (01342) 810567
Vowels Lane   *Fax* (01342) 810080
East Grinstead RH19 4LJ   *E-mail* gravetye@relaischateaux.fr

♕ *César award in 1991*

"Truly a luxury hotel. Dinner was excellent, as always." "It never disappoints; 'cosseting' just begins to describe the service." Plaudits continue for this creeper-covered Elizabethan manor (Relais & Châteaux). Set in magnificent grounds designed by William Robinson, pioneer of the English natural garden, it has been run for four decades by Peter Herbert, now in his 70s, and his wife Sue. There are "lots of nice country house touches": home-made biscuits at tea, served by an open fire in the Tudor drawing room with its carved wooden ceiling; fruit, books and magazines in the "soothing bedrooms" (most are large). Changes have taken place in the panelled and *Michelin*-starred restaurant this year: the *à la carte* menu has gone, replaced by two *prix-fixe* menus, one longer and more expensive than the other, and both priced according to whether two or three courses are taken. But coffee and petits fours are £4 extra. "Truly memorable" dishes served by Mark Raffan include, eg, tian of Cornish crab and cherry tomatoes, roast scallops and jus épice; roast young pigeon with foie gras; lightly poached exotic fruits with crème caramel. The wine list is huge, with "eyebrow-raising prices". Light lunches, with limited choice, are available. "Lovely berries with natural yogurt" are available for breakfast. Not cheap, but "for a special occasion, it is hard to beat". Gatwick is 20 minutes' drive away. Local attractions include the gardens of Wakehurst Place, Leonardslee and Sheffield Park. (*Prof. Wolfgang Stroebe, RF, and others*)

Open All year. Restaurant closed to non-residents Christmas night.
Rooms 16 double, 2 single.
Facilities 3 sitting rooms, bar, restaurant; private dining room. No background

music. 30-acre grounds: gardens, croquet, 3-acre lake (fishing). Unsuitable for &.

Location 5 miles SW of East Grinstead, off B2110 to West Hoathly. Train: East Grinstead, 5 miles, Gatwick Airport, 12 miles; then taxi.

Restrictions No smoking in restaurant. No children under 7, except babies. No dogs in house (kennels in grounds).

Credit cards MasterCard, Visa.

Terms [2000] Room: single £90–£140, double £120–£280. Breakfast: continental £14; full English £16. Set meals (2 or 3 courses): lunch £19 or £26; dinner £38 or £48. Off-season rates. 1-night bookings refused Sat.

EAST STOKE Dorset   **Map 2**

Kemps	*Tel* (01929) 462563
East Stoke	*Fax* (01929) 405287
nr Wareham BH20 6AL	*E-mail* kemps.hotel@euphony.net

"An excellent hotel." "Truly welcoming." Recent praise for this small Victorian rectory, which overlooks the Frome valley and Purbeck Hills. The owners, Paul and Gillian Warren, are "helpful, and full of useful advice about sightseeing". The bedrooms in the main house are "traditionally comfortable" with good views. Larger ones, in a purpose-built annexe, have a pretty decor; some have a spa bath, and one has a four-poster bed. There are also rooms in a coach house set well back from the nearby road and railway, but these are the least popular; some bathrooms are tiny, and sound insulation can be poor. The restaurant, with its west-facing conservatory extension overlooking the garden, is popular locally, particularly for the traditional Sunday lunch. And there is one report this year of a meal that was disorganised because a large wedding reception had been taking place. The wide-ranging *table d'hôte* menu changes daily, serving modern dishes, eg, air-dried tomato tartlet with a black olive tapenade; shank of lamb in a port wine and redcurrant sauce. A vegetarian option is available, as is a brasserie menu, and bar lunches are also served. Breakfast includes a buffet with fresh fruit, toast made from home-made bread, and unpackaged jams, marmalades and butter. The National Trust coastline is nearby; so is entertainment for all tastes: Monkey World, a tank museum, Corfe Castle. (*Mr and Mrs D Grogan*)

Open All year. Restaurant closed Sat lunchtime.

Rooms 14 double. 4 in coach house, 6 in annexe. 2 adapted for &.

Facilities Lounge, study, bar, restaurant (light classical background music during meals); function/conference facilities. 1½-acre garden: pond. Sea, safe bathing 10 mins' drive.

Location On A352, 5 miles W of Wareham.

Restrictions Smoking banned in dining room, discouraged in bedrooms. Dogs by arrangement.

Credit cards All major cards accepted.

Terms [2000] B&B: single £56–£76, double £84–£130. Set lunch £9.95, dinner £21.95; full alc £30. Child accommodated in parents' room: under 7, free; 7–12, £5; 13 and over, £15. Special breaks. Christmas package. 1-night bookings sometimes refused. *V*

ERPINGHAM Norfolk   **Map 2**

The Ark   *Tel* (01263) 761535
The Street
Erpingham NR11 7QB

A restaurant-with-rooms, "with a home-spun air", in a brick-and-flint
house on a small country road. Sheila Kidd is the "imaginative and
enthusiastic" chef; her husband Michael is front-of-house, *sommelier*
and waiter. "They do everything they can to make one's visit a happy
one," says a visitor this year. The large garden, recently much
improved, supplies many of the organic ingredients used in the
kitchen. The quality of the Elizabeth David-influenced country cooking earned it an East Anglia Country Cooking award in the *Good Food
Guide 2000*. Dishes on the small but varied menu include, eg, marinated free-range chicken salad with raisins and pine nuts;
Gressingham duck with apple, sage and onion purée; fresh raspberry
syllabub. A vegetarian main course is always available. Everything,
from bread to chocolates, is home made. The wine list ranges from
reasonably priced house wines up to the £80 mark. The dining room
has "a homely atmosphere: attractively laid tables, an open fire, a
lovely Edwardian inlaid cabinet". The lounge, warmed by a wood-
burning stove, was redecorated this year. Only three bedrooms,
crammed, like the rest of the house, with knick-knacks. One (suitable
for dog-owners) has a shower and a private garden: the Attic Room,
reached up a narrow, twisting staircase, is "arranged as a pleasant sitting room cum bedroom". It has a bathroom under the eaves. The
smaller Tulip Room has a shared bathroom. Breakfast, served round
one large table, is at flexible times. No menu, but it includes freshly
squeezed orange juice, fresh croissants and home-baked bread, home-
made marmalade, and local kippers. The grounds of two estates
owned by Lord Walpole – Wolterton Park close by, and Mannington
Hall two miles to the north-west – are worth visiting. Two fine
National Trust houses, Blickling Hall and Felbrigg Hall, and some
wonderful beaches are nearby, and the tiny church at Ingworth, which
has a thatched roof and the original box pews, is worth a visit. (*MJ*)

Open All year, except part of Oct.
Rooms 3 double. 2 with *en suite* facilities; 1 with shared bathroom. 1 on
ground floor. No telephone.
Facilities Lounge, bar, restaurant, breakfast/private dining room. No back-
ground music. 1-acre garden: croquet. Lakes and rivers 3–10 miles, sea
7 miles.
Location 4 miles N of Aylsham. Left off A140, just before Alby Centre.
Restrictions No smoking: restaurant, bedrooms. Dogs in garden bedroom
only, not in public rooms.
Credit cards None accepted.
Terms D,B&B: single £70–£77.50, double £120–£135. Set lunch £15.25, dinner (2 to 4 courses) £21.25–£28; full alc £31. Off-season breaks.

If the *Guide* is unavailable, or poorly displayed, in your local
bookshop, please complain to the manager and/or let us know.

The Saracen's Head   `BUDGET`   *Tel* (01263) 768909
Wolterton, nr Erpingham   *Fax* (01263) 768993
Aylsham NR11 7LX   *Website* www.broadland.com/guest/aylsham/saracen

An agreeably eccentric pub run in humorous style by owner/chef
Robert Dawson-Smith; he signs himself: "Innkeeper (humble)." His
aim, he writes, is a relaxed atmosphere, "with unusual and simple food
(no chips, peas, scampi or prawn cocktails) and without the intrusion
of piped music and fruit machines". Built as a coaching inn for the
Walpole family in 1806, it has a "comfortably bold" decor: candles
and log fires, plants and "all kinds of interesting artefacts". The
"charmingly old-fashioned patio" gives it "the feel of a Tuscan farmhouse". This is "not a place for those who want to be fussed over; the
approach is casual and friendly". It is a popular local eating place, with
a menu that changes at every meal; booking is advised. Mussels are a
speciality – sometimes served with cider and cream. Pan-fried monkfish with orange and ginger, and medallions of venison with red fruit
are also on the menu. Herbs and tomatoes are liberally used.
"Heavenly puddings", eg, nutty banana and Marsala crumble; old-
fashioned treacle tart. Three of the bedrooms, reached up steep steps,
are in the roof; they have rounded dormer windows, sloping ceilings
and simple pine furniture. Breakfast includes freshly squeezed orange
juice, fresh fruit, good bread, good kippers. In summer, meals are
served alfresco. Shows of work by local artists are held, and also wine
tastings. The Blickling estate is close by (Mr Dawson-Smith also manages its pub, the *Buckinghamshire Arms*). Other local attractions: the
gardens of Wolterton Park and Mannington Hall (with an outstanding
collection of roses), the north Norfolk coast, Holkham Hall and
Norwich. This is also a rich area for windmill and railway enthusiasts.
(*Good Pub Guide, and others*)

Open All year, except 25 Dec.
Rooms 4 double. No telephone.
Facilities Parlour, 2 bars; function room. No background music. 1-acre
grounds: walled patio. Only bar areas suitable for &.
Location Turn W off A140 to Erpingham. Instead of bearing right towards
Aldborough, go straight on, passing church on left and following signs to
Itteringham. Pub ½ mile on right, in field.
Restrictions Smoking discouraged in eating areas, banned in bedrooms. Dogs
by arrangement; in bedrooms only.
Credit cards All major cards accepted.
Terms B&B: single £30–£50, double £45–£65. Set lunch from £5.50; full alc
£27. Winter breaks. 1-night bookings sometimes refused weekends. ***V***

ETON Berkshire *See SHORTLIST*   **Map 2**

> The "Budget" label by a hotel's name indicates an establish-
> ment where dinner, bed and breakfast cost around £50 per
> person, or B&B about £30 and an evening meal about £20.
> These are only rough guides and do not always apply to single
> accommodation, nor do they necessarily apply in high season.

EVERSHOT Dorset   **Map 1**

Summer Lodge   *Tel* (01935) 83424
Evershot DT2 0JR   *Fax* (01935) 83005
                              E-mail reception@summerlodgehotel.com
                              Website www.summerlodgehotel.com

Ω *César award in 1985*

"A wonderful hotel." "A peaceful setting; a warm welcome." This
luxurious country house hotel (Relais & Châteaux) is set in a lovely
garden, in a Dorset village. A long-time *Guide* favourite, it was once
the dower house of the Earls of Ilchester. Some bedrooms are in a converted coach house. Nigel and Margaret Corbett have presided for
over 20 years; son-in-law Daniel Hostettler is now manager. "They are
totally dedicated to their guests' enjoyment," writes one of many
devoted fans. "The ambience and decor is friendly, and cosy rather
than grand," adds another visitor. The house is "beautifully furnished,
warm and comfortable". Mrs Corbett's "magnificent flower arrangements" are much admired. Bedrooms are lavish and well appointed.
Most are large, but No. 5 is "extremely small". Bedroom lighting may
be too soft for some, but the efficient showers and "fluffy towels" are
appreciated. A two-bedroomed cottage with its own garden is now
available. We'd like reports on the cooking of the new chef, Gregory
Nicholson, ex-*Browns Hotel*, London. He serves modern dishes, eg,
pan-fried scallops on pineapple, red pepper and cucumber salsa; breast
of Gressingham duck with fondant potatoes, roast foie gras, and bittersweet orange sauce. There is a daily set menu with two choices of each
course, as well as a *carte*. If you stray from the set menu, prices can
mount, but the light lunches are "good value". Breakfast has "21
cereal packets to choose from", and "the finest raspberry jam in the
world", but thin toast. The staff is "mostly French, young and well
trained". Children are genuinely welcomed. Not cheap, but the half
board prices include early morning tea, a newspaper and a lavish
cream tea. Shooting parties are sometimes accommodated. There is
good walking in a large deerpark nearby. Local attractions include
Parnham House, Stourhead, Hardy's cottage, Montacute and Kingston
Lacy. Ten golf courses are within 25 miles. (*Heather Sharland,
Michael and Maureen Heath, Edwin Prince; also Anne and Denis
Tate, and others*)

Open All year.
Rooms 1 junior suite, 13 double, 3 single. 6 in coach house 20 yds (3 on
ground floor, 2 with private terrace). Also 2-bedroomed cottage.
Facilities Ramps. 2 lounges, bar, restaurant. No background music. 4-acre
grounds: garden, swimming pool, croquet, tennis. Golf, fishing, hunting
nearby; sea, shingle beach 12 miles. Civil wedding licence.
Location 10 miles NW of Dorchester. Entering village turn left into Summer
Lane; drive on right. Train: Yeovil/Dorchester; then taxi.
Restrictions No smoking in restaurant. Dogs by prior arrangement; not in
public rooms.
Credit cards All major cards accepted.
Terms [2000] Room: single £85–£125, double £120–£245; suite £195–£285;
D,B&B (min. 2-night stay): single £125–£180; double £195–£345, junior
suite/cottage £260–£395. Breakfast £14.50. Set lunch £15.50, dinner £42.50;

full alc £50. Off-season breaks. Christmas, New Year packages. 1-night book-ings occasionally refused Sat.

EVESHAM Worcestershire   Map 3

The Evesham Hotel   *Tel* (01386) 765566
Cooper's Lane, off Waterside   *Fax* (01386) 765443
Evesham WR11 6DA   *Freephone* 0800 716969 (reservations only)
                                     E-mail reception@eveshamhotel.com
                                     Website www.eveshamhotel.com

 Q *César award in 1990*

Toadstool tables, a tiny front door set low in a bedroom wall, gnomes sitting on beams, a mad hatter's tea party laid out in a corner – all these greet the young visitor in the Alice in Wonderland family suite in this "wonderfully eccentric" yet professionally run hotel, a long-time *Guide* favourite. Other suites are based on tropical fish and on ancient Rome, and there is a new annexe this year, good for a family or a dis-abled visitor. The sitting room has board games and more toys. Children under 12 are charged according to age and amount of food eaten (see below). The wise-cracking brochures, toy ducks in the bath, and teddy bears strewn about the place may make some visitors won-der if they have wandered through the looking glass, but John and Sue Jenkinson show "intelligence and thoughtfulness, genuine good humour, and warmth to all comers". They are supported by a caring staff, and "everything is done with a great sense of fun". Mindful of other guests, the Jenkinsons try "to establish a balance by not having too many children at the same time". The house stands on a quiet road on the edge of the market town. Built in 1540, it was remodelled in Georgian times; a bedroom wing was added in the 1980s. The popular restaurant, overlooking a huge 200-year-old cedar of Lebanon in the large rear garden, offers exotic fare from around the world; dishes like pork Shoga-Yaki, lamb Neluska are jokingly explained on the menu; plainer dishes are also available, and there are always seven vegetar-ian main courses. Lunch includes a 50-dish buffet. The huge wine list avoids, on principle, French and German vintages; it was offering Chilean wines long before the fashion took hold, and you can order Lithuanian mead, absinth, or pastis. Evesham, in a fruit-growing area, has attractive old houses and riverside walks. Stratford-upon-Avon is 13 miles away. (*A and CR, and others*)

Open All year, except 25/26 Dec.
Rooms 3 suites (1 suitable for &). 32 double, 5 single. 10 on ground floor.
Facilities 2 lounges, bar, restaurant; function facilities; small indoor swim-ming pool. No background music. 2½-acre grounds: croquet, putting, swings, trampoline.
Location Off Riverside Rd. 5 mins' walk from town centre, across river. Parking. Station 1 mile.
Restrictions No smoking: restaurant, 1 lounge, 5 bedrooms, pool area. No dogs in public rooms.
Credit cards All major cards accepted.
Terms B&B: single £63–£71, double £98, suite from £145; D,B&B (2 nights min.) £55–£68 per person. Full alc £27. Child accommodated in parents'

room: under 12, £2 or £3 for each year of life, depending on season (eg, £12 for a 6-year-old in winter). Christmas, New Year rates. 1-night bookings sometimes refused.

EXETER Devon *See SHORTLIST*   **Map 1**

EXFORD Somerset   **Map 1**

The Crown   *Tel* (01643) 831554
Exford TA24 7PP   *Fax* (01643) 831665
                          E-mail bradleyhotelsexmoor@easynet.co.uk
                          Website www.gratton.co.uk/crown

Overlooking the green and a row of old houses in a picturesque village in Exmoor National Park, this old coaching inn has been sympathetically modernised by its owner, Michael Bradley. Catering for the horsy brigade (there are stables at the back), it is also popular with the non-horsy set who find it "pleasant and comfortable with good food". The atmosphere is described as "very unforced", the service "is splendid", and the lack of piped music is appreciated. There is a pleasant water garden, with stream, stone bridges, lawn and overhanging trees. The lounge is decorated in country style, with sporting prints and magazines; the yellow-and-green dining room has well-spaced tables and good napery. The new chef, Mathew Gardner, who claims to use only the freshest of ingredients, serves modern English dishes, eg, seared scallops with confit tomatoes; pan-roasted red mullet with aubergine caviar. There is a small selection of desserts and West Country cheeses. Simpler meals are served in the bar for those who find the restaurant food "marginally too elaborate". Breakfasts include freshly squeezed orange juice, home-made walnut bread and a wide choice of cooked dishes. The bedrooms are good sized, most of them spacious and light, with "supremely comfortable" beds. The problem of poor reading lights appears to have been resolved, though the switch may be difficult to find. This is the centre of *Lorna Doone* country; handy for the North Devon and Somerset coast. (*Josie Mayers, Nigel Rodgers*)

Open All year.
Rooms 14 double, 3 single.
Facilities 2 lounges, public bar, cocktail bar, restaurant; meeting room. No background music. 1-acre grounds: water garden, terrace garden, stabling for visiting horses. River 5 mins' walk; shooting, clay-pigeon shooting nearby. Unsuitable for &.
Location Centre of village in Exmoor National Park.
Restriction No dogs in public rooms, except bar.
Credit cards Amex, MasterCard, Visa.
Terms B&B £40–£47.50; D,B&B £61–£69. Bar meals. Set dinner £25; full alc £31. Child accommodated in parents' room charged only for meals. Exmoor breaks. Christmas package.

Make sure that the hotel has included VAT in the prices it quotes.

FALMOUTH Cornwall   Map 1

Penmere Manor   NEW   *Tel* (01326) 211411
Mongleath Road   *Fax* (01326) 317588
Falmouth TR11 4PN   *E-mail* reservations@penmere.demon.co.uk
                                           Website www.penmere.co.uk

A Georgian country house now a conventional hotel (Best Western),
owned by Andrew Pope and Elizabeth Rose. It is set amid subtropical
gardens and woodland near the south Cornwall coast, about a mile
from the town centre. Sandy beaches are a mile away. The decor may
be somewhat anodyne, but it is a "dependable place, with a happy
atmosphere". One visit in 1999 got off to a good start: "I booked, 18
months in advance, for the Eclipse. They did not put their prices up,
and for a year they did not ask for a deposit." The food is "unpretentious, varied and good, served with enthusiasm", and eating arrangements are flexible. *Bolitho's Restaurant* has a long four-course menu
that changes daily: many seafood starters, a sorbet to follow, and a
long list of main courses (several with a supplementary charge); you
pay according to number of courses taken. It also has a menu dedicated solely to lobster. You can lunch or dine more informally in the
bar in the Fountains Leisure Club, which also has a gym, a large
indoor swimming pool, solarium, beauty treatments, etc. The walled
garden shelters a heated outdoor pool. The best bedrooms, in the garden wing, are spacious, with a sitting area and king- or queen-size bed.
There are conference and business facilities. Falmouth golf club is
nearby (booking necessary), as are Land's End, Pendennis and
St Mawes castles and Trebah, St Austell and Trevarno Gardens.
(*HJM Tucker*)

Open All year, except 24–28 Dec.
Rooms 27 double, 10 single.
Facilities 2 lounges (guitar/piano music Apr–Oct), bar/brasserie, restaurant.
Leisure club: gym, solarium, beauty room; indoor and outdoor swimming
pools. 5-acre grounds: children's play area. Beach, sailing, windsurfing,
abseiling, golf nearby. Unsuitable for &. Civil wedding licence.
Location 1 mile SW of Falmouth. From Truro, take A39 towards Falmouth,
right at Hillhead roundabout. After 1 mile, left into Mongleath Road. Train:
Penmere Station 1 mile; local buses.
Restrictions No smoking: restaurant, bedrooms. No dogs in public rooms.
Credit cards All major cards accepted.
Terms [2000] B&B: single £53–£60.50, double £64–£71.50; D,B&B: single
£75–£82.50, double £86–£93.50. Full alc £27.50. Off-season breaks. *V*

FERRENSBY North Yorkshire   Map 4

The General Tarleton   *Tel* (01423) 340284
Harrogate Road   *Fax* (01423) 340288
Ferrensby   *E-mail* gti@generaltarleton.co.uk
nr Knaresborough HG5 0QB   *Website* www.generaltarleton.co.uk

In a small, pretty village with a duck pond, and red brick cottages
standing in flowery gardens, this 18th-century inn is named for Sir

Banastre Tarleton, barrister, soldier and MP. It has been transformed by Denis and Juliet Watkins and John Topham (he is the chef) into a "thoroughly modern" operation. The bar/brasserie occupies the original pub, with its alcoves, oak beams, and big old fireplace. "The cooking is far removed from what is normally thought of as 'bar food'," says a visitor this year (eg, smoked salmon blinis; pot-roast lamb; tiramisu), "and we were impressed by the large selection of wines sold by the glass." Prices are reasonable: most main courses cost under £10; sandwiches are available at lunchtime. The restaurant, in an extension, is "arranged with some elegance". It has exposed stone walls; upholstered high-backed chairs, smartly set tables, and "knowledgeable waiters". It serves three-course fixed-price meals. The food, on big plates, is "ambitiously up-to-date, and highly satisfactory", eg, crisp tomato tart with pesto; chicken breast wrapped in Parma ham with tarragon jus. There is a choice of wines from most wine-producing countries. The bedrooms, in a new extension, are "superior chain-like in design", but they have attractive fabrics, cheerful prints, excellent lighting, and a functional bathroom. A "perfect breakfast", served in a glass-roofed courtyard, includes freshly squeezed juices, "wickedly soft and buttery" croissants, toasted walnut bread and unsalted butter. "No lounge, so don't go for socialising," one visitor wrote. "The keen young staff were friendly, but we did not see a member of management." The owners' other old inn, the *Angel* at Hetton, near Skipton, is run on similar lines, but it has no bedrooms. Harrogate and York, the Yorkshire dales and moors are nearby. (*Ran Ogston, DW*)

Open All year; except 25 Dec.
Rooms 14 double. Some on ground floor.
Facilities Lounge, bar/brasserie, restaurant; small conference facilities; covered courtyard. No background music.
Location 2 miles NE of Knaresborough. From A1, take A6055 to Knaresborough. The inn is 4 mins' drive away on right.
Restrictions No smoking: restaurant, bedrooms. No dogs in public rooms.
Credit cards Amex, MasterCard, Visa.
Terms [2000] Room: single/double £65. Breakfast £9.95. Bar meals. Set dinner £25. Champagne, golfing, gourmet, sport, shopping breaks. ***V***

FILEY North Yorkshire   **Map 4**

Downcliffe House   BUDGET   *Tel* (01723) 513310
6 The Beach   *Fax* (01723) 513773
Filey YO14 9LA   *E-mail* paulmanners@onyxnet.co.uk
                                        Website www.fileytourism.co.uk

On seafront of Edwardian resort on edge of Yorkshire wolds, 7 miles S of Scarborough: Paul and Angela Manners' unpretentious small hotel (Les Routiers), in Victorian house across road from 6 miles of sandy beach. "Well decorated, clean, with pleasant atmosphere. Special breaks remarkable value." Lounge, bar, restaurant (no smoking), small terrace. Generous breakfasts; snacks available all day; good traditional dinners on set-price menu (mixed background music). Unsuitable for &. Croquet, tennis, bowls, walking, fishing,

sailing, birdwatching nearby. Small carpark. Railway station ½ mile.
10 bedrooms, most sea-facing. Closed Jan. No dogs in public rooms.
MasterCard, Visa accepted. B&B £35–£37, D,B&B £48–£53. More
reports, please.

FLEET Dorset   **Map 1**

Moonfleet Manor   *Tel* (01305) 786948
Fleet   *Fax* (01305) 774395
nr Weymouth DT3 4ED   *E-mail* info@moonfleetmanor.com
                               Website www.moonfleetmanor.com

In a "great location" overlooking the "amazing" Chesil Beach and
Lyme Bay, this Georgian manor, managed by Neil Carter, is one of the
Luxury Family Hotels group (see also *Woolley Grange,* Bradford-on-
Avon, *Fowey Hall,* Fowey and *The Old Bell,* Malmesbury). Like the
others, it aims to be both child- and adult-friendly, and though the
atmosphere may be a bit too casual for some, everyone agrees that the
staff are "quite delightful" and the food "excellent". The chef, Phil
Adams, presides over the formal dining room and the more casual
Verandah bar/restaurant, serving modern dishes in "nouvelle portions", eg, red pepper mousse on an orange and avocado salad; crab
risotto with a cappuccino bisque and baby vegetables; breaded
escalopes of pork fillet with basmati rice, spring onions and lemon and
herb butter. The wine list consists almost exclusively of New World
wines. Breakfast "is reminiscent of the best of British Rail", wrote one
well-travelled reporter. Facilities include a "Den" with full-time nannies, an indoor swimming pool, aromatherapy treatments, and much
more (see below); visits to the surrounding farm can be arranged.
Large, comfortable public rooms have a colonial feel (tiger skins on
walls). Bedrooms vary in size; some may seem a little cramped; and
some, not yet refurbished, have a "rather utilitarian" feel, but are
cheaper. There is no access to the beach, and strong currents rule out
swimming, but there are good walks in either direction along the Coast
Path, and the seaside attractions of Weymouth are a short drive away.
(*William Keegan, and others*)

Open All year.
Rooms 5 suites, 32 double, 2 single. 3 in adjacent coach houses. 3 on ground
floor.
Facilities Lift. 3 lounges, 2 restaurants; no background music; meeting room;
games room/nursery, Smugglers' Disco, Blackbeard's Arcade; indoor swimming pool, sauna, solarium, sunbed, aromatherapy, snooker, etc. 5-acre
grounds: children's play areas, tennis, bowls, squash, badminton, etc. Golf,
sailing nearby.
Location 5 miles W of Weymouth. A354 from Dorchester. Right at Manor
roundabout to Weymouth centre; right at Chafey's roundabout to
Chickerell/Bridport; through golf course to Wessex roundabout, left to
Chickerell, right at junction; 1.7 miles to Moonfleet mini-roundabout; turn
left; 2 miles on towards sea. Train: Weymouth; then taxi.
Restriction No smoking in restaurant.
Credit cards All major cards accepted.
Terms [2000] B&B: single £75, double £115–£185, suite £220; D,B&B:
single £80–£90, double £125–£220, suite £230–£255. Child accommodated in

parents' room charged for meals only. Bar meals. Set dinner £26.50. Spring, autumn breaks. Christmas package.

FLEETWOOD Lancashire *See SHORTLIST*   **Map 4**

FLITWICK Bedfordshire *See SHORTLIST*   **Map 2**

FOWEY Cornwall   **Map 1**

Fowey Hall   *Tel* (01726) 833866
Hanson Drive   *Fax* (01726) 834100
Fowey PL23 1ET   *Website* luxury-family-hotels.co.uk

This Italianate Victorian mansion may have been the model for Toad Hall, and the owners, Nigel Chapman and Nicholas Dickinson, have named eight bedrooms in a converted coach house after characters in *The Wind in the Willows*. Like other members of the Luxury Family Hotels group, this is a child-friendly destination for an upmarket clientele, and you can cram as many children as you like into your room for no charge. The manager, Hazel Brocklebank, is co-owner of *Brock's* restaurant, Padstow. The honey-coloured stone house was built by the Victorian industrialist Sir Charles Hanson. Inspectors in 2000 found it "appealing, with a big pillared portico, huge terrace with a wonderful view over rooftops to the estuary". Some bedrooms in the attics (no lift) have a steeply sloping ceiling and no view. Public rooms have Baroque plasterwork, panelling, marble fireplaces, oriental rugs and potted plants, "a hotchpotch of furniture, much of it repro Jacobean". There are two "cosy lounges" and a child-free "quiet room". The Four Bears Club has trained nannies who will take children off their parents' hands for several hours during the day. In the large grounds there is a courtyard with "every manner of amusement: tractors, bicycles, sandpits, slides", and a shallow swimming pool in a conservatory. The chef, Tony Duce, presides over two restaurants: the "lovely and light" *Palm Court* serves home-made soups, salads, all manner of seafood. In the "more staid" dining room, menus include pressed foie gras, chicken liver and apple terrine; fillet of monkfish in Parma ham with roast saffron potatoes; dark chocolate brioche and butter pudding with clotted cream. But one couple found the cooking disappointing this year. The young staff are "uniformly pleasant", and the aromatherapist, Tina, is strongly recommended. Early morning tea and a newspaper are included in the price. More reports, please.

Open All year.
Rooms 12 suites, 13 double. 8, some on ground floor, in coach house.
Facilities 2 lounges, TV room, billiard room, gun room, 2 restaurants; Four Bears Club (nursery, supervised 10 am–6 pm), games room. No background music. 5-acre grounds: garden – covered heated swimming pool, croquet, badminton. Sea 2 miles. Civil wedding licence.
Location Top of town; arriving in Fowey, at mini-roundabout, go straight ahead towards centre, down ravine. Right into Hanson Drive; hotel on right. Parking. Train: Par; then bus.

Restrictions No smoking in restaurants. No dogs in public rooms.
Credit cards Amex, MasterCard, Visa.
Terms [2000] B&B: double £90–£165, suite £135–£250. Set dinner (2 to 3 courses) £24.50–£29.50. Child accommodated free in parents' room. Christmas package. 1-night bookings sometimes refused.

FRANT Kent   **Map 2**

The Old Parsonage   *Tel/Fax* (01892) 750773
Church Lane, Frant   *E-mail* oldparson@aol.com
nr Tunbridge Wells TN3 9DX   *Website* www.s-h-systems.co.uk/hotels/oldpars

"The atmosphere is unique; not only the house, which is beautifully decorated, but the village, which represents for me merry old England. On a return visit, arriving late, I was welcomed more like a friend than a guest." A report from Germany this year on Mary and Tony Dakin's "excellent-value establishment". No humble parsonage this; it was built for the third son of the local peer, Lord Abergavenny, in the 18th century, and it remained in clerical hands until 1989 when the Dakins took over. Two sets of oak double doors lead into a grand hall; the spacious bedrooms are up an equally grand staircase; a fourth room, with a four-poster, is new this year. There are antiques throughout the house, photos on walls, a large lounge, and a Victorian conservatory, where tea and drinks are served. A balustraded terrace leads to the walled garden. Breakfast, served at a refectory table, is continental, with ham, cheese and croissants, or English, with eggs, bacon, etc, or kedgeree. No evening meal, but there are two pubs on the doorstep. "The *George* is excellent, but be sure to reserve for food." Or you could try the *Hotel du Vin & Bistro* at Tunbridge Wells (*qv*), two miles away. Frant is a conservation village on a ridge with extensive views. Its green, surrounded by superb timber-framed and Georgian houses, "makes a perfect setting for cricket". Sightseeing within a 15-mile radius includes Hever, Bodiam and Leeds castles, Penshurst Place, Ightham Mote, Batemans, Chartwell, Sissinghurst. (*Thomas Guder*)

Open All year, except Christmas.
Rooms 4 double. No telephone.
Facilities Drawing room (classical background music morning/evening), conservatory, breakfast room. 2-acre grounds: terrace, lawns, croquet. Lake, trout-fishing 3 miles; reservoir, leisure facilities 5 miles. Unsuitable for &.
Location By church in village 300 yds off A267, 2 miles S of Tunbridge Wells. Train: Tunbridge Wells; then bus/taxi.
Restrictions Smoking in conservatory only. No children under 7. Dogs allowed in bedrooms if owners bring their own blankets; only guide dogs allowed in public rooms.
Credit cards MasterCard, Visa.
Terms B&B: single £45–£59, double £65–£79. 1-night bookings refused weekends in season.

Deadlines: nominations for the 2002 edition of this volume should reach us not later than 25 May 2001. Latest date for comments on existing entries: 1 June 2001.

FRIETH Oxfordshire   Map 2

Little Parmoor BUDGET   *Tel* (01494) 881447
Frieth   *Fax* (01494) 883012
nr Henley-on-Thames RG9 6NL

The "wonderful panelled drawing room" of this tall red brick Georgian
house made one visitor this year "feel like a character in a Jane Austen
novel". In winter, logs burn in its handsome fireplace. Other visitors
wrote of the "splendid hospitality" offered by Wynyard and Julia
Wallace, the "charming couple" who run it as a B&B (an evening meal
is no longer served). "The garden is lovely, and the rural location marvellously peaceful." Set in open farmland on the edge of the Chiltern
hills, the house is in a designated area of outstanding natural beauty. Its
lovingly tended grounds contain a profusion of herbaceous plants,
mature trees and old roses, and a small walled garden bounded by brick
walls and yew hedges. The two large double bedrooms are cream-and-
white panelled, with a view over the garden; one has a bath, the other a
shower; both have a TV and tea/coffee-making facilities. Portraits and
watercolours, and a catholic collection of books, fill the house. The full
English breakfast is served in a vine-shaded patio in summer. Some
foodies use the house as a base for dining at the *Michelin* two-starred
Ortolan near Reading; there are also many pubs in the area serving
good food. A good base for visiting the Thames valley. Though quiet
(it is on a small road with almost no traffic) the house is convenient for
the M4, the M40 and Heathrow. (*Siân James*)

Open All year.
Rooms 2 double, 1 single. No telephone.
Facilities Drawing room, breakfast room. No background music. 1-acre gar-
den. Unsuitable for &.
Location 1 mile SW of village, which is NE of Henley. Follow road through
village and left at sign for Hambleden/Henley; house ¾ mile on right.
Restrictions No smoking. Children by arrangement. Dogs by arrangement.
Credit cards None accepted.
Terms B&B £26–£28. 1-night bookings sometimes refused weekends.

GATESHEAD Tyne and Wear *See SHORTLIST*   Map 4

GATWICK West Sussex *See SHORTLIST*   Map 2

GILLAN Cornwall   Map 1

Tregildry   *Tel* (01326) 231378
Gillan, Manaccan   *Fax* (01326) 231561
nr Helston TR12 6HG   *E-mail* trgildry@globalnet.co.uk
                                         Website www.tregildryhotel.co.uk

♔ *César award in 1998*

"The staff are wonderful. The location is perfect." "A beautiful spot.
The views from the garden are magnificent." A civilised small hotel,

run "with style" by its owners, Lynne and Huw Phillips. Set above Gillan Creek, it has panoramic views of the Helford River, Falmouth Bay and beyond. A private path leads down to a small stony cove; the Coast Path is nearby. Sandy beaches, eg, the National Trust's Poldhu, are reached via winding Cornish lanes. The decor provides a warm Mediterranean ambience: apricot walls, white paintwork; wicker/rattan furniture. Large lounges, broken up into separate areas, have sofas, fresh flowers, panoramic views in all directions, up-to-date glossy magazines, books about local flowers, birds, etc. The bedrooms are bright, well lit; even the small ones have "wonderful views", but one *en suite* bathroom was thought "old-fashioned" this year, and one couple were unhappy with their ground-floor suite: entered via the dining room, and fronted by a roped-off area of the public terrace, it did not provide the privacy they wanted. Huw Phillips is the chef, serving "modern British cooking with French influences" on "well balanced menus", eg, apple and parsnip soup, or roasted goat's cheese on lettuce with hazelnut dressing; fillets of lemon sole on spinach with cardamom and ginger sauce; chargrilled steak with parsley butter; always a vegetarian dish. The restaurant has well-spaced tables and wide archways, and comments on the food range from "good, rather than excellent" to "exceptional". The wine list is "inexpensive and good", if a bit short for some tastes, and one couple in 2000 found the piped music "irritating and out of place". A limited selection of sandwiches is available during the day. The welcome can be "a little rushed", and one guest would have liked breakfast time to be extended, to allow for "a leisurely lie-in", as well as more information about local walks. The nearby village of Helford is "a delight". (*John Whiting, Bridget Bentley, J and A Markwick; also Andrew Long, and others*)

Open Mar–Oct.
Rooms 2 suites, 7 double, 1 single.
Facilities 2 lounges, bar, restaurant (light classical background music during dinner). 4-acre grounds. Private path to Coast Path and cove: bathing, sailing, fishing, windsurfing. Golf nearby. Unsuitable for &.
Location 12 miles SE of Helston. Take A3083 towards the Lizard. 1st left for St Keverne; follow signs for Manaccan/Gillan.
Restrictions No smoking: restaurant, 1 lounge, bedrooms. No children under 8. Dogs by arrangement; not in public rooms.
Credit cards MasterCard, Visa.
Terms D,B&B £70–£80. Set dinner £24. 3–7-night breaks. 1-night bookings sometimes refused.

GITTISHAM Devon   **Map 1**

Combe House   NEW   *Tel* (01404) 540400
Gittisham   *Fax* (01404) 46004
nr Honiton EX14 3AD   *E-mail* stay@thishotel.com
                                 Website www.thishotel.com

"We loved it," say inspectors of this Grade I listed Elizabethan manor house with 19th-century additions. Backed by venerable trees, it stands on a hill at the end of a mile-long drive bordered with camellias and rhododendrons, and is surrounded by a vast Devon estate of wood-land, meadows, pastures with Arabian horses. Inside are panelled public rooms, huge fireplaces with Grinling Gibbon-style carvings, family coats of arms, magnificent plastered ceilings, ancestral portraits, a sweeping oak staircase. "But the overall effect is not intimidatingly grand. The staff are particularly friendly, the antique furniture looks meant to be used, rather than admired, and arrangements of garden flowers are prolific. On a rainy day, our bedroom, with sprigged fabric on walls, paint in two shades of yellow, tall shuttered windows, a most comfortable bed, was a warm haven." The owners, Ruth and Ken Hunt, have spent two years restoring the house and grounds from a neglected condition. Their chef, Philip Leach, was *sous-chef* at the *Michelin*-starred *Horn of Plenty*, Gulworthy (*qv*): "Dining was a treat: we chose starters of seared scallops on saffron risotto, and crispy duck rolls; then best end of lamb on parsnip mash, and John Dory on coriander risotto; finally, glazed rhubarb tart, and cold rice pudding with home-made ice-cream. The Hunts' serious interest in wine is evident. Breakfast had yogurt, fruit, cereals, the usual fry-ups, good coffee. We thought the midweek break good value." Plenty of toys and games for children (the owners have two young sons), and an early supper is available. "You can walk your socks off on one of Devon's finest estates," the Hunts say (they offer their guests a two-hour "hawk walk"). Gittisham, a picturebook Devon village, has thatched cream-and green-walled cottages, a Saxon church, a gourmet food shop in an old bakery. In nearby Honiton, there are 38 antique shops. Nine golf courses are within easy reach, and the hotel has one and a half miles of private fishing on the River Otter. Dartmoor and Exeter are within 30 minutes' drive.

Open All year.
Rooms 3 suites, 12 double.
Facilities Great Hall, sitting room, bar (background music "according to guests' mood"), restaurant, private dining room; pianist Fri, Sat nights in winter. 10-acre garden in 3,500-acre estate. Private fishing on River Otter; coast 9 miles. Only restaurant suitable for &. Civil wedding licence.
Location 2 miles SW of Honiton. Train: Exeter, Tiverton parkway, Taunton.
Restrictions No smoking: restaurant, 4 bedrooms. "Well-behaved" dogs in 2 bedrooms, not in restaurant.
Credit cards MasterCard, Visa.
Terms [2000] B&B £60–£112.50; D,B&B £83–£130. Set lunch £15, dinner £32. Child accommodated in parents' room: under 10, £10. Midweek, seasonal breaks. Christmas, New Year packages. 1-night bookings refused Fri, Sat. *V*

GLEWSTONE Herefordshire   **Map 3**

Glewstone Court   *Tel* (01989) 770367
Glewstone   *Fax* (01989) 770282
nr Ross-on-Wye HR9 6AW   *E-mail* glewstone@aol.com
                        Website www.smoothhound.co.uk/hotels/glewston

A listed country house, less than half a mile from the A40, but secluded in its wooded grounds with mature fruit orchards, and a Cedar of Lebanon reputed to be the oldest in the West of England. Bill and Christine Reeve-Tucker (she is chef) are informal owners, who welcome families with children and dogs – they have three dogs and three cats of their own. The decor is homely, with log fires in drawing room and restaurant, photos, old pictures and an abundance of family clutter. The bedrooms are named after the owners' daughters and nieces: Lucy, Katriona, Jasmine, Clementine, etc. Large, if sometimes a bit "frayed around the edges", they have stencilled walls, floral drapes and a big bed. Some bathrooms may be "rather cramped". The large drawing room/bar has French windows opening on to the garden; informal lunches and dinners are served here, from an extensive bistro menu. The Georgian restaurant serves "modern English/classic French" meals with lots of choice, eg, ginger and lime marinated tiger prawns; escalope of Welsh organic veal with wild mushroom and Madeira cream; home-made Italian trifle. Sunday lunch is a family occasion, with reduced rates for children under ten, and no charge for occupants of high chairs. CDs of '20s, '30s and '40s music are played in the public rooms much of the time, but it will be turned off upon request. Breakfasts, served until 10 am, include thick granary toast and scrambled eggs with smoked salmon. The River Wye is nearby: canoeing and fishing can be arranged, and there is good walking. Well placed for touring Brecon Beacons, Hay-on-Wye, the Cotswolds. More reports, please.

Open All year, except Christmas.
Rooms 7 double, 1 single.
Facilities Hall, drawing room/bar, restaurant; private dining room; function facilities. Background jazz/swing in public rooms. 2-acre grounds: croquet. Only restaurant suitable for &.
Location 3 miles SW of Ross-on-Wye. Turn right off A40 Ross–Monmouth (dual carriageway), signposted Glewstone. Court ½ mile on left.
Credit cards Amex, MasterCard, Visa.
Terms [2000] B&B: single £45–£75, double £92–£108. Set dinner £27. Child accommodated in parents' room: B&B £15. 2-day breaks, except bank holidays. 1-night bookings sometimes refused weekends. *V* (Sun–Thurs, min. 2 nights, max. 5 nights)

GLOSSOP Derbyshire   Map 3

The Wind in the Willows   *Tel* (01457) 868001
Derbyshire Level   *Fax* (01457) 853354
off Sheffield Road   *E-mail* info@windinthewillows.co.uk
Glossop SK13 7PT   *Website* www.windinthewillows.co.uk

With a willow tree in its garden and bedrooms called after Kenneth Grahame characters, this Victorian house stands by a nine-hole golf course at the foot of Snake Pass, on the edge of the Peak District National Park. New owners, Ian and Alison Wilkinson, took it over as a going concern in late 1999. Little has changed in the decor, inspectors tell us: "Atmosphere of a smart family home. Delightful antiques everywhere; multi-patterned carpets and curtains in the lounge, also flowers, books, up-to-date glossy magazines, a huge oak dresser stocked with drinks, an open fire. Lots of dark wood and excellent lighting in our beautifully furnished bedroom, Toad Hall, and a copy of Thomas Crapper's *Flushed with Pride* in the bathroom. Dinner, in a blue and beige dining room, included smoked salmon with Derbyshire oatcakes; honey-roast duck on a bed of creamed parsnips and herbs – very tasty; warm apple and mincemeat parcels of filo pastry with ice-cream. Breakfast included packaged fruit juice, a faultless poached egg, commercial marmalade." Old Glossop is mainly 17th-century, with narrow streets and pretty houses; the town centre, and the cotton mills which brought prosperity, were built in the early 19th century. Chatsworth and Haddon Hall are 40 minutes' drive away. The bedrooms vary in size; Mr Mole, at the top, is "cosy". A visitor in 2000 wrote of a "pleasant and peaceful weekend", but thought the wine and food overpriced.

Open All year. Restaurant closed for lunch.
Rooms 12 double.
Facilities Drawing room with dispense bar, study, dining room; conference room. No background music. 1-acre garden, 4 acres fields; fishing lodge. Golf course adjacent; pot-holing, riding, gliding, boating nearby. Unsuitable for &.
Location 1 mile E of Glossop. Turn off A57 opposite *Royal Oak* pub. Hotel 400 yds on right. Train: Glossop; then taxi.
Restrictions No smoking: restaurant, study. No children under 10. No dogs in public rooms, unattended in bedrooms.
Credit cards All major cards accepted.
Terms B&B: single £74–£92, double £99–£119. Set dinner £24. *V*

GOLCAR West Yorkshire   Map 4

The Weavers Shed   *Tel* (01484) 654284
Knowl Road   *Fax* (01484) 650980
Huddersfield HD7 4AN   *E-mail* stephen@weavers-shed.demon.co.uk

"The food is terrific, and the rooms are a bargain, and intelligently planned to provide maximum comfort within a limited budget." An endorsement this year for this restaurant-with-rooms in a stone-built village south of Huddersfield. The owners and their staff are "really friendly", and "despite the high aspirations, there is a homely Yorkshire feel". The accent is on the modern cooking of the chef/*patron* Stephen Jackson and his co-chefs, Ian McGunnigle, Robert Jones and Cath Sill; each is responsible for one course. The garden supplies much of the fruit, herbs and vegetables used in the kitchen. A pamphlet in the bedrooms lists the local suppliers of meat, fish and game. The restaurant is in a former cloth-finishing mill, with a flagstone floor, old beams, and framed menus from famous restaurants on the walls. The cooking, on a "sensibly short" *carte*, is modern, with a choice of five first courses (eg, soft-boiled egg with truffle toasts; smoked haddock risotto), and six main ones (eg, braised lamb shank; roast supreme of local chicken). To end, you might choose warm Eccles cake, hot chocolate fondant or cheese. The bedrooms, each named after a local textile mill, are in a substantial house next door. Original features – old fireplaces, moulded ceilings, etc, have been retained. The largest room, Brook, is admired: "It looks across the garden to the terraces over the road. White walls, modern pine furniture, attractive and effective lighting; heavy cream curtains; a decanter of sherry; a useful information pack. A big bathroom with a generous supply of fluffy towels and endless hot water. Good breakfasts too, with properly cooked scrambled eggs, excellent bacon" (but the toast was thought disappointing this year). Golcar is not particularly attractive, but there is much to see nearby. (*David and Kate Wooff, and others*)

Open Hotel: all year, except 25/26, 31 Dec, 1 Jan. Restaurant closed Sun, Mon, 25, 26 Dec; lunch on Good Friday.
Rooms 5 double. In adjacent house. 2 on ground floor.
Facilities Lounge/bar, restaurant; light classical background music; function/conference room.
Location 3 miles W of Huddersfield. Turn on to B6111 off A42 towards Oldham. They will send detailed directions.
Restriction Guide dogs only.
Credit cards All major cards accepted.
Terms B&B: single £40–£50, double £55–£65. Set lunch £13.95; full alc £30. Weekend, midweek breaks. Honeymoon package.

GRANGE-IN-BORROWDALE Cumbria   Map 4

The Borrowdale Gates   *Tel* (017687) 77204
Grange-in-Borrowdale   *Fax* (017687) 77254
Keswick CA12 5UQ   *E-mail* hotel@borrowdale-gates.com
                                    Website www.borrowdale-gates.com

Many changes have taken place at Terry and Christine Parkinson's extended Victorian house: a major refurbishment of the public rooms, continuing renovation of bedrooms (some of these have, in the past, been thought not up to the rest), and the return of Michael Heathcote as chef. Most visitors continue to enjoy the "warm welcome" and, above all, the "wonderful setting", in wooded grounds on the edge of an ancient hamlet in the Borrowdale valley, at the head of Derwentwater. With craggy peaks close by, this is a good base for walking and climbing. The staff "are delightful", and the decor is traditional. Picture windows in the open-plan public areas make the most of the views; there are antiques, books and magazines, plants and flowers; log fires in winter. Everybody enjoys the dishes chosen from the long menu: starters like smoked haddock and leek risotto, or seared scallops; main dishes such as seared fillet of seabass on pesto-crushed potatoes, or chargrilled rib-eye beef steak; then a choice of elaborate puddings or farmhouse cheeses. Bread and cakes are home baked. The most characterful bedrooms are in the main building; others are in a 1970s extension and a wing. Many rooms have good views, but one overlooks the carpark. (*John and Margaret Myring, GF Garston, and others*)

Open 1 Feb–2 Jan.
Rooms 26 double, 3 single. 10 on ground floor.
Facilities Ramp. 4 lounges, bar, restaurant. No background music. 2-acre grounds. Derwentwater 10 mins' walk: boating, fishing, windsurfing, etc.
Location SW of Keswick. Take B5289; after 4 miles turn right over double hump-back bridge at Grange. Hotel ¼ mile on right. Bus or taxi from Keswick.
Restrictions No smoking in restaurant. No children under 7 in restaurant at night. No dogs.

Credit cards Amex, MasterCard, Visa.
Terms B&B £44.50–£72.50; D,B&B £59.50–£92.50. Set Sun lunch £15, dinner £30; full alc £45. Child accommodated in parents' room: under 3, free; 4–8, £17.50; 9–12, £22.50. Off-season breaks. Christmas, New Year packages. 1-night bookings sometimes refused.

GRASMERE Cumbria   Map 4

Michael's Nook   *Tel* (015394) 35496
Grasmere LA22 9RP   *Fax* (015394) 35645
                              E-mail m-nook@wordsworth-grasmere.co.uk
                              Website www.grasmere-hotels.co.uk

A substantial Lakeland stone house, built on the steep slopes of Greenbank Fell, and set in large, landscaped gardens. It is named for Wordsworth's shepherd, who dwelt "upon a forest side at Grasmere Vale". Visitors this year liked it a lot: "It has character. The food is great, if a little challenging. The welcome is pleasant. Our bedroom was bright, tastefully furnished; French windows led on to a sunny balcony." In the public areas, mahogany panelling and fine plasterwork set off antiques, Oriental rugs, prints and porcelain, collected by the owner for over 30 years, Reg Gifford, a former antiques dealer who also keeps Crufts-winning Great Danes. There is a grand piano in the lounge, a spinet in the hall, splendid flower displays, potted plants "and the occasional glimpse of an exotic cat". The *Michelin*-starred dining room, where white cornices contrast with deep red walls, has a collection of antique tables, a log fire. Chef Michael Wignall serves modern English food "with a French influence", eg, frogs' legs, morels and cep pasta; roast quail with herb dumplings; Bramley apple mousse. There is a separate menu of British cheeses. Vegetarians are catered for, given advance notice. The wide-ranging wine list includes many half bottles. The cooking is "superb, modish, technically impressive and attractively presented". Breakfast is "just as good" (freshly squeezed juices, leaf tea, impeccably cooked dishes and also cold meats, cheeses, etc), and the staff "go out of their way to comply with guests' requirements". A mahogany staircase leads up to bedrooms of varying sizes, furnished in elegant country house style; all bathrooms have now been modernised. One suite opens on to a terrace with views; the other has a private patio. Good walks start from the door; guests may use the health facilities and swimming pool at the sister hotel, the *Wordsworth*, down the hill nearby; and there is free golf at a local championship course. Wordsworth's house, Dove Cottage, and Beatrix Potter's home at Sawrey are nearby. (*David Wooff, and others*)

Open All year.
Rooms 2 suites, 12 double.
Facilities Hall, drawing room, bar, 2 dining rooms; conference room. No background music. 3-acre garden adjoining 10-acre woodland: croquet. Access to leisure facilities at the *Wordsworth* nearby. Free river/lake fishing nearby. Unsuitable for &. Civil wedding licence.
Location Turn up between *Swan* hotel and its carpark on A591 just N of village. Hotel 400 yds on right. Train/bus: Windermere; then bus/taxi.
Restrictions No smoking in restaurant. Children by arrangement. No dogs.

Credit cards All major cards accepted.
Terms D,B&B £90–£205. Set lunch £37.50, dinner £48. Midweek, weekend breaks off-season. Christmas, New Year house parties. Winter breaks. 1-night bookings refused Sat, bank holidays. *V*

White Moss House
Rydal Water, Grasmere LA22 9SE

Tel (015394) 35295
Fax (015394) 35516
E-mail sue@whitemoss.com
Website www.whitemoss.com

This grey stone, creeper-covered house was once bought by William Wordsworth for his son Willie. Wordsworth senior is said to have written some poems while sitting on its porch. Now owned by Peter and Sue Dixon, it is run as a restaurant-with-rooms, and it has had an entry in the *Good Food Guide* since 1974. Peter Dixon and co-chef Robert Simpson serve a fixed-price, five-course dinner at 7.30 for 8 pm (except Sundays) with no choice until dessert. They are admired for their "unshowy interpretation of English country house cooking", eg, courgette and chervil soup; stuffed brill wrapped in smoked salmon with a watercress and dill sauce; roast fillet of Cumbrian wild venison with blueberry and blackberry sauce; Mrs Beeton's chocolate pudding, or mango sorbet with baby pineapple. British cheeses with home-baked oat biscuits round off the meal. The wine cellar has a choice of over 300 bins, and plenty of wines are available by the glass. The house looks to Rydal Water across the A591, but windows are double-glazed, and there is little traffic at night. The most peaceful bedrooms are in the cottage up the hill, which is let as a unit. In the main house, bedrooms are small, with a tiny bathroom; they are packed with extras, including herbal bathsalts, fresh flowers, books, magazines, a sewing kit, trouser press, etc. Breakfast continues the English theme, with kippers, Cumberland sausage, etc. The Dixons tell us that *White Moss* is now a popular venue for private house parties, birthdays, reunions and other celebrations. Walking of all kinds is the main outdoor attraction; Wordsworth's two homes, Dove Cottage and Rydal Mount, are nearby, and the gardens of Rydal Hall are worth a visit.

Open Mid Feb–end Nov. Closed Christmas and New Year. Restaurant closed midday, Sun evening.
Rooms 7 double, 2-room cottage on hillside (10 mins' drive or via direct footpath).
Facilities 2 lounges, restaurant; terrace. ⅔-acre garden, 1-acre woodland. Near Rydal Water, River Rothay: swimming, fishing, boating. Free use of nearby leisure club: swimming pool, sauna, gym, etc. Unsuitable for &.
Location 1 mile S of Grasmere on A591 (heavy lorries banned; double glazing; cottage rooms quietest). Train: Windermere, 8 miles; then bus to door.
Restrictions No smoking in restaurant. No small children in restaurant. No dogs, except in cottage suite.
Credit cards MasterCard, Visa.
Terms [2000] D,B&B: £65–£90. Set dinner £29.50. Off-season breaks. 1-night bookings occasionally refused. *V*

GRASSINGTON North Yorkshire   Map 4

Ashfield House   BUDGET   *Tel/Fax* (01756) 752584
Summers Fold   *E-mail* keilin@talk21.com
Grassington,   *Website* www.ashfieldhouse.co.uk
nr Skipton BD23 5AE

A few yards from Grassington's main square, set up a little cobbled
drive, this small 17th-century guest house is owned and run by Linda
and Keith Harrison. "Their gentle, unassuming and friendly stamp is
everywhere," says a returning visitor this year. They provide "excellent value for money, combined with a warm welcome". Colourful
flower baskets around the front door welcome guests in summer; and
"even in the chilliest of Yorkshire winters, the old stone house is warm
and cosy". The decor is simple: bare stone walls, beams, old oak and
pine furniture, log fires, modern fabrics. Most of the small bedrooms
have an efficient shower *en suite*; one has a private bathroom adjacent.
The home-cooked dinner (no choice of main course) is served punc-
tually at 7 pm at separate tables. "Meals are straightforward; the food
is fresh, and beautifully cooked," eg, pear with blue cheese dressing,
or watercress soup; spiced chicken and potato casserole; baked chocolate tart, or cheese. Some ingredients are home-produced. The wines
"are brilliant value". The walled garden is a peaceful refuge when the
village is crowded with day-trippers. Rupert, the resident cat, presides.
"Good for walkers, drivers, cyclists, and lovers of Yorkshire comfort."
(*Trevor Lockwood, and others*)

Open Mid-Feb–New Year, but closed Christmas. Restaurant closed Sat, also
Wed evening May–Oct.
Rooms 7 double. No telephone (pay-phone available).
Facilities 2 lounges (1 with honesty bar), dining room; drying room. No back-
ground music. ⅓-acre garden. River, fishing ¼ mile. Unsuitable for ⅖.
Location 50 yds off village square: turn left into Summers Fold when coming
up main street. Private parking. Train/bus: Skipton, via Leeds; then bus.
Restrictions No smoking. No children under 5. Guide dogs only.
Credit cards MasterCard, Visa.
Terms B&B £33.50–£43.50. Set dinner £17. Child accommodated in parents'
room: 50% of adult rate. Seasonal breaks; Dickensian festivities in Dec. 1-
night bookings refused bank holidays, some Sats.

GREAT DUNMOW Essex   Map 2

The Starr   *Tel* (01371) 874321
Market Place   *Fax* (01371) 876337
Great Dunmow CM6 1AX   *E-mail* terry@starrdunmow.co.uk
                                        Website www.zynet.co.uk/menu/starr

Brian and Vanessa Jones have for many years run their restaurant-
with-rooms, which stands in the market place of this old Essex village.
The handsome green-walled building, fronted by window boxes, dates
in part from the 15th century. The beamed dining room, with its
timbered ceiling, uneven floors, small windows and bright conservatory extension, is admired for the eclectic cooking of Mark Fisher, on

a daily-changing menu. Seafood is a speciality, eg, scallops in filo pastry with fennel, tomato and chervil cream; roast seabass with chorizo, aubergine caviar and basil leaves. "If only there were more places like this," one visitor wrote, praising the "outstanding service and attention to detail". The bedrooms, all redecorated this year, are in the courtyard stable block; four are above bays where guests can park their car. Each has its own colour scheme, and is well supplied with local information, books, magazines, mineral water, etc. Some have antique or period furniture and a bed with a brass or wooden head; the Oak Room has a four-poster with a freestanding Victorian bath at its foot, as well as a separate shower room. The Blue Room, "very small", was thought over-priced this year. Only snags: some noise from passing traffic; no lounge (at quiet times, residents can sit in the conservatory). Good breakfasts. Easton Lodge, with beautiful gardens, is close by. In Little Dunmow, two and a half miles away, are the remains of Dunmow Priory, where an old custom allows a couple who have survived a year of marriage unscathed to claim a flitch of bacon. Stansted airport is 15 minutes' drive away. (*RH, and others*)

Open All year, except 2–6 Jan.
Rooms 8 double, all in rear courtyard.
Facilities Reception/bar (background music sometimes), restaurant, conservatory; function/conference facilities. Unsuitable for &.
Location Central (some traffic noise). Courtyard parking. Train: Bishops' Stortford, 8 miles, Stansted airport 15 miles; then taxi.
Restrictions No smoking: restaurant, bedrooms. No dogs in public rooms.
Credit cards All major cards accepted.
Terms [2000] B&B: single £65, double £100–£120. Set lunch £11.50–£26, dinner £25–£35. Weekend rate for diners. *V*

GREAT MILTON Oxfordshire   Map 2

Le Manoir aux Quat'Saisons   *Tel* (01844) 278881
Church Road   *Fax* (01844) 278847
Great Milton OX44 7PD
                                       E-mail lemanoir@blanc.co.uk
                                       Website www.manoir.co.uk

Ꙩ *César award in 1985*

"A really lovely place. It takes a Frenchman to bring out the best in an English country house hotel. And it is *so* child-friendly." An experienced traveller's comment this year on Raymond Blanc's famous domaine (Relais & Châteaux) in a village near Oxford. Sixteen years old this year, it is now managed by Philip Newman-Hall. Another guest wrote of the "very good taste" of the decor, and the "interesting and varied" gardens: "Lovely roses, acres of immaculately laid out produce; heavenly herbs, old apple tree; ancient pond." The restaurant, with two *Michelin* stars for M. Blanc's sophisticated cooking, eg, Jerusalem artichoke mousse; roast guinea fowl with a lime and ginger jus; caramel soufflé with prune and Armagnac ice-cream, attracts a wealthy international clientele, and lots of outside diners, leading sometimes to comments about "an impersonal feel". The conservatory-style restaurant serves a seasonally changing *à la carte* menu, a four-course *menu du jour* at lunchtime, and a seven-course *menu gourmand* (not for the faint of stomach) at night. Vegetarians are well catered for, and the very young have their own appetising menu: "We don't just tolerate children, we welcome them," is the *Manoir*'s philosophy. Toys and garden games are provided. Service "is impeccable throughout", with "slick valet parking", though one couple felt "rather like goldfish in a bowl, there are so many staff around all the time". Fine fabrics and antique furniture abound. The new bedrooms, round the courtyard, designed by Emily Todhunter, are "cutting edge modern". Opium, with saffron and red silk and warm lighting, looks over a Zen garden. Mermaid Rose has a "very romantic" bathroom, reached by spiral stairs, with side-by-side bathtubs. Other rooms are more traditional. One couple were surprised that their bedroom, two floors up (no lift), had its bathroom across a corridor that also served as a fire exit. (*DW, NM Mackintosh, and others*)

Open All year.
Rooms 9 suites, 23 double. 23 in garden extensions. Some on ground floor.
Facilities 2 lounges, champagne bar (background music at night), restaurant with conservatory; function room; cookery school. 27-acre grounds: gardens, croquet, tennis, lake, fishing. Civil wedding licence.
Location 8 miles SE of Oxford. From London: M40 exit 7, from Birmingham exit 8a; left on to A329 towards Wallingford; 2nd right to Great Milton. From Oxford: A40 exit for Thame; right on to A329 towards Wallingford, 2nd right. Train: Oxford; then taxi; limousine service from London, Gatwick, Heathrow.
Restrictions No smoking in restaurant; no dogs in house (free kennels).
Credit cards All major cards accepted.
Terms B&B: single/double £230–£340, suite £395–£550. Cooked breakfast £6 supplement. Set lunch £35; *menu gourmand* (lunch, dinner) £84; full alc £90. Midweek breaks, residential cookery courses. Christmas package. 1-night bookings refused Sat Apr–Sept.

GREAT SNORING Norfolk   Map 2

The Old Rectory   *Tel* (01328) 820597
Barsham Road   *Fax* (01328) 820048
Great Snoring   *E-mail* greatsnoringoldrectory@compuserve.com
Fakenham NR21 0HP   *Website* www.norfolkcountryhouse.co.uk

Admired again this year (it has had a *Guide* entry since 1984), this Tudor manor house, with Victorian additions, stands in a large walled garden with old trees (a magnificent beech is floodlit at night). It has two hexagonal towers and a terracotta frieze with alternating male and female carved heads, possible portraits of the Shelton family, the original owners. The current owners, Mrs Tooke and her daughter and son-in-law, Mr and Mrs Scoles, offer "country house accommodation", and the whole place can be taken over by a house party. It has polished floor tiles, lots of dark wooden furniture, and flowers; oriental carpets and rich red flowered wallpaper in the large lounge. The bedrooms vary in size: some are quite small; others are spacious. They are comfortable rather than luxurious, but all have bath, telephone and TV; early morning tea is brought to the room. A traditional English dinner is served in a room with mullioned windows, heavy beams, and oak tables set with good silver, plate and glass. No written menu and no choice of main course, which might be casserole of  venison or ostrich stroganoff; four starters to choose from, eg, baked banana and stilton fondue; desserts include mulled wine pudding and apple charlotte. A good base for the Heritage Coast, Sandringham and Holkham Hall. (*H Norrington, and others*)

Open All year, except 24–27 Dec. Dining room closed midday.
Rooms 6 double.
Facilities Drawing room, dining room. No background music. 1½-acre walled garden. Golf nearby. Unsuitable for &.
Location Behind church on road to Barsham, in village off A148, 3 miles NE of Fakenham. Train: King's Lynn, 23 miles.
Restrictions No smoking in dining room. Children by arrangement. No dogs.
Credit cards Amex, MasterCard, Visa.
Terms B&B: single £71–£78, double £93–£101. Set dinner £25. Special breaks by arrangement.

GRIMSTON Norfolk   **Map 2**

Congham Hall   NEW   Tel (01485) 600250
Lynn Road   Fax (01485) 601191
Grimston, King's Lynn PE32 1AH   *E-mail* reception@conghamhallhotel.com

"The setting is idyllic. This must be one of the best hotels in the country." A visitor in 2000 was bowled over by this handsome Georgian manor (Pride of Britain), on an unspoilt estate near King's Lynn. It stands in large, manicured grounds, with a flower-filled front garden, a large herb and flower garden, a swimming pool (said to be in need of repair), and a tennis court. "The new owners, Von Essen Hotels, have given *Congham Hall* a fresh lease of life, and it is flourishing under the charming manager, Andrew Chantrell, and his keen young staff. The garden suite could not be bettered as regards space, decor, and attention to detail. From the conservatory restaurant, we watched wildlife – barn owls, pheasants, squirrels, rabbits – and a sinking sun. The chef, James Parkinson (formerly of *L'Aubergine*, London), deserves praise for his imaginative cooking: starters of seared scallops and potted crabs were both superb; of the main dishes we liked the pan-fried halibut, the honey-roasted duck, the vegetarian dishes (all served fashionably with elaborate sauces featuring ceps and black lentils). The assiette of four rhubarb puddings was scrumptious, ditto pavé of chocolate, and hazelnut pyramid. Home-made ice-creams are all wonderful. Breakfast was excellent, too: delicious fruit compote, granary bread, home-made marmalade." Other guests wrote of their "well-appointed bedroom", the "courteous, attentive service", but a disappointing cooked breakfast. The spacious public rooms have flowers and herb baskets everywhere, modern nude bronzes (one visitor though they struck "a jarring note"). A white-painted "serpent" staircase leads to chintzy bedrooms, stocked with flowers, pot-pourri, books, etc (some rooms are small). Conferences and weddings are catered for. Nearby attractions include Sandringham, Houghton Hall, the RSPB reserve at Titchwell; King's Lynn has an attractive waterfront and many fine old buildings. (*Alan Blyth, G and A Smeed*)

Open All year.

Rooms 2 suites (1 on ground floor), 11 double, 1 single. (More suites planned.)

Facilities Hall/lounge, lounge, bar, restaurant; function/conference facilities. No background music. 30-acre grounds: herb garden, unheated swimming pool, tennis, parklands, orchards, stables. Cricket pitch adjacent; nature reserves, fishing, golf, riding nearby; coast, sandy beaches 12 miles. Unsuitable for &. Civil wedding licence.

Location 6 miles NE of King's Lynn. Right towards Grimston off A148; hotel 2½ miles on left. Do not go to Congham. Train: King's Lynn; then taxi.

Restrictions No smoking: restaurant, bedrooms. No children under 7. No dogs in house (kennels available).

Credit cards All major cards accepted.

Terms B&B: single £85, double £130–£175, suite £205–£230. Set meals (2 to 3 courses): lunch £11.50–£15.50, dinner £27.50–£34; full alc £45. 2-days half-board rates from £190 per person. 1-night bookings refused Sat. ***V***

GUILDFORD Surrey *See SHORTLIST*   **Map 2**

GULWORTHY Devon   **Map 1**

The Horn of Plenty   NEW   Tel/Fax (01822) 832528
Gulworthy   *E-mail* enquiries@thehornofplenty.co.uk
nr Tavistock PL19 8JD   *Website* www.thehornofplenty.co.uk

Michelin-*starred restaurant-with-rooms 3 miles W of Tavistock. In creeper-covered stone Georgian house, up long drive through 4-acre grounds with garden, orchards, stunning views of Tamar valley. Chef Peter Gorton is now co-owner with Paul and Andie Roston (they also own the* Carved Angel *restaurant, Dartmouth). Ambitious cooking; "exceptionally helpful" staff. "Light classical" background music throughout public rooms. 10 bedrooms; 6 spacious ones, with balcony, small bathroom, are in stable block; some have* & *access. Renominated with some reservations: "Noisy water system; restaurant a bit dismal after dark, and meal service sometimes slow." Closed Christmas, 2–15 Jan; restaurant closed Mon midday. Smoking in drawing room only. No children under 10 in restaurant at night. No dogs in public rooms. Amex, MasterCard, Visa accepted. B&B: single £95–£190, double £120–£200. Set lunch £23.50, dinner £37. More reports, please.*

****

Hotel in Somerset. The information book in the hotel bedroom contained a number of restrictive rules, eg, don't touch the fridge except to remove drinks; if you open any drink that you have brought in, a corkage charge of £3 is made; don't entertain any friends in your room if you have come in a group.

****

HALIFAX West Yorkshire   Map 4

Holdsworth House   *Tel* (01422) 240024
Holdsworth   *Fax* (01422) 245174
Halifax HX2 9TG   *E-mail* info@holdsworthhouse.co.uk

"Truly a magnificent house, with public rooms and bedrooms full of
character and arranged with exquisite taste. The atmosphere is
unique. The decor cannot be faulted, and maintenance is good. A
delicious meal." A trusted *Guide* correspondent writes in praise of
this 17th-century manor house. The outlook from the sides and back
is uninspiring, however, due to the location north of the city centre.
The hotel has been owned by the Pearson family for over 30 years.
Kim Pearson and Gail Moss (they are sisters) are currently in charge,
with manager Peter Phillips and a "polite but unobtrusive staff".
During the week, it has a mainly business clientele, and it caters for
conferences; good-value breaks are offered to weekend visitors. Old
buildings frame an attractive courtyard. Inside, panelling, mullioned
windows, oil paintings, log fires and oak furniture "make you feel that
you have stepped into a Dutch painting". The lounge/bar, in a converted stable, is "light, smart, and immensely pleasant to sit in". The
dining rooms are formal with candlelight, fresh flowers, sparkling
glass and silverware and impeccable napery. The chef, Neal Birtwell,
serves modern dishes on a four-course menu, eg, Thai spiced prawns
with lime; caramelised shank of Yorkshire lamb with potato gratin.
But he will produce a simple grill on request. Desserts are prepared
to order, including baked apricot and cardamom charlotte with
mulled winter fruits; chocolate brûlée with a caramelised orange
sauce The bedrooms, in a well-crafted modern wing, vary greatly in
size (some, though attractive, may be a bit small for comfort).
Superior rooms have a brass or a four-poster bed and "delightful
pieces of furniture". Good modern bathrooms. Children are welcomed, as are dogs by prior arrangement. The gardens have been
landscaped to a 17th-century design; a Grade II listed Jacobean
gazebo can be hired for small weddings and dinner parties. Nearby
attractions include the Eureka Children's Museum in Halifax, the
Brontë parsonage at Haworth, and the David Hockney art gallery at
Saltaire. (*Francine Walsh*)

Open All year, except Christmas. Restaurant closed midday Sat, Sun.
Rooms 5 suites, 23 double, 12 single. 2 adapted for &.
Facilities Lounge/bar, restaurant (jazz/classical background music); 4 private
dining rooms, function room. 4-acre garden: gazebo. Golf, clay-pigeon shooting, go-karting nearby. Civil wedding licence.
Location 2½ miles N of centre. Take A629 Keighley road. Right after
1½ miles on to Shay Lane. Hotel 1 mile on right. Train: Halifax, Bradford, 5
miles, Leeds, 13 miles; then taxi.
Restrictions No smoking: restaurant, some bedrooms. No dogs in public
rooms.
Credit cards All major cards accepted.
Terms B&B: single £85, double £104, suite £134; D,B&B: single £90, double
£122, suite £148. English breakfast £8.25. Set lunch £10; full alc £32.75.

HALNAKER West Sussex   Map 2

The Old Store BUDGET   *Tel/Fax* (01243) 531977
Stane Street, Halnaker   *E-mail* alandavis@theoldstore.fsnet.co.uk
nr Chichester PO18 0QL

A modest B&B, run by Alan and Iris Davis in a red brick 18th-century
Grade II listed house, once the village store and bakery of the adjacent
Goodwood estate. "It makes a good alternative to the pricey and generally inadequate hostelries of nearby Chichester, and it has the added
attraction of rural peace," said the nominator. This is now endorsed:
"Good value for money; a welcoming hostess. From our room we had
a view across fields to Chichester Cathedral." The bedrooms have a
shower *en suite*; one is suitable for a family. The "excellent breakfast"
includes free-range eggs cooked in many ways, locally made
sausages, home-made marmalade. Plenty of interesting sightseeing:
Arundel, Petworth, Fishbourne Roman palace, etc. (*Pat Harman, BM*)

Open All year, except possibly mid-Jan–mid-Feb.
Rooms 1 family, 5 double, 1 single. 1 on ground floor. No telephone.
Facilities Lounge, breakfast room. ¼-acre garden. Unsuitable for &.
Location 4 miles NE of Chichester, off A285 to Petworth. Bus from Chichester.
Restrictions No smoking. No dogs.
Credit cards MasterCard, Visa.
Terms [2000] B&B: single £22–£28, double £50–£55. Child accommodated
in parents' room: under 5, free; 5–12, 50% of adult rate. *V*

HAMBLETON Rutland   Map 2

Hambleton Hall   *Tel* (01572) 756991
Hambleton   *Fax* (01572) 724721
Oakham LE15 8TH
                                    E-mail hotel@hambletonhall.com
                                    Website www.hambletonhall.com

꘡ *César award in 1985*

"Everything was perfect," one visitor wrote of her stay at this "immaculately presented" Victorian pile (Relais & Châteaux). Here, Tim and
Stefa Hart "benignly and alertly" preside, along with Rupert Elliott, the
manager since October 1999. Others sang the praises of the "impeccable service", and the "glorious setting". "Yes, it is expensive, but worth
every penny." Surrounded by manicured gardens with mature trees, it
is on a peninsula in Rutland Water, the largest man-made lake in northern Europe, with fishing, sailing and water sports. The swimming pool
and terrace, where breakfast or drinks may be ordered in fine weather,
"are perfectly placed from which to enjoy the views". The decor is
sophisticated: fine fabrics, good antiques and paintings; flowers everywhere. The *Michelin*-starred cooking of Aaron Patterson is appreciated
too ("fish is a particularly strong suit"). "Dinner was the best ever.
Poached tails of langoustines with chilled essence of tomato made a
perfect start – each flavour separate, intense, perfectly balanced. Then,
roasted fillet of seabass with basil-flavoured pasta and a fennel and
vanilla sauce – heaven! Caramelised lemon tart with a compote of
blackberries gave a wonderfully fresh finish. The wine waiter

recommended a different glass of wine with each course – an excellent idea. The set lunch was equally impressive and tremendous value." Only niggles: "the *amuse gueules* and petits fours were always the same"; and the "superb rolls available at dinner are not served at breakfast". "Every possible luxury" is supplied in the bedrooms. The best ones overlook Rutland Water ("even the loo has a view"); some, particularly one called Chota (Urdu for "small"), are not large. The new Croquet Pavilion suite guarantees extra seclusion, and would be good for a family – children are welcomed. Oakham is a famous fox-hunting centre. Some famous stately homes – Burghley, Belton, Boughton and Belvoir – are nearby, and so is the superb garden of the late Geoff Hamilton at Barnsdale. Tim Hart also owns a restaurant, *Hart's*, in Nottingham. (*Sue Davies, Alan Blyth, Janet L Sleep, and others*)

Open All year.
Rooms One 2-bedroomed suite, with kitchenette, in croquet pavilion (40 metres), 15 double.
Facilities Lift, ramp. Hall, drawing room, bar, restaurant; small conference facilities, 2 private dining rooms. No background music. 17-acre grounds: swimming pool, tennis, cycling; helipad; lake: trout-fishing, windsurfing, sailing. Riding, shooting by arrangement. Civil wedding licence.
Location 3 miles E of Oakham. Follow Hambleton sign off A606 to Stamford. Train: Peterborough/Kettering/Oakham (branch line); then taxi.
Restrictions No smoking: restaurant, 1 bedroom. "Children in the restaurant must be old enough to sit on a proper chair." "Well behaved dogs" by arrangement; not in public rooms.
Credit cards MasterCard, Visa.
Terms B&B: single £140–£160, double £170–£320, suite £450–£550. Set lunch £16.50–£35, dinner £35–£40; full alc £50. Winter rates. Christmas package. 1-night bookings sometimes refused Sat.

HAMSTERLEY FOREST Co. Durham   **Map 4**

Grove House   BUDGET   *Tel* (01388) 488203
Hamsterley Forest   *Fax* (01388) 488174
nr Bishop Auckland DL13 3NL   *E-mail* xov47@dial.pipex.com
                                      Website www.come.to/grovehouse

A place of "exceptional delights", says a visitor this year of Helene Close's unusual guest house. He relished its "away-from-it allness", deep in a green forest. The accommodation is in one wing of a grandiose shooting lodge, built about 1820 by a member of the Surtees family. Surrounded by beautifully kept gardens, it stands in a valley with two small rivers on either side; beyond are 5,000 acres of mixed woodland and moorland. The house is full of treasures: the remarkable backplate of the dining room fire, brought from France by the original owners, was once in a royal palace of the Valois; much of the furniture, including Art Deco chairs, 1920s lamp fittings, etc, was brought from Germany by Mrs Close's grandfather, escaping in 1939. The bedrooms are "large, stylish, comfortable and home-like, with such generous touches as lotions and potions in big bottles in the bathroom, rather than teeny packages". But one visitor reported a few lapses in the housekeeping this year. The lounge is "very comfy"; with open fire, TV, stereo, family mementos. Dinner is served at flexible times in a "splendidly eccentric" room hung with portraits. "The five-course evening meal (no choice) was delicious: mushrooms picked that morning in the forest, and sautéed; duck with a blackcurrant coulis; a delectable sweet of baked bananas with a caramel sauce, lemon ice and pancake; a selection of local cheeses. Not hotel food at all, but sympathetic home-entertaining cooking." No licence; bring your own wine. At breakfast "the sideboard is weighed down with fruit, cereals, etc, and there is a wide range of cooked dishes to follow". "Superb value for money." Good walking; mountain bikes can be borrowed. The former gardener's cottage is let on a self-catering basis. Barnard Castle is 20 minutes' drive away; Durham is half an hour. (*HR, Dr A Bowen, and others*)

Open Mid-Jan–mid-Dec. Dining room closed for lunch (packed lunch available).
Rooms 3 double. No telephone/TV. 1 self-catering cottage.
Facilities 2 lounges, dining room. No background music. 1½-acre grounds. Unsuitable for &.
Location From A68 turn W to Hamsterley village (ignore signs for Hamsterley Forest). Through village, continue for 2 miles to sign for "The Grove"; follow road to right, then left; after ½ mile, turn right at *Grove House* sign. Continue *c.* 2½ miles. House is across old stone bridge.
Restrictions No smoking. No children under 8. No dogs. No drinks licence.
Credit cards None accepted.
Terms B&B £23.50–£38.50. Set dinner £19.50. Child accommodated in parents' room: B&B £18. Weekly rates.

HARROGATE North Yorkshire   Map 4

Ascot House   NEW   *Tel* (01423) 531005
53 Kings Road   *Fax* (01423) 503523
Harrogate HG1 5HJ
                                  E-mail admin@ascothouse.com
                                  Website www.harrogate.com/ascot

In the middle of the old spa town, a short walk from the conference and exhibition centre, this Victorian house is now a small hotel managed by its owner, Stephen Johnson. "He is very pleasant," says a regular *Guide* correspondent. "We had booked two singles but were upgraded to two nice doubles, each with a good bathroom. In the distinctly elegant dining room we had good, genuine food, including an excellent breakfast, with helpful service. Highly recommended for anyone wanting modest and friendly comfort." The decor is traditional (patterned carpets and an open fire in the sitting room, chandeliers and a moulded ceiling in the restaurant). The set-price menus, with choice, are traditional too, eg, liver pâté with Cumberland sauce; grilled lamb cutlets with parsley butter. The *carte* is more adventurous (dishes like deep-fried baby camembert with a red onion marmalade; lemon sole with a cream prawn, saffron and chive sauce). Cots, high chairs and toys are provided for young children. Small conferences are held, "but they are not obtrusive". (*Ran Ogston; also C and R Stone*)

Open All year, except New Year, and possibly 27 Jan–11 Feb. Lunch not served.
Rooms 15 double, 4 single.
Facilities Lounge, bar lounge (soft taped music), restaurant; banqueting room. Small garden. Unsuitable for &. Civil wedding licence applied for.

Location Central (light sleepers should ask for a side or back room). Follow signs for centre/conference centre. In Kings Rd, pass exhibition centre; *Ascot House* on left, immediately after open parking area up hill. Carpark.
Restriction No dogs in public rooms.
Credit cards All major cards accepted.
Terms B&B: single £49.50–£61, double £75–£95; D,B&B (min. 2 nights): single £59.50–£76.50, double £98–£126. Set dinner £15.50; full alc £23. Child accommodated in parents' room: under 14, B&B £5. Stay 6 nights, get B&B free on the 7th. Christmas package. *V*

See also SHORTLIST

HARTEST Suffolk   **Map 2**

The Hatch   BUDGET   *Tel/Fax* (01284) 830226
Pilgrims Lane, Cross Green
Hartest IP29 4ED

"Marvellous." "A more peaceful place you could not find. The love of Bridget and Robin Oaten for their house subtly envelops all guests. Everything gleams with cleanliness and care." Rave reviews continue for this 15th-century timber-framed and thatched cottage on what was once the Pilgrims' Way (it is now a dead-end lane). The Oatens made their reputation at the *César*-winning *Hancocks*, near Cranbrook in Kent, and they have imbued their new venture with the same care and attention to detail. Both the dining room and drawing room have an inglenook fireplace, fine antiques, and views of "idyllic Suffolk countryside". The "beautiful bedrooms" have goose-down duvets, linen sheets, fresh flowers, a decanter of sherry, fruit, sweets, quality toiletries. "Old beams add to the ambience; tall people should mind their head." The suite has its own entrance off the drive. The "lovely garden" is filled with old English roses, and a large paddock is populated by "splendid grazing horses". Breakfast also receives its share of plaudits: "One of the best we have ever had," wrote one couple. "The highlight of our day," echoed visitors from Germany, who loved the home-baked scones, chocolate muffins, and the daily-changing selection of fresh fruit and compotes. Bridget Oaten occasionally prepares an evening meal by arrangement, particularly for regular clients and *Guide* readers. She describes her cooking as "English with a French accent and a few North American influences". There is a good pub, *The Crown*, on the village green, and plenty of restaurants are within 15 minutes' drive. Bury St Edmunds is seven miles away; Ickworth (National Trust) and Melford Hall, a turreted Tudor mansion, are also within striking distance. (*JD Crosland, Vonnie Haisell, Karin and Jörg Wöhrag; also PE Carter*)

Open All year, except Christmas, occasional closures; dinner sometimes served.
Rooms 1 suite (on ground floor), 1 double, 1 single. Telephone in suite.
Facilities Drawing room, sitting room, dining room. 1-acre garden and meadows.
Location From Bury St Edmunds take A143 S towards Haverhill. Left on B1066. Left after 6 miles, after Hartest sign, at cluster of cottages on corner; house is 1st down lane, on right.

Restrictions No smoking. No children 2–9. Dogs in suite only; not in public rooms.
Credit cards None accepted.
Terms [2000] (*Not VAT-rated*) B&B: single £30–£45, double/suite £56–£65. Set dinner £12.50–£25. Weekly rates. 1-night bookings sometimes refused Sat.

HARTFIELD East Sussex   Map 2

Bolebroke Mill   *Tel/Fax* (01892) 770425
Edenbridge Road   *E-mail* b+b@bolebrokemill.demon.co.uk
Hartfield TN7 4JP

"An idyllic spot." "Most romantic." Set well back from a busy road up a winding track, this Domesday-old water mill, its Elizabethan barn and its mill house have been skilfully converted by David and Christine Cooper, into a "most appealing" B&B. A tree-lined stream, with ducks and geese, flows under the mill towards the Ashdown Forest; its "new" building (17th-century) continued to grind corn until 1948. It was used as a location for the 1995 film *Carrington* (starring Emma Thompson and Jonathan Pryce). Each of the five bedrooms is different, "furnished with cottagey charm and bristling with dried flower arrangements and rustic beams". They all have facilities *en suite*, TV, a coolbox with fresh milk for early morning tea. Three rooms, including the Honeymooners' Hayloft with its four-poster bed, are in a barn. Two are up "seriously steep" loft ladders in the white weather-boarded mill. Both buildings have a spacious sitting room, "with comfortable sofas and bookshelves, amid a startling array of agricultural implements, assorted hunting trophies, African carvings and weaponry, suggesting a former overseas life". The "excellent breakfast" has won awards; it is communally served in the tile-hung brick Mill House. Imaginative creations, such as huge stuffed mushrooms or fruit pancakes, are offered as alternatives to a routine fry-up; jams are home made. Its steep stairs and changes of level make *Bolebroke* "suitable only for the nimbler sort of guest", but those who are sufficiently spry agree: "Very quiet at night; it is a memorable hideaway." Pooh bridge at AA Milne's former home down the road is much visited, leading to defoliation of the nearby trees; you should bring your own twigs if you wish to play Pooh Sticks. (Chartwell, Sissinghurst, Glyndebourne, Hever Castle, and countless other attractions are nearby) (*A and CR*).

Open 10 Feb–19 Dec.
Rooms 5 double. 2 in mill, 3 in barn. No telephone.
Facilities 2 lounges, breakfast room. No background music. 6½-acre grounds: garden, millpond, rowing, woodland walks. Unsuitable for &.
Location A264 East Grinstead–Tunbridge Wells for 6 miles. Right at crossroads on to B2026 towards Hartfield. After 1 mile, just past Perryhill Nursery, left into unmade lane. Follow signs.
Restrictions No smoking. No children under 8. No dogs.
Credit cards Amex (*5% surcharge*), MasterCard, Visa (*2½% surcharge on both*).
Terms B&B: double £65–£78; single occupancy £5 less. 10% reduction for 3-day stay. 1-night bookings refused weekends.

HARVINGTON Worcestershire   Map 3

The Mill at Harvington   *Tel/Fax* (01386) 870688
Anchor Lane   *Website* www.millatharvington.co.uk
Harvington, nr Evesham WR11 5NR

Converted from a Georgian house and red brick mill, this hotel has
stood the test of time and nature, having been seriously damaged by
the flooding of the Vale of Evesham in 1998. It is now fully restored,
and the owners, Simon and Jane Greenhalgh and Richard and Susan
Yeomans, with their "friendly staff", provide an atmosphere of "quiet
elegance". "They are very much in sympathetic control," says a visitor this year. "We were accommodated with imagination." All the
bedrooms overlook the wooded garden and river, where guests may
fish for chub, roach, dace and barbel; enjoy such wildlife as herons,
hare, pheasants and minks; or simply enjoy the recently extended
grounds. There have been changes in the kitchen: Adrian Billings, ex-
Café Roux, Amsterdam, has joined the team, the dinner menu is now
fixed-price, and Simon Greenhalgh writes that the dishes are "more
subtle and varied", eg, fish cakes on roasted black olives and tomatoes
with a basil sauce; fillet of seabass with roast couscous and citrus
sauce. But a simpler meal of home-made soup, and prime Scottish fillet steak is always available. The wine list is "extensive, with a modest mark-up". Light lunches and dinners are available in the less
formal *Chestnut Tree.* Breakfasts, which include freshly squeezed
orange juice, are enjoyed. Local attractions include Stratford-upon-
Avon, only ten miles away, the medieval castles of Warwick,
Kenilworth and Sudeley, and the Cotswolds. (*JR, and others*)

Open All year, except Christmas.
Rooms 21 double. 6 in garden annexe. Some on ground floor.
Facilities Lounge, conservatory/café, restaurant; private dining room, func-
tion facilities. No background music. 8-acre grounds: heated swimming pool,
tennis, 200 yds river frontage, fishing.
Location On banks of River Avon. Turn SE off Norton–Bidford Rd, opposite
Harvington village. Down Anchor Lane; hotel 3rd left. Train: Evesham;
then taxi.
Restrictions No smoking in restaurant. No children under 10. No dogs.
Credit cards All major cards accepted.
Terms B&B: single £63–£78, double £103–£145. Set lunch £14.25, dinner
£22.75; full alc £31. 2-night breaks. 1-night bookings sometimes
refused. *V*

HARWICH Essex   Map 2

The Pier at Harwich   *Tel* (01255) 241212
The Quay   *Fax* (01255) 551922
Harwich CO12 3HH   *E-mail* info@thepieratharwich.co.uk
                                    Website www.talbooth.com

A restaurant-with-rooms on Harwich's waterfront. Its decor is "both
nautical and tasteful", says a recent visitor. "Food, service and accommodation are all excellent." Others wrote of "first-rate meals, with

wines to match, at not outrageous prices." The handsome Victorian building overlooks the confluence of the Stour and the Orwell. It was built to accommodate passengers on the packet boat to Holland, and is now owned by the Milsom family of *Maison Talbooth*, Dedham (*qv*). The manager/chef, Chris Oakley, runs it with a "cheerful and informal" staff. There are two restaurants. The *Harbourside* on the first floor overlooks the harbour, and it serves oysters, lobster from its own tanks, and fish cooked in many ways. The approach is flexible: many dishes can be ordered in a large or a smaller portion, priced accordingly. A pianist sometimes plays. On the ground floor, the cheerful *Ha'penny Bistro* provides fish and chips, baked haddock, chargrilled steak and so on. The bar is smart, with smoked glass, granite bar tops and a copper ceiling. Breakfasts have good cooked dishes but no fruit or yogurt. The bedrooms, on the top floor, have a pastel decor, and are "well furnished, large and smart". Front ones have "an exciting view of the estuary and its shipping". With the acquisition of *The Angel* pub next door, seven new bedrooms and an attractive, large lounge were added in 2000. (*RH, CR*)

Open All year.
Rooms 4 suites, 10 double. 7 in adjacent building. 1 on ground floor.
Facilities Lounge, restaurant (varied background music during week; live pianist Sat), bistro. Unsuitable for &.
Location On quay. Parking. Train: Harwich station (5 mins).
Restrictions Smoking discouraged in restaurant. Guide dogs only.
Credit cards All major cards accepted.
Terms (*Excluding 10% service charge on meals*) B&B: single £68, double £91, suite £121–£161. English breakfast £5.50. Set lunch £18, dinner £20.50; full alc from £35.

See also SHORTLIST

HASSOP Derbyshire   **Map 3**

Hassop Hall   *Tel* (01629) 640488
Hassop   *Fax* (01629) 640577
nr Bakewell DE45 1NS   *E-mail* hassophallhotel@btinternet.com

The grey, bow-windowed building is a stately pile, full of history, but it has a "real family atmosphere", says an inspector this year. She liked the "absence of the trappings of self-conscious luxury", and the unpretentious style. The owner, Thomas Chapman, has presided since 1975, and his son and daughter are in attendance. Built of local stone, it is quietly set outside Baslow, and has "glorious views of Derbyshire fields". The public rooms have carved plaster ceilings, stone fireplaces, good views, also open fires and family photos; there is a panelled bar. Earlier visitors wrote of the "friendly service, and thoroughly nice atmosphere", and this is now endorsed: "Our cases were carried, we were given tea at 6.30 pm without demur; Mr Chapman came to chat, without being intrusive. In the long, attractive dining room, the menu was traditional: we had starters of potted shrimps, and asparagus; then salmon (fat and delicious), and halibut

meunière (less good)." Desserts come on a trolley. Breakfast (continental or English; and "fine, apart from the marmalade") is served in
bedrooms (they have a traditional chintzy decor; best ones look over
fields with sheep). Hotel guests have access to a 60-acre arboretum.
Local stately homes include Haddon Hall, Chatsworth, Eyam Hall.
Sheffield is 17 miles away.

Open All year, except Christmas/New Year; restaurant closed Sun evening/
midday Mon.
Rooms 1 suite, 13 double.
Facilities Lift, ramp. Hall (pianist Fri, Sat evening). Sitting room, bar, 3 dining
rooms; conference facilities; ballroom. 5½-acre grounds: tennis, helipad;
access to arboretum; golf nearby. Civil wedding licence.
Location 2½ miles N of Bakewell. From M1 exit 29: Chesterfield town centre;
A619 to Baslow, A623 to Calver. Left at traffic lights on to B6001. Hassop
1 mile.
Restrictions Smoking discouraged in restaurant, banned in sitting room. No
dogs in public rooms.
Credit cards All major cards accepted.
Terms [2000] B&B: single £86.95–£148.95, double £94.90–£158.90;
D,B&B: single £113.70–£182.20, double £148.40–£225.40. Child accommo-
dated in parents' room: ⅔ of adult rate. Set lunch: weekdays £15.90, weekends
£20.95; dinner: weekdays £26.75, weekends £33.25. £5 reduction per person
for 2-night stays 1 Nov–31 Mar.

HASTINGS East Sussex *See SHORTLIST*   **Map 2**

HATHERSAGE Derbyshire   **Map 3**

The George NEW   *Tel* (01433) 650436
Hathersage S32 1BB   *Fax* (01433) 650099
                                          E-mail info@george-hotel.net
                                          Website www.george-hotel.net

Acquired in 1996 by Eric Marsh of *The Cavendish*, Baslow (*qv*), and
given a massive facelift, this old inn was much enjoyed by inspectors
in 2000: "The young manager, Gerald Chislett, runs a tight ship, and
standards are high. The decor is sympathetic with the age of the building, preserving original stone walls, oak beams, open fires; and there
are many good antiques. The restaurant is stunningly decorated, in
dark blue and terracotta. It is open much of the day, serving breakfast
until noon, coffee, snacks, lunches. Our dinner was mostly very good:
succulent breast of guinea fowl, and superb ham and pistachio terrine;
robust beef cooked in with root vegetables, fish not so good; desserts
'sinful but worth it'. Breakfast has poor fruit juice, very good pastries,
some of the hot dishes a bit hit and miss. Our bedroom was large and
light, with a pristine decor, pleasant pictures, lovely fabrics, a functional bathroom." The village has connections with Charlotte Brontë,
who often visited – she called it Morton in *Jane Eyre* (the hotel was
owned by one James Eyre in her day).

Open All year.
Rooms 15 double, 4 single.

Facilities Lounge, restaurant (background CDs); 2 function rooms. Courtyard. Only restaurant suitable for ♿.
Location 8 miles N of Bakewell, in village centre (rear rooms quietest). Parking.
Restrictions No smoking in restaurant. No dogs.
Credit cards All major cards accepted.
Terms B&B: single £59.50–£79.50, double £89.50–£119.50; D,B&B £69.75–£99.50 per person. Full alc £35. Midweek reductions; off-season break: stay 2 nights, get the 3rd free. Christmas package. *V*

HATTON Warwickshire   Map 3

Northleigh House   BUDGET   *Tel* (01926) 484203
Five Ways Road   *Fax* (01926) 484006
Hatton, Warwick CV35 7HZ   *Website* www.northleigh.co.uk

Set on a small road in countryside just north of Warwick, this unpretentious B&B is run by its owner, Sylvia Fenwick. It continues to please most *Guide* readers, though there is one report this year of a cold room. Most visitors write of "a warm welcome" and praise the "comfortable bedrooms". Each has a different colour theme. The Blue Room (the priciest) has a kingsize bed in a blue-curtained alcove, blue sofas, pine furniture, a huge bathroom and a kitchenette. Others include Chinese, Gold, Italian, Poppy, etc. Each has a hair-dryer and a fridge. The panelled lounge has a wood-burning stove, books and original paintings. The "excellent English breakfast", with a toaster on each table, is served in a spacious room overlooking the garden. A home-cooked evening meal or supper tray can be arranged; a local map and information about local pubs and restaurants is provided. Mrs Fenwick writes in the brochure: "If you want anything – a large table to work at perhaps, a hot-water bottle or laundry service – just ask. We are happy to help." There is a pleasant garden, and a fenced paddock, "nice for dogs". "Excellent value for money." Warwick Castle is five miles away; Stratford-upon-Avon is 12; Birmingham is a 30-minute drive. (*Warmly endorsed in 2000 by Jonathan and Deborah Oxley*)

Open Mid-Jan–mid-Dec. Evening meal by arrangement.
Rooms 6 double, 1 single. 1 with kitchenette. 2 on ground floor. No telephone (pay-phone available).
Facilities Sitting room, dining room. No background music. 1½-acre grounds: garden, access to fields.
Location 5 miles NW of Warwick off A4177. At Five Ways roundabout take Shrewley road for ½ mile.
Restrictions No smoking. Dogs by arrangement; not in public rooms.
Credit card MasterCard, Visa.
Terms [2000] B&B: single £35–£42, double £50–£60. Supper tray from £6.50; evening meal £17.50. *V*

HAWKSHEAD Cumbria   Map 4

Highfield House   *Tel* (015394) 36344
Hawkshead Hill   *Fax* (015394) 36793
Hawkshead LA22 0PN   *E-mail* highfield.hawkshead@btinternet.com
           Website www.lakes-pages.co.uk

Set in peaceful gardens on a hillside overlooking Hawkshead, Pauline and Jim Bennett's Lakeland stone house, "ideal for a walking/cycling holiday", has beautiful views over Ambleside and across the fells to Kirkstone pass. "It is a very friendly hotel," says a visitor this year. "My lasting memory is lying on the bed before dinner, watching the sun set. In the morning, the mountain tops rose above the early morning mist, out of which, during breakfast, the valleys slowly appeared." Inspectors found the place "professionally run; good value; a happy place". The decor is simple, with bits of old furniture, patterned carpets, William Morris fabrics and wallpaper. There is a lounge, warmed by an open fire and full of books and local information, and a small bar. In the restaurant, popular with locals, diners enjoy the view through picture windows, and tables are close enough for conversation. Jason Spedding's menus, "with robust flavours and hearty portions", always include a vegetarian main course. "The descriptions are a little OTT, but we enjoyed mint and pea soup and home-made pâté, followed by poached cod with fettucine." To end, puddings such as baked marmalade roly poly with egg custard, and a good cheeseboard. Breakfast includes "very good scrambled eggs" but commercial orange juice, and the coffee was not liked this year. Children of all ages are welcomed: cots, baby seats, high teas are provided, and laundry facilities are available. William Wordsworth went to school in Hawkshead, a pretty grey stone village with old cottages and cobblestones, and a ban on traffic in its centre; day-trippers must park in large carparks on its edge. The National Trust runs the Beatrix Potter Gallery here – she lived at Near Sawrey, close by (*Highfield* was built by her husband's uncle). (*Sue Davies, and others*)

Open 1-Feb–3 Jan, except Christmas. Restaurant closed midday (bar lunch available).
Rooms 9 double, 2 single.
Facilities Lounge, bar, restaurant (occasional classical background music); laundry facilities, drying room. 2½-acre garden: children's play area. Fishing, boating, access to leisure facilities nearby. Unsuitable for &.
Location ¾ mile NW of Hawkshead on B5285 to Coniston. Train: Windermere; then taxi/infrequent bus.
Restrictions Smoking banned in restaurant, discouraged in lounge, 2 bedrooms. Dogs by arrangement, not in public rooms.
Credit cards MasterCard, Visa.
Terms [to 31 Mar 2001] B&B £40–£47.50; D,B&B £57–£64.50. Set dinner £20. Child accommodated in parents' room: under 2, free; 2–12, B&B £15. Weekly package, winter breaks. 1-night bookings sometimes refused Sat.

> Most hotels have reduced rates out of season and offer "mini-break" rates throughout the year. It is always worth asking about special terms.

Rough Close `BUDGET`   *Tel* (015394) 36370
Hawkshead LA22 0QF   *Fax* (015394) 36002

An unpretentious guest house in a peaceful position above Esthwaite
Water; from its garden there are views of sheep-dotted fells and woodland. It has many regular visitors who enjoy the beautiful setting, the
unpretentious comfort, the friendliness of the "unobtrusive owners",
Marylin and Anthony Gibson, and the socialising by the fire in the
lounge. Everyone finds it "excellent value for money". The dining
room layout is different this year, but otherwise little has changed. The
five-course dinner at 7 pm is "English with some imported elabora-
tion", say the Gibsons, eg, cream of mushroom soup; smoked trout
with horseradish cream; pork medallions in apple and Calvados sauce;
Swiss plum tart or chocolate ice-cream. The Gibsons share the cooking, and Mr Gibson serves at table and acts as wine waiter (each menu
suggests a wine, priced at about £13, to match the food). Substantial
breakfasts are served between 8.45 and 9.15 am. All the bedrooms
have private facilities, but one bathroom is not *en suite*. There is good
walking from the grounds, and excellent birdwatching, and the knowledgeable Gibsons can advise about local trips. Beatrix Potter's home,
Hill Top, is one mile away. More reports, please.

Open Mar–end Oct; sometimes in winter by arrangement. Lunch not served.
Rooms 5 double. No telephone.
Facilities Lounge, bar with TV, dining room. No background music. 1-acre
garden: *boules*. Lake, boating, fishing nearby. Unsuitable for &.
Location 1¼ miles S of Hawkshead on Newby Bridge road. Infrequent bus
service.
Restrictions No smoking: dining room, bedrooms. No children under 12. No
dogs.
Credit cards MasterCard, Visa.
Terms B&B £28.50–£32; D,B&B £41.50–£45. Single rate by negotiation. Set
dinner £14. Reductions for long stays. 1-night bookings sometimes refused.

HAWORTH West Yorkshire   **Map 4**

Hill Top Farmhouse `BUDGET`   *Tel* (01535) 643524
Haworth Moor
Haworth BD22 0EL

In a "lovely position" on Haworth moor, where the Brontë sisters once
walked, this is "one of the best B&Bs I have stayed in", one reporter
wrote this year. The 17th-century farmhouse stands in a large garden
(spectacular in summer when the heather is in flower). It has wide
views over farms, villages and the Lower Laithe reservoir to the distant hills. Mrs Brenda Fox and her husband, Alan, are "most welcoming hosts, interesting to chat to", others said, and the atmosphere is
"relaxed and homely". The old whitewashed cottage has been sensitively enlarged and furnished. "Our big bedroom had TV and a simple
but adequate shower room." One room might hear voices in the
kitchen below during the day. Packed lunches are available by
arrangement, and so is an evening meal, found "excellent: including
home-made soup with delicious bread; chicken with perfectly cooked

vegetables". Vegetarians are catered for. No licence; bring your own wine. The "delicious complimentary afternoon tea on arrival, with home-made scones", and the "memorable breakfasts" are also praised. "A real bargain" (£70 D,B&B for two). Haworth parsonage is 15 minutes' walk away; the Keighley and Worth Valley Railway (of *Railway Children* fame) is nearby. (*S and TT, and others*)

Open All year, except Christmas, New Year.
Rooms 3 bedrooms, all with shower. No telephone.
Facilities Lounge, dining room (soft background music). Large grounds. Unsuitable for &.
Location From Haworth take minor road to Colne; 1st turning left (signed Peniston Hill Country Park). *Hill Top* is 1st building on right.
Restrictions No smoking. No dogs in house.
Credit cards None accepted.
Terms [2000] B&B £23, D,B&B £35.

Weaver's	*Tel* (01535) 643822
15 West Lane	*Fax* (01535) 644832
Haworth BD22 8DU	*E-mail* colinjane@aol.com

"An excellent meal; good value," says a visitor to this restaurant-with-rooms on a cobbled street behind the Brontë Parsonage Museum. And this year owners/chefs Colin and Jane Rushworth gained a *Michelin Bib Gourmand* in recognition of the quality of their "modern/ traditional" British regional cooking. Using fresh, and mostly local, ingredients, they serve such dishes as fishcakes with tomato sauce; roast belly and fillet of port with cider gravy; steak-and-kidney pie (which comes with a free bottle of Hammond's Yorkshire Sauce for you to take home); there is always a vegetarian option. The home-made puddings and ice-creams include sticky toffee pudding; old school pud' wi' custard. The wine list is wide-ranging, with a good selection of half bottles, and a low mark-up. Regulars appreciate Jane Rushworth's re-working of the menu every few months: "a few old favourites are kept, and new dishes are introduced – a sign that someone really enjoys cooking." The "high standards" and "attention to detail" are admired: "The warmed coffee cups at breakfast are a nice touch." "Listening to sparrows through our window in the early morning was pleasurable; not so good was the church clock which chimed every 15 minutes." Old photographs, modern paintings, antiques, bric-à-brac, and mementos of the spinners' craft fill the house, once a barn and a row of weavers' cottages. The bar and lounge "can be crowded in a friendly sort of way". The "stylish and idiosyncratic" bedrooms, up a narrow staircase, have lace-trimmed pillowcases, fresh milk, a cafetière with ground coffee, and satellite TV. They "are maintained to a high standard". (*WK Wood, Chris Kay*)

Open All year, Tues–Sat from 6.30 pm, except 25 Dec–5 Jan, 1 weekend June.
Rooms 2 double, 1 single.
Facilities Bar/lounge, restaurant. Mixed '40s/'70s background music at night. Unsuitable for &.
Location By Brontë Parsonage Museum: use its pay-and-display carpark. Ignore sign for Brontë village/Tourist Information. Train: Keighley; then bus/taxi.

Restrictions No smoking in restaurant. No restriction on children, but baby cots unavailable. No dogs.
Credit cards All major cards accepted.
Terms B&B: single £50, double £75. Set menu (6.30–7.15 pm) £14.50; full alc £27.50. *V*

HAYTOR Devon   Map 1

Bel Alp House   *Tel* (01364) 661217
Haytor   *Fax* (01364) 661292
nr Newton Abbot TQ13 9XX

"A really warm welcome, incomparable views, fresh, simple food and a cosy atmosphere." Inspectors in 2000 were charmed by this Edwardian country house, high on a hill on the south-east edge of Dartmoor. One of its chief glories is the panoramic view across fields with sheep, a church, faraway towns, with glimpses of the distant sea – it is well worth paying extra for one of the large front bedrooms. The house was much altered in the 1920s by its then owner, the tobacco millionairess Dame Violet Wills, and the interior is light and spacious, with arches, bay windows, stained glass and a homely decor. It is run in a generous spirit by its owners, Mary and Jack Twist. She is the cook, he the solicitous front-of-house. "The level of personal attention is high, but they are never intrusive," other visitors wrote of this "lovely, peaceful place". Dinner is served on a glazed-in balcony – "as we ate, we watched the sun set, and the twinkling lights of far-away houses start up – rather magical". The hand-written two-choice-per-course menu might include tomato, orange and red pepper soup (seconds offered); cod with a herb crust; pork fillet with a creamy prune sauce; masses of vegetables. Mealtimes are flexible – "they urged us to lie in on Sunday, if we wished". Breakfast has toast made from home-made bread, and "excellent cafetière coffee", but cooked dishes may be rather hit and miss. There is direct access to the moor from the house. Charlie, the golden retriever, will take guests for walks. Many local attractions: houses, gardens, the Lydford Gorge, etc.

Open All year, except Christmas, New Year.
Rooms 1 suite, 8 double. 1 on ground floor.
Facilities Lounge, drawing room, restaurant. Background music if requested. 8-acre grounds. Riding, golf nearby.
Location From A38, take A382 to Bovey Tracey, then B3387 to Haytor/Widecombe. After 1½ miles, cross cattle grid on to moor; fork left after 500 yds into hotel drive, crossing 2nd cattle grid. Train: Newton Abbot; then taxi.
Restrictions No smoking: restaurant, bedrooms, 1 lounge. No dogs in dining room.

128 ENGLAND

Credit cards All major cards accepted.
Terms B&B: single £60–£75, double £120, suite £150. Packed lunch available. Set dinner from £22.50. 10% discount for 3 or more nights.

HAZLEWOOD North Yorkshire Map 4

Hazlewood Castle *Tel* (01937) 535353
Paradise Lane *Fax* (01937) 530630
Hazlewood *E-mail* info@hazlewood-castle.co.uk
nr Tadcaster LS24 9NJ *Website* www.hazlewood-castle.co.uk

Historic fortified "knights residence" and former monastery in 77 acres of parkland and landscaped grounds SW of Tadcaster (off A1M at A64 junction between Leeds and York). Chef/patron John Benson-Smith, with brother Matthew, has created an idiosyncratic but stylish hotel with conference centre, banqueting suites, cookery school. Civil wedding licence. Public rooms have moulded ceilings, ornate fireplaces; bedrooms combine tradition with up-to-the-minute amenities. Bistro-style meals in casual Prickly Pear Café; *serious dining in chic* 1086 Restaurant *(originally the orangery). Both have "easy listening" music. 21 rooms (including 11 suites), 11 in Grade II listed building in courtyard. No smoking: restaurants, some public rooms. Guide dogs only. All major credit cards accepted. B&B: single £95, double £125, suite £300. Set lunch £17.50, dinner £29.50 [2000]. More reports needed.*

HEDDON'S MOUTH Devon Map 1

Heddon's Gate Hotel *Tel* (01598) 763313
Heddon's Mouth, Parracombe *Fax* (01598) 763363
Barnstaple EX31 4PZ *E-mail* info@hgate.co.uk
Website www.hgate.co.uk

🅠 *César award in 1990*

"We loved this hotel," says one of many accolades this year. "The rooms are beautiful yet homely, with many caring details." Other visitors wrote of the "relaxing, music-free atmosphere", "value for money" and "interesting, well-balanced meals". Owner/chef (for over three decades) Robert Deville and his wife, Heather, "are perfectionists", their staff are long-serving, and the setting of their Swiss/Victorian lodge is "lovely, peaceful, but with many opportunities for outings". It stands in large grounds with steeply terraced gardens, in a remote position on the edge of Exmoor. "Sitting on the terrace, sipping a whisky before dinner as the sun falls into the sea, is one of the pleasures." The decor (lace tablecloths, patterned carpets, embroidered cushions) is quite old-fashioned, one of the charms for its many devotees. They love the personal service (beds turned down at night, etc), and the "friendly atmosphere: like-minded people to chat with, and plenty of laughter in the bar". Afternoon tea with home-made cakes is included in the price, so is after-dinner coffee with "luscious hand-made chocolates". Dinner, with limited choice, is served promptly at 8 pm (guests are expected to dine in). The cooking on the daily-changing menu is traditional "and excellent", with main courses like grilled local venison with red cabbage; baked salmon with chive sauce. But several visitors this year wished that the ambience of the dining room was "more romantic". Breakfast is brought to the table, rather than self-service, and it includes freshly squeezed orange juice, local bacon and kippers. No midday meal, but packed lunches are available. The bedrooms, named for their original occupants – Grandmama's, Nursemaid's, etc – vary greatly, and are priced accordingly. Some are large, with a spacious bathroom. The cottages in the garden are convenient for dog-owners. There is good walking in the "superb coastal countryside". Arlington Court (National Trust) is eight miles away. (*Carolyn and Steve Cardwell, Richard Neale, Mrs PM Glover, JA Fisher; also Rupert Wheeler, and others*)

Open 1 Apr–31 Oct. Dining room closed for lunch.
Rooms 4 suites (3 in cottages, on ground floor), 9 double, 1 single.
Facilities Lounge, bar lounge, library, piano/card room, dining room; table-tennis room. No background music. 20-acre grounds. River, fishing, riding, pony-trekking nearby. Sea ¾ mile. Not really suitable for &.
Location 6 miles W of Lynton. From A39, after 3 miles, take road to Woody Bay/Martinhoe; follow signs for *Hunter's Inn*; hotel drive on right. Train/coach: Barnstaple, 16 miles; then taxi.
Restrictions No smoking in dining room. Children "must be old enough to dine with parents at 8 pm". Dogs by arrangement, not unattended in bedrooms.
Credit cards MasterCard, Visa.
Terms [2000] D,B&B £66.10–£79.80. Set dinner £26. Child accommodated in parents' room: 50% of adult rate. Weekly rates. 3-day breaks. 1-night bookings occasionally refused.

HELMSLEY North Yorkshire   Map 4

The Pheasant   NEW   *Tel* (01439) 771241
Harome, Helmsley YO62 5JG   *Fax* (01439) 771744
E-mail pheasant@binks-harome.freeserve.co.uk

Formed from the former village smithy, two cottages and a shop, the Binks family's unpretentious small hotel stands near the pond in an old stone-built Yorkshire village. "It is first rate, without fuss," says a visitor this year. Other guests wrote of the "air of friendliness". "Not for those who want nightlife, but for tranquillity, courteous attention and delightful surroundings, this is the place." The "no-nonsense menus, serving food that you can really taste", are praised too. Smoked local trout, roast guinea fowl, bilberry and apple pie, and English cheeses all feature on the daily-changing menus, served in the dining room and a new orangery. The small oak-beamed bar and large drawing room open on to a terrace by a stream. Buildings across the courtyard house a swimming pool and some suites – one of these was found rather dark this year. (*Sir William Gladstone, Frank Slater, Don Parker; also John Knott*)

Open Mid-Mar–mid-Nov.
Rooms 2 suites (across courtyard), 8 double, 2 single. 1 ground-floor room.
Facilities Lounge, bar, dining room, orangery; indoor heated swimming pool. No background music. Courtyard; ½-acre garden; access to deerpark.

Location Near church of village 3 miles SE of Helmsley. Take A170 towards Scarborough; after ¼ mile turn right to Harome.
Restrictions No smoking in restaurant. No dogs in public rooms or unattended in bedrooms.
Credit cards MasterCard, Visa.
Terms [2000] B&B £40–£50, D,B&B £60–£68.50. Bar lunches. Set dinner £21.

HELSTON Cornwall   Map 1

Nansloe Manor   *Tel* (01326) 574691
Meneage Road   *Fax* (01326) 564680
Helston TR13 0SB   *E mail* info@nansloe-manor.co.uk
                                  Website www.nansloe-manor.co.uk

Owned and run by the Ridden family since 1997, this Grade II listed Georgian building is approached by a long tree-lined drive through its wooded grounds. The busy road to Penzance is nearby, but here "everything is calm and efficient – even during busy times". Visitors this year appreciated the "family feel" and the friendly service. The public areas and bedrooms were recently refurbished, but the decor remains "conventional, with boring pictures", says one guest who felt it "lacked flair". The large lounge/bar has log fires in a Victorian fireplace. The best bedroom, No. 3, is huge, with sofa, easy chair, flowery fabrics, flower prints, and a garden view, but some other rooms are small. Howard Ridden's British/Mediterranean cooking is liked, and the menu descriptions, though still elaborate, have been improved this year. Main courses include, eg, grilled seabass on a mussel, aubergine and tomato bouillabaisse; pan-seared maize-fed chicken stuffed with mango, served with a broth of Thai spices, Puy lentils and ginger wine. Smart dress is expected at dinner, where "prices are reasonable" and "the mark-up on wine is fair". RNAS Culdrose is nearby, but there is little night flying. A good base for exploring the Lizard peninsula. The ancient stannary town of Helston, in the Loe valley, is known for its flower festival; Loe Pool, nearby, is the largest freshwater lake in Cornwall. (*HR, and others*)

Open All year.
Rooms 6 double, 1 single.
Facilities Drawing room, restaurant; classical/"easy listening" background music during meals. 4-acre grounds: croquet. Sea 2 miles: sandy/rock beaches. Unsuitable for &.
Location Off A394 Helston–Falmouth, near junction with A3083 to Lizard. Train: Redruth; then taxi.
Restrictions No smoking in restaurant. No children under 10. No dogs.
Credit cards MasterCard, Visa.
Terms B&B £35–£65; D,B&B £54–£89. Set lunch £13, dinner £19–£24. 2-night rates. Christmas package.

We quote either prices per room, or else the range of prices per person – the lowest is likely to be for one person sharing a double room out of season, and the highest for a single room in the high season.

HENLEY-ON-THAMES Oxfordshire   Map 2

The Red Lion   *Tel* (01491) 572161
Hart Street   *Fax* (01491) 410039
Henley-on-Thames RG9 2AR   *E-mail* reservations@redlionhenley.co.uk
     Website www.redlionhenley.co.uk

A creeper-clad 16th-century red brick inn, looking over the Royal
Regatta course on the River Thames. It stands by a busy bridge, but
windows are double-glazed. Recently refurbished by the owners, the
Miller family of *Durrants*, London (*qv*), it has antique panelling and
furniture in its public rooms, and flagstones, an open fire and rowing
memorabilia in the bar. The riverside restaurant serves a mix of
modern and traditional dishes: seared salmon with ginger and chilli
sauce, and boudin of chicken and mushroom appear on the *table
d'hôte* menu; pea and ham soup, and roast beef and Yorkshire pudding
at Sunday lunch. The traditional bedrooms have flowery fabrics and a
marble-tiled bathroom, and there are some impressive antique beds.
The manager, James Shawcross, and his staff are not the least snooty,
as this report shows: "I arrived in the early evening, dressed in cycle
shorts, T-shirt and reflecting strips, and carrying a rucksack. I was welcomed by a smiling Mr Shawcross, who did not bat an eyelid. My
small but lovely room overlooked the river. The food was beautifully
presented and full of flavour. The staff were attentive but not over-
bearing, with a sense of *joie de vivre*." (*Briony Southcott*)

Open All year.
Rooms 1 family, 22 double, 3 single.
Facilities Lounge, bar, restaurant (classical background music); conference/
function facilities. On river: boat hire, river picnics arranged. Unsuitable for ♧.
Location By Henley bridge (rooms double-glazed). Trains to Henley from
London, Reading. Large carpark.
Restrictions Smoking discouraged in restaurant. No dogs.
Credit cards Amex MasterCard, Visa.
Terms [2000] (*Excluding "optional" 10% service charge on meals*) Room:
single £95, double £130, family £160. Breakfast: continental £8.50, English
£12.50. D,B&B £95–£120 per person. Set lunch/dinner (2 to 3 courses)
£12.50–£16; full alc £32. ***V***

HINTLESHAM Suffolk   Map 2

Hintlesham Hall   *Tel* (01473) 652268
Hintlesham   *Fax* (01473) 652463
Ipswich IP8 3NS   *E-mail* reservations@hintlesham-hall.co.uk
     Website www.hintlesham-hall.co.uk

A Grade I listed country house, Tudor in origin with a Georgian
façade, set in beautiful grounds near Ipswich. The interior is sumptuous, with panelling and mouldings, fine fabrics and antiques. The staff
are "well schooled by Tim Sunderland, the manager, in the cosseting
of guests". The spacious bedrooms vary in style; suites are huge and
opulent; some have a gas log fire, some a real one; some are up two
floors (no lift); some are in a stable block. Guests' accommodation
tends to be upgraded at no extra cost when possible. In its huge

grounds are a trout lake, a leisure club (the swimming pool may be too small for the vigorous) and an 18-hole championship golf course, well hidden by trees. The place is quite formal: men are asked to wear a jacket, and a tie or tailored shirt at dinner, and "smart casual wear" is required in the clubhouse (said to be an agreeable place for a light lunch). In the restaurant, the modern cooking of the long-serving chef, Alan Ford, is generally praised (you should book a table when reserving your room). The four-course dinner menu includes, eg, tempura of fresh anchovies and squid with saffron and white wine dressing; breast of pheasant with watercress and chestnut; Grand Marnier and candied kumquat soufflé. There is a separate vegetarian menu and "a really well-chosen wine list". "Breakfast was ok," says a visitor in 2000, but "we found our rooms a bit cold." "Good children" are welcomed, but under-tens are not allowed in the lounge and restaurant at night. All around is Constable country. (*RB, and others*)

Open All year.
Rooms 4 suites, 29 double. 11 in courtyard wing 20 yds. 8 on ground floor.
Facilities 4 lounges, 3 dining rooms; conference/function rooms; snooker room. No background music. 175-acre grounds: leisure club, small outdoor swimming pool (heated), tennis, croquet, 18-hole golf course with clubhouse, trout lake, fishing, riding, shooting. Civil wedding licence.
Location 5 miles W of Ipswich on A1071 to Sudbury.
Restrictions No smoking in dining rooms. No children under 10 at dinner. No dogs in public rooms, or unattended in bedrooms.
Credit cards All major cards accepted.
Terms [2000] B&B: single £94–£112, double £120–£230, suite £250–£350. English breakfast £7.50. Set lunch £21, dinner £27; full alc £45. Child accommodated in parents' room £20. 2-day breaks; golf breaks. Christmas package. 1-night bookings refused bank holidays.

HINTON CHARTERHOUSE Somerset   Map 2

Homewood Park `NEW`   *Tel* (01225) 723731
Hinton Charterhouse   *Fax* (01225) 723820
Bath BA3 6BB   *E-mail* res.@homewoodpark.com
                                    Website www.homewoodpark.com

An ivy-clad, bay-windowed, grey stone, mainly 18th-century house in a village on the edge of the Limpley Stoke valley, a designated area of outstanding natural beauty outside Bath. It has a country house decor: fine fabrics, antiques, Oriental rugs, and works by local artists. Log fires burn in the lounge and bar in cold weather. The Fentum family who owned the house have sold it, but Frank Guening remains as manager, and visitors this year were pleased: "Mr Guening and his staff are charming." "Seamless service." "We appreciated being warned, on booking, that a wedding reception might create noise on our first evening. We were upgraded to a spacious suite. Breakfast included freshly squeezed juices, delicious croissants and brioches, and beautifully presented yogurt with fresh fruit. The dishes at dinner were light and delicious. The half-board rate was good value." This year, Nigel Goodwin has been promoted to head chef, so we'd like more reports on the *Michelin*-starred restaurant, please. It serves elaborate modern dishes, eg, mosaic of poultry with caramelised apple and Sauternes jelly; monkfish with clams, cockles, wild mushrooms and a red wine sauce; plum and frangipane tart with apricot ice-cream. Most bedrooms are spacious, and overlook the immaculate garden. One of the suites has been sponsored by Marks and Spencer. There is a secluded swimming pool, "long enough to swim in". Children are welcomed. Some traffic from the busy road nearby. (*EP, Mary Woods, GD*)

Open All year.
Rooms 2 suites, 2 semi-suites, 15 double. 4 on ground floor.
Facilities Drawing room, bar, restaurant. No background music. 10-acre grounds: swimming pool, tennis, croquet.
Location 5 miles SE of Bath, opposite Hinton Priory. A46 from M4; A36 to Warminster; left at 2nd turning to Freshford. Some traffic noise; rooms double-glazed. Train: Bath; then taxi.
Restrictions No smoking in restaurant. Guide dogs only.
Credit cards All major cards accepted.
Terms [2000] B&B: single £88–£109, double £112–£177, suite £209–£249; D,B&B: single £144, double £209–£319. Set lunch £19.50, alc dinner £50. 2-day breaks. 1-night bookings sometimes refused.

HOCKLEY HEATH Warwickshire   Map 3

Nuthurst Grange   NEW   *Tel* (01564) 783972
Nuthurst Grange Lane   *Fax* (01564) 783919
Hockley Heath B94 5NL
                                    E-mail info@nuthurst-grange.com
                                    Website www.nuthurst-grange.com

"Extremely comfortable, with good food, excellent service and staff." A report this year restores this hotel/restaurant to the *Guide* after a time with no reports. It is a red brick Edwardian house in a large village on the Stratford-upon-Avon Canal, handy for Birmingham. Low and pleasant, it has a terrace, creeper-clad walls, bay windows with leaded panes, dormer windows in the roof. It stands amid landscaped gardens, fountains, ponds and a vegetable garden; you approach by an immaculate drive through woodland. The front looks down across the M40, half a mile away (some traffic noise) to open country. The public rooms have lavish fabrics, stylish flower arrangements, lots of pink. Two light sitting rooms overlook the garden. The spacious bedrooms are traditional, with flowery fabrics, reproduction furniture, fruit, "useful extras", and a bathroom with an air spa bath. The restaurant, set out in a string of rooms, serves the "competent modern British cooking" of owner/chef David Randolph at well-spaced tables. He offers a three-course menu with three choices of each course, eg, galantine of duck, with plum and grenadine compote; escalope of salmon with roast vegetables, saffron and chive sauce; steamed date sponge with butterscotch. Or you can eat off a four-course menu and pay according to the number of courses taken. "Breakfast is good and efficiently served. They prefer you to take it in the bedroom, but will serve it in the dining room if asked. Reception is efficient; pleasant staff." "Suitable for children who are well behaved," says the brochure. A popular venue for weddings, small meetings, and functions. Three impressive castles, Warwick, Broughton and Berkeley, are nearby. (*John and Thérèse Hall, and others*)

Open All year, except a few days over Christmas.
Rooms 1 suite, 14 double. Some on ground floor.
Facilities 2 lounges, restaurant; function/private dining rooms. No background music. 7½-acre grounds: gardens, croquet, ponds, woodland, helipad. Riding, hunting, tennis, golf, clay-pigeon shooting, canal boating nearby. Civil wedding licence.
Location 10 miles NW of Warwick. Off A3400 ½ mile S of Hockley Heath. Turn right at hotel sign.
Restrictions No smoking: restaurant, 1 lounge, some bedrooms. Dogs by arrangement; not in public rooms.
Credit cards All major cards accepted.
Terms B&B: single £128, double £145–£155, suite £175. Set dinner £26.90; full alc lunch £25. Weekend breaks: D,B&B £82.75–£95 per person. ***V***

HOLFORD Somerset   Map 1

Combe House BUDGET	*Tel* (01278) 741382
Holford	*Fax* (01278) 741322
nr Bridgwater TA5 1RZ	*E-mail* enquiries@combehouse.co.uk

"Very good for families, with unsophisticated, nice accommodation at reasonable rates," says a report in 2000 on Denice and John Page's converted 17th-century tannery. Long, low and pink-washed, and still with its waterwheel, it is peacefully set at the end of a narrow lane in a combe that leads up to the Quantock hills. "Not for those seeking luxury; it will suit walkers and lovers of the English countryside," wrote returning visitors who liked its "air of having grown rather than been designed, and ambience of a homely country house" – small public rooms, log fires, beams, creaking stairs and floors, patterned carpets, and "a variety of furniture apparently bought at long-ago auctions". The long-serving chef, Lynn Gardner, serves traditional dinners "of a high standard", eg, home-made chicken terrine; roast pork with sage and onion stuffing; lemon meringue pie. Wines are reasonably priced. "The beds are comfortable, the bedrooms warm and clean (some are quite small). No night-life, just the ripple of the stream through the gardens, the sound of wind in the trees, the song of birds." Breakfasts are lavish. Packed lunches and cream teas are available. A rock beach is nearby; Cleeve Abbey and Dunster Castle are within 20 minutes' drive. (*D Fisher, R and JG*)

Open All year, except Jan.
Rooms 1 suite, 11 double, 4 single. 1, on ground floor, suitable for partially &.
Facilities Lounge, smoking room, bar, restaurant. 3-acre grounds: tennis, covered swimming pool, stream. Golf, riding, walking, rock beach nearby.
Location A39 Bridgwater–Minehead. Turn between Plough Inn and Holford garage. Left at T-junction, left at fork; hotel on right. Train: Bridgwater, Taunton; then local bus.
Restrictions Smoking in 1 lounge only. No dogs in public rooms, except bar.
Credit cards Amex, MasterCard, Visa.
Terms B&B: single £28–£38, double £56–£87, suite £67–£87; D,B&B £46.75–£56.75 per person. Bar lunches from £2.50. Set dinner £19.50. 2- to 5-night breaks. Christmas, New Year packages. 1-night bookings refused bank holidays. ***V***

HOPE Derbyshire   Map 3

Underleigh   `BUDGET`   *Tel* (01433) 621372
off Edale Road   *Fax* (01433) 621324
Hope S33 6RF   *E-mail* underleigh.house@btinternet.com
                                    Website www.underleighhouse.co.uk

*19th-century house set amid quiet fields, near a Domesday-old village
in Hope valley. New owners this year, Philip and Vivienne Taylor, and
"delightful Border terrier, Tess", offer B&B only (but "plenty of
hostelries are close at hand"). Good welcome, good service; good
breakfast around large oak table in beamed, flagstoned room: Aga-
cooked porridge warmly recommended. 1 suite, 5 double bedrooms,
recently refurbished, with plenty of toiletries, views over countryside
or garden. Drinks served in large lounge with wood-burning stove, or
on terrace. Maps, packed lunches provided for walkers; good birdwatching nearby. Closed Christmas, New Year. No smoking. No background music. Not really suitable for ♿. No children under 12. Guide
dogs only. MasterCard, Visa accepted (5% surcharge). B&B: single
£33–£46, double £60–£66, suite £70–£80 [2000].*

HOPESAY Shropshire   Map 3

 The Old Rectory   *Tel* (01588) 660245
Hopesay, Craven Arms SY7 8HD   *Fax* (01588) 660502
César award: Guest house of the year

Much enthusiasm again this year for Roma and Michael Villar's 17th-
century rectory: "A lovely retreat." "The high standards never slip."
"From the first greeting we felt like welcome guests. The owners could
not have been more kind. We didn't want to leave." "We think Mrs
Villar doesn't realise how excellent a cook she is." "Offers the Wolsey
Lodge experience par excellence." The house stands in landscaped
gardens by a 12th-century church ("its bells add to the atmosphere")
in a hamlet above the Clun valley. It has been "beautifully restored,
with a perfect balance between formality and informality". The Aga-
cooked evening meal is served communally at 8 pm around a polished
oak refectory table. The cooking is "quite sophisticated, using the
freshest products". "We enjoyed chilled tomato soup; tender chicken
in a tarragon sauce, with vegetables from the garden; chocolate
roulade to die for." "This is almost the only 'hotel' in the country
where we regularly order good wine; mostly it is a rip-off – not here."
"The silhouette of the hill seen from the dining room as the sun sets is
the final touch to make dinner a rare treat." The drawing room has an
Adam fireplace, Georgian sash windows opening on to a terrace,
antique and period furniture, and a self-service drinks trolley. The
"spotlessly clean", spacious bedrooms have TV, up-to-date magazines, armchairs; two have an emperor-size bed. "Michael Villar plays
up his host role amusingly when taking orders for his perfectly timed
and cooked breakfasts" – they include home-made yogurt and preserves, fruit compote, home-baked bread, and traditional cooked

items. Afternoon tea, with home-made biscuits and cakes, is included in the rates. "Altogether a lovely place to stay as long as people understand that this is someone's home, not a hotel." Guests should not arrive before 4 pm without prior arrangement. There is much to enjoy in the lovely countryside of south-west Shropshire: good birdwatching from local RSPB bird hides, as well as in the rectory's garden; Powis and Stokesay castles, Offa's Dyke and Long Mynd are near, and one reader recommends the "wheely wonderful cycling" offered by Patchfield Farm, Elton: "Excellent bikes, and up to 40 miles of virtually flat cycling through quiet lanes and voluptuous countryside." (*Philip and Eileen Hall, Margaret Kershaw, Alice Wilkinson, Daisy Berger; also Ann Pickering, and many others*)

Open All year, except Christmas/New Year. Occasionally closed at other times.
Rooms 1 suite, 2 double. No telephone.
Facilities Drawing room, dining room. No background music. 2-acre garden. Unsuitable for &.
Location 3 miles W of Craven Arms. B4368 to Clun; at Aston-on-Clun turn right over humpback bridge to Hopesay. Hotel 1½ miles, by church.
Restrictions No smoking. No children. No dogs.
Credit cards None accepted.
Terms B&B £37.50. Set dinner £22.50.

HOPWAS Staffordshire   Map 3

Oak Tree Farm   BUDGET   *Tel/Fax* (01827) 56807
Hints Road
Hopwas, nr Tamworth B78 3AA

"First class," says one report this year on this "little rural oasis". The owner, Sue Purkis, "has a genius for hospitality, and provides a tranquil environment," say other visitors. "She shares her home with her guests with infectious enthusiasm" and "her staff are excellent". The renovated farmhouse stands in grounds between the River Tame (coarse fishing) and a canal (good walks). "A cornucopia of a hanging basket sways in the breeze; swallows swoop; a cat blinks on the lawn." There is a swimming pool in a conservatory, and a lounge with a wood-burning stove. Spotless bedrooms, of decent size, have a sofa, armchairs, TV, a desk, books, magazines and much else. "They are some of the nicest, most tastefully furnished and best-equipped rooms that we know." Breakfast, which includes freshly baked bread, is served from 7 am until 10. The village has two good pubs (one is open all day). The market town of Tamworth, across the river, has an old castle, a Norman church and a snow dome for indoor skiing. Lichfield, the cathedral city and birthplace of Samuel Johnson, is five miles away; Drayton Manor pleasure park is nearby; Birmingham is 13 miles. (*Mrs CM Parkes, Mary Bryden, Edit and Barry Westwood, John Shaw*)

Open All year, except New Year.
Rooms 6 double. 5 in barn. No telephone (pay-phone available).
Facilities Drawing room, breakfast room; conservatory with swimming pool. No background music. 4-acre grounds of river, fishing. Golf nearby. Unsuitable for &.

Location From A51, turn into Hints Rd at *Tame Otter* pub. Last house on left at fork in road. Train: Tamworth; then bus to village.
Restrictions No smoking: breakfast room, bedrooms. No children. No dogs in public rooms.
Credit cards Amex, MasterCard, Visa.
Terms [2000] B&B: single £52, double £64.

HORLEY Surrey   **Map 2**

Langshott Manor   *Tel* (01293) 786680
Langshott   *Fax* (01293) 783905
Horley RH6 9LN   *E-mail* admin@langshottmanor.com
                                        Website www.langshottmanor.com

Close to Gatwick, but not on a flight path, this airport hotel with a difference is owned by Peter and Deborah Hinchcliffe and managed by
Kenneth Sharp. The Grade II listed timber-framed Elizabethan manor
house, "wonderfully romantic", stands in a traditional English garden
with roses, herbaceous borders and a lake. With sturdy chimneys,
leaded windows, beamed ceilings, wooden staircases, fresh flowers, it
is a world apart from the chain hotels nearby. "The building is charming and the gardens are a marvel," says one report. "The lounges are
warm and inviting." Poshest bedrooms are in the main house. Those
in the converted mews may have less character, but they are comfortable and have views over gardens or fields and treetops. Some bathrooms have a four-poster bath. The lounge and bar areas have now
been extended, and a new restaurant, looking over the lake, opened in
April 2000. We'd be grateful for reports on the work of the chef,
Stephen Toward. He has worked in *Michelin*-starred restaurants in
Germany, and also at three other *Guide* hotels, *Mallory Court*,
Bishop's Tachbrook, *New Hall*, Sutton Coldfield, and *Longueville
Manor* in the Channel Islands. His "modern European" menus
include, eg, ham and pease pudding terrine; pot roast local wood
pigeon; Bourbon and vanilla soufflé. The rates include a week's free
parking at a nearby airport carpark. Many packages are offered,
including visits to famous gardens and houses (Wisley, Wakehurst
Place, Bateman's, etc); learning to fly, using a flight simulator; trips to
horse races. (*Dr Michael Dods; also Richard Neale*)

Open All year.
Rooms 1 suite, 14 double. 8 in mews 50 yds. Some on ground floor.
Facilities Ramps. 2 lounges, bar (piano CDs, evenings), restaurant; confer-
ence/private dining room. 3-acre garden: croquet. Courtesy car to Gatwick (2½
miles). Civil wedding licence.
Location From A23 in Horley take Ladbroke Rd (3rd exit off large round-
about by *Chequers* hotel) to Langshott. Hotel ¾ mile on right. Train: Gatwick
or Horley; taxi.
Restrictions No smoking: restaurant, 1 lounge, bedrooms. No dogs in house
(kennels available).
Credit cards All major cards accepted.
Terms B&B: single £145, double £155–£165, suite £250. Set lunch £25, dinner £35; full alc £55. D,B&B: single £180, double £210–£220, suite £310.
Special breaks; Christmas package. *V*

HUDDERSFIELD West Yorkshire *See SHORTLIST*   **Map 4**

HUNSTRETE Somerset   **Map 2**

Hunstrete House   `NEW`   *Tel* (01761) 490490
Hunstrete, Chelwood   *Fax* (01761) 490732
Nr Bath BS39 4NS   *E-mail* info@hunstretehouse.co.uk
                          Website www.hunstretehouse.co.uk

"One of the most attractive hotels we have ever stayed in," says its
nominator. "It is small for a country house, beautifully decorated, with
one of the most interesting gardens we know. Everything is understated, carefully considered, and in excellent taste." Built of grey stone
in the 18th century and now owned by an American partnership (see
also *Culloden House*, Inverness, Scotland), it stands in large grounds
on the edge of the Mendip hills, amid woodland, a deerpark, an outdoor
heated swimming pool, magnificent gardens with a flourishing kitchen
garden. This supplies many ingredients for *Michelin*-starred kitchen –
Stewart Eddy is the chef. His *table d'hôte* dinner menu might include
terrine of duck confit and root vegetables; a potage of Cornish fish and
shellfish with asparagus and a bouillabaisse sauce; chocolate confit
mousse with orange sauce and chocolate sorbet. There is also a more
elaborate *menu dégustation,* and an imaginative children's menu. The
public rooms have chandeliers, antiques, mirrors, portraits, open fires.
Bedrooms are luxurious too, and 24-hour room service is available.
"Expensive, but very good value." A gym and more "superior" bedrooms are planned for 2000. (*Sir Geoffrey Chipperfield*)

Open All year.
Rooms 3 suites, 19 double, 1 single. Some in coach house.
Facilities 3 lounges, bar, restaurant; classical background music. 92-acre
grounds: gardens, swimming pool, woodland, deerpark, pond, fishing. Civil
wedding licence.
Location 7 miles SW of Bath, 10 miles SE of Bristol. From Bath take A4
towards Bristol; A39 through Marksbury; A368 towards Weston-super-Mare.
Turn off at Historic House signpost.
Restrictions No smoking: restaurant 8 bedrooms. No dogs.
Credit cards All major cards accepted.
Terms B&B: single £80–£120, double £100–£180, suite £230–£250. Set
lunch £14.95 and £19.95, dinner £35 and £55. Full alc £70.

HUNTINGDON Cambridgeshire   **Map 2**

The Old Bridge   *Tel* (01480) 424300
1 High Street   *Fax* (01480) 411017
Huntingdon PE18 6TQ   *E-mail* oldbridge@huntsbridge.co.uk

*On River Ouse, near town centre, handsome, creeper-covered 18th-
century building, once a bank, now an "efficient modern hotel", often
catering to a business clientele. Belongs to John Hoskins' small group
of hotels run by manager/chefs: Martin Lee and his wife, Jayne, are
new this year. Busy road nearby: riverside garden and conservatory*

provide a "relatively peaceful retreat". 23 bedrooms (some are "wonderful", with large freestanding bath), with triple-glazing, air-conditioning, CD system. "Excellent decor." Some have found the atmosphere impersonal, but others wrote of "very friendly welcome to our dogs". International-style cooking in panelled restaurant or less formal terrace room, with large mural. Very good wine list. Bar lounge serves real ales. No background music. Terrace, 1-acre garden. Civil wedding licence. No smoking: restaurant, bedrooms. All major credit cards accepted. B&B: single £79.50–£110, double £89.50–£139.50. Full alc £25. *V*

IPSWICH Suffolk   Map 2

The Marlborough   *Tel* (01473) 257677
73 Henley Road   *Fax* (01473) 226927
Ipswich IP1 3SP   *E-mail* reception@themarlborough.co.uk

In a residential area of Ipswich, this Victorian town house stands across a busy road from Christchurch Park. Visitors this year continued enthusiastic about Simon Barker's traditional cooking (eg, terrine of Suffolk meats with red onion marmalade; venison with red cabbage and pink peppercorn sauce), though one found the meal service inept. The restaurant gives access to the pretty garden (floodlit at night), and has well-spaced tables, good napery. The newly refurbished bedrooms have period furniture, good reading lights and television sets with a low maximum volume guaranteeing the neighbouring rooms peace. One visitor had a room that he described as "adequate, but compact". The hotel is run by Robert Gough for his mother Mary, but this year he seems to have been busy with refurbishment of the sister hotel, the *Angel,* in Bury St Edmunds, and visitors found themselves well looked after by manageress Nancy Innes and Karen, the "charming receptionist", and there was praise for the staff's "flexibility and eagerness to please". Business visitors are catered for during the week; there are good weekend reductions. Ipswich, the birthplace of Cardinal Wolsey, and the possible home of Chaucer, is a busy inland port and agricultural centre on the River Orwell. Despite modernisation, it retains some fine old buildings. A good base for touring Suffolk, and visiting the Snape Maltings and the music festival at Aldeburgh. (*Moira Jarrett, H Darby, and others*)

Open All year.
Rooms 1 suite, 17 double, 4 single. Some on ground floor.
Facilities Ramps. Lounge, bar (jazz/classical background music all day), restaurant; private dining room, small conference room. ⅓-acre garden. Civil wedding licence.
Location ½ mile from centre (quietest rooms at rear). N of Christchurch Pk; turn S off A1214. Private parking.
Restrictions No smoking in restaurant. No dogs in public rooms.
Credit cards All major cards accepted.
Terms [2000] Room: single £72–£82, double £82–£89, suite £110. Breakfast: continental £7.95, English £10.65. Set lunch £18.95, dinner £24.95; full alc £40. Weekend breaks: D,B&B from £42 per person per night. Christmas, New Year, Easter packages. *V*

KIMBOLTON Herefordshire   Map 3

Lower Bache House   `BUDGET`   *Tel* (01568) 750304
Kimbolton
nr Leominster HR6 0ER

A substantial 17th-century stone farmhouse and granary in a lovely
Herefordshire valley near Leominster – "a wonderful setting". With
its low beams and half-timbered walls, it has been sympathetically
restored by Rose and Leslie Wiles, who run it in friendly country guest
house style. Family dogs and cats roam around. Offering "comfort,
rather than elegance", it is "good value, very quiet". Each bedroom has
a small sitting room and old pine furniture. The sitting/dining room,
where cider was once made, has the old cider mill, a vaulted ceiling,
and a flagstone floor. Organic ingredients are used in imaginative
cooking, eg, grilled tiger prawns with a garam masala and turmeric
mayonnaise; duck breast with a port and wild mushroom sauce.
Vegetarians are catered for. Dinner must be ordered by midday;
preferences are discussed in advance. But one visitor would have liked
a little more flexibility: he asked for cheese as an alternative, when
confronted by a rich chocolate roulade, and was surprised to be told:
"We have no cheese." Much of the produce is home grown. Breakfast
is interesting, including unusual dishes cooked from free-range eggs;
also home-smoked kippers, home-made sausages, bread and marmalade. "The owners are enthusiastic, and they take trouble over their
guests," said the nominator. But a check-out time of 10.30 am on
Sunday was thought "extremely early". Much interesting sightseeing
nearby: castles, gardens, Hereford Cathedral with the Mappa Mundi,
etc. (*JAS, AG*)

Open All year.
Rooms 4 double. 1, on ground floor, across courtyard. No telephone.
Facilities Lounge/dining room. No background music. 14-acre grounds:
meadows, wildlife. Walking, cycling, riding, golf, horse-racing, fishing
nearby.
Location 4 miles NE of Leominster. From A4112 between Kimbolton and
Leysters, follow signs to Lower Bache.
Restrictions No smoking. No children under 8. No dogs.
Credit cards None accepted.
Terms B&B: single £34.50, double £59. Set dinner £15.50–£21.50. Bargain
breaks. Christmas package.

KINGHAM Oxfordshire   Map 2

The Tollgate Inn   `NEW/BUDGET`   *Tel* (01608) 658389
Church Street   *Fax* (01608) 659467
Kingham OX7 6YA

In a pristine Oxfordshire village, this handsome old Georgian farmhouse stands near the church; the bedrooms are in extensions at the
back, by a gravel drive (interspersed with flowerbeds) where cars are
parked. The owners, Penny Simpson and Jeff Fergus, took it over in a
run-down state in 1998 and have refurbished from top to bottom. "We

welcome children and dogs, and aim to fit into your plans, not the other way round," they write. "We have no residents' lounge, so we're not great for visitors who want to be around all day." The lounge/bar and restaurant are done in "sophisticated, arty" style, says an inspector, and the emphasis here is on the food (the chef, Matthew Laughton, was formerly head chef at the renowned *Marsh Goose*, Moreton-in-Marsh). His eclectic menus include main courses like roasted cod with orange-braised fennel; lamb sweetbreads with wild mushrooms and Madeira; sweet potato, date and fresh fig tagine. The owners' interest in wine is obvious (wines of the month are chalked up on a board, "with zappy comments, like 'Wow'"), and they also offer a selection of exotic cocktails. Meals and drinks are served in the walled garden in fine weather. The bedrooms, all different, are named for their decor: Lilac, Green ("not for the faint-hearted"), Gingham, etc. The Hayloft, with a separate entrance and a vaulted ceiling, is suitable for a family. "Our room was stylish, very pretty, with views of pastureland and gentle Cotswold hills beyond, but its bathroom lacked places to put things. At breakfast, service was "smiling, if a bit distrait". More reports, please, especially on the food.

Open All year, except 1st 2 weeks Sept, New Year. Only B&B at Christmas.
Rooms 1 family, 9 double. 2 on ground floor.
Facilities Bar (occasional background music). Restaurant. Small walled garden. Golf, fishing, riding, walking, cycling nearby.
Location Centre of village. Trains from London.
Restrictions Smoking in bar only. Dogs in some bedrooms, not in public rooms except bar.
Credit cards MasterCard, Visa.
Terms B&B: single £45–£55, double £50–£85; D,B&B: single £65–£75, double £75–£115. Full alc £27.50. 3-night breaks. *V*

KINGTON Herefordshire   **Map 3**

Penrhos Court NEW   *Tel* (01544) 230720
Kington HR5 3LH   *Fax* (01544) 230754
                                            E-mail martin@penrhos.co.uk
                                            Website www.penrhos.co.uk

A tranquil collection of ancient buildings set around a pond (home to moorhens, coots and mallards) off a road in the hilly Welsh borders. The owners for 30 years, Martin Griffiths and Daphne Lambert (the chef), have lovingly restored it, creating a smoke-free, muzak-free, eco-friendly hotel. Its organic restaurant was the first in Britain to get the Soil Association's symbol, and stickers in the entrance ("We are allergy aware"; "Please don't buy battery chickens") emphasise the point. The oldest part is a flagstone-floored medieval hall, dating from the time of Edward I; there is an Elizabethan wing, and a large modern wing, "beautifully integrated with the rest". Bedrooms, named after local birds, are large; some are huge, with lovely views. "Old-fashioned comfort and creaky wooden floors combine with modern conveniences such as TV and a shower that would measure up to the most exacting standards," say inspectors. "A delicious dinner, served at rustic wooden tables and with some choice, included potato and lovage soup; roast vegetable salad; brill with mustard sauce, and out-standing puddings – we tried them all; the chestnut, raisin and brandy ice-cream was the best ever." There is a wide range of organic and vegetarian wines. For breakfast there were freshly squeezed fruit and vegetable juices ("delicious frothy cucumber juice"); a loaf of whole-meal bread at each table; organic honey and preserves. No fry-up, but Welsh rarebit or tofu sausages. Daphne Lambert runs a school of food and health; gardening weekends are held with Bob Flowerdew, the organic gardener. Close by are the Hergest Croft gardens; also castles, stately homes, and Offa's Dyke.

Open All year.
Rooms 15 double. Some on ground floor.
Facilities Ramps. Lounge, cruck hall, Elizabethan room; function facilities; usually no background music. Garden. Civil wedding licence.
Location ½ mile E of Kington, on A44.
Restrictions No smoking. No dogs.
Credit cards Amex, MasterCard, Visa.
Terms B&B from £55; D,B&B from £80. Set dinner £31.50.

KNUTSFORD Cheshire   Map 4

Belle Epoque   BUDGET   *Tel* (01565) 633060 and 622661
60 King Street   *Fax* (01565) 634150
Knutsford WA16 6DT   *E-mail* belleepoque@compuserve.com

"A delightful place," says a visitor this year to Keith and Nerys Mooney's brasserie-with-rooms. "Not luxurious, but idiosyncratic and comfortable", it is "a popular venue of the 'Cheshire set'", and it has an "efficient young staff". Once a coffee house, the building (with a quirky tower) is considered to be the crowning achievement of Richard Harding Watt, a well-travelled Manchester glove merchant/architect, active locally at the turn of the 19th century. It has a dra-matic Art Nouveau decor: deep green and purple walls, mirrored alcoves, a Venetian glass floor. Fabrics are lavish; tables have heavy cloths, good cutlery and glassware, flowers in tall glass vases, wicker chairs. The Mooneys' son David (who has worked with Raymond Blanc and Marco Pierre White) is chef, serving menus that "embrace all influences", eg, Bury black pudding with potato pancakes; local Cumberland sausage; Cheshire cheese sausage; fish and chips. "A good dinner, with good wines" was enjoyed this year, but one visitor, who asked for chips with his steak, reported that this request was turned down "in a cocky manner". There is a terrace for alfresco meals. The bedrooms are upstairs; some have a dark and dramatic decor; others are plainer; lighting may be poor and storage space limited. One room has French doors leading on to the roof terrace – "here, we breakfasted in privacy on two sunny mornings". Guests are warned of possible aircraft noise – "this was not too bad, but they need a smoking policy – both the restaurant and our room smelt of smoke." With cobbled alleys, courtyards, and narrow streets rich in antique shops, pubs and interior designers, Knutsford is a small commuter town, 18 miles from Manchester. It is named for King Canute (said to have forded the River Lily here in 1016); Mrs Gaskell, who grew up in Knutsford, used it as the model for *Cranford*. It has two Palladian mansions (both National Trust): Tatton Park, in large grounds with magnificent gardens by Humphry Repton and a working farm, and Tabley House. (*Jaime Ribeiro dos Santos, RSL*)

Open All year, Mon–Fri only, except Christmas, bank holidays. Brasserie closed Sat lunch, all day Sun.
Rooms 6 double.
Facilities Restaurant (background music); function rooms; terrace, roof garden. Unsuitable for &.
Location Town centre. Street parking. Regular trains from Manchester.
Restrictions No children under 12. No dogs.
Credit cards All major cards accepted.
Terms [2000] B&B: single £50, double £60. Full alc £25.

Longview BUDGET
51 and 55 Manchester Road
Knutsford WA16 0LX

Tel (01565) 632119
Fax (01565) 652402
E-mail longview_hotel@compuserve.com
Website www.longviewhotel@freeserve.co.uk

Pauline and Stephen West's small hotel, composed of 2 Victorian houses separated by a private home. 2 mins' walk from station. Looks across busy commuter road to wide common (quietest rooms at rear). "Charming proprietors and staff"; welcoming feel: open fire in reception, cosy cellar bar (with Punch prints). Light classical background music in public areas 6.30 am–11 pm. 26 bedrooms, 3 suites, all recently made over: most with mahogany Victorian-style furniture and thoughtfully equipped, but some walls are thin. Careful traditional cooking, eg, smoked haddock rarebit; saddle of wild boar; pineapple charlotte; also good vegetarian dishes, served in no-smoking restaurant with chandelier, dressers, clock with resonant chime. Light meals available in bar and bedrooms. Substantial breakfast. Small roof garden. Open 7 Jan–24 Dec. Restaurant closed midday; also Sun, bank holidays. Unsuitable for & (steep steps). No dogs in public rooms. All major credit cards accepted. B&B: single £47.50–£77.50, double £66.50–£92.50, suite £100–£120. Full alc £24.

LACOCK Wiltshire
Map 2

At the Sign of the Angel
6 Church Street
Lacock, Chippenham SN15 2LB

Tel (01249) 730230
Fax (01249) 730527

♀ *César award in 1989*

"Very good service, very good food, great wine list, bedrooms small but full of character. Great atmosphere. One of the best *Guide* hotels I have stayed in," says an endorsement this year for this quintessentially English 15th-century half-timbered inn. It is in the middle of this lovely old wool village, now preserved in its entirety by the National Trust. The Levis family have run it for 46 years. Chef/*patronne* Lorna Levis and manager/*sous chef* George Hardy preside. With low doorways and beams, oak panelling, antique furniture, open fires, and squeaky floorboards, it is not for those seeking luxury. It is liked for its "no-frills style and intimacy", "friendly but not gushing" service, and peaceful garden. The bedrooms are simple and pretty; some are compact, "and not the most modern, but none the worse for that". Inevitably there's imperfect sound insulation between some rooms. The quietest ones are probably those in the garden cottage across a stream. The restaurant is often busy with diners enjoying the "robustly satisfying English cooking, using excellent local produce", eg, stilton and walnut pâté; pan-fried fillet of beef with horseradish butter; warm treacle and walnut tart with clotted cream. There is always a roast of the day, and a vegetarian option. "Breakfasts are wonderful." Only grumble this year: "No non-smoking area." (*FR, and others*)

Open 1 Jan–22 Dec.
Rooms 10 double. 4 in garden annexe. 1 on ground floor.
Facilities Lounge, 3 dining rooms. Garden: stream. Only restaurant suitable for &.
Location 7 miles S of M4 exit 17; E of A350 Chippenham–Melksham. Garages, off-street parking. Train: Chippenham, 3 miles.
Restriction No dogs in public rooms.
Credit cards All major cards accepted.
Terms B&B: single £85, double £99–£137.50. Full alc £29.50. Winter, summer breaks. No single bookings Sat.

LANGAR Nottinghamshire   Map 2

Langar Hall   *Tel* (01949) 860559
Langar NG13 9HG   *Fax* (01949) 861045
                          E-mail langarhall-hotel@ndirect.co.uk
                          Website www.langarhall.com

Q *César award in 2000*

"An utterly delightful atmosphere; beautiful food and a fantastic wine list." "The decor is faded country house style, but charming and comfortable." "Imogen Skirving has her finger on the pulse as far as hospitality is concerned; her staff are, without exception, sweet natured." Once again, there are many eulogies for this "endearingly, though only slightly, eccentric" apricot-coloured Regency house, the family home of Ms Skirving. Filled with portraits, antiques, Oriental rugs, ornaments, plants and flowers, it stands by the ancient church (with fine monuments) of a village in the Vale of Belvoir (pronounced Beaver). The housekeeping may not be immaculate, and one couple this year found the lighting a bit dim, but *Langar Hall* is loved for its personal style, and is much favoured by lawyers as a retreat from nearby Nottingham. Refurbishment of public rooms and some bedrooms is in progress: "This should dispel the scruffiness without changing the style," says Ms Skirving. The large rooms in the main house are the most expensive; Barristers resembles an old-fashioned solicitor's office. Edwards is "for dreamers and lovers". Smaller rooms, looking over the graveyard, are "just as nice"; plainer ones are in a separate building. In the busy restaurant, the chefs, Toby Garratt and Chris Ansell, serve simply cooked dishes using organic ingredients and light sauces. Roast turbot, roast duck, chargrilled local lamb and saddle of venison are followed by desserts such as passion fruit tart and chocolate fondant, and a cheeseboard that includes Colston Bassett, the stilton cheese made a mile away. There is one report this year of a breakfast not up to the standard of dinner; but another visitor enjoyed "the best poached eggs in the country". Weddings and parties are catered for, which can disturb the peace at times. Occasional opera performances take place after dinner, and there is an annual open-air Shakespeare production. In the extensive grounds are gardens, canals, medieval fishponds and a croquet lawn. (*GS, Martin and Jane Bailey, Padi Howard, Sue Davies*)

Open All year.
Rooms 1 family, 9 double, 1 single. 1 in chalet. 1 on ground floor.
Facilities Ramp. Drawing room, study, bar, dining room (classical background music when required); private dining room; small conference facilities. 30-acre grounds: gardens, children's play area, croquet, ponds. Civil wedding licence.
Location 12 miles SE of Nottingham (hotel will send directions). Train: Grantham or Nottingham; then taxi.
Restrictions No smoking: restaurant, bedrooms. Dogs by arrangement.
Credit cards All major cards accepted.
Terms [2000](*Excluding 5% discretionary service charge added to restaurant bills*) B&B: single £75–£95, double £100–£150, family £150. Set lunch £10, dinner £20; full alc £35. 2-night weekend breaks: 25% reduction. ***V***

LANGFORD BUDVILLE Somerset   **Map 1**

Bindon Country House   *Tel* (01823) 400070
Langford Budville   *Fax* (01823) 400071
nr Wellington TA21 0RU   *E-mail* bindonhouse@msn.com
                          Website www.prideofbritainhotels.com

"Everything is in pleasing order, and reception is warm," says a recent visitor to this "splendidly bizarre" house (Pride of Britain). In a "glorious position", and set in well-kept grounds, it dates back to the 17th century, but a Victorian make-over gave it the appearance of a Baroque Bavarian hunting lodge. Though only ten minutes from the M5, it is deep in Somerset countryside, next to the huge Langford Heath nature reserve. Wellington, the town from which the Iron Duke took his title, is nearby, and the hotel's "personable young owners", Lynn and Mark Jaffa, have turned it into something of a shrine to him: pictures of the battles that he fought, and memorabilia of his life, adorn the public rooms. The bar and the "handsome and light" restaurant are called Wellington and Wellesley, respectively. But the "rather staid" drawing room (with heavy drapes and dark furnishings) is Bonaparte. The bedrooms have the names of famous Wellingtonian victories: Waterloo, Talavera, Douro, etc. They vary in size, but all are well equipped. The young chef, Patrick Roberts, from Brittany, serves a mixture of classical French and modern British dishes, on a set menu with plenty of choice, eg, tian of crab and peppers, or scallops on a broccoli purée; grilled Dover sole, or beef Wellington; banana Tatin, or chocolate fondant with pistachio ice-cream. There is also a short *carte*. "The service is friendly, if a bit amateurish," say visitors this year, who thought the food "ambitious and not always successful". But others considered the cooking "seriously good". The gardens and woodland, which have been restored to their original splendour, include a small swimming pool, a hot tub, a croquet lawn, a tennis court and a private chapel. The hotel is child-friendly – the Jaffas have young children themselves. Dunster Castle, Barrington Court and Hestercombe house and gardens are within driving distance. (*EB*)

Open All year.
Rooms 2 junior suites, 9 double, 1 single. Some on ground floor.
Facilities Drawing room, bar, restaurant, orangery; TV/conference room; classical background music in public rooms at night; pianist on Sat. 7-acre grounds: swimming pool, tennis, croquet, chapel, woodland. Nature reserve adjacent; riding, fishing, boating, nearby. Civil wedding licence.
Location 4 miles NW of Wellington. Take B3187 towards Langford Budville. After 4 miles follow sharp left-hand bend into village. Through village; right towards Wiveliscombe; right at next junction. After 1 mile, pass Bindon Farm; hotel 450 yds further (next right). Train: Tiverton (7 miles), or Taunton.
Restrictions No smoking in restaurant. No dogs in public rooms.
Credit cards All major cards accepted.
Terms [2000] B&B: single £85, double £95–£185, suite £125–£135. Set lunch £14.95, dinner £29.50; full alc £40. 2 children under 14 accommodated free in 2 suites. Short breaks all year; Christmas package. *V*

LANGHO Lancashire   **Map 4**

Northcote Manor   *Tel* (01254) 240555
Northcote Road, Langho   *Fax* (01254) 246568
Blackburn BB6 8BE   *E-mail* admin@northcotemanor.com
                                     Website www.northcotemanor.com

The dining room at Nigel Haworth and Craig Bancroft's *Michelin*-starred restaurant-with-rooms is the main attraction, by all accounts, and local customers are "very much at the core". Its recent renovation is "absolutely stunning", says a visitor this year: sunny yellow walls, crockery specially designed by Wedgwood, toned-down lighting; daytime views over a Japanese-style flowerbed "add another dimension". But the lounge was thought "dingy" by contrast, particularly in the afternoon, and the loud jazz played throughout dinner was disliked. Nigel Haworth, who describes his cooking as "modern British with rustic undertones", has researched old regional recipes for such dishes as black pudding and pink trout with mustard and watercress sauce; Scotch beef with marrowbone, tarragon jus and honey-roast potatoes; apple crumble soufflé. Many vegetables and herbs are home-grown organically. The wine list is wide-ranging, with house wines at £14.50, and a "fine selection of half bottles". The bay-windowed red brick Victorian house, set in wooded grounds, looks across to Pendle Hill, above the county town of Clitheroe. The busy A59 road is close by (windows are double-glazed), "but the views are ravishing". Most of the bedrooms are spacious, with good-quality fabrics, old furniture, ornaments and games. Some are reached via a handsome wooden staircase; some are down "a maze of narrow corridors". A new telephone system gives guests "total e-commerce access". "One cannot fault the breakfast for choice": it includes freshly squeezed orange juice, an "artistically arranged" plate of fresh fruit, black and white puddings, "delicious wholemeal bread". The place is informally run; service can be "haphazard" at times, and a visitor this year disliked the "optional" 10% service charge. There is good walking in the Ribble Valley and the Forest of Bowland; nearby are ruined abbeys, interesting museums, and historic villages – many associated with witches. (*Francine Walsh, Richard Fitzherbert, and others*)

Open All year, except 25 Dec, 1 Jan.
Rooms 1 suite, 13 double. 4 on ground floor, 1 adapted for &.
Facilities Ramp. Lounge, drawing room, bar, restaurant (jazz during dinner); private dining/meeting room. 2-acre garden. Shooting, hunting, fishing, golf nearby. Civil wedding licence.
Location From M6 exit 31, follow signs to Skipton, Clitheroe. At first set of traffic lights, turn left on to A59. Straight ahead at new roundabout at Mellor. After 8 miles turn left, immediately before large roundabout at Langho. Train: Preston, 14 miles; then bus/taxi.
Restrictions No smoking: restaurant, some bedrooms. No dogs.
Credit cards Amex, MasterCard, Visa.
Terms (*Excluding "optional" 10% service charge*) B&B: single £80–£100, double £90–£110, suite £110–£130. Set lunch £16, dinner £25–£40; full alc £52. 2- to 3-night gourmet breaks.

LANGLEY MARSH Somerset   **Map 1**

Langley House   *Tel* (01984) 623318
Langley Marsh   *Fax* (01984) 624573
Wiveliscombe   *E-mail* user@langley.in2home.co.uk
nr Taunton TA4 2UF

A gold grasshopper sign marks the entrance of this restaurant-with-rooms, owned by a "nicely tactful" couple, Peter and Anne Wilson. He is the chef, she is front-of-house, "anxious to please". The Grade II listed house, dating from the 16th century, stands in large grounds, with mature gardens, a pond and a tiny stream, on the edge of Exmoor. The decor "emphasises comfort as well as elegance, using vibrant colours". Antique furniture, rich fabrics, and fresh and dried flowers abound. The medium-sized bedrooms, up a curved staircase, have a floral decor, good lighting. Dinner, in the small beamed pink-and-green dining room, consists of three courses on weekdays, four (including cheese) at the weekend. Fresh ingredients – fish from Brixham and local lamb, for example – are cooked with herbs and vegetables from the walled garden. "I liked the no-choice menus; they inspired me with confidence that the chef had chosen the best ingredients for the day," one correspondent wrote of Mr Wilson's modern British cooking. No choice until dessert (which might be "icky sticky pudding" with toffee sauce, or elderflower and elderberry syllabub). Morning tea is brought to the bedroom. "Toast at breakfast comes with the hot dishes so that it, too, is hot." "A thoroughly pleasurable, if quite expensive, stay" (extra charges, for after-dinner coffee and chocolates, newspapers, etc, can bump up the bill). The Brendon Hills are nearby, and so are several famous gardens: Knightshayes, Stourhead, Montacute, etc. (*AL, and others*)

Open All year.
Rooms 1 family, 6 double, 1 single.
Facilities 2 lounges, restaurant, conservatory, private dining room. 4-acre garden: croquet. Unsuitable for &.
Location B3227 to Wiveliscombe; right at town centre, signposted Langley Marsh; house is ½ mile to N, on right. Train: Taunton; then bus to Langley Cross.
Restrictions No smoking: restaurant, 2 bedrooms. No dogs in public rooms.
Credit cards Amex, MasterCard, Visa.
Terms B&B: single £77.50–£85, double £93–£127.50, family £150–£162.50; D,B&B: single £105–£117.50, double £148–£192.50, suite £205–£227.50. Set dinner (3 to 4 courses) £27.50–£32.50. Discount for 2 nights or more. 1-night bookings sometimes refused weekends, bank holidays. *V*

## LASTINGHAM North Yorkshire					Map 4

Lastingham Grange						*Tel* (01751) 417345
Lastingham YO62 6TH						*Fax* (01751) 417358
E-mail lastinghamgrange@aol.com
Website www.lastinghamgrange.co.uk

Ω *César award in 1991*

"*Lastingham Grange* is always the highlight of our trip," says a Californian visitor who enjoys the peace and quiet of this traditional hotel. Its chief attraction is the "marvellous position" in the North Yorkshire Moors National Park; you can step straight out of the door on to the moor. The owners, Dennis and Jane Wood, have been here for years, and their many loyal visitors love the "homely atmosphere". "I do not know of a more pleasant hotel," one supporter writes this year. Another praised the "outstanding dedication" of the proprietor, and the "conscious effort to treat every guest as an individual". The 17th-century stone-walled farmhouse, built round a courtyard, is surrounded by gardens, mature trees and fields. Mr Wood "is generous with the loan of maps, and has obviously walked the moors himself". The house is well maintained, and the decor is thoroughly traditional (patterned carpets everywhere; flowery fabrics and wallpaper in the "spotless" bedrooms). Asked in the *Guide*'s questionnaire whether background music is played, Mr Wood writes: "Certainly not!" The food is as traditional as the rest, with dishes like melon and Parma ham or leek and ham tartlet; guinea fowl with cranberry sauce or grilled venison steak. There is always a vegetarian main course. Mr Wood is "very attentive in the dining room, without being intrusive." Prices are considered high, but newspapers, morning coffee, afternoon tea and shoe-cleaning are included. Children are welcomed – they have their own playground and ponies. The village, where St Cedd built an abbey in the 7th century, makes an excellent base for walking. Nearby attractions include Castle Howard, and Rievaulx and Fountains abbeys. (*HRL, Douglas M Ward, Mrs Ann H Edwards, and others*)

Open Beginning Mar–end Nov.
Rooms 10 double, 2 single.
Facilities Hall, lounge, dining room; laundry facilities. No background music. 10-acre grounds: garden, adventure playground. In National Park, near moors and dales; riding, golf, swimming nearby. Unsuitable for &.

Location Off A170, 5 miles NE of Kirkbymoorside. Turn N towards Appleton-le-Moors 2 miles E of Kirkbymoorside.
Restrictions No smoking in dining room. No dogs in public rooms.
Credit cards None accepted.
Terms [2000] B&B: single £82–£85, double £155–£160; D,B&B: single £98–£110, double £185–£204. Set lunch £17.50 (£21.50 on Sun), dinner £31.75. Light or picnic lunches available. Child accommodated in parents' room: under 12, free. Reductions for long stays; winter breaks.

LAVENHAM Suffolk   Map 2

The Great House   *Tel* (01787) 247431
Market Place   *Fax* (01787) 248007
Lavenham CO10 9QZ   *E-mail* info@greathouse.co.uk
                                       Website www.greathouse.co.uk

In the middle of "one of England's finest medieval towns" stands this French establishment, surrounded by many other lovely old houses. The 16th-century building with its Georgian façade was painstakingly restored in the 1930s, and the house was later the home of the poet Stephen Spender. It has been a restaurant-with-rooms since 1985, and was found "wonderful; charming though not luxurious" again this year. Accommodation is mainly in suites; the best ones have antiques, old beams and a smart new bathroom; homelier ones are on the top floor. "We liked the thoughtful details, eg, halogen lights in the antique four-poster, enabling us to read in bed. It was wonderful to have a separate sitting room; we watched the comings and goings in the market place." The "consistently courteous service" is praised, and so is the Gallic atmosphere; children are made welcome in true French style. Régis Crépy (the owner/chef) and his wife Martine run the place with a French staff, and traditional French dishes are served in the oak-beamed, candlelit dining room, with its bare floorboards and original inglenook fireplace. Ravioli of lobster and courgette fondue with a langoustine bisque; scallops on a risotto and Parmesan gâteau with a goat's cheese sauce; tarte au citron with a red fruit coulis, might feature on the *carte*; the *prix fixe* menu offers plenty of choice and good value. Light lunches are served from Tuesday to Saturday; Sunday lunch is a set three-course affair. The mainly French wine list includes plenty of reasonably priced bottles. There is a little sitting room/bar, a patio with tables under sunshades, where alfresco meals are served on fine days, and a walled garden. The restaurant is popular, so you should book a table when reserving your room, and one visitor found the piped music irritating this year. Lavenham is a good base for visiting Bury St Edmunds (where the Crépys own another restaurant, *Maison Bleue at Mortimers*), Colchester, Long Melford, Dedham, etc; Newmarket is 30 minutes' drive, Cambridge 45. (*Lesley and Carl Powell, Stewart Douglas-Mann; also AB*)

Open Feb–Dec. Restaurant closed 3 weeks Jan, Sun night/Mon, except bank holiday Mon.
Rooms 4 suites, 1 double.
Facilities Lounge/bar, restaurant (French background music). ½-acre garden: patio, swings, children's toys. Unsuitable for &.

Location By Market Cross, near Guildhall. Public carpark. Bus 753, Colchester–Bury.
Restrictions No smoking: restaurant, bedrooms. No dogs in public rooms.
Credit cards Amex, MasterCard, Visa.
Terms [2000] B&B: single £55–£120, double/suite £70–£140; D,B&B: single £74.95, double £109.90, suite £129.90. Set lunch £9.95–£15.95, dinner £19.95; full alc: lunch £18, dinner £35. 3-night breaks: D,B&B £52.95–£62.95. Child accommodated in parents' room: under 2, free; 3–12, £15. 1-night bookings refused Fri/Sat.

Lavenham Priory   NEW
Water Street
Lavenham CO10 9RW

Tel (01787) 247404
Fax (01787) 248472
E-mail pitt@btinternet.com
Website www.lavenhampriory.co.uk

No ordinary B&B, this. With Elizabethan wall paintings, oak floors and a variety of exotic beds (four-poster, bateau, polonaise) in the "bedchambers", it is a Grade I listed house, once owned by Benedictine monks, that dates from the 13th century. Later it was the home of an Elizabethan merchant. Now it has been lavishly restored by the current owners, Tim and Gilli Pitt. Original features, carefully preserved, include beamed, sloping ceilings, an oak Jacobean staircase and a Tudor inglenook fireplace in the Great Hall. "The setting is idyllic, in a lovely garden, and the house is quite beautiful," says an inspector in 2000. "Everything is done with taste, like a comfortable home. Our bedroom was huge, romantic, with a soaring ceiling, large pieces of antique furniture, nice views. The bathroom, oh so pretty, had a large slipper bath, and there was a separate shower room with a power shower. At breakfast, served round one large table in another antique-filled room, you squeeze your own orange juice, and make your own toast from good bread; there is a buffet with fresh fruit, compotes, etc; and well-cooked egg dishes, etc. The owners are very nice, chatty and helpful." In summer, breakfast and pre-dinner drinks are served in the courtyard herb garden. Dinner is sometimes served, by arrangement, and there are good restaurants very near, eg *The Great House* (see above). Guests can sit in the Great Hall or a lounge (with TV, videos, books and a fire).

Open All year, except Christmas, New Year.
Rooms 5 double.
Facilities Great Hall, reading room, breakfast room. No background music. 3-acre garden: courtyard, herb garden. Unsuitable for &.
Location Central. From A1141 to Lavenham turn by *Swan* on to Water St right after 50 yds into private drive. Parking.
Restrictions No smoking. No children under 10. No dogs.
Credit cards MasterCard, Visa.
Terms [2000] B&B: single £59–£69, double £78–£98. 1-night bookings refused Sat.

LEAMINGTON SPA Warwickshire *See SHORTLIST*   **Map 2**

LEDBURY Herefordshire *See SHORTLIST*   **Map 3**

LEEDS West Yorkshire   Map 4

42 The Calls   *Tel* (0113) 244 0099
42 The Calls   *Fax* (0113) 234 4100
Leeds LS2 7EW   *E-mail* hotel@42thecalls.co.uk
                                    Website www.42thecalls.co.uk

♈ *César award in 1995*

"Stunningly good." "Just about the nicest, most unusual small city
hotel we have stayed in." "I loved the extraordinary attention to detail,
the individual rooms." "What a wonderful place." Almost all reports
are highly enthusiastic again this year about this unusual hotel in a
former warehouse in the waterfront area of central Leeds, though one
couple wrote in 2000 of lax housekeeping. The decor is modern, with
smart, air-conditioned public rooms, and bedrooms all different and
recently sound-proofed, with original pictures, a CD-player, satellite
TV, three telephones. They vary from "studio" to "Director's" (the
latter "are exceptional"). Many rooms overlook the River Aire: one
couple was pleased to find a fishing rod by the window, with a suggestion that they try their luck. A family with four children "were
given a suite of rooms, which were the utmost in comfort and luxury".
Other guests liked the "huge bed with lovely sheets", the "delicious
breakfast" delivered through a hatch, the "very good room service
meals" and the jokey touches (frog-shaped bath soap, Smarties left on
pillows at night). "Beautiful black-and-white bathrooms" are lavish.
The staff, led by the manager, Belinda Dawson, is "unfailingly polite
and helpful". If you breakfast downstairs (in a "restful" canal-side
room) there is squeeze-your-own juice, a range of 20 jams, and
cooked dishes such as "the juiciest kippers I have ever eaten", nine
types of exotic sausage (eg, wild boar and black sheep) and "ten different, delicious breads". The bustling *Brasserie 44* serves "excellent,
straightforward food" with a Mediterranean influence. The restaurant,
Pool Court at 42 (*Michelin* star), serves "classically inspired modern
cooking" in black-and-white surroundings, and it has a waterfront balcony for summer meals. Jeff Baker's menus might include creamed
eggs with shaved truffle; sautéed calf's liver with polenta and
pancetta; organic lemon sponge with mandarin sorbet. The hotel is
business-orientated during the week; at the weekend it offers generous
reductions to independent travellers. Difficult to find by car, but they
will send a map, "and we regularly talk people in on their mobile
phone". Valet parking is provided, at £4.95 a day. The nearby
Victorian arcades and shops include the northern branch of Harvey
Nichols. The hotel is now part of the Scotsman Hotel Group; its
founder, Jonathan Wix, is converting the *Scotsman* building in
Edinburgh into a 68-bedroom hotel. (*Anne-Marie Sutcliffe, William
Goodhart, Roland Philipps, Karen Palmer, Pat and Jeremy Temple,
and many others*)

Open All year, except 4 days at Christmas. *Pool Court* closed bank holidays.
Rooms 3 suites, 31 double, 7 "study". 1 suitable for ♿.
Facilities Lift. Lounge, 2 bars, breakfast room, restaurant, brasserie;
24-hour room service; conference facilities. Background music: lounge,
breakfast room.

Location Central, near Corn Exchange (rooms double/triple-glazed; quietest ones overlook river). Valet parking.
Restrictions No smoking: restaurant, breakfast room. "Well-behaved dogs" by arrangement.
Credit cards All major cards accepted.
Terms (*Excluding 10% service charge on meals*) Room: single £98 (£80 weekend), double £150 (£85 weekend), suite £250 (£130 weekend). Breakfast: continental £8.95, English £11.50. Restaurant: set lunch £14.50–£19, dinner £29.50–£50; brasserie: light lunch from £5; set meals £9.75–£12.95; full alc £28. Child accommodated in parents' room: £5. 1-night bookings refused bank holidays, some weekends. *V*

Haley's   *Tel* (0113) 278 4446
Shire Oak Road   *Fax* (0113) 275 3342
Headingley, Leeds LS6 2DE   *E-mail* info@haleys.co.uk
                                         Website www.haleys.co.uk

A "country hotel in the city", John Appleyard's turreted Victorian house is in a leafy suburb near the university. It is named for a local stonemason prominent at the turn of the century, and it has been carefully restored to its original splendour. There are open fires, period furniture, lavish drapes in the public rooms; pictures everywhere, many with a cricketing theme in honour of the famous cricket ground nearby. "It has a delightful atmosphere, friendly staff, very comfortable rooms," says a visitor this year. Others liked the "quiet surroundings, well-trained young staff", the "lack of sycophancy" and the free parking. "The quality of food and service are high." Many weekday visitors are here on business (each bedroom has two telephones and a desk); there are good weekend reductions. The bedrooms in the turrets are large, with a bay window. The one in the garden has "well-designed period touches", a tiny lobby/lounge and a decent-sized bathroom. Extras range from a trouser-press and an ironing board to Harrogate toffee. In the restaurant, with its striking brown-and-cream decor, chef Jon Vennell's monthly-changing menu of modern cooking includes, eg, terrine of carrots and wild mushrooms; braised lamb shank; always a vegetarian option; desserts such as strawberry shortbread tower; warm banana and chocolate pudding. Breakfast is Yorkshire or continental. (*AB Ballantine*)

Open All year, except 26–30 Dec. Restaurant closed midday Mon–Sat, to non-residents Sun evening.
Rooms Two 2-roomed suites, 18 double, 9 single. 7 in annexe, *Bedford House*, next door.
Facilities Ramp. Lounge/bar, library, restaurant; function/meeting room. Jazz/classical background music at night. Small front and back lawns. Unsuitable for &. Civil wedding licence.
Location 2 miles N of centre. Turn off A660 Leeds–Otley between Yorkshire and HSBC banks in Headingley. Private parking.
Restrictions No smoking: restaurant, library, some bedrooms. Guide dogs only.
Credit cards All major cards accepted.
Terms [2000] B&B: single £60–£120, double £85–£165, suite £185–£230. Set Sun lunch £17.50, dinner £25; full alc £37.50. Weekend breaks. *V*

Malmaison NEW   *Tel* (0113) 398 1000
Sovereign Quay   *Fax* (0113) 398 1002
Leeds LS1 1D2   *E-mail* leeds@malmaison.com
                                                       Website www.malmaison.com

A new *Malmaison,* by the River Aire, decorated, like the rest of the
group, with contemporary chic: bold stripes and "fashionable brown/
grey/purple colours". "Efficient, professional and smart," was the verdict of an inspector, visiting anonymously. She felt "really cared for"
in the "pleasant, stylishly lit" brasserie: "I was given a good table, and
addressed by name. Good, robust food was accompanied by modern
jazz." She thought the bar "a bit crepuscular", but enjoyed her room-
service breakfast, served Sushi-style on a black tray, though other
visitors thought it "a bit, trendy – we would have preferred toast and
marmalade to pastries". A cooked breakfast is served in the brasserie.
"Rooms more spacious than the norm"; "the best bedroom lighting
ever," are other comments. (*Anne-Marie Sutcliffe, and others*)

Open All year.
Rooms 1 suite, 97 double, 2 single. 5 suitable for &.
Facilities Lift. Lounge, bar, brasserie; background jazz/blues; gym.
Location Central. Some rooms might get noise from bars opposite.
Restrictions No smoking in some bedrooms. No dogs.
Credit cards All major cards accepted.
Terms [2000] Room: single £79, double £105–£110, suite £140. Breakfast
£8.50–£10.50. Set lunch £9.50, dinner £20; full alc £30. Christmas package.

LEONARD STANLEY Gloucestershire   **Map 3**

The Grey Cottage BUDGET   *Tel/Fax* (01453) 822515
Bath Road, Leonard Stanley
Stonehouse GL10 3LU

♕ *César award in 1999*

Many tributes came again this year to Andrew and Rosemary Reeves.
"Their kindness and hospitality is second to none. Immaculate attention to detail." "The *César* award is well deserved." "Superb hosts; we
were made incredibly welcome." Their small, simple stone guest
house, 170 years old, was once the meeting place for the local
Methodist movement. Its colourful flower garden, enclosed by a nine-
foot yew hedge, is dominated by a 100-foot sequoia, planted in 1865.
The three spacious bedrooms, filled with "quality furniture", are supplied with dressing-gowns, chocolates, fruit, "all the toiletries one
could need", "crisp white linen and good thick towels". One room has
its bathroom down a short hall. Dinner, by arrangement, is served at a
polished table in front of a log fire, or in a conservatory. No choice;
preferences are discussed in advance, and local produce, organic when
possible, is used. It is "a feast, and cheap at the price", says a visitor
who enjoyed warm stilton and walnut tart with a broccoli sauce; roast
partridge with grape and ginger stuffing and "*real* bread sauce"; honey
ice-cream with Moroccan oranges in Cointreau. There is a "very
acceptable choice of wine". The "pleasant and varied breakfasts"

include freshly squeezed orange juice, kedgeree, smoked salmon with scrambled eggs, home-made jams. A Norman church is all that

remains of the medieval priory that once stood in the village. Local attractions include the Wildfowl and Wetlands Trust at Slimbridge, Berkeley Castle, the Weston-birt Arboretum. (*Graham Dyster, David and Janet Austin, Pamela and Tim Moorey, Sue and Colin Raymond, and many others*)

Open All year, except occasional holidays. Advance booking essential.
Rooms 2 double, 1 single. No telephone.
Facilities Sitting room with TV, conservatory, dining room. No background music. ¼-acre garden. Unsuitable for &.
Location 3 miles from M5 exit 13. 3 miles W of Stroud. 1 mile S of A419, between King's Stanley and Leonard Stanley. Train: Stonehouse, 1½ miles; then local bus.
Restrictions No smoking: dining room, bedrooms. No dogs.
Credit cards None accepted.
Terms B&B: single £35–£38, double £48–£60; D,B&B: single £55–£58, double £68–£80. Reductions for 3 nights or more.

LEWDOWN Devon   **Map 1**

Lewtrenchard Manor   *Tel* (01566) 783256
Lewdown   *Fax* (01566) 783332
nr Okehampton EX20 4PN   *E-mail* s&j@lewtrenchard.co.uk
                                Website lewtrenchard.demon.co.uk

"A superbly tranquil setting, obliging staff, lovely garden." "Extremely comfortable; the proprietors are affable but not pushy." Set in large grounds, with a lake with swans, this is the "Victorian–Elizabethan fantasy" of the Revd Sabine Baring-Gould, author of the hymn "Onward, Christian Soldiers" (he is buried in the little church at the end of the drive). It has an avenue of beech trees, a dovecote and a sunken garden. The stone manor house (Pride of Britain) "is exquisite", say visitors this year, with its ornate plaster ceilings, oak panelling, stained glass, large log fires, portraits, antiques, gleaming brass door handles. The bedrooms, off a long music gallery, are reached by an impressive staircase – it is worth asking for a garden view. Their "traditional, uncluttered" country house decor is liked; a small bottle of champagne greets new arrivals. No keys on doors, but you can bolt yourself in. The South African owners, James and Sue Murray, and their three black labradors, Duma, Ben and Holly, are much in evidence. The chef, David Swade, "treads the fine line between the pretentious and the acceptable", says a visitor this year (eg, warm squab pigeon salad with pickled wild mushrooms; brill roasted with cinnamon, lemon and ginger, crushed potato and honey-roasted baby fennel; vanilla mousse with champagne-poached strawberries). She thought her meal "excellent, with first-rate ingredients – but the courses appeared at very long intervals", and one guest reported that the menu did not change during a two-night stay. Vegetarian and special diets are catered for. Nearby are Dartmoor, Cothele House, Buckland Abbey, the Lydford Gorge, good fishing. (*Michael and Maureen Heath, Anne Laurence*)

Open All year.
Rooms 1 suite, 8 double.
Facilities Stair lift. Lounge, bar lounge, restaurant (classical background music during dinner), breakfast room; ballroom. 11-acre grounds: garden, croquet, lake (fishing, from boat only). Clay-pigeon shooting, river fishing nearby. Civil wedding licence.
Location S of A30 between Okehampton and Launceston. Take slip road for A386 Tavistock–Plymouth. Right at T junction, then immediately left on to old A30, signposted Bridestowe/Lewdown. Left, after 6 miles, at sign to Lewtrenchard.
Restrictions No smoking in restaurant. Children under 8 by arrangement. No dogs in public rooms, unattended in bedrooms.
Credit cards All major cards accepted.
Terms [2000] B&B: single £85–£110, double £115–£160, suite £144–£170. Set lunch £19.50, dinner £32. 7-day rates; off-season discounts. Christmas 3-night house party. 1-night bookings refused bank holidays.

LEWES East Sussex   Map 2

Berkeley House   BUDGET   *Tel* (01273) 476057
2 Albion Street   *Fax* (01273) 479575
Lewes BN7 2ND   *E-mail* rp.berkeleyhse@lineone.net
                                 Website www.berkeleyhousehotel.co.uk

"The town is delightful, and our stay was a great success," says an aficionado of this small B&B, who also enjoyed "a pleasant hour with a beer on the eccentric roof terrace". The cream Grade II listed house is part of a Georgian terrace in a small side street, and its admirers enjoy its off-beat style and good value. The owner, Roy Patten, is "a charming and helpful host", a fund of local information, and an opera enthusiast. The bedrooms are on the small side, with a shower *en suite*. The one at the top "is not for the arthritic or overly tall". Breakfasts, served in a light room overlooking the "micro-garden" are "copious and good". Drinks, tea and coffee are available "at all reasonable times". The county town of East Sussex has lots of antique shops, and the South Downs Way (splendid walking), is a mile away; Glyndebourne is close; Brighton and Charleston Farmhouse are 20 minutes' drive. (*Simon Willbourn*)

Open All year, except Christmas, New Year.
Rooms 1 suite, 4 double. All with shower. No telephone.
Facilities Lounge, breakfast room. No background music. Roof terrace. Leisure centre, outdoor swimming pool nearby. Unsuitable for &.
Location Central. Limited private parking opposite (advance booking advised); public carpark nearby.
Restrictions No smoking: breakfast room, 1 bedroom. No children under 8. No dogs.
Credit cards All major cards accepted.

Terms B&B: single £40–£50, double £50–£60, suite £75. 1-night bookings sometimes refused Sat May–Sept. *V*

Shelleys　　NEW
High Street
Lewes BN7 1XS

Tel (01273) 472361
Fax (01273) 483512

Once inhabited by the poet's aunts, this "grand and spacious" Georgian house, "very much a part of the town's life", is now part of the Thistle hotel chain. It is liked for its "good ambience" and good food (main courses such as roast seabass with braised red cabbage; monkfish tail wrapped in Parma ham, are served by chef Robert Pierce). The nominator found it "delightfully stylish", and was given a warm welcome. "Breakfast, excellent in all respects, had fresh ingredients and a good, but not fussy, choice. The manager, Graeme Coles, gives very personal, yet discreet, attention to guests. Prices are steep, but it was a faultless stay." Bar lunches, morning coffee, afternoon teas and room-service meals are available, and there are benches and tables in the quiet rear garden. Chintzy fabrics and pastel colours in the bedrooms; some have a four-poster. (*Richard Parish*)

Open All year.
Rooms 3 suites, 15 double, 1 single.
Facilities Lounge, bar, restaurant (light classical background music at quiet times). 2-acre garden. Unsuitable for &.
Location Central (roadside rooms double-glazed). Carpark. Train/bus stations nearby.
Restrictions No smoking: restaurant, bedrooms. No dogs in public rooms.
Credit cards All major cards accepted.
Terms Room: single £130, double £170, suite £250. Breakfast: continental £10.25, English £12.50. Set lunch £20, dinner £30; full alc £45. Off-peak breaks. Christmas package. *V*

LIFTON Devon　　　　　　　　　　　　**Map 1**

The Arundell Arms
Lifton PL16 0AA

Tel (01566) 784666
Fax (01566) 784494
E-mail arundellarms@btinternet.com

"Very well managed, with delicious meals and snacks," says a plaudit this year for this creeper-covered coaching inn in a small Devon town just off the A30. It has been run for 40 years by the owner, Anne Voss-Bark, much in evidence, with a pleasant, mostly local staff. The manager, Sally Hill, has been here for 22 years, and Roy Buckingham, the fishing instructor, has been a riverkeeper on the River Tamar for 35 years. Mrs Voss-Bark and her husband, Conrad, are expert fly-fishers – both have written books on the subject. They have 20 miles of trout, sea trout and salmon fishing on the Tamar and four of its tributaries, and a three-acre stocked lake. Fishing courses of all kinds are offered (you need to book early). There is good shooting, too, and families and non-sporting guests are also welcomed. "Mrs Voss-Bark is charming and thoroughly professional. The ghillies are knowledgeable and entertaining. Picnic hampers are provided, and when you return in the

evening there is a comfortable lounge for a restorative dram."
Following the redecoration of the large lounge last year, the restaurant
(formerly Lifton's assembly rooms), where a young French manager
now presides, has had a major facelift: a lighter, more contemporary
look, with intimate lighting, now complements its high ceilings and
large windows; facilities are being developed to provide alfresco
meals. The much-admired chef Philip Burgess (assisted by Nick
Shopland) has presided over the kitchens for 20 years. Eating arrangements are flexible, and the food in the bar is as highly thought of as
that in the restaurant. The menus, based on local ingredients, include
grilled asparagus with parmesan; casserole of sole, seabass, lobster
and scallops; braised oxtail with prunes and root vegetables.
Vegetables and herbs are organically home grown; fresh fish comes
from Cornwall, cheeses from nearby Tavistock. The bedrooms vary
greatly (some, on the road, are plain). In the terraced garden behind is
one of the few remaining cockpits in England. All manner of off-
season packages are offered; functions and conferences are catered
for. Local sightseeing includes Castle Drogo, Cothele, Lanhydrock
and Buckland, the National Marine Aquarium in Plymouth, and the
Eden 2000 project – a huge indoor garden. (*BC, and others*)

Open All year, except 3 days over Christmas (but Christmas lunch served).
Rooms 20 double, 8 single. 5 in annexe opposite. 4 on ground floor.
Facilities Ramp. Lounge, cocktail bar, public bar, 2 dining rooms (taped back-
ground music); conference/meeting rooms; games room, skittle alley. ½-acre
terraced garden. 20 miles fishing rights on River Tamar and tributaries, 3-acre
stocked lake, fishing school for beginners. Civil wedding licence applied for.
Location Half mile off A30, 3 miles E of Launceston (road-facing rooms
double-glazed). Train: Exeter, 40 miles; then taxi.
Restrictions No smoking in restaurant. No dogs in restaurant.
Credit cards All major cards accepted.
Terms [2000] B&B: £45–£74; D,B&B (min. 2 nights) £70–£90. Bar meals
from £3.50. Set lunch £17–£21, dinner £29.50–£36.50. Child accommodated
in parents' room: under 16, free. 2–6-night breaks all year; off-season breaks:
sporting, gourmet, etc. *V*

LINCOLN Lincolnshire   **Map 4**

D'Isney Place Hotel   *Tel* (01522) 538881
Eastgate   *Fax* (01522) 511321
Lincoln LN2 4AA   *E-mail* info@disneyplacehotel.co.uk
                                   Website www.disneyplacehotel.co.uk

"The most luxurious B&B we know, refreshingly consistent over
many years," say returning visitors to David and Judy Payne's red
brick Georgian house. Named for the local worthy who built it in
1735, it was extended in Victorian days. The medieval wall of the
cathedral close forms the southern boundary of its garden. The bedrooms vary greatly in size and style: the best ones are "lovely and
spacious, with gorgeous old furniture"; some have a view across the
town to country. One has a four-poster bed, two have a spa bath; some
are suitable for a family; the simplest ones have a shower. Some rooms
get traffic noise (but they have double glazing), others are "remarkably

quiet". No public rooms: a "very good" breakfast is served in the bedrooms. Fresh orange juice, fresh fruit and, if wanted, a "megaplateful" of sausages, mushrooms, bacon, etc, are "charmingly presented, with fresh flowers and bone china". Service is "unobtrusive but solicitous". The weekend breaks are good value. The *Wig and Mitre*, a pub/café/restaurant, and *The Jew's House* (in one of the oldest inhabited houses in Britain) are recommended for meals. The castle and the Usher Gallery are close by. (*John and Joan Wyatt, Jane Cummins*)

Open All year.
Rooms 1 suite, 14 double, 1 single. 2 in cottage annexe with sitting room, kitchen, dining room. Some on ground floor.
Facilities Ramp. No background music. 1-acre garden.
Location By cathedral. Front rooms double-glazed; back ones quietest. Small carpark; street parking after 6 pm. Bus, taxi from station.
Restriction No smoking in 13 bedrooms.
Credit cards All major cards accepted.
Terms [2000] B&B: single £61.50–£71.50, double £63–£99, suite £158. Weekend breaks. ***V***

LISKEARD Cornwall   Map 1

Pencubitt House   `BUDGET`   *Tel/Fax* (01579) 342694
Station Road   *E-mail* claire@penc.co.uk
Liskeard PL14 4EB   *Website* www.penc.co.uk

Victorian wool merchant's house in 2-acre mature gardens in elevated position on edge of old market town, on B3254 near railway station. Owned since 1996 by young couple, Michael Kent (the chef) and wife Claire (front-of-house), who are refurbishing. Lovely views of East Looe valley. 5 bedrooms. Spacious public rooms: 2 lounges, bar, candlelit restaurant (no smoking; classical background music). Good modern British cooking (eg, globe artichoke and asparagus salad with parmesan; oven-roast cod with a herb crust); friendly service. MasterCard, Visa accepted. Unsuitable for &. No children under 12. No dogs in public rooms. B&B £30–£40; D,B&B £50–£65. Set lunch/dinner £24 [2000]. More reports, please. ***V***

LITTLE MALVERN Worcestershire   Map 3

Holdfast Cottage   *Tel* (01684) 310288
Marlbank Road   *Fax* (01684) 311117
Little Malvern WR13 6NA   *E-mail* holdcothot@aol.com
                                          Website www.holdfast-cottage.co.uk

"Excellent, and competently run." "A nice, unpretentious place, with unobtrusive service." Two reports this year on Stephen and Jane Knowles's small hotel, a 17th-century cream-and-brown cottage with Victorian extensions. Long and low, it is set back from the road between Little Malvern and Pershore. From its wisteria-covered terrace there are wide views of the Malvern Hills. Entrance is via a plant-filled conservatory into a small hall with low black beams and the original cast iron range. The diminutive Victorian-style bar, and the "very pretty" blue-and-white candlelit dining room (with prints on walls; flowers and knick-knacks on old oak tables), overlook the garden. The bedrooms, reached up little staircases, are small too, with a "slightly old-fashioned" decor of flowered fabrics and patterned wallpaper. The rooms with the most character are in the older part of the house. "Our bathroom was fun, with a bath under the eaves." Mrs Knowles is the chef, offering five choices for each course, eg, avocado and pink grapefruit salad; roast guinea fowl breast with creamy wild mushroom sauce. Rolls are home baked, ice-creams home made, herbs home grown. Breakfast "is in the best English tradition; no plastic containers". Children are welcomed; there are toys, and a Wendy house in the garden. Around are trees and farmland. Sir Edward Elgar is buried in the Roman Catholic cemetery in the village. Gloucester, Worcester, Hereford and Tewkesbury, Eastnor Castle and Little Malvern Court are all within easy reach. (*John and Hazel Williams, Alice Wilkinson*)

Open All year, except Christmas, 1st 2 weeks Jan.
Rooms 7 double, 1 single.
Facilities Hall, lounge, conservatory, bar, restaurant. No background music. 2-acre grounds: croquet, Wendy house, small wood. Unsuitable for &.
Location On A4104 midway between Welland and Little Malvern. Train: Great Malvern; then taxi.
Restrictions No smoking: dining room, lounge, bedrooms. No dogs in public rooms.
Credit cards MasterCard, Visa.
Terms [2000] B&B: single £48–£60, double £90–£92; D,B&B £64–£84 per person. Set dinner £24. Short breaks all year; 10% reduction for weekly stays. 1-night bookings sometimes refused Sat. *V*

LITTLE PETHERICK Cornwall   Map 1

Molesworth Manor   `BUDGET`   *Tel* (01841) 540292
Little Petherick
nr Padstow PL27 7QT

This handsome Grade II* listed 17th-century stone house, originally the rectory of nearby St Petroc's church, was converted into a manor in the 19th century by Sir Hugh Molesworth. The coat of arms can be seen in the tall windows on the elaborately carved main staircase. The house is reached up a narrow drive flanked with flowers. The garden is formal; "the silence is broken only by squabbles from the rookery". Peter Pearce and Heather Clarke run it informally as a B&B, with "the feel of a private home", an inspector says. "It is all Christian names here; guests are made to feel they can relax anywhere." The bedrooms vary in grandness; their "upstairs, downstairs" names reflect the house's history: Her Ladyship's and His Lordship's on the first floor, Butler's and Maid's above. Most are spacious; some have antiques and a large brass bed. One or two bathrooms are private rather than connecting. There is a two-room family suite, but no TV in the rooms. Instead, there are ground-floor lounges for reading, TV and music, "which makes for a peaceful atmosphere". Afternoon tea is served on the terrace; breakfast in the conservatory boasts a lavish cold buffet of fruits, cereals, cold meats, cheeses, yogurt, and four kinds of specially baked bread. No dinners, but the dining room table is willingly laid for those guests who bring their own food ("don't leave crumbs in your room"), and the Pearces are licensed to sell wine. Plenty of pubs, bistros and restaurants are nearby, including the famous *Seafood Restaurant* (*qv*) in Padstow, which can be reached on foot by a coastal path. The Heritage Coastline and Lanhydrock House (National Trust) are nearby; a birdwatcher's paradise.

Open Jan–end Oct.
Rooms 2 suites (1 family), 7 double, 1 single. No telephone/TV.
Facilities Drawing room, library, morning/TV room, music room, conservatory, dining room. No background music. 1-acre garden. Close to sea: fishing, boating, sailing, etc. Unsuitable for &.
Location 2 miles SE of Padstow. From A39 Wadebridge–Truro, take A389 to Padstow; through St Issey into Little Petherick; over hump-back bridge; house 300 yds on right. Train: Bodmin, 14 miles; then taxi.
Restrictions No smoking. No dogs in bedrooms or public rooms.
Credit cards None accepted.
Terms B&B £23.50–£32.50.

LITTLE STRETTON Shropshire   **Map 3**

Mynd House   NEW   *Tel* (01694) 722212
Ludlow Road   *Fax* (01694) 724180
Little Stretton SY6 6RB   *E-mail* myndhouse@go2.co.uk
                              Website www.go2.co.uk/myndhouse

In an area of outstanding natural beauty, with direct access to Long Mynd: Mr and Mrs Oatham's red brick Edwardian house (built for a bachelor department store owner in 1902), above small road in Shropshire hamlet. 7 bedrooms. Unassuming, friendly, with extensive views across valley (and distant railway line). "Very good food, comfy bedroom; my 10-year-old nephew was kindly treated," says nominator. 2 lounges (1 with log fire), bar. Candlelit restaurant (open to public) serves, eg, rack of lamb with Shrewsbury sauce; venison with parsnip crisps and juniper ginger sauce. Extensive wine list. Small, steep rear garden. Good walking all around. Open Feb–Dec. Unsuitable for &. Smoking in bar only. Dogs in 1 bedroom, not in public rooms. Amex, MasterCard, Visa accepted. B&B £35–£45; D,B&B £55–£85. Set lunch £12.50, dinner £26. Child under 10 accommodated free in parents' room. More reports, please. *V*

LIVERPOOL Merseyside   **Map 4**

Woolton Redbourne   *Tel* (0151) 421 1500
Acrefield Road   *Fax* (0151) 421 1501
Woolton, Liverpool L25 5JN   *E-mail* woolton@bestloved.com

In an exclusive residential area on the southern edge of the city, this Grade II listed mansion, red brick and bay-windowed, was built by the Victorian industrialist Sir Henry Tate for his daughter, Katherine,

when she married in 1884. It is now a "very special hotel", owned by
Paul Collins, and run for residents only. A busy road passes the front,
but rear rooms, overlooking the landscaped gardens, are quiet. All the
bedrooms are different, and "charming", with some eccentric features.
One couple stayed in the Gardener's Suite, a lodge in the grounds:
"We were delighted by the pictures and the goodnight message from
the hotel cat, placed on our pillows on the enormous Victorian bed.
There was a vast freestanding bath. Room-service breakfast included
exquisite pastries." One suite has a four-poster spa bath as well as a
four-poster bed. "The sitting room is delightful," another guest wrote,
"with antiques, Oriental rugs on polished floors, chandeliers, bowls of
fresh fruit and Turkish delight. They brought me tea on a tray with
flowers. Light meals are also served there." Dinner is for residents
only. The cooking is good, "if slightly rich" (dishes like fillet of beef,
glazed under a grain mustard sabayon, with a red wine sauce; langoustines and scallops with a lobster butter sauce); vegetarians are
well catered for. Children are welcomed. Good weekend reductions.
Liverpool airport and Beatles sites (eg, Eleanor Rigby's grave and
Strawberry Fields orphanage) are nearby; the city centre is
25 minutes' drive away. More reports, please.

Open All year.
Rooms 5 suites, 11 double, 5 single. 3 in mini-annexe across carpark. Some on
ground floor.
Facilities Lounge, bar, restaurant; classical background music all day; func-
tion/conference facilities. 2-acre garden: gazebo.
Location 6 miles SE of city centre. M62 exit 4, left on to A5058. Left at 3rd
traffic lights into Woolton Rd/Acrefield Rd. Hotel 2 miles on left (front windows double-glazed).
Restrictions No smoking: restaurant, some bedrooms. No dogs in public
rooms.
Credit cards All major cards accepted.
Terms [2000] B&B: single £63–£82, double £92, suite from £120. Set dinner
(2 to 3 courses) £18.95–£22.95. Weekend breaks.

See also SHORTLIST

LODDISWELL Devon   **Map 1**

Hazelwood House   BUDGET   *Tel* (01548) 821232
Loddiswell   *Fax* (01548) 821318
nr Kingsbridge TQ7 4EB

In a magnificent setting, in large, rambling grounds with meadows and
woods, sloping down to the River Avon, this early Victorian house is
reached up a long drive. It is informally run by the owners, Jane
Bowman, Gillian Kean and Anabel Farnel-Watson, who rescued it
from dereliction in 1988. They are involved in the Dandelion Trust,
which organises conservation and cultural projects in the UK, and
"Through Heart to Peace" projects in Ethiopia and central Europe, and
they run a busy programme of courses, lectures and concerts (the
Medici string quartet often appears). There are also regular weekends

with entertainments (jazz, painting, story-telling, philosophy, etc). The Christmas package invites guests to bring "harps, lutes, guitars, stories and poems". The place won't suit all comers. It does not offer hotel facilities; some bedrooms are small, most do not have facilities *en suite*, and they are heated by electric fires (no central heating). But the "genuinely warm hospitality", "non-commercial atmosphere", "feeling of peace and friendliness" and "excellent food" are loved by its devotees. "Atmosphere of a house party, but you are under no pressure to socialise if you prefer to sit by the fire and read." "We visited with four children – they were made most welcome." The decor, a "delightful mix" of simple furniture, antiques and paintings, is not at all smart. The meals are "beautifully prepared" in the enormous Victorian kitchen; the short menu, based on organic ingredients, might include avocado with grilled pimento; smoked haddock with a cheese sauce; pink grapefruit sorbet. Vegetarians are well catered for. Water comes from the house's own spring, and there is a small choice of wines (some are organic). "Two or three cats roam around, and the small terrier loves having her tummy tickled." (*Liz and Ken Bartlett, CR, CK*)

Open All year.
Rooms 2 suites, 11 double, 4 single. 1 with bath, 1 with shower. 1 on ground floor. No telephone/TV. 6 self-catering cottages.
Facilities Hall with piano, sitting room, drawing room, library/TV room, dining room; chapel; function/conference facilities, concerts, courses, talks. 67-acre grounds, river, boat house.
Location 1 mile N of Loddiswell. From California Cross on B3207 Dartmouth–Modbury take road to Kingsbridge/Loddiswell. Left after *c.* ¾ mile to Hazelwood. Down lane; entrance gate with stone pillars on right. Train: Totnes, 14 miles; then taxi.
Restrictions No smoking: bedrooms, public rooms on request. Dogs by arrangement; not in restaurant.
Credit cards MasterCard, Visa.
Terms (*Excluding VAT*) B&B £25–£50; D,B&B £48–£77. Set lunch £18, dinner £20. Child accommodated in parents' room: under 4, free; 4–12, 50% of adult rate. Negotiable rates for parties, groups, etc. Cultural events and courses. Christmas package.

LONDON   Map 2

Basil Street Hotel   *Tel* (020) 7581 3311
8 Basil Street   *Fax* (020) 7581 3693
London SW3 1AH   *E-mail* info@thebasil.com
                                   Website www.thebasil.com

"A haven of civilisation," says a regular visitor to this old-established hotel in Knightsbridge. Managed by David Brockett, it has many regular visitors who love its country house feel and "old-world standards". Most reports tell of the "courteous staff", but one visitor this year was critical of the welcome. The public rooms have antiques, Oriental rugs, mirrors and paintings – and a ban on the use of mobile phones. In the "lovely dining room", candlelit at night and with a pianist, traditional meals, eg, avocado and crab terrine; grilled Dover sole; chargrilled steaks; desserts on a trolley, are served by formally dressed waiters. House wines are reasonably priced. Female guests have their own domain, the Parrot Club. At breakfast you are waited on, and nothing is packaged. The bedrooms are not lavishly endowed with extras, and they vary greatly; but many are smoke-free, and refurbishment is on-going. Some rooms are spacious and smartly decorated, with antiques and a large bathroom; some baths are large, too. There are a few two-bedroomed family suites (children are welcomed). Some rooms get noise from traffic, a nearby fire station or neighbouring bedrooms. But many rooms are double-glazed and earplugs can be provided. Those overlooking a courtyard are quiet, if small. (*Richard Creed*)

Open All year.
Rooms 4 family, 43 double, 28 single.
Facilities Lift. Lounge bar, ladies' club, dining room (pianist at night); function facilities.
Location Central; public carpark nearby. (Underground: Knightsbridge.)
Restrictions No smoking in 40 bedrooms. No dogs in public rooms.
Credit cards All major cards accepted.
Terms (*Excluding VAT on accommodation*) Room: single from £128, double from £190, family from £250. Breakfast: continental from £10, English £14. Set lunch (3-course) £19, dinner £24; full alc £30. Extra bed for child £20. Concessions to regular visitors; special rates Aug, winter, bank holidays; long-stay rates. Christmas package.

The Beaufort
33 Beaufort Gardens
London SW3 1PP

Tel (020) 7584 5252
Fax (020) 7589 2834

E-mail thebeaufort@nol.co.uk
Website www.thebeaufort.co.uk/index.

At this small town house hotel on a quiet Knightsbridge square, the price (quite steep at first glance) covers drinks (champagne around the clock), free use of a local health club, a free one-way airport transfer for those occupying the junior suites, and a no-tipping policy. *The Beaufort*, owned by Diana Wallis and her husband Sir Michael Wilmot, has a pretty decor, a collection of original English floral watercolours, a "professional", mainly female, staff. On arrival in the hall which, says a visitor this year, has "a lovely, friendly feel", guests are given a front-door key. The bedrooms contain a brandy nightcap, shortbread and chocolates, a fax, a video recorder, a restaurant guide and a jogging map. There is a complimentary bar in the drawing room, where afternoon tea is served. No restaurant, but light meals are included in the price of the junior suites. Continental breakfast is served in the bedrooms on Wedgwood china. "Great service, interiors, location," says one visitor, but another writes: "I like an inclusive pricing policy, but I would prefer them to include VAT rather than champagne." Not everyone is too keen on Bunter, the old ginger tomcat, and one visitor complained that his "large" room was, in fact, cramped and cheaply furnished, and its bathroom was "in need of a refit". But most have found the atmosphere "delightful". "A haven in a big city." Harrods is round the corner and free passes are available for the South Kensington museums; they are within walking distance. (*Prof. Wolfgang Stroebe, Frances Viola, and others*)

Open All year.
Rooms 7 junior suites, 16 double, 5 single.
Facilities Lift. Drawing room with complimentary bar, CD, piano music some evenings. Air-conditioning. Free membership of nearby health club.
Location Central, near Harrods. Meter parking; public carpark nearby. (Underground: Knightsbridge.)
Restrictions No smoking in 5 bedrooms. No dogs.
Credit cards All major cards accepted.
Terms (*Excluding VAT*) B&B: single £155–£165, double £180–£260, suite £295–£320. Child accommodated in parents' room: in cot, free; on sofabed, £25. *V*

Blooms	*Tel* (020) 7323 1717
7 Montague Street	*Fax* (020) 7636 6498
London WC1B 5BP	*E-mail* blooms@mermaid.co.uk
	Website www.bloomshotel.co.uk

Round the corner from the British Museum (underground: Russell Sq): 18th-century town house, with bay trees, flowers in tubs, in front; pleasant rear garden, where good breakfast can be served. Bar lounge and room service provide light meals with "sensibly priced" wines. Library has newspapers, games, books, flowers, background music all day. 27 bedrooms, some small; quietest ones at rear look on to the museum. Unsuitable for ♿. No smoking in breakfast room. Guide dogs only. All major credit cards accepted. B&B (including welcome sherry, newspaper): single £100–£130, double £125–£205. Light meal alc £20–£24 [2000]. Liked by earlier visitors for "friendly air; helpful staff". New manager this year, Oliver Brown, so we'd like more reports, please.

The Cadogan	*Tel* (020) 7235 7141
75 Sloane Street	*Fax* (020) 7245 0994
London SW1X 9SG	*E-mail* info@cadogan.com
	Website www.cadogan.com

In a prime location near Sloane Square and Chelsea, this long-established hotel has quite a history. Its discreet charm attracted Lillie Langtry; her house next door now forms part of the premises. While staying here, Oscar Wilde was arrested by two plain-clothes policemen, an event commemorated in verse by John Betjeman: "We must ask yew tew leave with us quoietly/For this *is* the *Cadogan Hotel*." Managed by Malcolm Broadbent, it is now one of a small group of distinguished buildings owned by Richard Broyd's Historic House Hotels Ltd (see also *Hartwell House*, Aylesbury; *Middlethorpe Hall*, York; *Bodysgallen Hall*, Llandudno, Wales). It is luxurious in a traditional way, with panelled public rooms, Arts and Crafts wallpaper, antiques and lots of sofas and armchairs. Most bedrooms are air-conditioned and have fine cotton sheets, floral fabrics, fresh flowers. There is one account this year of a visit that went wrong, but most guests have felt "well looked after by the friendly staff". The lounge is a popular place for tea. The Edwardian-style restaurant is run by Graham Thompson, who says he enjoys cooking offal, but who also caters to more conservative tastes with dishes like chicken consommé with quail's eggs and truffle; baked seabass with a herb crust; grilled fillet of Scotch beef with foie gras and Madeira. Guests have access to the large gardens in Cadogan Place opposite, which many rooms overlook. More reports, please.

Open All year. Restaurant closed Sat midday.
Rooms 4 suites, 54 double, 7 single. 1 adapted for &. All air-conditioned.
Facilities Lift, ramp. Drawing room, bar, restaurant; function facilities. No background music. Access to gardens opposite: tennis. Civil wedding licence.
Location Central (rear rooms quietest). Meter parking; NCP carpark opposite. (Underground: Sloane Sq, Knightsbridge.)
Restrictions No smoking in 16 bedrooms. Dogs by arrangement; not in restaurant.
Credit cards Amex, MasterCard, Visa.
Terms [2000] (*Excluding VAT on accommodation*) Room: single £175, double £190, suite £250–£330. Breakfast: continental £12, English £16.50. Set lunch £18.90, dinner £27; full alc £49. Child accommodated in parents' room: under 5, free. Weekend rates. Theatre, Christmas packages.

The Capital
22–24 Basil Street
London SW3 1AT

Tel (020) 7589 5171
Fax (020) 7225 0011
E-mail reservations@capitalhotel.co.uk
Website www.capitalhotel.co.uk

Built 30 years ago by David Levin as a "grand hotel in miniature", *The Capital* is in a busy little street near Harrods. Its restaurant, now run by Eric Crouillère Chavot, was mostly enjoyed this year: "Fully lives up to its *Michelin* star; outstandingly courteous service." "A joy – some of the best food we have had anywhere; the staff were charming." At dinner there is a choice between a five-course set dinner at £60, or an *à la carte* menu with a choice of seven dishes for each course: starters at £18 (eg, salad of foie gras and honey-roasted bacon), main courses at £22 (eg, blanquette of John Dory with croquant vegetables), desserts at £9 (eg, dark chocolate vacherin with fresh peppermint). The simpler lunch is thought good value (£24.50). The meals are served amid a Nina Campbell decor of chandeliers, mirrors, honey-coloured walls and tapestry chairs. There is a pale-panelled bar. The bedrooms are lavish, with heavy fabrics, original oil paintings, flowers, double glazing, a marble bathroom and 24-hour room service, but there is one report this year of noisy air-conditioning, disorganised reception, and communication problems with the foreign members of staff, all adding up to a disappointing stay. A new manager, Olivia Hetherington, has since arrived, so we'd like more reports, please. The hotel's residents can also eat in the *Metro* wine bar in the basement of its less expensive sister, *L'Hotel* (*qv*), almost next door.

Open All year.
Rooms 8 suites, 22 double, 12 single.
Facilities Lift. Lounge, bar, restaurant; 2 private dining rooms, business facilities. No background music.
Location Central (rooms double-glazed; rear ones quietest). Garage for 12 cars (£20 per night). (Underground: Knightsbridge.)

Restrictions No smoking in some bedrooms. Dogs at management's discretion; not in public rooms.
Credit cards All major cards accepted.
Terms [2000] (*Excluding VAT on accommodation*) Room: single £180, double £235–£305, suite £350. Breakfast: continental £12.50, English £16.50. Set lunch £24.50, dinner £60; full alc £69. Weekend rates.

The Connaught	*Tel* (020) 7499 7070
Carlos Place	*Fax* (020) 7495 3262
London W1Y 6AL	*E-mail* info@the-connaught.co.uk
	Website www.savoy-group.co.uk

"Discreet and grand", this "splendid time warp hotel", 103 years old, is a large red brick building in Mayfair, owned by the Savoy group and managed by Duncan Palmer. It is named after the Queen's great-great uncle, Prince Arthur, Duke of Connaught, the third son of Queen Victoria. "Staying here is an experience to remember – at a price," say visitors this year, who liked "being known by name, not by room number", and added: "Breakfast and Sunday lunch were a pleasure." Other reporters loved the surroundings, with antique shops, galleries and designer boutiques, and described the hotel's look as "carefully preserved mid-fifties Edwardian". The dress code (no sneakers, tracksuits or shorts; jacket and tie for male diners at night), and the ban on mobile telephones, help maintain the old-fashioned feel. Michel Bourdin has presided for 22 years over the *Michelin*-starred kitchen. It serves both the mahogany-panelled restaurant, grandly elegant with arched windows and a huge crystal chandelier, and the more intimate green-walled Grill Room. The royal theme continues on the menus, with dishes like sole jubilée (created to celebrate the Queen's silver jubilee) and noisettes d'agneau Edward VII. There is always a traditional dish of the day: Irish stew; steak, kidney and mushroom pie, etc, and a joint under a dome. Tail-coated waiters wheel trolleys, carve meat, and heat sauces over flames. "With all this going on, you don't need a cabaret." From the huge breakfast menu you can order kedgeree, grilled chicken, all manner of fruit; "delicious croissants, but the toast is commercial". The cocktail bar is said to be "one of the best in London". There is nothing designerish about the bedrooms and suites that lead off a five-storey wood-panelled staircase under a cupola; they are as traditional as the rest, with large damask armchairs, curtains patterned with big flowers, old gilt mirrors, his and hers chests of drawers and wardrobes, crisp sheets on a huge bed, a marble bathroom with a large bath, big cakes of soap. But one couple would have liked fresh flowers. The affluent clientele includes foreign royalty, famous actors and international businessmen, drawn by the old-fashioned style and "commitment to personal service". Despite the grandeur, "there is no hint of snootiness – from the uniformed doorman with shiny shoes, umbrella at the ready, to reception and waiting staff, everyone is friendly". Children of all ages are welcomed. Guests may use the rooftop swimming pools of the sister hotels, *The Berkeley* and *The Savoy*, and the health and fitness facilities at *Claridge's*. No garden, but you can sit under the plane trees in Mount Street Gardens, adjacent to the Farm Street Roman Catholic church around the corner, and Hyde Park is close by. Some traffic noise, but it dies down at night, and most rooms are air-conditioned. (*John and Ann Smith, A and CR*)

Open All year.
Rooms 24 suites, 36 double, 30 single. Most air-conditioned.
Facilities Lift. 2 lounges, cocktail bar, Grill Room, restaurant; private dining room, function/meeting facilities. Complimentary use of health facilities at *The Berkeley*, *The Savoy*, *Claridge's*. No background music.
Location Central. Limited private parking. (Underground: Bond St, Green Pk.)
Restriction No dogs.
Credit cards All major cards accepted.
Terms (*Excluding VAT on accommodation, 15% service charge on breakfast*) Room: single £290–£335, double £370–£425, suite £695–£1,600. Breakfast: continental £16, English £21. Set lunch £28.50 (Sun £33.50), dinner £58; full alc from £60. Luxury breaks: up to 40% reduction. Christmas packages.

Durrants	*Tel* (020) 7935 8131
George Street	*Fax* (020) 7487 3510
London W1H 6BJ	*E-mail* reservations@durrantshotel.co.uk
	Website www.durrantshotel.co.uk

In a "wonderfully convenient location", this is "a very easy place to stay", says a visitor this year to one of London's oldest privately owned hotels. Opened in 1790, and run since 1921 by the Miller family, it is "remarkably well staffed, reminiscent of another era"; "a fascinating rabbit warren, behind a Georgian façade" (it is composed of a row of terraced houses). Small panelled lounges with leather settees and chairs lead off a quaint, rambling corridor. Original paintings, prints and engravings of London hang above antique furniture. "The polish on the brass is a wonder to behold, and there is not a finger mark on the sparkling glass panels in the doors." The bedrooms are well maintained, but they vary greatly – some are "poky with nondescript furniture": the largest, at the front, get some traffic noise. At the back, "you would not think you were in central London". An American guest was pleased to find "an efficient shower, for once". Sixteen rooms were refurbished this year. The panelled restaurant, run for many years by Luigi Boito, has a short daily set menu, with dishes like steak, kidney and mushroom pie or grilled swordfish; and a long *carte,* serving more ambitious dishes, eg, millefeuille of Scottish salmon and leaf spinach with champagne sauce; also grills. The barman is "very helpful, providing good sandwiches after theatre or for a late lunch". Breakfast has "decent marmalade and excellent smoked haddock". Women travelling alone are welcomed, and so are children (high chairs, cots, baby-sitters, early suppers are available). The Wallace Collection (one of the world's finest art collections, recently completely refurbished, with free entry) is opposite; the Wigmore Hall is close by. The Millers also own the *Red Lion* in Henley-on-Thames (*qv*). (*Jean Chothia, Sandra Beddows*)

Open All year. Restaurant closed for dinner 25 Dec.
Rooms 4 family, 4 suites, 68 double, 16 single. 29 air-conditioned. 7 on ground floor.

Facilities Lift. Lounges, bar, breakfast room, restaurant; function facilities. No background music. Sports centre nearby.
Location Central (rear rooms quietest). Public carpark 5 mins' walk. (Underground: Bond St, Baker St.)
Restrictions No smoking in breakfast room. No dogs.
Credit cards Amex, MasterCard, Visa.
Terms (*Excluding 12½% "optional" service charge on restaurant bills*) Room: single £92.50, double from £140, suite from £265. Breakfast: continental £9.95, English £12.95. Set lunch £20, dinner £20; full alc £40.

Egerton House
17–19 Egerton Terrace
London SW3 2BX

Tel (020) 7589 2412
Fax (020) 7584 6540
E-mail bookings@egertonhousehotel.co.uk
Website www.egertonhousehotel.co.uk

"We always feel totally contented here," say the most devoted fans of this tall Victorian town house, close to Knightsbridge. "The manager, Gareth Absalom, and reception staff are welcoming, helpful, relaxed. We were upgraded to a large deluxe room with a high, pitched ceiling, easy chairs, fresh flowers. 'Chintzy' may be a bit 'eighties' compared with the newer boutique hotels, but that makes *The Egerton* refreshingly different. The fabrics are of superior quality, antique furniture is real not repro, marble bathrooms are impressive. Breakfasts are excellent, with fresh orange juice, good coffee, good choice of bread and rolls, though you may not always get what you order." Power showers and a two-line telephone with voicemail and a modem link are among the hotel's modern attributes. The bedrooms vary in size; most overlook private gardens. "Even the small rooms are cleverly arranged, so that you are happy to spend time in them. The beds are supremely comfortable." Breakfast is taken in the bedrooms or in a pretty basement room. Afternoon tea is served in the drawing room, with its marble fireplace, stuccoed walls, oil paintings and "rather pricey" honesty bar. The extensive room-service menu ranges from toasted sandwiches to liver and mashed potatoes, salmon fishcakes, apple crumble. A newspaper is included in the rates (regular visitors' preferences are recorded on a database). The owner, David Naylor-Leyland, also owns *The Franklin*, nearby, and *Dukes, St James's* (see Shortlist). Knightsbridge department stores and the South Kensington museums are close at hand. (*David and Kate Wooff*)

Open All year.
Rooms 21 double, 8 single. All air-conditioned.
Facilities Lift. Drawing room, honesty bar, breakfast room; private dining room. No background music. 24-hour room service. Unsuitable for &.
Location Central. Valet parking. (Underground: Knightsbridge, South Kensington.)
Restriction No dogs.
Credit cards All major cards accepted.
Terms (*Excluding VAT*) Room: single £155, double £180–£240. Breakfast: continental £10, English £16; full alc £30. Easter, Christmas, summer holiday rates.

Make sure that the hotel has included VAT in the prices it quotes.

The Goring
Beeston Place
Grosvenor Gardens
London SW1W 0JW

Tel (020) 7396 9000
Fax (020) 7834 4393
E-mail reception@goringhotel.co.uk
Website www.goringhotel.co.uk

♕ *César award in 1994*

"There will always be a Mr Goring at *The Goring* to welcome you." So says George Goring, OBE. His sedate, traditional hotel (Pride of Britain), in a small street near Victoria and close to Buckingham Palace, was built by his grandfather in 1910, and his own son, Jeremy, is a director. Many staff are long-serving: the doorman has been here for 32 years; the general manager, William Cowpe, for 29; others, including a porter and chambermaid, for more than 20. This was the first hotel in the world to have a private bathroom and central heating in every room. Top priority is "a high standard of decor and cleanliness". Each of the 75 bedrooms is individually designed, with mouldings, striped wallpaper, writing desk and easy chairs, and a bathroom in marble and wood. Many look over a private garden (not for guests' use); some have a balcony, where breakfast can be served on fine days. Guests may be upgraded when better rooms are free. In the formal restaurant, where Mr Goring is often in attendance, and a pianist plays at night, the long menu has some quite adventurous starters, eg, carpaccio of tuna with soya and lime dressing; wild mushroom and artichoke salad with a walnut dressing; main courses might be steak and kidney pie; noisettes of lamb with white pudding, girolles and a rosemary sauce. Service, by waiters in tailcoats, is "polished", but can be leisurely. The wine list is "extensive and fairly priced". Bar lunches are served, and tea may be taken in the lounge where woolly replica sheep add a comic touch, or the indoor terrace, which overlooks the garden. More reports, please.

Open All year.
Rooms 7 suites, 47 double, 20 single. All air-conditioned.
Facilities Lift, ramps. Lounge, bar, terrace, restaurant (pianist in evening); function facilities. Free use of nearby health club. Civil wedding licence.
Location Central, near Buckingham Palace (front rooms double-glazed). Garage, mews parking. (Underground: Victoria.)
Restriction No dogs.
Credit cards All major cards accepted.
Terms [2000] Room: single £172.50, double £210, suite £320. Breakfast: continental £11, English £15. Bar meals. Set lunch £28, dinner £35. Christmas, Easter, weekend breaks.

Halkin Hotel
5 Halkin Street
London SW1X 7DJ

Tel (020) 7333 1000
Fax (020) 7333 1100
E-mail sales@halkin.co.uk
Website www.halkin.co.uk

"If you like an understated style, this is your place," says a recent visitor to this small hotel in a residential street in Belgravia. Behind a sober Georgian-style façade, the decor is the last word in post-modern Italian designer chic. The "marvellous staff", all dressed by Armani, are "warm and friendly, without a hint of attitude". (The Singaporean owner, Christina Ong, also owns the 155-bedroom *Metropolitan* in Park Lane, with a similarly minimalist decor and a staff dressed by Donna Karan.) Many weekday guests are here on business: a Reuters area supplies up-to-date financial news. The bedrooms are on five floors "with black-walled corridors and acres of marble", and each floor has a theme relating to a natural element: water, air, fire, earth and sky. The rooms are "immaculate, stylish with not a floral print in sight"; they have a sitting area, fax, video, two telephone lines, e-mail, voice-mail, 24-hour room service; also "glorious toiletries". In the small restaurant, overlooking the garden (to which guests have no access), black-clad waiters serve Stefano Cavallini's *Michelin*-starred modern Italian cooking (eg, salad of venison with black truffle and apple; stuffed saddle of rabbit with olives, polenta and mushrooms; orange crêpes with strawberry sorbet and chocolate sauce). Light meals are served in the bar and the lobby. A gym was added in 2000. More reports, please.

Open Hotel all year; check for restaurant closures.
Rooms 11 suites, 30 double. 24-hour room service.
Facilities Lift. Lobby (live harp/guitar at night), bar, restaurant, private dining/meeting room; gym.
Location Central (double glazing). (Underground: Hyde Park Corner.)
Restriction Guide dogs only.
Credit cards All major cards accepted.
Terms [2000] (*Excluding VAT on accommodation*) Room: single/double £265–£345, suite £415–£575. Child accommodated in parents' room: under 12, free. Breakfast: continental £14, English £17. Set lunch from £23, dinner from £55; full alc £70. Weekend rates.

Hazlitt's	*Tel* (020) 7434 1771
6 Frith Street	*Fax* (020) 7439 1524
London W1V 5TZ	*E-mail* reservations@hazlitts.co.uk
	Website www.hazlittshotel.com

A conversion of three 18th-century terrace houses in Soho, called after the essayist, who died here in 1830. The bedrooms are named after famous residents and visitors to the house; the decor is Victorian and, since this is a listed building, there is no lift. But the hotel is up to date, too, and popular with people in film, fashion, music and publishing. "We are equipped with all the necessary modern communications and life support systems," they tell us. In the course of a recent refurbishment, some original Georgian panelling was discovered and restored, and air-conditioning was installed in the small top-floor rooms. Most bedrooms are light, with a high ceiling, though some look on to a dark inner courtyard. All have prints and plants, an 18th- or 19th-century bed (many are four-poster or half-tester), and decent linen. Some bathrooms have a freestanding bath. Street noises can be a problem, but back rooms are quiet. A continental breakfast is brought to the bedroom, and room-service snacks (baguettes with exotic stuffings; pasta, blinis, etc) are available. *Hazlitt's* now has a residential liquor licence. The staff are "extremely helpful", says a regular visitor. Dogs are allowed in bedrooms and public rooms. Within easy walking distance are theatres, museums and countless restaurants. *The Gore*, in South

Kensington, and *The Rookery*, in Clerkenwell (see Shortlist for both), are also owned by the *Hazlitt's* proprietor, Peter McKay. (*HRL*)

Open All year.
Rooms 1 suite, 17 double, 5 single. 3 on ground floor.
Facilities Sitting room. No background music. Unsuitable for &.
Location Central (rear rooms quietest). NCP nearby. (Underground: Tottenham Court Rd, Leicester Sq.)
Credit cards All major cards accepted.
Terms [To 31 Mar 2001] (*Excluding VAT*) Room: single £140, double £175, suite £300. Continental breakfast £7.25.

L'Hotel	*Tel* (020) 7589 6286
28 Basil Street	*Fax* (020) 7823 7826
London SW3 1AS	*E-mail* l'hotel@capitalhotel.co.uk
	Website www.capitalgrp.co.uk

The "no-frills atmosphere, and very helpful reception" were admired this year by visitors to this upmarket B&B, owned by David Levin of *The Capital* (*qv*), next door but one. It is relatively inexpensive for this part of London, aiming for "an ambience of quietness and discretion" without a large staff and lots of facilities. Reception at night is shared with the *Capital*; there is no residents' lounge. The bedrooms have a country-style decor, with pale colours, patterned wallpaper, pine furniture, wooden shutters, good fabrics, "but dim lighting made reading difficult". Each has a kettle, crockery and a fridge; best ones have a gas fire. A continental or English breakfast is served between 7.30 and 10.30 am in the basement wine bar, the *Metro*, run by the sister hotel's distinguished chef, Eric Crouillère Chavot. It is open to the public for bistro-style meals (soups, salads, bangers and mash, etc), and has a jazzy modern decor: granite, chrome and leather (service can be slow). Wines of quality are sold by the glass. Afternoon teas are served between 3.30 and 5.30 pm. Rooms above the *Metro* can be noisy. The manager, Nathalie Jarnot, is new this year. (*Brian and Eve Webb*)

Open All year. *Metro* closed Sun, bank holidays, except for residents' breakfast.
Rooms 1 suite, 11 double. 1 on ground floor.
Facilities Lift. Reception, wine bar ("easy listening" background music all day).
Location From Underground (Knightsbridge, Harrods' exit) turn left into Hans Cres, then 1st left. Rear rooms quietest. NCP opposite.
Restriction No dogs.
Credit cards All major cards accepted.
Terms [2000] B&B: double £170.38, suite £193.88. English breakfast £6.50. Full alc £24.

Knightsbridge Green Hotel	*Tel* (020) 7584 6274
159 Knightsbridge	*Fax* (020) 7225 1635
London SW1X 7PD	*E-mail* theKGHotel@aol.com
	Website www.theKGHotel.co.uk

"Wonderful, up to date, with a friendly staff." "My home from home in London. We have stayed nine times. The service is always helpful, the double rooms are spacious and quiet. A winner in every way." Two

Americans write in praise of this "spotlessly kept" small hotel close to Hyde Park. Owned by the Marler family for over 30 years, it offers "excellent value for such a central position". The best accommodation is in large suites "somewhat plainly furnished, but well provisioned", with a double bedroom, a sitting room and a large tiled bathroom (towels may be "on the thin side"). The quietest rooms, at the back, overlook a courtyard, but all rooms are double-glazed. The air-conditioning was "a great relief" during a heatwave. An "excellent and fresh" breakfast is delivered to the room: "express" at 7 am, with croissants, and continental or cooked from 7.30 am on weekdays, between 8 and 10 on Sunday. There is a lounge, and a Club Room on the first floor providing free tea and coffee during the day. Guests may use a nearby health club. Reception is staffed from 7.30 am to 10.30 pm, and porters are on duty between 7 am and 8 pm. The Marler family also owns the *St Enodoc Hotel* at Rock, Cornwall (*qv*). (*Dr Mary Tilden-Smith, Marilyn L Gardner*)

Open All year.
Rooms 12 suites, 9 double, 7 single. All air-conditioned.
Facilities Lift. Lounge, Club Room with complimentary refreshments 9 am–8 pm. No background music. Access to nearby health club. Unsuitable for &.
Location Central (rooms double-glazed; quietest ones at rear). NCP carpark nearby. (Underground: Knightsbridge.)
Restrictions No smoking. No dogs.
Credit cards All major cards accepted.
Terms Room: single £110–£121.50, double £145–£166, suite £170–£191. Breakfast: express £3.50, continental £7, English £10.50. *V*

Langorf Hotel   *Tel* (020) 7794 4483
20 Frognal   *Fax* (020) 7435 9055
Hampstead   *E-mail* langorf@aol.com
London NW3 6AG   *Website* www.langorfhotel.com

Managed by Caroline Haynes, and reasonably priced for the city, the *Langorf*, composed of three Edwardian houses, is in a residential area of north London. It is quiet and comfortable, with good-sized, pleasantly decorated bedrooms, some suitable for a family; those at the back are quietest; some bathrooms are small. Staff are "friendly, informal and mostly female". Plenty of choice at the buffet breakfast, served in a room overlooking the sloping rear garden; there is a licensed bar and a 24-hour room service snack menu. *Casa Giovanni*, a nearby Italian restaurant, is warmly recommended. Street parking only, said to be expensive. The Freud museum is close by, Hampstead village is five minutes' walk, and the city centre is reached by a quick tube journey. More reports, please.

Open All year.
Rooms 31 double. Some on ground floor. Also five 2-bedroomed self-catering apartments.
Facilities Lift. Lounge/bar, breakfast room (classical background music). Walled garden. Unsuitable for &.
Location Between Finchley Rd and Fitzjohn's Ave. Street parking. (Underground: Finchley Rd.)

Restrictions No smoking in breakfast room. No dogs.
Credit cards All major cards accepted.
Terms B&B: single £77–£82, double £95–£100. Winter rates. Child accommodated in parents' room: under 8, 50% of adult rate.

The Leonard
15 Seymour Street
London W1H 5AA

Tel (020) 7935 2010
Fax (020) 7935 6700
E-mail the.leonard@dial.pipex.com
Website www.theleonard.com

Close to Marble Arch and handy for the West End, four Grade II listed 18th-century town houses have been converted into this "tucked away gem", warmly praised this year. The manager, Angela Stoppani, and her staff are "keen to assist at all times", and the atmosphere is "unquestionably hospitable". The accommodation is mostly in suites; some are large, with a kitchenette. Rooms at the front can be noisy. The high-quality bedlinen and power showers are appreciated. One couple were put out to find that their "celebration double" was in fact two singles zipped together, "but the room-service breakfast was a feast for both stomach and eyes". Antiques, fine fabrics, paintings, plants and flowers combine with the latest technology: video, hi-fi and (in the suites) a dedicated line for fax or modem. The café/bar, with sofas and dining tables, serves breakfast, and drinks and light Mediterranean-style meals all day. There is a small exercise room. Guests may do their laundry in the utility room. (*Ara Ohanian, Debbie Peers-Smith*)

Open All year.
Rooms 20 suites, 9 double. Some on ground floor.
Facilities Lift. Lobby, café/bar (open 7 am–11 pm; varied background music at night); 24-hour room service; function facilities; exercise room. Access to garden square with tennis.
Location Central, near Marble Arch (rooms double-glazed). NCP carpark 2 mins' walk. (Underground: Marble Arch.)
Restrictions No smoking in some bedrooms. No dogs.
Credit cards All major cards accepted.
Terms Rooms: single £211.50, double £235, suite (1–2 bedrooms) £293.75–£587.50. Breakfast: continental £12.50, English £17. Full alc £25. Weekend rates.

Miller's
111a Westbourne Grove
London W2 4UW

Tel (020) 7243 1024
Fax (020) 7243 1064
E-mail enquiries@millersuk.com
Website www.millersuk.com

A treasure house of slightly faded splendour in a street near Notting Hill Gate, where antique shops and restaurants are two a penny, and there is also a wholefood emporium. Entrance is via a maroon door next to a launderette. A staircase hung with shabby rugs brings you to "a dimmed sanctuary, a complete contrast to the busy world outside". Martin Miller (author of the eponymous antiques guide) has filled the large drawing room with old furniture, ornaments, busts, bric-à-brac, paintings and antiques. It has a huge oak fireplace; candles often burn at night, supplementing the light from French brass chandeliers. One visitor called it a "Portobello junk shop look". Another wrote: "The effect is embracing, eclectic, entertaining. Classical music, played for much of the day, dims the sound of traffic outside." A staircase with maroon walls densely hung with pictures and prints, "quaintly modern or antiquated risqué", leads up to the bedrooms. Each is named after an English poet. They are theatrically furnished, with heavy brocades and velvets and a lavish bed, but also equipped with voicemail, and a TV with video. Aberrations, eg, a nylon rug, a luminous rainbow-coloured triangle on the bathroom door, "add to the humour of the place". Dust cannot be kept at bay in such a decor, and housekeeping may not be perfect, but the atmosphere generated by the manager, Anthea Pouli, is "genuinely hospitable" and unfussy. Guests are given a key, and told to help themselves to drinks from an honesty bar. Breakfast, served round one large table, is largely self-service: you toast your own bagel, help yourself to fruit and yogurt, make your own tea. One warning: If you give your credit card number to guarantee a booking, £200 will be blocked on your account a week before your arrival. Mr Miller, who often visits, also owns *Chilston Park*, at Lenham, Kent, also antique-filled and eccentric, with staff in period dress. More reports, please.

Open All year, except 25/26 Dec.
Rooms 3 suites, 4 double.
Facilities Drawing room (classical background music all day). Unsuitable for ♿.
Location Above *Rodizio Rico* restaurant (entrance in Hereford Road). (Underground: Notting Hill Gate, Bayswater, Queensway.)
Restrictions No smoking in some bedrooms. No dogs.
Credit cards Amex, MasterCard, Visa.
Terms (*Excluding VAT*) B&B: single/double £140, suite £160. Corporate rates on application. Lounge may be hired for functions.

Number Sixteen   *Tel* (020) 7589 5232
16 Sumner Place,   *Fax* (020) 7584 8615
London SW7 3EG   *E-mail* reservations@numbersixteenhotel.co.uk
                           Website www.numbersixteenhotel.co.uk.

"We loved it. The staff were immensely helpful. The location was great, with a neighbourhood feel." "Truly delightful – a quiet refuge." Praise this year and last for a popular hotel in a residential street near South Kensington station (direct underground trains to Heathrow airport). Owned by Ms Tan Lei Cheng, and managed by Jean Branham, with a "friendly, yet unobtrusive" staff, it is a conversion of four town houses. Bedrooms "vary in size and desirability"; some bathrooms may be "tight" – but they are "well updated, with nice marble". One couple were pleased to be given an upgrade to a quiet room with a view of the pretty garden (with flowers and a fountain) and they liked "being able to choose which room to have breakfast in: the lounge (yellow, chintzy, cheerful), the library (cranberry red with shelves to browse through), or our bedroom". The honesty bar provides drinks "at a steepish price", and it can get "a bit smoky". "No piped music – it's not that sort of place." Guests have access to a health and fitness centre at a nearby hotel, and there is a huge choice of local restaurants.

No stings on the bill: the rates quoted include VAT and service. (*Lesley and Carl Powell, RK and EA*)

Open All year.
Rooms 4 suites, 23 double, 9 single. 4 on ground floor.
Facilities Lift. Drawing room, library with honesty bar, conservatory. No background music. Small garden. Access to nearby health centre (£10). Unsuitable for &.
Location Central (quietest rooms overlook garden). Pay parking 5 mins' walk. (Underground: South Kensington.)
Restrictions No children under 12. No dogs.
Credit cards All major cards accepted.
Terms [To March 2001] B&B: single £95–£135, double £170–£195, suite £215. English breakfast £8.

One Aldwych	*Tel* (020) 7300 1000
1 Aldwych	*Fax* (020) 7300 1001
London WC2B 4BZ	*E-mail* sales@onealdwych.co.uk
	Website www.onealdwych.co.uk

A luxury hotel in a prime central position, in what was once a newspaper office and later a bank. The owner, Gordon Campbell Gray, aims to provide "understated luxury combined with cutting edge technology", and a reporter this year found the modern decor "restful rather than theatrical". An eclectic art collection is displayed throughout the building. It has two restaurants: *Axis* ("modern European"), on the lower ground floor, is run by Mark Gregory; *Indigo* ("healthy and creative"), with chef Julian Jenkins, is on the mezzanine. This overlooks the huge lobby, with a giant statue of an oarsman in his boat, "trendy, if tortured, flower arrangements", and a bar that serves "inventive cocktails". Bedrooms are equipped with modem plugs, fax lines, mobile phones, etc; fibre-optic lights allow discreet reading in bed; fresh flowers and fruit are replenished daily. There is a gym, an 18-metre lap swimming pool with underwater music; personal trainers are available, and two suites have their own private gym. Private travellers, as well as those on business, have almost all enjoyed their visit: "The best hotel I have ever stayed in. We were made to feel special. Our room, approached via the grooviest of lifts, had an enormous bed; the granite bathroom had a separate power shower, tiny TV and high-class toiletries." "Informal, helpful staff. Stunning views across to Waterloo Bridge. Excellent sound-proofing. Great choice at breakfast" (continental, healthy or English). The "high-energy" *Cinnamon Bar*, opening on to Aldwych, serves pastries, sandwiches, fruit juices. Within walking distance are theatres, Covent Garden, Trafalgar Square, Westminster. Easy access to the City. We'd like more reports, please, especially on the restaurants.

Open All year.
Rooms 12 suites, 93 double. 6 adapted for &. All air-conditioned.
Facilities Lifts. Lobby, 2 bars, 2 restaurants, private dining rooms; function facilities; newsagent, florist. Health club: indoor swimming pool, sauna, gym. Civil wedding licence.
Location Central, where Aldwych meets the Strand (rooms triple-glazed). Valet parking. (Underground: Charing Cross.)
Restrictions No smoking in some bedrooms. Guide dogs only.

Credit cards All major cards accepted.
Terms [2000] (*Excluding VAT*) Room: single £255–£310, double £275–£330, suite £395–£995. Breakfast: continental £11.50, English £16.50. Set lunch/dinner (2 to 3 courses): *Axis* £14.95–£18.95, *Indigo* £19.50–£24.50; full alc: *Axis* £35, *Indigo* £30. Reductions for children under 16. Weekend breaks.

The Pelham   *Tel* (020) 7589 8288
15 Cromwell Place   *Fax* (020) 7584 8444
London SW7 2LA   *E-mail* pelham@firmdale.com
                                      Website www.firmdale.com

With its lush interiors, sumptuous bathrooms, friendly staff, and copious breakfasts, this Victorian town house is "a delightful place to stay", say visitors this year. It is liked for its "atmosphere of a country house in London", and its useful location near South Kensington tube station, where three lines converge. It is one of a small group of luxury hotels owned by Kit and Tim Kemp. The decor is lavish, with chandeliers, rococo ceilings, heavily draped fabrics, panelling, antiques, china ornaments and elaborate flower arrangements. The bedrooms under the eaves are small; those lower down have a large bed (some are four-posters), chintz eiderdowns and curtains, and antique furniture. All are crammed with extras: bottled water, chocolates, classy bathroom goodies, etc, and they have "excellent air-conditioning", much appreciated in summer. Business facilities and 24-hour room service are available. The yellow-and-blue basement restaurant is popular with locals for its good-value set menus at lunch and dinner. The new chef, Jason Booker, serves modern dishes such as Thai fish-cakes with coriander, ginger and sweet chilli jam; breast of chicken on a black olive mash; lemon-poached pear with chocolate sauce. A light "express" lunch menu is also available. Hyde Park is close by; so are the "Albertopolis" museums. The manager, Deborah Scott, is new this year, so we'd like more reports, please.

Open All year.
Rooms 5 suites, 39 double, 7 single. 4 on ground floor. 1 mews flat. All with air-conditioning.
Facilities Lift. 2 drawing rooms; restaurant with bar (background jazz). Access to nearby health club. Unsuitable for &.
Location Central, by South Kensington tube station (rooms double-glazed). Meter parking; public carpark nearby. (Underground: South Kensington.)
Restriction Smoking discouraged in 1 drawing room.
Credit cards Amex, MasterCard, Visa.
Terms (*Excluding VAT, and 12.5% service charge on meals*) Room: single £145–£160; double £175–£190; suite £395. Breakfast: continental £11.50, English £13.50. Set meals (2 to 3 courses): lunch £14.95–£17.95, dinner £14.95–£17.95; full alc £48. Christmas package. ***V***

Pembridge Court   *Tel* (020) 7229 9977
34 Pembridge Gardens   *Fax* (020) 7727 4982
London W2 4DX   *E-mail* reservations@pemct.co.uk
                                        Website www.pemct.co.uk

In a quiet street (for London) close to Notting Hill and Portobello Road, this 19th-century town house offers "eminently well-run, unpretentious" accommodation. Owned by Derek and Karen Mapp, it is managed by the long-serving Valerie Gilliat, with two resident ginger cats, Spencer and Churchill, "a prima donna-ish pair, who even get mail". The bedrooms vary greatly in size; some are very small. One single was thought dowdy this year, but most are "pleasant to live in, decorated in mock-Victorian style, and well sound-proofed. Lights just about adequate for reading." All the bedrooms, except two small singles, were given air-conditioning this year; there is a new telephone system with voicemail, and new bedding (duvets). But some bathrooms may be in need of updating. There is a "cheerful, light lounge". The basement restaurant, *Caps* (extravagantly decorated with cricketing memorabilia), serves soups, salads and snacks to residents and their guests. "The staff could not have been more considerate," wrote one visitor who appreciated help with bags, "swift and efficient service, excellent bacon", and the lack of background music at breakfast. Restaurants of all kinds are nearby; there is good transport to the West End and the City. Visitors here are offered discounted rates at the *Cross House*, the Mapps' other hotel, in Padstow, Cornwall.

Open All year.
Rooms 14 deluxe, 3 small double, 3 single. Some on ground floor. 18 air-conditioned.
Facilities Sitting room, bar (taped background music), restaurant. Unsuitable for &.
Location Side street off Notting Hill Gate. (Underground: Notting Hill Gate.)
Restriction No dogs in public rooms, or unattended in bedrooms.
Credit cards All major cards accepted.
Terms B&B: single £120–£160, double £150–£190. Family rates on application. Reductions 24 Dec–1 Jan. *V* (1 night only)

The Portobello   *Tel* (020) 7727 2777
22 Stanley Gardens   *Fax* (020) 7792 9641
London W11 2NG   *E-mail* info@portobello-hotel.co.uk
                           Website www.portobello-hotel.co.uk

"It won't suit everyone, but for anyone tired of the average hotel, however good, *The Portobello* is a must experience," writes a regular *Guide* correspondent who has known this bohemian place over many years. "The laid-back style that I love is almost unchanged, and the themed bedrooms really are special; you should take the time to discuss them carefully when booking." Composed of two six-floor Victorian terrace houses on a residential street in Notting Hill and owned by Tim Herring, this a favourite with supermodels, rock and film stars and musicians. They appreciate its quirky decor (gilt mirrors, military pictures, marble fireplaces, potted palms, Edwardiana, cane and wicker furniture, etc) and its exotic bedrooms, which are frequently redesigned. The Round Room, with its round bed, was created for Alice Cooper; he kept his boa constrictor in its large freestanding Edwardian bathing machine. Room 22 overlooks the gardens at the rear (no access for residents) and has a Victorian decor, an antique carved four-poster bed, and a bathroom with a Jules Verne bath. Scary and Sporty Spice were the first to experience the two new Japanese water garden basement suites, each with an oversized bath. Most of the "micro-cabins" have gone, having been turned into bathrooms for the newly refurbished doubles. Porterage and room service operate only between 8 am and 4 pm, but reception is open day and night, as is the restaurant/bar, supervised by manager/chef Johnny Ekperigin. Parking is awkward. Tim Herring also owns *Julie's Restaurant*, and *Julie's Bar* in nearby Clarendon Cross (known for its arty little shops). Portobello Road, with its famous Saturday market, is close by. (*Iain Elliott*)

Open 2 Jan–23 Dec.
Rooms 9 suites, 11 double, 4 single. Some on ground floor.
Facilities Lift. Lounge/bar, restaurant (open 24 hours to residents). No background music. Access to health club nearby. Unsuitable for &.
Location Central. Meter parking. (Underground: Notting Hill Gate.)
Credit cards All major cards accepted.
Terms B&B: single £150, double £180, suite £250–£350. Full alc £25.

Tophams Belgravia	*Tel* (020) 7730 8147
28 Ebury Street	*Fax* (020) 7823 5966
London SW1W 0LU	*E-mail* tophams_belgravia@compuserve.com
	Website www.tophams.co.uk

Now with a posher new name (it used to be *Tophams Ebury Court*), this family-owned establishment has been upgraded recently, and the bedrooms "are fitted with every comfort you could wish for". But it still has a "delightfully old-fashioned" atmosphere, says one of its most loyal fans. Marianne Topham, of the third generation, runs it with her husband Nicholas Kingsford. Their aim is to evoke "the charm of an English country house", despite its busy central London location. Mirrors, pictures and pieces of china adorn the small public rooms; there are floral sofas and armchairs in the lounge. The basement brasserie ("rather luridly decorated", and open to the public) has a short menu, including haddock with a white wine, prawn and tarragon sauce; steak au poivre; treacle tart. The bedrooms are mostly small, but "tastefully done"; some have a "new, beautifully appointed" bathroom. Four singles are without facilities *en suite*, but bathrobes are provided for the trip down the corridor. The location of rooms varies widely, from those at the rear or in the mews (quiet) to those at the front, overlooking the street (noisy). Breakfasts, in a new room at the rear, include a "healthy option" of fruit and fat-free bagels, as well as old favourites like porridge and kippers. "One of my favourite hotels"; "We will definitely be back": typical comments from recent visitors. (*Ran Ogston, Prof. Wolfgang Stroebe*)

Open All year, except Christmas, New Year.
Rooms 1 suite, 31 double, 8 single (4 without facilities *en suite*). Some on ground floor.
Facilities Ramp, lift. Sitting room, bar (light background music), brasserie; private dining/function room.
Location Central (front rooms double-glazed). Meter parking. (Underground: Victoria.)
Restrictions No smoking in bedrooms. Guide dogs only.
Credit cards All major cards accepted.
Terms B&B: single £115, double £130–£170, family (for 4) £260. Full alc £22.

22 Jermyn Street
22 Jermyn Street
London SW1Y 6HL

Tel (020) 7734 2353
Fax (020) 7734 0750
E-mail office@22jermyn.com
Website www.22jermyn.com

🏵 *César award in 1996*

"Fabulous. A well-kept secret. What a treat it was to find this jewel."
"The staff were extraordinarily helpful, no matter what the request,
but they were never intrusive. Our children loved it, and I loved all the
thoughtful details – even live orchids in the rooms." Tributes continue
to arrive for Henry Togna's small luxury hotel, in a prime position in
St James's. It combines the ultimate in hi-tech – fax/modem lines,
Internet MasterCard, a CD-ROM library, private voicemail and an
individual e-mail address for every guest – with personal care.
Business visitors appreciate "the sheer practicality" of the services
provided. The in-house newsletters are detailed and wide-ranging,
offering theatre, exhibition and restaurant recommendations. Other
visitors "were upgraded to a spacious suite with a large sitting room
looking on to Jermyn Street, a lovely bedroom and a superb bathroom.
The air-conditioning, though noisy, was welcome on a sultry August
night." Mr Togna is a fitness fanatic: his guests may use the sporting
facilities at a nearby club, borrow a mountain bike, or go jogging with
him in St James's Park. His art-historian niece, Louise Hayward, con-
ducts tours of art galleries. The decor is an appealing blend of contemporary furniture and fabrics with antiques. Accommodation is
mostly in suites. No public rooms, but light room-service meals (salads, pasta, fish-cakes, sandwiches) can be served. West End theatres,
shops and eating places of all kinds are nearby. (*Alston Kerr,
Katherine Galligan*)

Open All year.
Rooms 13 suites, 5 double. All air-conditioned. 24-hour room service.
Facilities Lift. Reception (classical background music); small conference
facilities. Access to swimming pool, gym, squash courts at nearby club.
Location Central. Valet parking (expensive). (Underground: Piccadilly
Circus.)
Credit cards All major cards accepted.
Terms [2000] (*Excluding VAT*) Room £205, suite £290–£325. Extra bed £30.
Breakfast £11.55. Room service full alc £30–£40.

See also SHORTLIST

LORTON Cumbria   **Map 4**

New House Farm
Lorton
Cockermouth CA13 9UU

Tel/Fax (01900) 85404
E-mail hazel@newhouse-farm.co.uk
Website www.newhouse-farm.co.uk

A country guest house, surrounded by a garden, fields, woodland,
streams and ponds, and set amid some of the Lake District's most
spectacular and unspoilt scenery, on the edge of a traditional village.
The 17th-century Grade II listed whitewashed farmhouse has been

stylishly furnished by its helpful owner, Hazel Thompson (she has reverted to her maiden name). "She could not be more friendly," says a visitor this year, who enjoyed the "relaxing atmosphere". Others wrote: "Very professional. Not a hotel. You are definitely in some-one's house." Antiques, silver and bright colours in the small lounges complement the original oak beams and rafters, flagstone floors and open stone fireplaces. The home-cooked five-course dinner (no choice) might consist of local Solway shrimps; cream of tomato soup; pheasant cooked in cider; rhubarb crumble with cream. There is a short wine list. "Excellent breakfasts" include fresh grapefruit pieces, juicy prunes, eggs and bacon and home-made marmalade. Lunches and teas are served in the café, in a converted barn. Bedrooms, of vary-ing sizes, are "cosy and spotlessly clean", with "marvellous views". Some towels may have seen better days, but one guest wrote that her mattress "was of the highest quality". Dogs are allowed the run of the grounds. There is easy access to Loweswater, Crummock Water, Buttermere and the fells, and excellent birdwatching. (*Elizabeth Sandham, Carol Jackson, Patricia M Simpson*)

Open All year.
Rooms 5 double. 1 in stable. No telephone/TV.
Facilities 3 lounges, dining room. No background music. 14-acre grounds: garden, streams, woods, field. 3 lakes within 3 miles. Unsuitable for &.
Location Off B5289 S of Lorton.
Restrictions No smoking. No children under 8. No dogs in public rooms.
Credit cards None accepted.
Terms B&B £38–£50; D,B&B £58–£70. Packed lunch £6.50. Set dinner £22. Reduced rates for 3 nights or more. Christmas package. 1-night bookings sometimes refused.

Winder Hall NEW/BUDGET	*Tel/Fax* (01900) 85107
Low Lorton	*E-mail* winderhall@lowlorton.freeserve.co.uk
Cockermouth CA13 9UP	*Website* www.winderhall.co.uk

A country guest house, owned by Mary and Derek Denman. It is a Grade II listed building, 14th-century in origin with later additions, named for the family that built it. Thick Tudor walls, Victorian mul-lioned windows, and a huge fireplace with a priest-hole give it plenty of character. "It is a restful place," says the nominator. "The bed-rooms, all different, are beautiful" (two have a kingsize four-poster; all have flowers and chocolates). The grounds run down to a stretch of the River Cocker crossed by an old bridge. A four-course dinner is served at 7.30 pm in the panelled dining room. Two choices of starter and main course, eg, watercress soup or pear and stilton salad; pork ten-derloin with rosemary and apples, or wild mushroom risotto. Desserts might be baked chocolate fondant with white chocolate sauce or mango and passion fruit salad. There is a short wine list with some reasonably priced house wines. Breakfast is a generous affair, with a cold buffet, smoked fish, egg dishes, home-made preserves.

Open All year, except Christmas.
Rooms 6 double. No telephone.
Facilities Lounge with honesty bar, dining room (classical background music mealtimes). ½-acre grounds on River Cocker. Unsuitable for &.

Location From Keswick take A66 west, then B5292 Whinlatter Pass. At T-junction with B5298 turn left to Low Lorton. House on right, past *Wheatsheaf Inn*.
Restrictions No smoking. No children under 8. No dogs.
Credit cards MasterCard, Visa.
Terms B&B £30–£39; D,B&B £48–£55. Set dinner £20. Child accommodated in parents' room: under 10, £7; 11–15, £12. 1-night bookings sometimes refused.

LOUGHBOROUGH Leicestershire *See SHORTLIST*   **Map 2**

LOWER HENLADE Somerset   **Map 1**

The Mount Somerset   *Tel* (01823) 442500
Lower Henlade   *Fax* (01823) 442900
Taunton TA3 5NB

High up in the Blackdown hills, with "memorable views", this was originally a Tudor house, built by local landowners the Proctor-Anderdon family. In 1805 they employed an Italian architect to transform it into the white manor house it is today. Original features have been carefully preserved. Now owned by Countess von Essen (see also *Congham Hall*, Grimston), it is "immaculate and exceedingly comfortable", says a visitor this year. She also praised the "friendly young managers", Scott and Tracey Leeming, and enjoyed the "soothing atmosphere". The bedrooms are lavishly decorated. "Some might consider them OTT – bold flowery fabrics, huge bed – excellent, if ugly, huge bathroom, with state-of-the-art shower in separate cubicle, and whirlpool bath." The large dining room "is beautiful", in terracotta and white, with fresh flowers, heavy cutlery, crisp white napery. The chef, Ritchie Herkes, serves such modern dishes as foie gras and truffle terrine; marinated venison with a cassis jus; gingered quince broth with a black cherry and hazelnut ravioli. Wines are "reasonably priced", and the service "is excellent", but one guest found the cooking a little variable. Breakfast has a good cold buffet. Other pleasures: tea served with white bone china and home-made biscuits; gardens with peacocks and pine trees. "A little noise from a nearby road, but mostly beautifully quiet." Conferences and functions are held; you should check the position when booking.

Open All year.
Rooms 5 suites, 6 double.
Facilities Lift. Lounge/bar, restaurant, conservatory; conference/function facilities; piped background music or pianist during meals. 3-acre gardens. Fishing 20 mins.
Location 3 miles E of Taunton. From M5 exit 25 take A358, signposted Chard. Through Henlade, right at crossroads into Stoke Rd (to Stoke St Mary). Left at T-junction; drive on right after *c*. 100 yds. Train: Taunton; then taxi.
Restrictions No smoking in restaurant. No dogs.
Credit cards All major cards accepted.
Terms [2000] B&B: single £95–£115, double £110–£135, suite £155–£170. Set lunch £16.95, dinner £25; full alc £40. Weekend breaks. Christmas package.

LUDLOW Shropshire   Map 3

Dinham Hall   `NEW`   *Tel* (01584) 876464
by the castle   *Fax* (01584) 876019
Ludlow SY8 1EJ

Owned by the Mifsuds of The Lake, *Llangammarch Wells, Wales* (qv):
beautifully proportioned, Georgian house, "a tranquil spot", sur-
rounded by walled garden (with parking) in "enviable position",
opposite castle, with views of Teme valley, and "some of Ludlow's
loveliest houses and gardens". 15 bedrooms, best ones with elaborate
drapes, four-poster, etc, but in need of updating: 2 in cottage.
2 lounges. Pretty, beamed dining room (no smoking), with French
chef, Oliver Bossut. His cooking has been called "divine" by some but
"fussy" by others; breakfasts "so-so". "Charming staff." Unsuitable
for &. *No dogs in public rooms. All major credit cards accepted. B&B*
£55–£80; D,B&B £70–£95. Set lunch/dinner £26. New manager, Mr
Grainger, in March 2000. More reports, please. *V*

Mr Underhill's   *Tel* (01584) 874431
Dinham Weir
Ludlow SY8 1EH

& *César award in 2000*

"Very personally run" by its owners, the Scottish-born chef
Christopher Bradley and his wife Judy, this restaurant-with-rooms is
named for their large white cat (they also own Frodo, a British Blue).
The restaurant is unusual in having both a *Michelin* star and a *Bib
Gourmand*. Returning visitors this year again wrote of the "excellent
value", "simple, cheerful bedrooms", "friendly staff" and "modern,
intensely flavourful food". The Bradleys, they say, "are dedicated to
their profession". The setting is charming, below the ramparts of
Ludlow Castle and overlooking the River Teme. During recent reno-
vations, the façade was painted "the colour of straw", and the window
frames sage green. The garden has been restored, and there is now a
courtyard-style outdoor sitting area. In the restaurant (with red-striped
walls, modern pictures, red-and-green floral drapes, Wedgwood
china) there is no choice on the menu until dessert (you should make
sure you discuss preferences in advance). "Fresh, firm fillet of brill
with a light carrot and ginger sauce, beautifully timed" was enjoyed
this year; also chicken, "really tasting of chicken", on a cushion of
wild mushroom risotto; "wickedly creamy, but light" Italian panetone
bread and butter pudding; "excellent petits fours and good coffee".
The wine list "contains something for everyone". All the bedrooms
look across the river to Whitcliffe Common. They have good-quality
pine furniture, natural fabrics, a large bed, crisp linen, a small but
"well-arranged" bathroom. Some rooms are small, but two are being
enlarged this year, and given a new bathroom. Sound insulation may
not always be perfect. Breakfast includes fresh orange juice, home-
made muesli, organic bacon, sausage and eggs. "With their small staff,
the Bradleys may not be able to satisfy the most demanding of guests,

but they aim to provide high standards of cooking and housekeeping at affordable prices, without the trappings associated with many smart country house hotels." They do not insist that residents dine in, and will help with reservations elsewhere. (*Padi and John Howard, JD, and others*)

Open All year. Restaurant generally closed Tues.
Rooms 6 double.
Facilities 2 small lounge areas, restaurant; function facilities. No background music. ¼-acre garden on river: fishing, swimming. Unsuitable for &.
Location Below castle on bank of River Teme. Station ½ mile.
Restrictions No smoking: restaurant, bedrooms. No dogs.
Credit cards MasterCard, Visa.
Terms B&B: single £62.50–£92.50, double £75–£105. Set lunch £25, dinner £27.50. 1-night booking refused some Sats. *V*

Number Twenty Eight   BUDGET
28 Lower Broad Street
Ludlow SY8 1PQ

Tel (01584) 876996
Fax (01584) 876860
E-mail ross.no28@btinternet.com
Website www.no28.co.uk

"Perfection! A true home from home," is one comment this year on Patricia and Philip Ross's unusual B&B. "It is beautiful and original, the welcome was warm, and we left restored and happy." Set in a quiet street close to the River Teme, it consists of three separate small terrace houses. *Number Twenty Eight*, which houses the breakfast room, is early Georgian with 13th-century origins; *Broadgate Mews* is two joined Tudor cottages; *Westview* is part of a small Victorian terrace, said to have had the first internal water closets in town. Each house has a garden, and a "comfy sitting room" with an open fire, family photographs, books, maps, etc, and two bedrooms. Bathrooms have been added with respect for the houses' origins. One has an old fireplace next to the loo; all are well provided with toiletries and useful items like plasters and razors. The rooms are "charming, spotless and well organised", though some are quite small, and one bathroom "might be uncomfortable for a large person". The owners' "kindness and genuine concern for guests' comfort" is praised. "Daisy, the resident labrador, regarded us with benign affection, as if we were old and well-remembered friends." A continental breakfast is available in the bedrooms, which are equipped with a fridge and a toaster; a cooked breakfast is "competently served by Mr Ross"; the marmalade "is made by a leading light of the Women's Institute". Parking can be awkward. "There are more *Michelin*-starred restaurants within walking distance than anywhere else on earth," the Rosses write. These include *Mr Underhill's* (see above). Ludlow is well endowed with historic buildings (its entire centre is Grade II listed). A good base for touring Shropshire and the Welsh Marches. (*Ann Evans, Rosemary Wright, Sir Timothy Harford, and others*)

Open All year.
Rooms 6 double, in 3 separate houses.
Facilities 3 sitting rooms, breakfast room (classical background music). 3 gardens. Unsuitable for &.

Location 200 yds from centre; close to Ludford Bridge. Train: Ludlow; they will meet.
Restrictions No smoking. Dogs in mews cottage only; not in public rooms.
Credit cards MasterCard, Visa.
Terms B&B: single £60–£75, double £75–£85. 1-night bookings sometimes refused weekends.

LYDGATE Greater Manchester   **Map 4**

The White Hart   *Tel* (01457) 872566
51 Stockport Road   *Fax* (01457) 875190
Lydgate, nr Oldham OL4 4JJ   *E-mail* charles@thewhitehart.co.uk
                                        Website www.thewhitehart.co.uk

"The main business of *The White Hart* is food," says an inspector, but he also liked the "impressive views" and the "simple but tastefully furnished bedrooms". The old stone-built inn, in a Pennine village near Oldham, was saved from dereliction in 1994 by Charles Brierley and John Rudden (the chef); they have been busy making further improvements this year. There is a new ground-floor restaurant (the old one upstairs is now a private dining room), and seven bedrooms have been added. The brasserie (*Michelin Bib Gourmand*) serves "modern classics" like deep-fried cheese soufflés with tomato and chilli jam; seabass with crab risotto; all manner of locally produced sausages with mash. Some dishes are marked "H" for "healthy eating". In the restaurant, "fine contemporary cooking" is served on a menu that changes each month, eg, spinach risotto with poached egg, or glazed goat's cheese with olive beignets; fillet of beef with truffle risotto and a chanterelle jus, or veal cutlet with roasted parsnips. Only complaint: "The non-stop background taped music was intrusive." Some bedrooms have sweeping views towards Manchester and the Cheshire plains; they have "serviceable modern pine furniture, good lighting"; some are small. The "generous breakfast" has freshly squeezed juice, granary toast, home-made jams, "first-class eggs, mushroom and bacon". The inn caters for business visitors during the week, offering "advanced office technology". The staff are "well trained, slightly formal, but friendly". More reports, please.

Open All year.
Rooms 1 suite, 10 double, 1 single.
Facilities 2 bars, brasserie, restaurant, private dining room; business facilities; modern background music all the time. 2½-acre grounds. Unsuitable for &. Civil wedding licence.
Location 3½ miles E of Oldham. From Manchester, take A62 to Oldham; at Mumps roundabout take A669 to Lees. Through Lees, Springhead and Grotton. Up to brow of hill; turn right immediately after derelict garage; inn is 50 yds on left. Bus from Oldham.
Restrictions No smoking in restaurant. No dogs.
Credit card Visa.
Terms B&B: single £62.50, double £80, suite £105. Set lunch £12–£17, dinner £24.75; full alc (brasserie) £25. *V*

LYMINGTON Hampshire   Map 2

Stanwell House   *Tel* (01590) 677123
14 High Street   *Fax* (01590) 677756
Lymington SO41 9AA

Jane McIntyre's Georgian coaching inn is in the centre of this old port
and yachting station at the mouth of the River Lymington, where it
reaches the Solent. Run in relaxed style, it has a decor that is "slightly
wild and wacky – New England meets Gothic revival", one visitor
wrote. The bedrooms, often of strange shape and size, are "both fun
and comfortable". Some have a terrace overlooking the courtyard.
Suites have a roll-top bath and a four-poster. There are bright colours
everywhere, and lavish use of silk and velvet. The restaurant's colour
scheme ranges through amethyst, fuchsia, gold and paprika; the
bar/bistro, occupying three rooms and also brightly coloured, has
wooden chairs and tables and is popular with locals. There is a new
chef this year, Ian McCelland from Canada, and his GM-free menus
include, eg, breast of duck with a foie gras sauce; chargrilled tuna;
saddle of venison in a port sauce. Picnic hampers, "accompanied if
necessary by staff", are available. There is a conservatory lounge with
flagstones, plants, antiques and bric-à-brac, a clothing store that sells
goods by Mulberry, Burberry and others, and a two-bedroomed cottage, a few minutes' walk from the quay. A 50-foot yacht, *Alpha of
Devonport*, is available for charter. A good base for visiting the New
Forest and touring Dorset. Winchester and Salisbury are not far.
Parking can be awkward. "Small, well-behaved" dogs are allowed.

Open All year.
Rooms 6 suites, 21 double, 1 single. Some on ground floor. 2-bedroomed cot-
tage nearby.
Facilities Conservatory lounge, bar/bistro, restaurant (light background
music). Conference facilities. Walled garden; patio. Private yacht. Unsuitable
for &. Civil wedding licence.
Location High street. Rear rooms quietest. Train: Brockenhurst (main line)
(6 miles); Lymington 200 metres.
Restriction No smoking: restaurant, some bedrooms. No dogs in restaurant.
Credit cards All major cards accepted.
Terms [2000] B&B: single £55, double £105, suite from £125; D,B&B: single
£77.50, double £150, suite from £170. Set lunch £15, dinner £25; full alc £38.
Child accommodated in parents' room: from £15.

MALMESBURY Wiltshire   Map 3

The Old Bell   *Tel* (01666) 822344
Abbey Row   *Fax* (01666) 825145
Malmesbury SN16 0AG   *E-mail* info@oldbellhotel.com
                                         Website www.oldbellhotel.com

Built in 1220 by Walter Loring, abbot of Malmesbury, for visitors to
the library of the adjacent abbey, this inn is thought to be one of the
oldest in Britain. Extensions have given it a rambling character, and it
is now owned by Nicholas Dickinson and Nigel Chapman of Luxury

Family Hotels, and managed by Clare Hammond. They run it on the same lines as its siblings, *Woolley Grange,* Bradford-on-Avon, *Moonfleet Manor,* Fleet, and *Fowey Hall,* Fowey (*qqv*), aiming to provide a welcoming environment for the young as well as a civilised ambience for adults. Children of all ages are well looked after: between 10 am and 6 pm youngsters can be left in the "Den" (a supervised nursery), while older children can enjoy the computer wizardry of the "Cyber Room" (an Internet café); there's also a play area in the small garden. After children's supper at 5 pm, parents can dine in the Edwardian restaurant, where one couple this year found the food "surprisingly good". The chef, Mike Benjamin, serves modern dishes, eg, grilled chorizo sausage on a creamy herb and parmesan risotto; roast rack of lamb with a herb crust, vegetable stuffing and a tian of aubergine and tomato; glazed lemon tart with a red fruit sorbet. Light lunches, teas and suppers are served in the "Great Hall" (actually a collection of small rooms), with comfortable furniture, plenty of reading matter, interesting artefacts and greenery. Some visitors this year have written of the "attentive service", but it has also been thought "inexperienced, with no sign of anyone in charge". Recent reports on the bedrooms have also been mixed: one couple thought their large room in the front "depressing, with a large marble fireplace and a bathroom in great need of refurbishment"; other readers had a room that was "very pleasing; its spacious bathroom had a freestanding bath". Bedrooms in the modern annexe have a "minimalist" Japanese decor. A few rooms get traffic noise by day, but they are quiet at night. Westonbirt Arboretum, Bowood House and Lacock village (National Trust) are all within a 20-minute drive.

Open All year.
Rooms 4 suites, 24 double, 3 single. 15 in coach house. 6 on ground floor.
Facilities Ramp. 2 lounges, children's playroom, Great Hall (for brasserie-style meals), bar (varied background music), restaurant. Small garden. Fishing, riding, tennis, golf, dry skiing, water sports, cycling nearby. Civil wedding licence.
Location Central, by abbey. Carpark. Train: Chippenham 8 miles; then taxi.
Restriction No smoking in restaurant.
Credit cards All major cards accepted.
Terms [2000] B&B: single £65, double £95–£130, suite £165–£180. Set lunch £16, dinner £26; full alc £35. Children accommodated free in parents' room. Special breaks. Christmas, New Year packages. 1-night bookings sometimes refused weekends.

MALVERN WELLS Worcestershire   **Map 3**

The Cottage in the Wood   *Tel* (01684) 575859
Holywell Road   *Fax* (01684) 560662
Malvern Wells WR14 4LG   *E-mail* proprietor@cottageinthewood.co.uk
                                    Website www.cottageinthewood.co.uk

The "beautiful location, outstanding views and friendly welcome" were enjoyed again this year by visitors to this Georgian dower house. It stands amid woods and shrubbery high on the slopes of the Malvern Hills, where Edward Elgar loved to walk. Looking over the Severn valley to the distant Cotswolds, it is in a designated area of outstanding natural beauty. From the grounds you can walk straight out to a nine-mile range of the Malvern Hills and more than 100 miles of tracks. This is a family affair: John and Sue Pattin run the hotel with their daughters, Maria and Rebecca, and daughter-in-law, Romy. Son Dominic, who has worked in a number of *Michelin*-starred kitchens including *Le Manoir aux Quat'Saisons*, Great Milton (*qv*), presides over the restaurant with its Indian paintings, well-spaced tables, and "correct atmosphere". The cooking is mostly thought "very good", though one visitor, on a three-night stay, bemoaned the lack of a dish of the day. But the chefs' flexibility is appreciated; they will tailor size of portion to appetite, and cook dishes plainly if asked. The long *à la carte* menu changes monthly, offering, eg, monkfish wrapped in Parma ham; loin of lamb on buttered leeks; "delicious home-made ice-creams". The half-board rates include a £26 allowance for dinner. The huge wine list includes many half bottles and three pages of English wines – John Pattin promises a refund if you try one of these and don't like it. Light lunches are served on weekdays; on Sunday there is a *table d'hôte* menu. "Breakfast was excellent in every respect," says a visitor in 2000. The bedrooms vary greatly; the best ones, in the main house, have a traditional decor; home-made shortbread and Malvern water are supplied, and most rooms have binoculars. Major alterations are in progress, including renovation of the least appealing rooms, in the Coach House annexe. The public rooms have antiques, and picture windows overlooking the view; the bar is "amazingly well stocked". Dogs are welcomed, except in the main house. Guests have access to the local golf and squash clubs. (*John RC West, Sue Davies, and others*)

Open All year.
Rooms 20 double. 4 in Beech Cottage 70 yds, 8 in Coach House 100 yds.
Facilities Lounge, bar, restaurant; function facilities. 7-acre grounds leading to Malvern Hills. Golf, squash nearby. Unsuitable for &.
Location Off A449 to Ledbury, 3 miles S of Malvern; turning is 500 yards N of B4209 junction, on opposite side of road. Do not approach from S end of Holywell Rd. Train: Malvern.
Restrictions No smoking in restaurant. No dogs in main house.
Credit cards Amex, MasterCard, Visa.
Terms [2000] B&B: single £75–£85, double £89.50–£145; D,B&B (min. 2 nights) £62–£97 per person. Set lunch: £11.95–£14.95 Mon–Sat, £16.95 Sun; full alc £37.50. Bargain breaks all year. Christmas, New Year packages. 1-night bookings sometimes refused Fri/Sat. *V*

MANCHESTER Map 4

Eleven Didsbury Park NEW   *Tel* (0161) 448 7711
11 Didsbury Park   *Fax* (0161) 448 8282
Didsbury Village   *E-mail* enquiries@elevendidsburypark.com
Manchester M20 5LH   *Website* www.elevendidsburypark.com

"A godsend," says an inspector this year of this new hotel, a conversion of a Victorian town house in a conservation area of the city (the centre is reached by a 20-minute bus ride). A member of Planet, a small international consortium of "designer hotels" (see also *The Lace Market,* Nottingham), it was opened in late 1999 by its owner, Eamonn O'Loughlin, who is much in evidence – "his delightful Irish manner contributes much to the informal atmosphere". His designer wife Sally, "equally charming", is responsible for the "fairly minimal" modern decor: public rooms have white walls, large steel-framed mirrors, a huge stone fireplace topped by three large stones, coffee tables made of old trunks, goldfish in a tall bowl. Large casement windows lead on to a small gravel terrace with pots and shrubs, and an attractive large garden with mature trees. "Our bedroom had white walls, a beige carpet, dark polished furniture, an extra-large bed, a small wardrobe, a CD-player, but nothing in the way of mineral water, flowers, etc. Breakfast, in a pleasant, airy room with framed montages of cutlery on the walls, had a small buffet, an interesting selection of cooked dishes (eg, a full Irish breakfast of black pudding, white pudding and potato cake; free-range eggs prepared in many ways; eggs Benedict), but nasty packages of butter and jam – not good enough for a place of this quality." Arriving visitors are greeted by the friendly manager (he styles himself "host") Justin Hanson, with "excellent coffee". No restaurant, but you can order dishes from a "Deli Menu" (salads, soups, pasta, etc), the hotel's car will ferry guests to local restaurants, and the owners sometimes hold a barbecue in the garden.

Open All year.
Rooms 1 junior suite, 13 double.
Facilities Lounge, veranda, breakfast rooms; background music all day. Large walled garden, rooftop terrace: hot tub. Unsuitable for &.
Location Didsbury Park 3 miles from centre (regular buses). From A34 take A5145 (Wilmslow Rd); right up Didsbury Pk. Parking.
Restrictions No smoking: breakfast room, 11 bedrooms. Dogs by arrangement; not in public rooms.
Credit cards Amex, MasterCard, Visa.
Terms Double room £99.50–£119.50 (£69.50–£89.50 weekends), suite from £155.50 (£125.50 weekends). Breakfast: continental £7.50, English £9.50.

Malmaison	*Tel* (0161) 278 1000
Piccadilly	*Fax* (0161) 278 1002
Manchester M1 3AQ	*E-mail* manchester@malmaison.com
	Website www.malmaison.com

"Must be *the* place to stay in Manchester," says one visitor to this *Malmaison,* two years old, and liked for its "combination of high style and no nonsense", and ethos of "trying to give good value at a fair price". Not a great setting, in a busy street close to Piccadilly station, and one guest thought the place "over-trendy", but other views were positive: "The public rooms are comfortable and uncluttered, and the bedrooms well maintained." "Reception and restaurant staff were outstanding, and the food was excellent – just as well; it would be a trek to find better." The entrance hall is "dark, solid and serious, with splashes of colour: exotic, classy flowers, huge bowls of fresh lemons and limes, designerish furniture, eg, angular padded chairs". Upstairs is "more like a standard hotel (bedrooms leading off beige corridors)", but the rooms are chic: bold stripes, bright colours, lots of cushions, a

CD-player, a smart bathroom with a "first-class shower" (but sound-proofing is not always perfect). The mini-bar has a tab sheet with an "Amount scoffed" column. You can call your bill up on the TV screen and see how much you have spent. The French-style brasserie serves unfussy food in generous portions, eg, eggs Benedict; braised lamb shank with polenta; lemon tart. And "the francophilia extends to the announcements in the lift: 'Les portes ferment', etc". "Good breakfast, with freshly squeezed juices and a good croissant." Leisure facilities include the "gymtonic" and "Le petit spa", with sauna, solarium and "lifestyle treatments". An extension with 55 more bedrooms will be completed by 2001, so we'd like reports, please. (*Prof. David Taylor, HW*)

Open All year.
Rooms 8 suites, 104 double. 5 adapted for &.
Facilities Lift. Lounge, bar, brasserie; private dining room; leisure centre. Background contemporary music all day.
Location By Piccadilly station; 2 mins' walk from centre. Valet parking.
Restrictions No smoking in some bedrooms. Dogs by arrangement, not in public rooms.
Credit cards All major cards accepted.
Terms [2000] Room: single/double room £110, suite £165. Breakfast: continental £8.50, English £10.50. Set lunch £12.50, dinner £15; full alc £35.

See also SHORTLIST

MARKINGTON North Yorkshire   **Map 4**

Hob Green   *Tel* (01423) 770031
Markington   *Fax* (01423) 771589
nr Harrogate HG3 3PJ   *E-mail* hobgreen.hotel@virgin.net

A well-appointed, traditional hotel (Best Western) in a "delightful rural setting", not far from Ripon. "It offers good value, meals of a high standard, and excellent service," says a report this year. Reached up a tree-lined drive, the 18th-century house "is no great beauty, but it is enhanced by its setting in a huge estate, with extensive floral and vegetable gardens" (they have won a "Yorkshire and Humberside in Bloom" prize). It was converted into a hotel in 1982 by the long-time owners, the Hutchinson family. The manager, Gary Locker, welcomes guests in a "warm and natural" manner. The public rooms have an old-fashioned style: original panelling and moulding, antiques, fresh flowers, open fires, and views across the valley. The bedroom decor varies from traditional to modern. "Room 1 was large and attractive, with a good view, a mini-bar containing fresh milk, lots of bathroom goodies." No bar; drinks are served in the hall or the pretty lounge. "You should not make too great an inroad into the crudités, given the size of the main courses at dinner." The cooking is "English with a Mediterranean twist", with a wide choice, including, eg, mussels Provençale; fanned supreme of duckling with apricot and thyme sauce; apple and blackberry crumble with custard. There is a "decent selection of reasonably priced wines." Plenty of choice for breakfast.

Conferences and functions are catered for. Within 20 minutes' drive are Fountains Abbey, Ripley Castle, the cathedral city of Ripon, and many other attractions. (*Donald J Barnes*)

Open All year.
Rooms 1 suite, 8 double, 3 single.
Facilities Hall, drawing room, sunroom, restaurant; function facilities. No background music. 880-acre grounds: farm, woodlands, garden, croquet. Unsuitable for &.
Location SW of village 9 miles N of Harrogate. From Harrogate: A61 to Ripon. B6165 to Pateley Bridge. After 1 mile turn right at sign to Fountains Abbey. After 2 miles, right at *Drovers' Inn*; hotel 1 mile further. Look for brown signs.
Restrictions Smoking discouraged in restaurant. No dogs in public rooms.
Credit cards All major cards accepted.
Terms [2000] B&B: single £85, double £95–£105, suite £120–£125. Set lunch £13.95, dinner £24.50; full alc £35. 1-night bookings sometimes refused weekends. *V*

MARLBOROUGH Wiltshire *See SHORTLIST*   **Map 2**

MATLOCK BATH Derbyshire   **Map 3**

Hodgkinson's Hotel   BUDGET   *Tel* (01629) 582170
150 South Parade   *Fax* (01629) 584891
Matlock Bath DE4 3NR
♧ *César award in 1994*

The large oval sign hanging in front of the oldest hotel in the old spa town dates from the 1830s, when it was bought by Job Hodgkinson, a wine merchant. The house is cut into the cliff face at the rear; the caves behind were used as a cellar, and much of the ground floor has hardly changed since Hodgkinson's day. From outside it can appear a bit run down, but it has been carefully restored by Nigel Shelley, an interior designer, and Malcolm Archer, who has a hairdressing salon on the first floor. Once within, guests enjoy the stained glass of the lobby, the "slightly louche atmosphere", and a treasure trove of Victorian ephemera. William Morris wallpaper, old prints, and Staffordshire china adorn the public rooms. Fox furs, hats, gloves, shoes, Dinky toys, Minton china, figurines, Art Nouveau relics, a dressmaker's dummy, birdcages, and exotic paintings enliven the climb up the stairs – four floors, no lift. Most of the bedrooms look across a busy road to the River Derwent, and they have a small shower room. They are priced according to size; the single is tiny. There are some splendid old beds. "Lovely room; great food; very friendly people," one reader said. Another had "a clean, bright room; attractive view; plenty of hot water". The owners share the cooking. There are five choices of the first two courses at dinner, which might include grilled mussels, stuffed with green pepper, garlic and parsley; fillet of lamb with a honey and lavender sauce. There is also a vegetarian menu. "The restaurant has good chairs and first-class napery. No half bottles in the cellar, but decent house wine by the glass. Adequate breakfast with good tea." There is a small rear garden with mature roses and a pergola built of brick, old chimney pots and timber. Set in a gorge, the town is now a tourist centre for the Derbyshire dales. Despite amusement arcades and fish-and-chip shops, it still retains some of its Victorian appeal, and it is a good base for exploring the Peak District. There is some challenging rock climbing close by. (*PT, and others*)

Open All year, except Christmas. Restaurant closed midday.
Rooms 6 double, 1 single.
Facilities 2 lounges, restaurant (varied background music at night). ¼-acre garden. Opposite River Derwent: fishing. Unsuitable for &.
Location Central (2 quiet rooms at rear). Private carpark.
Restrictions No smoking in restaurant. No dogs in public rooms.
Credit cards Amex, MasterCard, Visa.
Terms B&B: single £35, double £60–£90. Set dinner £19.50–£24.50. 2- to 4-day breaks.

MAWNAN SMITH Cornwall   **Map 1**

Meudon   *Tel* (01326) 250541
Mawnan Smith   *Fax* (01326) 250543
nr Falmouth TR11 5HT
                                            E-mail info@meudon.co.uk
                                            Website www.meudon.co.uk

"Particularly welcoming to families"; "very attentive staff" are two comments this year on this thoroughly traditional hotel. Run by its owners, father and son Harry and Mark Pilgrim, it consists of a mellow stone mansion connected by a glassed-in "bridge", which doubles as a sun lounge, to a utilitarian modern bedroom wing. Its chief glories are its subtropical garden, which was laid out in the 18th century by Capability Brown, and its location in 200 acres of protected Cornish coastline between the Fal and Helford rivers, at the head of a valley leading down to a private beach. Old-fashioned services are offered: cases carried, beds turned down at night, shoes cleaned, early morning tea brought to the room (tea-making facilities are also available). The bedrooms are good-sized and well equipped, but not luxurious; the suites are "particularly good", says a visitor this year. Many bedrooms and bathrooms have been refurbished, and the Pilgrims write that they have abolished single supplements: "a twin double is now allocated for single occupancy at half the double rate". Breakfast is of a "calorific nature", including black pudding with a huge mixed grill; lashings of toast and coffee. Afternoon tea is taken outdoors, or in front of a log fire in the lounge. A new head waiter, David Pitcher, presides over the restaurant, where chef for 17 years, Alan Webb, serves a traditional five-course dinner, with lots of choice: sorbet in the middle, fish, steaks, etc, to follow (lobster and crab can be specially ordered – you pay extra); properly cooked vegetables; a trolley of old-fashioned desserts; an excellent cheeseboard, and a decent range of reasonably priced wines. Another lovely garden, Trebah, is close by. (*LH*)

Open 1 Feb–3 Jan.
Rooms 4 suites, 25 double/single. 16 on ground floor (some equipped for &).
Facilities Lift, ramp. 3 lounges, bar, restaurant. 10-acre grounds: gardens, private beach, fishing. Golf, riding, windsurfing nearby.

Location 4 miles S of Falmouth. From Truro: A39 towards Falmouth for about 9 miles. Right at Hillhead roundabout; follow signs for Meanporth (*ignore* signs for Mawnan Smith). Follow narrow, winding road (marked "Unsuitable for long vehicles"). Hotel on left ½ mile after Meanporth beach, 1 mile before Mawnan Smith. Carpark; 2 lock-up garages £5. Train: Truro; then taxi/hire car.
Restriction No dogs in public rooms.
Credit cards All major cards accepted.
Terms [2000] B&B: single £39.50–£85, double £89–£170, D,B&B (min 2 nights): single £49.50–£95, double £99–£190. Suite £60 supplement. Set lunch £12.50, dinner £25.50. Reductions for children in adjoining rooms July/Aug. 3-day breaks. Christmas package. *V*

MEMBURY Devon   Map 1

Lea Hill Hotel   *Tel* (01404) 881881 and 881388
Membury, nr Axminster EX13 7AQ   *Fax* (01404) 881890
                                            Website www.leahillhotel.co.uk

"We love the peaceful location," says a returning visitor to this 14th-century thatched longhouse. Another wrote of the "excellent hosts and relaxed atmosphere – everyone chatting in the bar". Reached by narrow rural roads, it has a beautiful position on a Devon hilltop in a designated area of outstanding natural beauty. From the large grounds there are wide views of woodland and meadows. Inside the handsome building are ancient beams, flagstone floors, and inglenook fireplaces. The efficiency, and the welcome by owners Chris and Sue Hubbard, is praised, and so is the "first-class cooking" of their son, James, though one visitor would have liked one slightly simpler alternative to each course. The "very pleasant restaurant" (it has wooden tables and chairs, fat candles, fresh flowers) is open to the public. A sample menu includes local wild rabbit with soft-fried polenta chips; ballotine of lamb with roasted shallots, parsnip crisps and a red wine and redcurrant veal jus; coconut sponge with raspberry sauce. On Sunday evening, when the restaurant is closed, there is an informal buffet in the bar. "Breakfasts as good as I've had anywhere," was another compliment. The buffet includes freshly squeezed orange juice, and cooked dishes include local bacon, sausages and black pudding, Manx kippers, poached smoked Finnan haddock. Most bedrooms are in converted barns; many have a private garden or patio. They are "beautifully decorated, with good-quality fabrics and excellent lighting". Membury, a pretty village on the borders of Devon, Somerset and Dorset, was a Quaker centre in the 17th and 18th centuries; it has a Quaker burial ground and meeting house. The coast and an abundance of National Trust properties are close by. (*Joan Lee, Brian Beedham*)

Open All year, except 2 Jan–28 Feb. Restaurant closed midday, all Sun.
Rooms 2 suites, 9 double. 9 in 2 converted barns. Most with private patio or garden.
Facilities Lounge study, bar, restaurant; light background classical music/jazz evenings; meeting room. 8-acre grounds: garden, 6-hole par 3 golf course. Riding, hunting, fishing nearby; sea, safe beaches 10 miles. Unsuitable for &.
Location 2½ miles NW of Axminster. From *George Hotel* take road to Membury. Through village, past trout farm. House on right after ½ mile.

Restrictions No smoking, except in bar. No children under 16. Dogs by arrangement: in bar, certain bedrooms only.
Credit cards Amex, MasterCard, Visa.
Terms [2000] B&B £56–£68; D,B&B £78–£89. Set dinner £25.95. Wine and food weekends, painting holidays, midweek breaks. 1-night bookings refused Christmas, New Year, Easter. *V*

MIDDLEHAM North Yorkshire   Map 4

Waterford House   *Tel* (01969) 622090
19 Kirkgate   *Fax* (01969) 624020
Middleham DL8 4PG

"A jewel of a small Georgian hotel/restaurant," says an inspector. "An antique dealer's dream. The food is superb, and the wine list is an oenophile's delight." Brian and Everyl Madell run their Grade II listed stone house almost single-handed. It stands in a corner of the village square; you enter through a paved garden, colourful in summer with flowers in tubs. Inside is an "amazing collection" of silver, copper and glassware; walls are crammed with pictures; there are books galore. The residents' lounge has a grand piano, a log fire, a huge pine dresser. The bedrooms, equally crammed with ornaments and old furniture, are warm and quite spacious, and they have expensive fabrics, good toiletries, fruit, sherry, chocolates, plenty of local information, but lighting can be "somewhat dim", and the shower room "poorly designed". Two bedrooms were refurbished this year. Mrs Madell, "an energetic, charming lady" who has a young son, "is absolutely lovely". And her cooking, served in the little dining room (only four tables), is much admired, though portions are too large for some. "Asparagus, tender and beautifully cooked; tournedos Rossini, well executed and accompanied by huge choice of vegetables; trifle brought in a large glass bowl; you help yourself – such indulgence. Delicious wines served in lovely antique glasses." Mr Madell's award-winning wine list has over 1,000 bins; more than 900 wines are available by the glass. Breakfast has a wide choice of cooked dishes – "scrambled eggs as good as we expected", also thick brown toast and "delicious stewed fruits with creamy yogurt". "Middleham is delightful, particularly the daily scene of racehorses on their way to the gallops." Visits to the stables can be arranged. (*JB, and others*)

Open All year.
Rooms 5 double.
Facilities 2 lounges, restaurant. No background music. Walled garden. Fishing nearby. Unsuitable for &. Civil wedding licence.
Location Centre of village. Parking. Train: Darlington; then taxi.
Restriction No smoking: restaurant, 1 lounge. No dogs in public rooms.
Credit cards MasterCard, Visa.
Terms B&B: single £50–£60, double £75–£95. Set lunch £19.50, dinner £22.50; full alc £32.50. Wine weekends, private parties. Christmas, New Year, bank holiday breaks. Weekly rates. *V*

MILBORNE PORT Dorset   Map 2

The Old Vicarage   `BUDGET`   *Tel* (01963) 251117
Sherborne Road   *Fax* (01963) 251515
Milborne Port DT9 5AT   *Website* www.milborneport.freeserve.co.uk

A large, listed Victorian stone house in a village near Sherborne. It
stands in substantial grounds with old trees, a pond, and views of
rolling countryside. The owners, Jörgen Kunath and Anthony Ma, formerly ran a popular restaurant, *Noughts and Crosses*, in Ealing, West
London. The decor has a strong Chinese feel (Mr Ma is from Hong
Kong), and there are some impressive beds in the main house. The
bedrooms in the coach house are smaller and cheaper. The spacious
lounge has bright colours, antiques and oriental pots, easy chairs, a
piano, books and games. It looks over the garden, as does the conservatory dining room. Dinner is served only on Friday, Saturday and
bank holiday Sundays. Eclectic menus include, eg, deep-fried strips of
Szechuan beef with fried spicy aubergine; pan-fried local hare with
redcurrant and brandy sauce; apple and blueberry Eve's pudding.
"The hospitality was outstanding," said the nominator. "The meals
were attractively presented, using local produce when possible. The
wine list is interesting and well priced. Jörgen is a mine of information
about local sights" (they include Montacute, Parnham and Stourhead).
"Chinese, German, French and Spanish are all spoken here," say the
polyglot owners. (*GJ*)

Open Feb–Dec. Dinner served Fri, Sat, bank holiday Sun.
Rooms 6 double, 1 single. 4 in coach house (20 yds).
Facilities Lounge (classical background music at night), dining room. 3½-acre
grounds. Unsuitable for &.
Location 3 miles NE of Sherborne, on A30 at W end of Milborne Port. Train:
Sherborne; then taxi.
Restrictions No smoking: dining room, bedrooms. No children under 5.
No dogs.
Credit cards Amex, MasterCard, Visa.
Terms B&B: single £27–£30, double £53–£95; D,B&B: single £48–£50,
double £86–£136. Set dinner £20.50. Weekend breaks. 1-night bookings
sometimes refused weekends.

MILTON KEYNES Buckinghamshire *See SHORTLIST*   Map 2

MORSTON Norfolk   Map 2

Morston Hall   *Tel* (01263) 741041
Morston, nr Blakeney   *Fax* (01263) 740419
NR25 7AA   *E-mail* reception@morstonhall.com.uk
                                 Website www.morstonhall.com.uk

Owned by Galton and Tracy Blackiston (Justin Fraser has left), this
flint-walled Jacobean house stands on a road by the North Norfolk
coast. Behind is a peaceful garden with a lily pond and fountain, roses
and a croquet lawn. *Morston Hall* is "professional yet relaxed; you feel

like guests in a country house", say visitors this year. The Blackistons' "personal involvement at all stages" is praised, and so is the *Michelin*-starred restaurant. Using local produce, the cooking is a combination of modern British and classical French, eg, pan-fried foie gras; fillet of turbot on a tomato fondue; roast pigeon and venison with boudin; Bourbon vanilla cream with a Granny Smith sorbet, or cheese. The four-course dinner menu changes daily; no choice until the end; preferences are discussed in advance. Portions are "not over-large, so you can enjoy the meal without feeling bloated". Breakfast includes home-made bread, fresh orange juice and local kippers. Cream teas are served. Most bedrooms are spacious and well furnished, with a CD-player, a video and a large bathroom; those in the attic have a sloping ceiling. Lighting may be rather dim. Dogs are welcomed; a small charge is made for those accommodated in the house, but kennels are free. Morston is in a designated area of outstanding natural beauty – the estuary is two minutes' walk away; local attractions include the Blakeney Point seal sanctuary, Sandringham, Felbrigg and Blickling halls, Sheringham Park and "some wonderful churches". (*G and A Smeed, Brian and Rosalind Keen, Marilyn Frampton*)

Open All year, except Christmas, 3 weeks Jan. Restaurant closed for lunch, except Sun.
Rooms 1 suite, 5 double.
Facilities 2 lounges, conservatory, restaurant. No background music. 3½-acre garden: pond, croquet. Sea, beaches, sailing, birdwatching nearby. Only restaurant suitable for &.
Location On A149 coast road, 2 miles W of Blakeney. Private parking. Train: Sheringham, via Norwich; then taxi.
Restrictions No smoking in restaurant. No dogs in public rooms.
Credit cards All major credit cards accepted.
Terms D,B&B £90–£130. Set Sun lunch £21, dinner £34. Child accommodated in parents' room: under 3, free; over 3, £20. 3-night off-season breaks. Cookery courses. 1-night bookings sometimes refused Sat.

MOULSFORD-ON-THAMES Oxfordshire   Map 2

The Beetle and Wedge   *Tel* (01491) 651381
Ferry Lane   *Fax* (01491) 651376
Moulsford-on-Thames OX10 9JF
 César award in 1993

The "magical location" of Richard and Kate Smith's old inn is quintessentially English, on the banks of the Thames in manicured lawns that lead to the stretch of the river immortalised by Kenneth Grahame in *The Wind in the Willows*. Jerome K Jerome lived here while he wrote *Three Men in a Boat*. But it has a distinct Frenchness of style, in the welcome to children, the emphasis on food, and the style of the cooking (the co-chef is Olivier Bouet). The mainly French young staff are "enthusiastic and courteous", though language difficulties can occur. Reports are in the main strongly positive: "Outstanding. Lovely grounds." "Expert service and management." "Impressive attention to detail." The two restaurants are popular with outside lunchers and diners. Locally grown produce, organic where possible, is used, and the menus vary according to supplies. The smart conservatory-style *Dining Room*, overlooking the river, serves sophisticated dishes, eg, warm onion tart with foie gras and truffle sauce; turbot and seabass with mushroom risotto and champagne sauce; hot Cointreau soufflé with raspberry sauce (thought "exceptional" this year). The wine list is strong on Italian and French vintages. No half bottles, but a "dip-stick" policy applies: you can order a whole bottle and pay only for what is consumed plus a surcharge of £1.25. The informal *Boathouse* restaurant, which has a different chef and kitchen, serves charcoal grills, salads, casseroles and traditional puddings, in large portions (service is sometimes slow). There is a water garden for summer meals. Most of the bedrooms have river views; some are large. They are furnished "with a mixture of old and modern" – a huge bed, a sofa, a "glorious, large old-fashioned bath" and "gorgeous toiletries" (but dim bedside lights and thin curtains were reported this year). Breakfast, served from 7.30 until 11, is a relaxed affair, and it includes freshly squeezed orange juice, porridge, smoked haddock and

poached eggs, kidneys and black pudding, "and the best coffee ever"). "Our children loved feeding the ducks and swans." A good base for visiting Henley, Oxford and the Cotswolds. Heathrow airport is 50 minutes' drive away. (*Katherine Galligan, Alan Greenwood; also HJ Martin Tucker, and others*)

Open All year.
Rooms 1 suite, 9 double. 4 in adjacent cottage. 2 on ground floor.
Facilities Lounge, 2 restaurants; private dining/function room. No background music. ½-acre grounds on river: water garden, boating, fishing, mooring.
Location From M4 junction 12 take A4 S; at 2nd roundabout take A340 Pangbourne/Streatley/Moulsford. In village turn to river on Ferry La. Parking. Train: Reading/Goring; then taxi.
Restrictions No smoking: Dining Room, bedrooms. No dogs in public rooms, 8 bedrooms.
Credit cards All major cards accepted.
Terms [2000] B&B: single £90–£120, double £135–£150. Bar meals; full alc £31.50–£48.50. Champagne weekends. ***V***

MUNGRISDALE Cumbria   Map 4

The Mill Hotel   *Tel* (017687) 79659
Mungrisdale, Penrith CA11 0XR   *Fax* (017687) 79155
Q *César award in 1993*

"A delight. The most child-friendly hotel we have stayed in," says one report this year on this popular place. "The warmth of Richard Quinlan's personal welcome extended from our initial phone enquiry right through our Easter visit, and wholeheartedly included our two small children. The dinners were delicious, especially the puddings."

The converted 17th-century former mill cottage, still with its millrace, waterfall and trout stream, is in a peaceful hamlet at the foot of the Skiddaw range of mountains. There is walking through "delightful woodland" from the door. The public rooms are small, and they can be crowded at times. The sitting room has an open fire; there is a sun-room, and a small reading room with "a catholic selection of reading matter". Some bedrooms are small, too, with a small bed. Tables in the dining room are close together, encouraging conviviality. Dinner is served at 7 pm by Mr Quinlan; his wife, Eleanor, is the chef. The five-course dinner, with choice, might include Roquefort tartlet with an orange and walnut salad; chard and chickpea soup; loin of lamb with caper sauce, or carrot and parsnip terrine with asparagus sauce; puddings such as steamed date and pecan pudding with maple toffee sauce, or poached plums in Madeira. Bread is home-baked. The "sheer professionalism of the Quinlans" is regularly admired. "It is matched by their concern that guests really enjoy their stay." Breakfasts are "first class". Dogs are welcomed. The Penrith exit of the M6 is only 12 miles away. (*Alison Forrester*)

Note: Not to be mistaken for the *Mill Inn*, with which it confusingly shares an entrance.

Open 1 Mar–1 Nov. Dining room closed for lunch.
Rooms 9 double, 6 with *en suite* facilities. 2 on ground floor. No telephone.
Facilities Lounge, reading room, sun lounge, dining room (classical background music during dinner); drying room. 2-acre grounds: millrace, waterfall, trout stream. Ullswater, fishing, sailing 5 miles. Unsuitable for &.
Location Small village 2 miles N of A66 Penrith–Keswick. M6 exit 40.
Restrictions No smoking in dining room. Dogs at proprietors' discretion; not in public rooms.
Credit cards None accepted.
Terms B&B: single £39–£50, double £69–£95; D,B&B: single £67–£79, double £120–£150. Set dinner £29. Reductions for 5 or more nights. *V*

NANTWICH Cheshire *See SHORTLIST*   Map 3

NAYLAND Suffolk   Map 2

The White Hart   NEW   *Tel* (01206) 263382
11 High Street   *Fax* (01206) 263638
Nayland CO6 4JF
                                             E-mail nayhart@aol.com
                                  Website www.whitehart-nayland.co.uk

In a small Suffolk town (with colour-washed old houses and a milestone obelisk), 15 minutes' drive from Colchester and Sudbury, this old inn is a rather surprising outpost of the empire of Michel Roux (see also the *Waterside Inn*, Bray). Standing in grounds on the River Stour, it dates back to the 15th century; in 1789 its frontage was changed to make a tunnel entrance through which carriages could pass. It has been given contemporary bedrooms (with bright checked fabrics, a kingsize bed). "It is all very French. The manager, Franck Deletang, and his wife and baby are charming," says an inspector this year. "Our bedroom, not large, was smart in blue and yellow, fine for a short stay. And the cooking is excellent." The chef, Neil Bishop (*Michelin Bib Gourmand*), provides informal lunches (eg, soups; moules marinière; confit of rabbit legs with pan-fried Jerusalem artichokes), and sophisticated dinners (roast quail on a bed of haricots verts with soft-boiled eggs; pan-fried chicken and duck livers on a bed of walnuts and raisin bread with button mushrooms, grapes and cider, are two of the starters, with grilled seabass on a black olive and basil tapenade, or wood pigeon on choucroute to follow, and desserts like baked apple stuffed with figs, plums, sultanas and almonds, or bread and butter pudding). "Breakfast was delicious, with fresh orange juice, large French-style coffee cups, perfectly cooked eggs." Functions are held (a marquee is sometimes erected on the terrace). Beautiful Suffolk countryside is all around.

Open All year, except 26 Dec–4 Jan. Restaurant closed Mon, except bank holidays.
Rooms 5 double, 1 single.
Facilities Lounge, bar, restaurant; mixed background music during meals; private dining/function rooms, terrace. Garden on river.
Location 6 miles N of Colchester. In village on A134. Private parking. Buses from Sudbury, Ipswich, Colchester.
Restrictions No smoking in bedrooms. Guide dogs only.
Credit cards All major cards accepted.
Terms B&B: single £64.50, double £69.50. Full alc £34. *V* (Sun–Fri)

NEAR SAWREY Cumbria　　　　　　　　　　　Map 4

Ees Wyke　　　　　　　　　　　*Tel/Fax* (015394) 36393
Near Sawrey　　　　　　　　　　　*E-mail* eeswyke@aol.com
nr Ambleside LA22 0JZ　　　　　　*Website* www.smoothhound.dir

"Excellent value for money, in an idyllic spot," says a report this year on this late-Regency mansion (much altered in the 20th century) in the vale of Esthwaite. It was once the holiday home of Beatrix Potter, who loved it so much she moved to the village; her farmhouse, Hill Top, managed by the National Trust, is nearby. Now run as a guest house by its hard-working owners, Margaret and John Williams, *Ees Wyke* looks across fields with sheep towards Esthwaite Water and distant hills. A gentle border collie, Ruff, lies in the entrance. The consistent standards were admired again by a regular visitor this year, and also the "good-humoured atmosphere". Others wrote of the "fresh and homely" decor (with tasselled lampshades and fringes, open fires, a medley of furniture in the bedrooms); "everywhere is immaculate". Each room is named for its colour scheme, and all but one have a lake view. They are good-sized and well decorated, with a "compact but charming bathroom". In the two pleasantly furnished sitting rooms, guests assemble for drinks at 7 pm, and socialise after a leisurely dinner. The cooking was found "well above average, with good raw materials, impressive timing". "Modern dishes, skilfully prepared" might include cream of parsnip and curry soup; fillet of pork with Dijon mustard sauce; "guests talk freely between the well-spaced tables". Breakfast is "startlingly copious"; "the fried eggs are a picture"; "Mrs Williams circulates with a groaning platter of mushrooms, black pudding, kidneys, fried bread, three kinds of sausage; guests choose what they fancy". Only snags: packaged orange juice and butter, and "the hot water comes on a bit late for early risers". (*Don Parker, David Wooff, and others*)

Open Mar–Jan (including New Year).
Rooms 8 double. 1 on ground floor. No telephone.
Facilities 2 lounges, restaurant. No background music. 2-acre garden. Access to lake; fishing, boating. Unsuitable for &.
Location On edge of village 1½ miles SE of Hawkshead, on road to Windermere ferry. Local bus from Windermere in summer.
Restrictions No smoking in restaurant. No children under 8. No dogs in public rooms.
Credit card Amex.
Terms B&B £48; D,B&B £62. Set dinner £23 to non-residents. Weekly rates. Christmas, New Year house parties.

Sawrey House
Near Sawrey
nr Ambleside LA22 0LF

Tel (015394) 36387
Fax (015394) 36010
E-mail enquiries@sawrey-house.com
Website www.sawrey-house.com

Adjacent to Beatrix Potter's home, Hilltop, but peacefully set in 3-acre gardens: Colin and Shirley Whiteside's Victorian country house (original features, eg, stained glass, retained). Period furniture, log fires, views of lake, forest and mountains. "Warm, but unobtrusive" welcome. Ambitious cooking; extensive, reasonably priced wine list in restaurant (with pianist); "easy-listening" background music in bar.

11 well-equipped bedrooms, some on ground floor. No smoking: restaurant, bedrooms. No children under 8 in restaurant at night. No dogs in public rooms. Open Feb–mid-Nov, Christmas, New Year. MasterCard, Visa accepted. B&B £45–£60; D,B&B £60–£75 [2000].

NEW MILTON Hampshire   **Map 2**

Chewton Glen
Christchurch Road
New Milton BH25 6QS

Tel (01425) 275341
Fax (01425) 272310
E-mail reservations@chewtonglen.com
Website www.chewtonglen.com

"Wonderful. Lovely staff. Very good food." "Not cheap, but we left happy. The staff make you feel special." "Must be one of the best hotels in the UK." Praise again in 2000 for Martin and Brigitte Skan's luxurious "hotel, health and country club", on the southern fringes of the New Forest. With the help of managing director Peter Crome and a large staff ("unfailingly helpful and charming"), they cater for an international moneyed clientele. A major attraction is health and sporting facilities (most are free to residents). Another is the restaurant, named for Captain Marryat (he wrote *The Children of the New Forest* here) – "like the bar, it has a warm, intimate feeling". Pierre Chevillard's "cooking with a light touch" is "refreshingly modern, but with no hint of unnecessary trendiness" (*Michelin* star for tomato and raclette cheese tart with pesto; seabass with shiitake mushrooms and beansprouts; chocolate fondant with pistachio ice-cream). The menu also includes "vegetarian and wellness" choices. Most visitors write of the "relaxed and efficient" meal service, but one Easter visitor found it "erratic" at times, with long waits between courses. Breakfast can be healthy (skimmed milk, wholemeal toast, decaffeinated coffee), traditional English (with New Forest sausages), or luxurious (champagne, scrambled eggs and smoked salmon). Lounges are large and light, with antiques and fine fabrics. Suites and bedrooms, some vast, are equally lavish, and have fruit (constantly replenished), sherry, biscuits, plentiful toiletries, huge towels, bathrobes. Some have a balcony or terrace; the two-storey suites in the coach house have a private garden. Six bedrooms and two suites are new this year. The sea is a short walk away, along a footpath. (*Val Hennessy, John Gibbon, Paul Hingston*)

Open All year.
Rooms 18 suites (2 in lodge in grounds), 37 double. Some on ground floor.
Facilities Ramps. 3 lounges (pianist in 1, Fri, Sat evening), bar, restaurant; function rooms; snooker room; health club: indoor tennis, swimming pool, gymnasium, beauty salon. 75-acre grounds: swimming pool, tennis, croquet, 9-hole golf course, lake, jogging course, helipad; bicycle hire. Beach, fishing, sailing, shooting, riding nearby. Chauffeur service. Civil wedding licence.
Location M27 to A31. Turn left towards Emery Down, right on to A35 (*don't follow New Milton signs*); after 11 miles, turn off to Walkford/Highcliffe. As you leave Walkford, road dips; turn into Chewton Farm road (immediately before roundabout sign). Entrance on right. Bus service nearby. Station 5 mins' drive.
Restrictions No smoking: restaurant, 1 lounge. No children under 7. No dogs (kennels nearby).
Credit cards All major cards accepted.
Terms Room: single £235–£255, double £235–£385, suite £455–£665; D,B&B: single £300–£320, double £365–£515, suite £585–£795. Breakfast £17.50. Lunch from £15.30. Set dinner £47.50. 5-night breaks; healthy breaks. Christmas, Easter and golfing packages. Min. 2-night bookings at weekends.

NEWCASTLE UPON TYNE Tyne and Wear   Map 4

Horton Grange   *Tel* (01661) 860686
Seaton Burn   *Fax* (01661) 860308
Newcastle upon Tyne NE13 6BU   *E-mail* andrew@horton-grange.co.uk
                                                      Website www.horton-grange.co.uk

"A hotel to be enjoyed." "The hosts are delightful. We felt that we were being rather spoiled in a friend's house." Enthusiasm this year and last for this small hotel and its owners, Sue and Andrew Shilton. They are "enthusiastic but unintrusive", and their staff are "friendly in a natural way". The handsome stone-built house, in open country six miles from the city centre, stands by a large farm with stables – horses look out over the hotel's carpark. The sitting room is light, with two fireplaces, sofas and chairs "arranged to provide privacy", attractive lighting from table lamps, arrangements of flowers and foliage. The "very pleasant" conservatory-style restaurant, all green and white, has a sloping roof, paper lampshades, a wooden floor with rugs, glass doors looking on to a Japanese water garden. Steven Martin's cooking is "first class, and imaginative", but not too complicated: his cooking of fish is particularly admired this year: "Excellent seared salmon on salade niçoise; interesting seabass oriental style." Wines are "good value" and many are available by the glass. Bedrooms are "pleasantly furnished, not designerish", with antiques and fresh flowers, fine linen sheets and an evening turn-down service. Bathrooms have good toiletries and "reliably hot water", but some baths are short, and rooms with a bath have no shower attachment. The suites in the "greenhouse-style" garden annexe have a desk. The bedrooms on the road are well insulated against traffic noise. At breakfast: "Tea was the real McCoy; perfectly cooked free-range eggs, excellent bacon – but no freshly squeezed orange juice." The airport is nearby. (*John Townsend, TW*)

Open All year, except Christmas, New Year. Restaurant closed Sun.
Rooms 4 suites (on ground floor, in garden), 5 double, 4 single.
Facilities Lounge, cocktail bar, restaurant (classical background music). 4-acre grounds: water garden. River 2 miles; beach 6 miles. Civil wedding licence.
Location 6 miles N of centre. From A1 western bypass take A19 Ashington/ Tyne Tunnel exit. At roundabout take 1st exit; left after 1 mile to Dinnington/ Ponteland. Hotel 2 miles on right. Large carpark. Taxi: from airport 4 miles; from station 6 miles.
Restrictions No smoking: restaurant, some bedrooms. No dogs.
Credit cards Amex, MasterCard, Visa.
Terms B&B: single £54–£74, double £75–£90; D,B&B from £75 per person. Set dinner £34.

Malmaison
The Quayside
Newcastle upon Tyne NE1 3DX

Tel (0191) 245 5000
Fax (0191) 245 4545

E-mail newcastle@malmaison.com
Website www.malmaison.com

"Ultra-modern, ultra-stylish", this is "*the* place to stay in the city centre", say visitors to the Newcastle *Malmaison* (see also Glasgow, Leeds and Manchester). Others wrote of the "enthusiastic young staff". The former Co-operative Society warehouse is in the newly developed Quayside area. Tall and square, it has an Art Deco-style metal canopy over the entrance. The ground-floor lobby is smart, with mirrors, wall-to-wall carpeting, bold contemporary furniture, taped jazz. The long reception desk has a "cheerful and unpretentious" staff, and the hotel "offers value for money, particularly at the weekend". It is run with a light touch; eg, instead of a "Do not disturb" sign you get one saying "Leave me alone"; a lift with recorded announcements in French takes you up to the bedrooms. Some are quite small; all are different, with a plain decor: striped fabrics, striped wallpaper, well-designed contemporary wooden furniture, a CD-player, interesting artwork, decent wines in the mini-bar, a well-planned bathroom.

Suites on the seventh floor have wide views. The dimly lit bar has wooden Venetian blinds, tables with blue lamps. The brasserie, overlooking the river, serves uncomplicated French dishes on a frequently changing menu: steak with garlic butter and pommes frites, and charred chicken with red pepper salad were enjoyed this year. Breakfast includes freshly squeezed orange juice, fruit, cheese, etc. There is a high-tech gym and long-term parking in a multi-storey carpark at the rear. (*HW*)

Open All year.
Rooms 18 suites, 98 double. 6 adapted for &.
Facilities Lounge, bar, brasserie; gym, spa; function facilities. Modern jazz in public areas 24 hrs.
Location ½ mile from centre; adjacent to law courts. Under Tyne bridge; head E for 200 yds. Parking.
Restrictions No smoking in some bedrooms. No dogs.
Credit cards All major cards accepted.
Terms [To Apr 2001] Double room £105, suite £145. Breakfast: continental £8.50, English £10.50. Full alc £30.

NEWLANDS Cumbria   **Map 4**

Swinside Lodge   *Tel/Fax* (017687) 72948
Grange Road
Newlands, nr Keswick CA12 5UE

In "wonderfully peaceful surroundings", 3 miles SW of Keswick in unspoilt corner of northern lakes: Victorian Lakeland house. Much admired in the past for high standards, excellent food. New owners, Mr and Mrs Kniveton, took over in spring 2000, but staff have stayed on, including chef Chris Astley (Michelin Bib Gourmand for not too fussy cooking on four-course menu, no choice until dessert). "Excellent home-made bread"; vegetarian dishes by arrangement. Bring your own drinks (but licence applied for; complimentary sherry before 7.30 pm dinner). Packed lunches available. Hearty Cumbrian breakfast with fresh orange juice. Open Feb–Nov, and Christmas. 7 bedrooms. 3 sitting rooms, dining room. No background music. ¾-acre garden. Derwentwater 5 mins' walk: shingle beach, safe bathing. Unsuitable for &. No smoking. No children under 10. No dogs. MasterCard, Visa accepted. D,B&B: single £77–£90, double £128–£170. Packed lunches. Set dinner £25–£28. First reports of new regime encouraging, but we'd like more, please.

NEWTON-LE-WILLOWS North Yorkshire   **Map 4**

The Hall   *Tel* (01677) 450210
Newton-le-Willows   *Fax* (01677) 450014
nr Bedale DL8 1SW

"It is a real joy to stay here," says an inspector this year of this handsome Georgian house on the edge of a tiny Bedale village (her only criticism was "dim bedside lighting"). The "beautiful, very friendly" owner, Oriella Featherstone, runs it in house-party style, providing "peace, quality, attention to detail" and "good Yorkshire value for money". The decor is theatrical: continental antiques and *objets d'art*, tapestries, Oriental rugs, heavy curtains fill the rooms. Rose-patterned fabrics and floral prints in the spacious bedrooms (named Apollo, Aphrodite, etc) echo the roses in the secluded garden (with ancient copper beeches, ponds and streams, it is set amid fields good for dog-walking). There is an honesty bar; tea, coffee and home-made fruit-cake are always available in the kitchen. A home-cooked evening meal is served round one large table. No choice on the menu, but there is prior consultation; vegetarians are catered for, and so are guests on special diets. All was found "delicious" this year: thick chicken and watercress soup; pork casserole with garlic and rosemary potatoes; apple crumble or trifle. Breakfast, served at flexible times, includes flavoursome local bacon and sausages, thick brown toast, sometimes goose eggs. Mulligan, a Fell terrier, will accompany guests for a walk. The family car is sometimes available to collect guests from Teesside airport or Darlington station. A good base for visiting the Dales, castles, ruined abbeys, gardens, and local racecourses. The A1 and the Middleham moors are ten minutes' drive away.

Note: This village is not to be confused with the Merseyside town of the same name.

Open All year.
Rooms 1 suite, 2 double. No telephone.
Facilities Drawing room, TV room/snug, breakfast room, dining room. Classical/modern background music morning/evening. 12-acre grounds: 2-acre gardens, stables and fields for visiting horses. Golf, fishing, riding, cinema and Georgian theatre nearby. Unsuitable for &.
Location In village 3 miles W of Bedale. From A1 go W on A684, through Bedale; pass golf course on left, sports centre on right; take 1st left towards Newton-le-Willows; turn right at T-junction. After 500 yds, in front of *Wheatsheaf Inn*, turn left; hotel on right. Train: Darlington; then taxi, or they will meet.
Restrictions No smoking: breakfast room, bedrooms. No children under 13 except by prior arrangement. No dogs in public rooms.
Credit cards None accepted.
Terms B&B £45–£50. Set dinner £25. Christmas house party can be booked.

NORTH BOVEY Devon   Map 1

Blackaller Hotel   *Tel* (01647) 440322
North Bovey   *Fax* (01647) 441131
nr Moretonhampstead TQ13 8QY   *Website* www.ourworld.cs.com/ukblackaller

"Our spirits lifted when we arrived on a lovely evening. The house, low and white, and the garden, with a clear stream running through, looked very attractive. The welcome was warm, and our bedroom was bright and clean." "The setting, half a mile from Dartmoor National Park, is peaceful and beautiful." On the edge of a delightful village (with granite and thatch houses and a large green with oak trees), this converted woollen mill, at the end of a long lane, is named for the black alder trees that grow locally. "A sophisticated operation, despite its simple appearance," one visitor wrote. The "charming, unassuming host", Peter Hunt, "is an ideal front-of-house". In his spare time he keeps bees, spins wool from his own Jacob sheep, and plays the sitar. A reporter on his fifth visit wrote of the "beautifully cooked and presented food". The four-course dinners, produced by Hazel Phillips, the "jolly hostess", and with two choices of each course, are based on local ingredients: organic lamb, fresh fish from Brixham, etc, and accompanied by reasonably priced New World wines. A vegetarian dinner can be ordered. Breakfast has home-produced yogurt, muesli and honey, toast made from "chunky brown bread". Antiques, china, flowers and family photos give a homely air to the public rooms. The bedrooms, some up a steep staircase, have a simple decor: oak beams, pine furniture, quality fabrics, and a bright bathroom. Cream teas are served, alfresco in fine weather. Garden chairs and tables are dotted about on the smooth lawn; it leads down to the River Bovey, where you might see a kingfisher flash by. Castle Drogo (National Trust) is close by; good walking all around. (*Marilyn Frampton, K Chard*)

Open Mar–Dec; closed New Year. Restaurant closed Sun, Mon.
Rooms 4 double, 1 single. 1 self-catering flat. No telephone.
Facilities Lounge, bar (classical background music in evening), restaurant. 3-acre garden on river: limited trout-fishing. Golf nearby. Unsuitable for &.
Location From Moretonhampstead follow sign to North Bovey. Sign on wall at edge of village. Train: Exeter, 14 miles; hosts will meet.
Restrictions Smoking in bar only. No children under 13. No dogs in public rooms.
Credit cards None accepted.
Terms B&B £31–£38. Set dinner £22. Special breaks: autumn, spring, Christmas, walking, bird photography. *V*

NORTH MOLTON Devon   **Map 1**

Heasley House   BUDGET   *Tel* (01598) 740213
Heasley Mill   *Fax* (01598) 740677
North Molton EX36 3LE   *E-mail* heasleyhouse@enterprise.net

*Former residence of local copper mine captains: John and Jane Ayres' Georgian dower house, Grade II listed, in hamlet just N of North Molton, 11 miles E of Barnstaple, in valley on S edge of Exmoor National Park. 7 bedrooms (no telephone/TV), 1 on ground floor. Liked for family feel, personal service, good food. Restaurant, open to the public, serves traditional Aga-cooked meals (eg, steak-and-kidney pudding, roast duck, treacle tart, trifle) in dining room with horse brasses, old hunting prints. 3 choices of starter and dessert; main course by agreement – vegetarians catered for. Well-stocked wine cellar. Lounge with log fire. Varied background music ("Fauré to Brubeck"), on demand, in public rooms. ¾-acre garden. Dogs welcomed (£3 per night). Unsuitable for &. No children under 12. No smoking, except in TV room. Credit cards not accepted. Closed 1 Feb–20 Mar, Christmas. B&B £25.50–£45. Set lunch £6–£15, dinner £17.50. More reports, please. *V*

NORTH WALSHAM Norfolk   Map 2

Beechwood `BUDGET`   *Tel* (01692) 403231
Cromer Road   *Fax* (01692) 407284
North Walsham NR28 0HD

"It goes from strength to strength," says a satisfied visitor this year to
Don Birch and Lindsay Spalding's ivy-clad 200-year-old house. With
red brick walls and sash windows, the former doctor's residence is
now a small hotel, recently taken over and redecorated by the "charming owners". They say they guarantee peace by taking no large groups,
wedding parties or conferences. The "friendly ethos" and the "delicious and varied meals" are admired, as are the "willing service", and
the two "adorable Airedale dogs", Clem and Emily. Chef Steven
Norgate's cooking, on a long menu, "combines New World and traditional styles", with dishes such as avocado, mango and prawn salad;
chargrilled tuna on a bed of Chinese leaves; always an interesting vegetarian main course. One bedroom has a four-poster, another a freestanding slipper bath. "The small garden, with shrubs, a long lawn and
a sunken area, is beautiful." In winter, visitors on a two-day weekend
break can stay on Sunday night as well with no charge for B&B, provided that they dine in. Lord Nelson was educated in this market town
(its church is the second largest in Norfolk). A good base for exploring the Norfolk broads. Sandy beaches are nearby, also Blickling,
Holkham and Felbrigg halls (National Trust) and Sandringham. "The
knowledgeable owners will advise about outings." (*Valerie Flindall,
and others*)

Open 8 Jan–23 Dec.
Rooms 10 double.
Facilities Lounge, bar, restaurant; light classical background music at meal-
times. 1¼-acre garden. Sea 5 miles. Golf, sailing, tennis, riding nearby.
Unsuitable for &.
Location Approaching North Walsham on B1150 from Norwich, turn left at
first set of traffic lights, right at the next set; *Beechwood* is on left.
Restrictions Smoking in bar only. No children under 10.
Credit cards MasterCard, Visa.
Terms B&B £35–£62; D,B&B £40–£84. Set lunch £12, dinner £24. 1-night
bookings sometimes refused weekends. *V*

NORTON Shropshire   Map 3

Hundred House `NEW`   *Tel* (01952) 730353
Bridgnorth Road   *Fax* (01952) 730355
Norton TF11 9EE   *E-mail* hphundredhouse@compuserve.com
                                   Website www.hundredhouse.co.uk

"Very enjoyable" is the verdict of inspectors visiting this quirky red
brick coaching inn owned by the Phillips family: Henry (he likes to
brew beer and make damson gin) and Sylvia, with their sons, David
and Stuart (the chef). "It is mildly eccentric, but professionally run."
Dried flowers and herbs hang from beams in the panelled public
rooms. Large fireplaces have a log fire or a range. The food is

considered "outstanding" by the *Good Pub Guide*, and it has an entry in the *Good Food Guide 2000*. Brasserie-style meals are flexibly served in the bar and a series of small rooms, all with a tiled floor and an assortment of wooden tables. "You can order as much or as little as you like" and there are vegetarian dishes and a children's menu. An *à la carte* menu is served in the restaurant: first courses of tomato and rosemary soup, and chicken liver pâté, followed by rack of lamb with butter bean mash, and braised shank of lamb were all thought good. To end, you could choose "the ultimate dessert", a selection of all eight puddings on the menu. The reasonably priced wine list has a good selection of wines by the glass. Upstairs, "someone's imagination has been allowed to run riot". The bedrooms are reached up stairs carpeted with bright patchwork, and with equally bright walls. "Our 'superior' room had a swing suspended from a wooden beam, an ornate glass chandelier, gold-painted ceiling paper, walls that were mauve with a pattern of stencilled gold hearts and cupids. The colourful carpet had a small, busy pattern, and the bed had a patchwork quilt that matched the curtains. The bathroom was functional." The house is surrounded by an old-fashioned garden with roses, shrubs, a "teddy bear's picnic", a large herb garden with a memorial corner. "The whole thing is carried off with great self-confidence and humour. The family are helpful, without being over-effusive." Only flies in the ointment: "Breakfast was eminently forgettable, apart from good granary toast." And the hotel stands on a busy road "but double glazing muffled the sound and there was not much traffic at night".

Open All year, except Christmas.
Rooms 9 double, 1 single.
Facilities Reception lounge, bar (varied background music), restaurant. ½-acre grounds. Unsuitable for &.
Location 6 miles S of Telford on A442.
Restrictions No smoking in restaurant. No dogs in public rooms.
Credit cards MasterCard, Visa.
Terms B&B: single £69, double from £95. Full alc £30. Child accommodated in parents' room: B&B free. 10% reduction for more than 5 nights.

NORWICH Norfolk   **Map 2**

The Beeches   *Tel* (01603) 621167
2–6 Earlham Road   *Fax* (01603) 620151
Norwich NR2 3DB   *E-mail* reception@beeches.co.uk
                                 Website www.beeches.co.uk

"Very nice", unpretentious hotel, owned by Keith and Lis Hill, managed by daughter Kate, with "unfailingly courteous" staff. In 3 buildings – 1 in middle of romantic Grade II listed Victorian garden in wooded hollow, with terraces, balustrades, Gothic fountain, mock ruins, massive rockery with cascades. On B1108, 10 mins' walk W of centre, c. 20 from cathedral. Ample parking. 36 bedrooms (10 on ground floor, 1 designed for &). Best ones are quiet, with lofty ceiling, good lighting. Bar/lounge (snacks served). Quite formal restaurant (jazz/classical background music) serves "slightly variable" meals, and "rather packaged" breakfasts. Closed New Year. Restaurant

closed for lunch. Smoking in bar only. No children. No dogs. All major credit cards accepted. B&B: single £54–£59, double £70–£76, superior £80–£88. Set dinner £14; full alc £24 [2000].

By Appointment
25–29 St Georges Street
Norwich NR3 1AB

Tel/Fax (01603) 630730

♺ *César award in 1999*

"For us, there is nowhere else to stay in Norwich," writes a visitor after a dose of TLC at Timothy Brown and Robert Culyer's "enjoyably eccentric" restaurant-with-rooms (he was visiting for a funeral). "We were well looked after in every way, and sent on our way cheerfully and solicitously. The welcome was sincere and thoughtful throughout." Another visitor wrote of a "wonderful weekend; friendly hosts". The 15th-century merchant's house in the historic city centre has a labyrinthine layout. You enter under an arch at the back of the street, through a tiny courtyard with a Della Robbia relief on the wall, and straight into the kitchen. The decor has been described as "Merchant Ivory, emphasised by trunks and panama hats". The restaurant is in four dining rooms, dotted around the house. The menus, displayed on gilt-framed blackboards, and read out loud before each meal, include, eg, home-made brioche filled with devilled lamb's kidneys; sea bream filled with a rich lobster mousse, with a champagne and lobster sauce; Jamaican banana crème brûlée. There is a separate vegetarian menu. The bedrooms are "a riot of Victoriana". "Our attic room had wonderful antique furniture, pincushions, hairbrush sets, cotton bedwear, hats; also TV, trouser-press, a cafetière with good coffee, a kettle and real tea, an amazingly comfortable bed." Bathrooms are "exotic but efficient" (one is a floor below the bedroom, adjacent to the loo used by diners in the restaurant). "Tim and Robert left loving goodnight notes with chocolates." At breakfast there is a choice of smoked salmon with scrambled eggs, fillet steak, fried eggs, mushrooms, sausages, bacon. (*Robin Houston, Mrs S Murphy, and others*)

Open All year, except 25 Dec. Restaurant closed lunchtime; also Sun, Mon.
Rooms 3 double, 1 single.
Facilities 2 lounges, restaurant (jazz/classical background music in evening). Tiny courtyard. Unsuitable for &.
Location Central; corner of St Georges St and Colegate (rooms double-glazed).
Restrictions No smoking: restaurant, bedrooms. No children under 12. No dogs.
Credit cards MasterCard, Visa.
Terms [2000] B&B: single £70, double £95. Full alc £33.

See also SHORTLIST

If you think we have over-praised a hotel or done it an injustice, please let us know.

NOTTINGHAM Nottinghamshire   **Map 2**

The Lace Market   NEW   *Tel* (0115) 852 3232
29–31 High Pavement   *Fax* (0115) 852 3223
Nottingham NG1 1HE   *E-mail* reservations@lacemarkethotel.co.uk
                                    Website www.lacemarkethotel.co.uk

A Georgian red brick building (once a probation office) in the renovated Lace Market area of the city. Now belonging to a small consortium of designer hotels (see also *Eleven Didsbury Park*, Manchester),
and managed by Mark Cox, it has been given a stylish modern decor.
"The location is great," say inspectors in 2000 – it is next to St Mary's,
"a gem of a church", and opposite the lovely 18th-century Galleries of
Justice (the basement entrance has the inscription "County Gaol" in
stone). "The atmosphere is easy-going, with a pleasant young staff.
Our bedroom was fashionably done in shades of brown. It had high
ceilings, four tall sash windows, good views, a spacious bathroom, a
plethora of today's 'must-haves': CD-player, tape deck, voicemail,
a 'grown-up desk'. But a certain quality monitoring was lacking, eg, a
bathrobe lacked a belt; the ordered newspaper was delivered one day,
but not the next. And one night our sleep was broken by a noisy party.
The restaurant has a rather predictable brasserie menu, but the dishes
were well handled: good, thick tomato, basil and white bean soup;
well-cooked cod with deep-fried cabbage leaf; grilled steak, perfectly
timed, with excellent chips; an impressive selection of cheeses with
very good bread. Breakfast was adequate, with a good buffet,
with fresh orange juice, but the bread was poor. But we enjoyed our
stay: a comforting place to return to." Bar meals are served from
11 am to 11 pm.

Open All year, except Christmas.
Rooms 3 suites, 23 double, 3 single. 24-hour room service.
Facilities Lift. Bar/café, restaurant; "easy listening" background music all
day; private dining room, boardroom. Unsuitable for &.
Location City centre (rooms double-glazed). Follow signs for Galleries of
Justice; hotel is opposite. No private parking.
Restrictions No smoking in reception. No dogs in public rooms.
Credit cards Amex, MasterCard, Visa.
Terms [2000] Room: single £65–£89, double £75–£99, suite £130–£165.
Breakfast: continental £7.50, English £10.50. Set lunch £12.50, dinner £16.50;
full alc £25. Off-season and weekend rates.

 Morgans   NEW   *Tel* (0115) 957 0017
The Townhouse   *Fax* (0115) 957 0018
34 The Ropewalk, The Park   *E-mail* info@morgans34.com
Nottingham NG1 5DW   *Website* www.morgans34.com

César award: Town house hotel of the year

"It has great style and charming owners. We were most impressed."
So say inspectors in 2000, visiting this "designer B&B", a Grade II
listed 19th-century house quietly set on a leafy ridge above The Park
(Nottingham's conservation area). The owner, Kathy Morgan,
American by birth, who does almost everything herself, says she set

out to create the sort of place she often looked for, but never could find. "My husband calls me obsessive, I call it passionate," she writes. And thoughtfulness is apparent everywhere: breakfast is served until noon; you are asked on booking whether you prefer feather or hypo-allergenic pillows, sparkling or plain water; beds have linen sheets and merino wool blankets; every evening Mrs Morgan and her husband, Clive, invite guests for a drink. (At other times they can serve themselves, no charge, in the former schoolroom of the children of a mayor of Nottingham, an earlier resident, and a prolific father.) "Now the panelled lounge, it has been charmingly furnished, with modern leather club chairs and sofas, '20s-style lights, potted palms. Our ground-floor bedroom, with fresh fruit and flowers, was enormous, very smart, cleverly modern while retaining original features – a decorative iron cornice, large bow windows with curved brass curtain poles. The vast bed had a large headboard in squares of three different timbers; one wall was pale green, the others pale yellow. The huge white tiled bathroom, one of the best we have seen in ages, had a sandstone floor, natural light, a spacious glassed-in separate shower." Breakfast, with newspapers, is served in a bright room, with mirrored and wooden panels. It has a buffet of fruit, croissants, jams, organic marmalade. "Scrambled and boiled eggs were perfect; toast OK, coffee excellent." Mrs Morgan, "who is always around to help", keeps menus of recommendable restaurants, eg, *Harts* (*Michelin Bib Gourmand*), owned by Tim Hart of *Hambleton Hall*, Hambleton (*qv*), and *Sonny's*, both nearby. Another boon: the electronically gated carpark.

Open All year, except 2 weeks in summer, Christmas, New Year.
Rooms 5 double. 1 on ground floor.
Facilities Lounge with complimentary bar (soft jazz/classical background music evenings), breakfast room.
Location Near castle, 5–10 mins' walk from centre; 1½ miles from station. Guests arriving by taxi or on foot should use the main entrance on The Ropewalk; Access to the carpark via Park Terr.
Restrictions No smoking in breakfast room. No dogs (because of resident dog, Kato).
Credit cards Amex, MasterCard, Visa.
Terms [2000] B&B: single £95–£120, double £110–£135. Discounts for 2 nights or if 2 rooms are booked.

See also SHORTLIST

OAKAMOOR Staffordshire   Map 3

Bank House   `BUDGET`   *Tel/Fax* (01538) 702810
Farley Lane   *E-mail* john.orme@dial.pipex.com
Oakamoor   *Website* www.smoothhound.co.uk/hotels/bank
nr Stoke-on-Trent ST10 3BD

With "thoughtful owners, excellent food, splendid bedrooms", this is no conventional guest house. It is run by John and Muriel Egerton-Orme (she won an AA award for the best landlady in the UK in 1996) with the aim of creating a "house-party ambience". It stands on the edge of a village below a steep hill on the edge of Peak District National Park. From its "lovely grounds" (with a formal garden, a bog garden and ponds) there are pastoral views, but it makes a good base for visiting Alton Towers a mile away. It was constructed by its owners in the style of a Derbyshire manor house, using bricks and stone quoins from a much older house on the same site. No brochure – a personal letter is sent to each prospective guest, explaining the accommodation in detail. Only three bedrooms: two can accommodate a family of four (one has a four-poster bed, another a spa bath). There is a hall with a grand piano, a drawing room and a library; also a large, friendly dog and some cats (if you are averse to pets you should advise the hosts when booking). In fine weather, meals can be served on a terrace. Breakfast, "where you like it, when you want it", includes home-made breads, pastries and preserves; also porridge, fruit, all manner of cooked dishes. A simple three-course evening meal is available by arrangement (eg, salmon mousse, or soup; pheasant casserole, or beef Wellington). The hosts often eat with their guests, or join them for a drink. There are also eating places of all sorts nearby, and good walking from the door. The Staffordshire Way is close by; also many stately homes – Chatsworth, Haddon and Kedleston halls, etc. (*RR, VH*)

Open All year, except Christmas week.
Rooms 3 double: 1 can accommodate an extra bed; 2 can accommodate 4. Telephone on request.
Facilities Hall, drawing room, library (both with TV), dining room. No background music. 1-acre grounds: garden, water garden, bog garden. Walking, golf, riding, cycling, etc, nearby. Unsuitable for &.
Location From A50 take B5030 at Uttoxeter. Follow signs to Alton Towers via Alton village. Pass theme park main entrance on right. After 400 yds turn left signed Farley (narrow lane). After ¾ mile, 2nd house on left (name on gate piers).
Restrictions No smoking. Dogs by arrangement.
Credit cards MasterCard, Diners, Visa.
Terms [2000] B&B double £58–£76. Single room supplement £15. Set dinner (by arrangement) £22 (with wine £30). Reductions for longer stays. Child accommodated in parents' room: under 5, £10; 5–12, £14; over 12, £16. 1-night bookings sometimes refused.

OXFORD Oxfordshire   **Map 2**

Cotswold House   *Tel/Fax* (01865) 310558
363 Banbury Road
Oxford OX2 7PL

Alan Clarke is the "charming manager" of this modest B&B in a double-fronted, flower-festooned Cotswold stone house in North Oxford. "It offers good value, given the location and the cost of other establishments nearby," says a visitor this year. The bedrooms are modern and immaculately kept, with pastel linens and flounces, pink dolls, pot-pourri, chocolates, TV, a fridge; fresh milk on request for tea-making. Duvet or blankets according to preference. One single is small. Shower rooms have ample towels and masses of hot water. Breakfast, traditional or vegetarian, is "excellent", with fresh fruit, home-made yogurt, and "warm toast served when wanted". Guests have access to the well-kept garden at the rear. The house is on a busy road, but double glazing mitigates traffic noise, and the city centre, one-and-a-half miles away, is reached by regular buses. *Blue Palms*, *Xian* and the *Greek Taverna* in Summertown, close by, are recommended for an evening meal. (*PMG, and others*)

Open All year.
Rooms 2 family, 3 double, 2 single, all with shower. 1 on ground floor. Payphone in hall.
Facilities Lounge, breakfast room (classical background music). Guests have access to garden at rear. Unsuitable for &.
Location 1½ miles N of centre, just inside ring road (A40), on W side of Banbury Rd (A4165) between Apsley Rd and Squitchey La. Carpark. Frequent buses to centre.
Restrictions No smoking. No children under 6. No dogs.
Credit cards MasterCard, Visa.
Terms [2000] B&B: single £41–£45, double £65–£72. Christmas package.

Old Parsonage   *Tel* (01865) 310210
1 Banbury Road   *Fax* (01865) 311262
Oxford OX2 6NN   *E-mail* info@oldparsonage-hotel.co.uk
                            Website www.oxford-hotels-restaurants.co.uk

"A lovely place," says a visitor this year to this wisteria-clad 17th-century building not far from the centre, where Oscar Wilde is said to have roomed. It is on a busy road which a few bedrooms overlook (and some overlook the carpark), but one traveller had a room that was "blissfully quiet". You enter through an ancient door from a small courtyard, into a large bar/brasserie. Here, drinks and informal meals are served all day, by young waiters wearing dark green aprons (they were thought both friendly and "very professional" this year). With walls crammed with pictures and cartoons, newspapers on sticks, and near-permanent background music, it is a busy place, much frequented by locals. Spinach and Parmesan soufflé; chargrilled quail with rosti; pan-fried scallops are some examples from the eclectic menu. The food was found "interesting" and the wines "cleverly selected" this year. The bedrooms are mostly small but "well designed", though some beds may be on the small side. The suites have a "small, pretty sitting room, an elegant bedroom and bathroom". In fine weather, residents may sit in the roof garden, and alfresco meals, including breakfast ("with plenty of choice, including nice fruity options") are served in the courtyard. Punting expeditions, with a picnic, can be arranged. The hotel's owner, Jeremy Mogford, recently opened the *Old Bank Hotel* nearby (see Shortlist). (*Prof. Wolfgang Stroebe, JS Rutter*)

Open All year, except 25–28 Dec.
Rooms 4 suites, 25 double, 1 single. 10 on ground floor.
Facilities Small lounge, bar/restaurant (jazz/classical background music "when appropriate"). Terrace, roof garden, small walled garden. Unsuitable for &.
Location NE end of St Giles (some traffic noise; rooms double-glazed).

Restriction No dogs.
Credit cards All major cards accepted.
Terms [2000] B&B: single £130, double £150–£175, suite £200. Full alc £30.
2-night breaks.

See also SHORTLIST

PADSTOW Cornwall   **Map 1**

The Seafood Restaurant and   *Tel* (01841) 532700
St Petroc's Hotel and Bistro   *Fax* (01841) 532942
Riverside   *E-mail* seafoodpadstow@cs.com
Padstow PL28 8BY   *Website* www.rickstein.com

Ω *César award in 1995*

"Rick Stein is a genius. Never have I met such helpful, utterly charming staff." "The food is tremendous. Even when we arrived at 10 pm after a horrendous journey we were greeted with the greatest courtesy and encouraged to take our time before coming down to eat." "Dinner is a great experience; the fish tastes as it does nowhere else in the country. Service is good and unfussy, and despite the two sittings (7.30 and 9.30) it does not feel hurried. Our room was wonderful, with a fridge full of goodies, a galleried ceiling, a sitting area looking over a pretty courtyard with a fountain to the estuary, a huge bathroom with a double shower cubicle." "The dining room is beautiful. We loved the simplicity and the relaxed atmosphere. It is not grandiose, and would not appeal to those in search of luxury, but you get everything you need." "My dog was made welcome (no charge)." Again the praise continues for this famous restaurant-with-rooms in a converted granary on the harbour of a fishing village on the Camel estuary. You have to book your dinner table weeks in advance. Fish and lobsters "come straight off the boats and through the kitchen door". Chargrilled Dover sole with sea salt and lime; roast turbot with Hollandaise sauce; grilled lobster with *fines herbes*; local cod, chips and tartare sauce are some of the dishes on the long menu. Breakfast includes "real crunchy French bread and heart-pumping coffee". The bedrooms are priced according to size and view; two have a balcony. Room 9, on the side, was thought cramped and overpriced, with an awkward bathroom. Other rooms, and a bistro, are in *St Petroc's House*, one of the oldest buildings in Padstow, just up the hill; this gets some traffic, and there is a report of some disappointing meals here this year. The cheapest rooms are above the *Middle Street Café*, which serves "delicious lunches". There is also a delicatessen, selling Stein's Jams, Stein's Pickled Products, Stein-embroidered aprons, etc; his recipe books and cassettes of his TV programmes are for sale everywhere, and he recently opened a cooking school offering residential and non-residential courses for cooks of all standards. "You feel you are in a film set with Rick Stein memorabilia everywhere, and people gawping outside the restaurant." (*VH, Anne-Marie Sutcliffe, Simon Irving and Susan Ganney, and others*)

Open All year, except 18–26 Dec. Restaurant closed 31 Dec (evening) and 1 May.
Rooms 28 double, 1 single. 13 at *St Petroc's*, 3 above café.
Facilities *Seafood*: conservatory bar, restaurant (Mrs Stein's father sometimes plays the piano at lunchtime). *St Petroc's*: lounge, reading room, bar, bistro. Sandy beaches ¼ mile. Unsuitable for &.
Location Central: *Seafood* on harbour; *St Petroc's* in New St (150 yds). Garage, parking. Train: Bodmin Parkway, 15 miles; then bus (infrequent) or taxi.
Restriction No children under 3.
Credit cards MasterCard, Visa.
Terms [2000] B&B: single £30–£45, double £70–£150. D,B&B: single £60, double £90–£165. Set lunch £30.50, dinner £36; full alc £50. 2-day breaks in low season. 1-night bookings sometimes refused Sat.

PAINSWICK Gloucestershire   **Map 3**

Painswick Hotel   *Tel* (01452) 812160
Kemps Lane   *Fax* (01452) 814059
Painswick   *E-mail* reservations@painswickhotel.com
GL6 6YB   *Website* www.painswickhotel.com

In a Cotswold hillside wool town looking across the Painswick valley, this is one of many lovely buildings: a Palladian-style ex-vicarage behind the church. Its owners (since 1998), Gareth and Helen Pugh, write: "Our policy is not to impose stuffy rules on our guests. We welcome children of all ages, we have no dress code, and we attempt to employ staff with personality, not technically skilled robots." Dogs are also welcomed, and the place "works on oiled wheels", according to recent guests. The public rooms are distinctive: a lounge "dramatic in purple, with cosy settees and antiques"; a restaurant in two rooms, one of them the panelled former chapel. It has an "elegant, restrained decor and impeccably set tables", and a new chef this year, Kevin Barron, so we'd be grateful for reports on his cooking. A sample dinner menu (you can choose two or three courses) consists of: spring vegetable soup, or Oriental duck leg on noodles; medallions of pork on celeriac purée, or sea trout with confit of aubergine and mussel ravioli; passion fruit tart with pear sorbet, or cheese with walnut bread. There is also a *carte*, and a Sunday lunch menu including a roast. The house wines are liked, but not always the background music. Many bedrooms are large: a garden room, one of the cheapest, was thought "lovely: a pretty decor, a welcoming note from the Pughs, handsome furniture, fresh fruit, ample storage space, an adequate, if slightly dated bathroom". Another bathroom "had two baths side by side, with taps at opposite ends to encourage conversation". The pretty garden has a smooth croquet lawn and a curious grotto, where a vicar once rehearsed his sermons. The churchyard is "a real curiosity", and the rococo gardens of Painswick Hall are sometimes open to the public. (*FW, and others*)

Open All year.
Rooms 17 double, 2 single.
Facilities 2 lounges, bar, restaurant (mixed background music), private dining/meeting room. Unsuitable for &. Civil wedding licence.

Location In village off A46. Turn down by church; follow road round; turn right at cross. Hotel down hill on right. Train: Stroud (5 miles).
Restrictions No smoking in restaurant. Dogs allowed in some bedrooms only; not in public rooms.
Credit cards Amex, MasterCard, Visa.
Terms B&B: single £85, double £120–£185; D,B&B: single £95–£105, double £170–£210. Set lunch £16, dinner £23–£26; full alc £42. Winter and summer breaks. Christmas package. 1-night bookings refused weekends.

PENZANCE Cornwall   **Map 1**

The Abbey Hotel   *Tel* (01736) 366906
Abbey Street   *Fax* (01736) 351163
Penzance TR18 4AR   *E-mail* glyn@abbeyhotel.fsnet.co.uk
                                      Website www.abbey/hotel.co.uk

Run with more than a touch of eccentricity, this 17th-century house, painted bright blue, is in a narrow street that runs down to the sea from the centre of this resort/fishing port, the most westerly town in Britain. The decor is distinctive: bright coloured walls set off curios, oriental rugs, paintings and flowers, and there is a large choice of books and audio tapes. The drawing room, with flowered sofas and a chandelier, looks on to the walled garden. The place is informally run. "The service provided is limited, especially room service," one visitor wrote. Others told of "lovely treatment by the staff". Meals are served by an open fire in the white-panelled dining room. The menu has three choices at each stage: quite straightforward dishes, eg, spaghetti with pesto sauce; cod with butter and cumin; chocolate steamed sponge pudding. There is always a vegetarian main course. The food can be variable. "It was often good," is one verdict, "but wine is not taken seriously (no vintage dates on the wine list)." Some bedrooms over-look the garden; others face the harbour (some get street noise); some are small, with a small shower room. Room 1 is huge, with antiques and a working fireplace, and a wood-surrounded bath in its large bathroom. The suite, which looks over the harbour and St Michael's Mount, is airy and "very comfortable". The Coxes recently took over the adjacent nightclub and are turning it into a restaurant, to be called The Abbey Seafood Restaurant. It should be open by Christmas. (*JF Bailey*)

Open All year, except Christmas.
Rooms One 2-bedroom suite (in adjoining building), 4 double, 2 single. No telephone.
Facilities Drawing room, dining room (classical background music evenings). Small walled garden. Sandy beach ¼ mile. Unsuitable for &.
Location Take road marked Sea Front; pass carpark on left; right after 300 yds, just before bridge, then left, up slipway, to hotel. Courtyard parking for 7 cars.
Restrictions No smoking: dining room, 1 bedroom. No children under 7. No dogs in public rooms.
Credit cards Amex, MasterCard, Visa.
Terms [2000] B&B: single £60–£135, double £80–£145, suite £120–£155. Set dinner £24. Weekend breaks; winter rates. 1-night bookings refused New Year, Easter.

The Summer House BUDGET *Tel* (01736) 363744
Cornwall Terrace   *Fax* (01736) 360959
Penzance TR18 4HL   *E-mail* summerhouse@dial.pipex.com
                                        Website www.cornwall-online.co.uk/summer-house

César award: Restaurant-with-rooms of the year

In a narrow street of Regency houses near the seafront, this quaint
Grade II listed corner house is an engaging restaurant-with-rooms. Its
decor "is charming", with lots of yellow, polished wood, fresh
flowers. A curving glass tower lights the house. The Neapolitan
patron/chef, Ciro Zaino, has worked at some of London's most distinguished restaurants, including *The Halkin* and *The Capital* (*qqv*).
His wife Lynda is the "endearingly enthusiastic" front-of-house. "The
hospitality is warm. It offers genuine value," one visitor wrote.
Another found it "a peaceful oasis in a busy town. The bedrooms are
calm. Lots of white linen." Everyone admires the cooking: "It is wonderful." "Dinners and breakfasts are varied and excellent." The restaurant, hung with local paintings, leads on to a walled garden with
terracotta pots and palm trees. Sample menus include: terrine of
chicken and spinach with pesto dressing, or Newlyn mussels and
clams with white wine, garlic and parsley; seabass with a cream and
white wine sauce and ginger, or red mullet with citrus and coriander
dressing; mango sorbet with raspberry coulis, or warm apple tart with
crème Chantilly and Calvados. Wines are predominantly Italian. Teas
are served at bright blue tables among potted plants and palm trees in
the walled garden. The bedrooms (some are spacious) have antique
furniture, Victorian-style lights, fresh flowers. Step out to the waterfront for views of St Michael's Mount to the left, Newlyn to the right.
(*JL, AS, and others*)

Open All year. Restaurant closed Mon to non-residents.
Rooms 5 double. No telephone.
Facilities Lounge, restaurant (classical/Celtic background music breakfast/
dinner). Small walled garden. Sea, beach, public outdoor swimming pool close
by. Unsuitable for &.
Location 5 mins' walk from centre. Drive along harbour; pass open-air swim-
ming pool; follow promenade; right immediately after *Queen's Hotel*. Hotel
on left. Carpark. Train/bus/helicopter to Penzance.
Restrictions No smoking: in restaurant until 10 pm, all bedrooms. No children
under 12. No dogs.
Credit cards MasterCard, Visa.
Terms [2000] B&B: single £40–£70, double £55–£75; D,B&B: single
£60.50–£90.50, double £96–£117. Set dinner (2 to 3 courses) £17.50–£20.50.
Off-season breaks. Christmas package. 1-night bookings refused Easter.

Tarbert Hotel BUDGET *Tel* (01736) 363758
11–12 Clarence Street   *Fax* (01736) 331336
Penzance TR18 2NU   *E-mail* reception@tarbert-hotel.co.uk
                                        Website www.tarbert-hotel.co.uk

*Former sea captain's residence, now a good-value simple hotel (Logis
of Great Britain). New owners in 2000, ex-teachers Jeff and Shirley
Maddern. Traditional cooking on varied menu (emphasis on fish and*

New World wines), served to "easy listening" tapes in no-smoking restaurant. Log fire in stone-walled lounge/bar (snack lunches available). Flowery patio; small carpark. 12 bedrooms, 1 with good-size bathroom, others with shower (some are small). Near centre, but no view; promenade with outdoor swimming pool close by. Closed 22 Dec–end Jan. Unsuitable for &. Guide dogs only. Amex, MasterCard, Visa accepted. B&B £26–£38; D,B&B £39–£56. More reports, please.

PLYMOUTH Devon *See SHORTLIST*   **Map 1**

POOLE Dorset   **Map 2**

The Mansion House   *Tel* (01202) 685666
Thames Street   *Fax* (01202) 665709
Poole BH15 1JN   *E-mail* enquiries@themansionhouse.co.uk
                        Website www.themansionhouse.co.uk

"It exudes warmth, style and excellence," says a visitor this year to this well-established hotel in an 18th-century town house – "a real gem, where you can enjoy yourself without breaking the bank". It stands in a quiet cul-de-sac near Poole's old parish church and busy quay. "The welcome is warm, the bedrooms tastefully furnished, the food interesting, with unobtrusive service." A grand sweeping staircase leads up from the entrance hall to a stylish residents' lounge. A "dedicated staff" is led by the "remarkable manageress", Jackie Godden; her husband, Gerry, supervises the kitchens. The bar/bistro provides "simple meals of excellent quality, with quick and charming service". The panelled restaurant, serving "modern British dishes with European and Asian influences", is a fashionable dining club of which the hotel's residents are temporary members. There is always a fish dish of the day; other main courses might be pan-fried scallops with stir-fried vegetables; breast of duck with Oriental sauce. On Saturday evening and at Sunday lunch there is an impressive hors d'oeuvre table. Most bedrooms are good-sized and luxurious, with fresh fruit, thermos with ice, and a telephone in the bathroom. Singles can be small. No charge is made for room service; early morning tea is brought to the room. "Breakfasts are wide-ranging and well prepared." Poole's magnificent natural harbour makes it a popular boating centre, and its beach, graded one of the cleanest in Britain, is overlooked by the lovely gardens of Compton Acres. There are many interesting places to visit, including Brownsea Island, Kingston Lacey, Athelhampton House, Edmonsham House, Corfe Castle and Sherborne. The tomb of Mary Shelley is also nearby; she is buried next to her husband's heart, plucked from his funeral pyre. (*CR Burns, AJB, and others*)

Open All year. Restaurant closed Sun evening, midday on bank holiday Mon.
Rooms 23 double, 9 single. 4, adjoining main building, with separate entrance.
Facilities Lounge, cocktail bar, bar/bistro, restaurant; classical background music during meals; private dining room. Poole Quay 100 yds: fishing, boating, sailing. Unsuitable for &. Civil wedding licence.

Location Follow signs to Channel ferry. Left at Poole bridge on to quayside, 1st left (James St), signposted to hotel. 2 private carparks. Train/bus ½ mile.
Restrictions Smoking discouraged in restaurant, banned in 4 bedrooms. No children under 5 in restaurant. No dogs.
Credit cards All major cards accepted.
Terms B&B: single £65–£88, double £98–£128; D,B&B: single £87–£110, double £142–£172. Set lunch £16.25, dinner (2 to 3 courses) £19.50–£23.50; full alc £32. Child accommodated in parents' room: under 12, free. Weekend rates. Midweek/weekend breaks. Christmas package. *V*

PORLOCK Somerset   **Map 1**

The Oaks   *Tel* (01643) 862265
Porlock TA24 8ES   *Fax* (01643) 863131
                                    E-mail oakshotel@aol.com

Tim and Anne Riley provide a "really friendly welcome", says a visitor this year to their gabled Edwardian pebbledash house. It is set amid lawns and oak trees, in an elevated position above the tiny fishing village with its narrow main street and old buildings. It has views across the Bristol Channel, and it is within earshot of a nearby weir. Exmoor lies behind. Regular visitors like the "quite old-fashioned" atmosphere and the traditional courtesies: help with suitcases, complimentary tea on arrival, etc. The newly decorated public rooms have chintzes, open fires, oil paintings and prints; flowery wallpaper and fabrics brighten the bedrooms. Meals are as traditional as the rest. A typical dinner menu includes, eg, cream of mushroom soup; grilled scallops with prawn sauce; Exmoor venison with a port and redcurrant sauce; banana and stem ginger ice-cream. A visitor this year found the starters and dessert "excellent", main courses more variable. Breakfast is "good, but to give a choice of fruit juice or cereal seemed somewhat mean". However, "the owners make up for any minor faults by their really kind approach". One warning: "The hotel's entrance is at a sharp angle of the main road." One of the smallest churches in England is at Culbone, three miles away. (*John Whiting, and others*)

Open Mar–Nov.
Rooms 9 double.
Facilities 2 lounges, bar, dining room (classical background music at night). 1-acre garden. Sea 1 mile. Unsuitable for &.
Location ¼ mile from village 6 miles W of Minehead.
Restrictions No smoking, except in bar. No children under 8. No dogs in public rooms.
Credit cards MasterCard, Visa.
Terms B&B: single £60, double £100; D,B&B (min 2 nights): single £80, double £140. Set dinner £27.50. Christmas package.

****

Hotel in Devon. The breakfast choice of smoked fish is limited to haddock or kippers "because of government fishing instructions". Moreover, unless you order the previous evening, you get the "standard" cooked breakfast with no option other than a continental breakfast.

****

PORLOCK WEIR Somerset   **Map 1**

Porlock Vale House   BUDGET   *Tel* (01643) 862338
Porlock Weir TA24 8NY   *Fax* (01643) 863338
E-mail info@porlockvale.co.uk
Website www.porlockvale.co.uk

"The setting is splendid, quiet" – in ancient oak woodlands on the
lower slopes of Exmoor, and with "superb views" over the Bristol
Channel to Wales. "The staff were exceptionally kind and helpful at
all times," says a visitor this year, "and it represents good value for
money." This is one of England's premier riding hotels, but non-riders
are welcome too. The owners, Kim and Helen Youd, have been
refurbishing since they took over four years ago, and the grounds have
been landscaped to create a woodland garden. The public rooms are
"well decorated" with deep chintz sofas, antique and period furniture,
sporting prints and antlers (a reminder that this was once a hunting
lodge). The panelled hall has a huge open fireplace and a small bar.
Some bedrooms may be less immaculate, with "slightly ramshackle"
furniture, but refurbishment is in progress, and a junior suite with a
kingsize bed is new this year. Most rooms, particularly the larger ones
at the back, have a peaceful view over garden and paddocks to a wide
sweep of beach and headland. In summer, the dining room opens on to
a flower-filled terrace. The food was thought "good on the whole" this
year. You are asked to order dinner in the morning, from a daily-
changing menu of traditional dishes, with an emphasis on West
Country produce and local game, eg, potted duck with sage, cider and
apple jelly; roast guinea fowl with bacon and onion stew; treacle and
whisky steamed sponge pudding and custard. The choices always
include fish and vegetarian dishes. Bar lunches (home-made soup and
sandwiches) are served. Breakfast is cooked to order. There is good
walking from the house up into the woods, and a short drive takes you
on to the moor. The owners will advise about outings. The remote
farmhouse where Coleridge "is reliably said to have written 'Kubla
Khan'" is close by. (*AD, JD, and others*)

Open All year, except 1st 2 weeks Jan; restaurant closed occasional midweek
evening Jan/Feb.
Rooms 1 junior suite, 13 double, 1 single.
Facilities 3 lounges (1 with TV), bar, dining room (occasional classical back-
ground music during dinner). 25-acre grounds running down to sea: gardens,
riding stables. Unsuitable for &.
Location Leave A39 at Porlock; drive through village; hotel is 1½ miles to
NW by lower Porlock Weir coast road. Train: Taunton (28 miles).
Restrictions No smoking: restaurant, 2 lounges, bedrooms. No children
under 12. No dogs in house (kennels available).
Credit cards All major cards accepted.
Terms B&B: single £25–£60, double £50–£95, suite £70–£110; D,B&B:
single £40–£80, double £84–£135, suite £104–£150. Set dinner £20. Short
breaks. Christmas, New Year packages. 1-night bookings sometimes refused
weekends.

If you find details of a hotel's location inadequate, please tell us.

PORT ISAAC Cornwall   Map 1

Port Gaverne Hotel   *Tel* (01208) 880244
Port Gaverne   *Fax* (01208) 880151
nr Port Isaac   *E-mail* pghotel@telinco.co.uk
PL29 3SQ   *Website* www.chycot.co.uk/hotels/port-gaverne

Owned for 31 years by one family – Mrs Marjorie (Midge) Ross is
now in command – this traditional hotel stands in a secluded cove near
the "quintessential fishing village" of Port Isaac. It is liked for its
"wonderful location", relaxed style (sometimes thought "marginally
chaotic"), simple English cuisine, and the welcome to families with
children and dogs. Most of the bedrooms are large, with a "proper
bathroom". An enthusiastic report came this year: "It copes brilliantly,
with hotel visitors on a few days' stay, and also with clients who see
it as their lovely local pub. My bedroom was beautifully furnished,
and warm. In the dining room, warm fish salad and mussels were
memorable starters, followed by delicious fresh fish dishes. At lunch I
had the best-ever crab sandwich with home-made brown bread. The
wine list, recently revamped, included some amazingly reasonable
bottles, and a most unusual plummy cabernet sauvignon from Israel."
Other reports spoke of the "delicious soups", "great puds", also provided by the chef, Ian Brodey. Vegetarians are well catered for. Close
by is a small beach, with sand, rocks, safe bathing. "Fantastic walks on
National Trust coastal paths, where wildlife and wild flowers are magnificent, thanks to the absence of pesticides." Bicycles can be hired
locally. (*June Goodfield*)

Open All year.
Rooms 14 double, 2 single. Also self-catering cottages.
Facilities Lounge, upper deck lounge (with sea-facing balcony), bar lounge,
cocktail bar, restaurant; occasional background music throughout, at quiet
times. Small garden. Sand/rock beach 60 yds; golf, fishing, surfing, sailing,
riding nearby. Unsuitable for &.
Location ½ mile N of Port Isaac (signposted off B3314).
Restriction No smoking: restaurant, 2 small bars.
Credit cards All major cards accepted.
Terms B&B £35–£55; D,B&B £50–£70. Full alc £24. Off-season breaks: 3
nights for the price of 2.

PORTHLEVEN Cornwall   Map 1

Tye Rock Country House   *Tel/Fax* (01326) 572695
Loe Bar Road   *E-mail* info@tyerockhotel.co.uk
Porthleven TR13 9EW   *Website* www.tyerock.co.uk

Dating back to 1883, this old manor house has an "interesting, if rather
bleak" location on a cliff near a charming village with large harbour.
Surrounded by National Trust land, it has wide views across Mounts
Bay from Land's End to the Lizard peninsula (stunning sunsets), and
it is "ideal for coastal path walkers, birdwatchers and sailors". The
owners, Pat and Richard Palmer ("personable and accommodating
hosts" say inspectors), have extensively renovated, and they offer

"excellent value for money". Behind the plain exterior are "pleasant public rooms" and exotically themed bedrooms (some quite small), all with a sea view. The Blue Room, based on local bluebell woods, has pictures of Cornish scenes; the African Room is decorated with Lua carvings and batik paintings; the 1920s room is Art Deco; another room is based on Cornish myths and legends. Some original fireplaces have survived. "The style is original, if a bit cluttered; a lot of thought has gone into detail." In the small dining room, with tightly packed tables, there are spectacular sea views, blue and white napery. The food is "not gourmet, but simple and fresh". The short *table d'hôte* menu (with choice; for residents only) might include avocado, mango and prawn salad, or grapefruit segments in crème de menthe; breast of duck Clementine, or wild boar and apple sausages with Cumberland sauce. Vegetarians are catered for. The wine list is "ample, with lots of choice at under £10". Only caveat: "The loud 1920s music detracted from our pleasure." The swimming pool in the grounds was destroyed by gales in 1999; it has been replaced by gardens, a sun terrace and promenade. "Murder Mystery" weekends are sometimes held; and one couple enjoyed a Victorian weekend, with an "adult Punch and Judy show". Local attractions include cliff walks and wildlife, gardens – including Heligan and the Eden 2000 project – historic houses and the Minack Theatre. (*PO, and others*)

Open All year, except 2 weeks Nov and Feb.
Rooms 7 double. Also 8 self-catering apartments.
Facilities 2 lounges, restaurant (light classical background music at breakfast and dinner). 3½-acre grounds; terrace. Unsuitable for &.
Location 10 mins' walk from harbour. From Helston, follow Porthleven sign; then Loe Bar sign. Train: Penzance; then taxi.
Restrictions No smoking. No children under 12. No dogs.
Credit cards MasterCard, Visa.
Terms Double room: B&B £82–£100; D,B&B £118–£136; single occupancy 25% off room rate. Set dinner £18; full alc £25. Christmas package. 1-night bookings sometimes refused high season. *V* (Oct–Mar)

PORTSMOUTH Hampshire *See SHORTLIST*   Map 2

PRESTBURY Cheshire   Map 3

The White House   *Tel* (01625) 829376
  Restaurant and Manor   *Fax* (01625) 828627
New Road   *E-mail* stay@cheshire-white-house.com
Prestbury SK10 4HP   *Website* www.thewhitehouse.uk.com

The red brick Georgian exterior of Ryland and Judith Wakeham's unusual hotel belies its exotic interior. All the rooms "give a feeling of luxury", says a visitor this year. Travelling on her own, she appreciated being able to dine and breakfast at a large table in her ground-floor bedroom – the restaurant is five minutes' walk away. Each bedroom has its own theme. The Studio has paintings, art books, lavish fabrics, a dramatic green-and-black bathroom. Glyndebourne has a sophisticated music centre and a collection of discs. Trafalgar is decorated with naval artefacts, burgundy drapes and gold braid, and has a power shower with body jets. The Crystal Room has a four-poster bed, crystal chandelier and a whirlpool bath. Minerva, with a Turkish steam room and a collection of antique sporting equipment, is all about sport and health. The millennium suite has an ultra-modern glass bed. In the low-ceilinged restaurant, Mark Cunniffe serves "contemporary British dishes" to a smart local clientele, eg, steamed mussels in a broth of fennel, Pernod and cheese; calf's liver on olive oil mash, with red onion and pancetta; warm pear clafouti with star anise. "Delicious breakfasts" can be continental, "healthy" or "full Cheshire"; all include fresh orange juice, thick brown toast, good coffee. Prestbury is a pretty village on the River Bollin. It has easy access to the ring of motorways reaching into Lancashire and across the Pennines, and Manchester airport is a short drive away. (*Sue Davies, and others*)

Open All year, except 25 Dec.
Rooms 8 double, 3 single. Some in coach house annexe.
Facilities Lounge, conservatory with honesty bar, restaurant; function facilities. ½-acre garden. Unsuitable for &.
Location Edge of village on A538, 2 miles N of Macclesfield. Some traffic noise.
Restrictions No smoking: restaurant before 10 pm, bedrooms. No children under 10 in bedrooms. No dogs.
Credit cards All major cards accepted.
Terms [2000] Room: single £40, double £70–£120. Breakfast £8.50. Set lunch £13.95, dinner (2 to 3 courses) £14.95–£17.95; full alc £32.

PURTON Wiltshire   **Map 3**

The Pear Tree at Purton   *Tel* (01793) 772100
Church End   *Fax* (01793) 772369
Purton, nr Swindon SN5 4ED
                                     E-mail stay@peartreepurton.co.uk
                                     Website www.peartreepurton.co.uk

"Very high standards; on a return visit we were greeted like old friends." "Deserves all accolades. Offers value for money." "Excellent food; professional yet friendly service. One of the few hotels where I feel comfortable alone in the restaurant." Again there is admiration for Francis and Anne Young's old stone house (Pride of Britain) on the edge of this Saxon village (the name means "pear tree enclosure"). Once the village rectory, it stood by the unusual twin-towered parish church, but it was moved, stone by stone, to its present site in 1912, when space for graves began to run out. Given its location, only a few miles off the M4, the hotel is much frequented by business travellers, and often used for weddings on Saturdays. But it is "unintimidating": "Whatever you ask is promptly and willingly attended to. The meals are well cooked, nicely presented, with first-class, unhurried service." In the conservatory dining room, candlelit at night, and with views of well-maintained gardens, chef Alan Postill serves ambitious modern British dishes at dinner, eg, scallops marinated in tomato and walnut vinaigrette; breasts of wood pigeon with wild mushrooms, truffle oil and rosti; lemon mousse cheesecake with cassis sauce. At lunch, simpler offerings include braised local sausages with grain mustard and chive mash; always a traditional hot pudding. Each bedroom is named after a character associated with the village. "They are well furnished, spotless", with fresh flowers that match the colour scheme, fresh fruit in prime condition, sweets, biscuits, etc. Bathrooms are "impeccable"; many have a spa bath. Purton is well placed for visiting Avebury, Rosemary Verey's gardens at Barnsley House, Dyrham Park, Bowood House, and STEAM, the recently opened museum of the Great Western Railway in Swindon. (*Gerald S Bernett, Tess Biggs, Sue Davies*)

Open All year, except 26–30 Dec. Restaurant closed Sat midday.
Rooms 2 suites, 15 double, 1 single. Some on ground floor.
Facilities Ramps. Lounge bar, library, conservatory restaurant; function facilities. No background music. 7½-acre grounds: croquet, jogging route. Civil wedding licence.
Location 5 miles NW of Swindon. From M4 exit 16 follow signs to Wootton Bassett/Purton; through Purton village, right at Spar grocer. Train: Swindon; then taxi.
Restriction No dogs in public rooms, unattended in bedrooms.
Credit cards All major cards accepted.
Terms B&B: single/double £95–£115, suite £115–£135. Set lunch £17.50, dinner £29.50. Child accommodated in parents' room: £10. Weekend breaks. *V*

RAMSGILL-IN-NIDDERDALE North Yorkshire   Map 4

The Yorke Arms   *Tel* (01423) 755243
Ramsgill-in-Nidderdale   *Fax* (01423) 755330
nr Harrogate HG3 5RL   *E-mail* enquiries@yorke-arms.co.uk
                                 Website www.yorke-arms.co.uk

Ǫ *César award in 2000*

In 1997, Frances and Bill Atkins took over this former shooting lodge, which stands on the green of an old dales hamlet close to the Gouthwaite Reservoir bird sanctuary. They rapidly acquired a reputation for serving some of the best food in the area, and in 2000, *Michelin* awarded a *Bib Gourmand* for the quality of the food produced by Mrs Atkins and her all-female kitchen staff, and served in both the bar and restaurant. Many of her main dishes are robust, based on local lamb and game. Starters include, eg, champagne, parsley and wild mushroom risotto; millefeuille of artichoke, avocado and tomato. There is a choice of 70 wines from around the world. But despite the sophisticated food, the place retains the atmosphere of an inn, with its flagstone floors, log fires, oak beams, wheelback chairs and wooden tables. Bill Atkins "is an exemplary 'Mine Host'". Visitors who call in for a drink are welcomed, and in summer the seats in front of the pub and in the small rear garden are full. Praise came again this year: "A super place to stay, with courteous owners, marvellous breakfasts." "Wonderful food, caring staff." The bedrooms are unpretentious (No. 6 is said to be very small); bathrooms are being upgraded. There is good walking from the door, through fields with sheep and lambs. Weekend breaks, with walks led by an ornithologist, are offered in low season. A good base for visiting Ripon Cathedral, Harewood House, Fountains Abbey (you need a car). (*Good Pub Guide, Mrs PD Pells, A and CR; also Mr and Mrs M Firth*)

Open All year.
Rooms 2 suites, 8 double, 3 single.
Facilities Lounge, 2 bars, restaurant; classical background music at customers' request; function facilities. 2-acre grounds. Unsuitable for &.
Location Centre of village. Take B6265 from Ripon/B6165 from Ripley to Pateley Bridge. Then Low Wath road to Ramsgill. Plane: Leeds/Bradford airport; train: Harrogate; then bus, or hotel will meet.
Restrictions Smoking banned in restaurant, discouraged in bedrooms. Dogs in bar only.
Credit cards All major cards accepted.
Terms D,B&B £85–£135. Full alc £30. Weekend breaks; walking weekends. Cookery courses. Christmas, New Year packages.

RAVENSTONEDALE Cumbria   Map 4

The Black Swan   *Tel* (015396) 23204
Ravenstonedale   *Freephone* 0800 0741394
nr Kirkby Stephen CA17 4NG   *Fax* (015396) 23604
                          E-mail reservation@blackswanhotel.com
                              Website www.blackswanhotel.com

Ravenstonedale (pronounced Rassendale) is a quiet village, with a "very special parish church", in a lovely area between the Lake District and the Yorkshire Dales. There is good walking on the Howgill fells close by, and good birdwatching. This hotel, in the centre of the village, also has access to a private stretch of fishing on the River Eden. It is a late 19th-century stone building which Gordon and Norma Stuart have run for many years. There is one report this year of a poor lunch with offhand service, and another of a cool welcome in the owners' absence, but most visitors find the place "friendly, with good beers, and rooms that are good value, clean and cosy". Local beef, lamb, venison and fish, elaborately sauced, are served in the restaurant, preceded by starters such as goat's cheese on marinated cherry tomatoes with quail's eggs; terrine of black pudding, baby leeks and foie gras. Breakfasts are "substantial". "The unspoilt setting and the friendly locals all contribute to the charms." Thomas, the cat, is friendly too. There is a residents' lounge, a stone-walled lounge bar, and a garden, bordered by a stream, across the road. Some bedrooms, which can be let on a self-catering basis, are in *The Nick* (formerly the police station) next door, which has a kitchen, sitting room and four bedrooms. More reports, please.

Open All year.
Rooms 20 double. 4 in annexe (can be self-catering). 3 on ground floor, 1 adapted for &.
Facilities 2 lounges, 2 bars, restaurant, small dining room. No background music. 2-acre grounds on stream. Fishing, golf, riding, tennis, bowling nearby.
Location Centre of village. From M6, exit 38, take A685 for Brough. Bus from Kendal.
Restrictions No smoking in restaurant. No dogs in public rooms.
Credit cards All major cards accepted.

Terms B&B: single £45–£52, double £70–£85; D,B&B: single £70–£77, double £120–£135. Bar meals. Set lunch £12, dinner £25. Off-season breaks. Christmas package. *V*

READING Berkshire *See SHORTLIST*   **Map 2**

REETH North Yorkshire   **Map 4**

Arkleside   *Tel/Fax* (01748) 884200
Reeth, nr Richmond   *E-mail* info@arklesidehotel.co.uk
DL11 6SG   *Website* www.arklesidehotel.co.uk

"It maintains its high standards. We were welcomed back as old friends," writes a visitor returning this year to Dorothy Kendall and Richard Beal's unpretentious, small hotel. Composed of a row of 17th-century miners' cottages, it is close to the green of this picturesque village in the middle of Swaledale. Bedroom 4 has "a wonderful view down the Swale valley and to Fremington Ridge". The suite, in a mews cottage, has its own lounge and a "Victorian bathroom"; other rooms have a shower, but there is a shared bathroom. The "home-like decor" is pleasing, and there are good views from the public rooms. The bar, which serves real ale, has a log fire and doors opening on to the garden, where pre-dinner drinks are served in summer. The dining room was recently redecorated, and a conservatory has been added. The food is traditional English, on a short menu that changes daily; eg, parsnip and apple soup; steak Bordelaise; rhubarb and ginger crumble. "It is unfailingly tasty," says a visitor this year, who also enjoyed the "intimate atmosphere". Gourmet weekends are held with a local wine expert in attendance, and Ms Kendall and Mr Beal sometimes lead walking weekends. On the subject of muzak, they write: "We are trying to get away from it, but some guests like it." Dogs are welcomed, and so are children over ten. Reeth is surrounded by beautiful scenery and it is usually peaceful, though it can be crowded in summer. A good base for visiting Barnard Castle, Teesdale and Wensleydale. (*Lynda Gillinson, Trevor Lockwood*)

Open All year, except Christmas, Jan. Restaurant closed midday.
Rooms 1 suite (with bath) in mews cottage, 8 double (with shower).
Facilities Lounge, conservatory, bar, dining room (background tapes/CDs/radio most of the day). Small grounds. Trout-fishing rights on River Swale ½ mile. Unsuitable for &.
Location 10 miles W of Richmond. Off top right corner of village green. Parking. Limited bus service from Richmond.
Restrictions Smoking in bar only. No children under 10. No dogs in public rooms.
Credit cards MasterCard, Visa.
Terms B&B: £34–£44. Set dinner £20. Walking, gourmet, dinner party, Dickensian weekends. Special breaks, Christmas, New Year packages. 1-night bookings refused New Year, Easter, bank holidays.

Give the *Guide* positive support. Don't leave feedback to others.

The Burgoyne   *Tel/Fax* (01748) 884292
On the Green   *E-mail* peter@carwardine.fsbusiness.co.uk
Reeth, nr Richmond   *Website* www.hotels.nettraders.co.uk/burgoynehotel
DL11 6SN

"What a lovely little hotel. Comfortable and spotless, with service
that's warm and perfectly friendly, yet never over-familiar." Praise
this year for this Grade II listed Regency house, which looks across a
small front lawn to the village green. Other guests called Peter
Carwardine (the chef) and Derek Hickson "two of the best hosts we
have ever met". "We never cease to be amazed by the warmth of the
welcome and the genuine courtesy that is shown to all. The house is a
delight, dining is a pleasure and the surroundings are outstanding."
There are antiques, a log fire, books and magazines in the spacious
lounge (where drinks are served), and a pink-and-green decor in the
restaurant, where dinner "with enough variety to keep everyone
happy", is "impeccably presented". It starts promptly at 8 pm. The traditional English cooking is unfussy, eg, fish-cake with tomato coulis;
roast best end of lamb with redcurrant jelly; bananas baked in brandy,
with ginger ice-cream. The wine list has a good choice of half bottles,
and if you order a full bottle of the house wine, you pay only for what
is consumed. The bedrooms (some redecorated this year) are named
after local hamlets; most are large, with a view of the green and the
hills beyond (the rear view is less attractive). Three have their bathroom across a corridor (a bathrobe and slippers are provided).
Breakfast is admired too: "beautifully cooked and served by the
chef/proprietor"; "delicious smoked haddock". (*IT Glendenning, Mr
and Mrs GA Lilley, Robert Thornberry, EB*)

Open 12 Feb–2 Jan. Restaurant closed midday.
Rooms 1 suite, 7 double, one suitable for &.
Facilities 2 lounges, dining room (jazz/classical background music during
dinner as required). ½-acre grounds. Trout-fishing rights on River Swale.
Location Centre of village, 10 miles W of Richmond. Parking.
Restrictions No smoking: dining room, 1 lounge, bedrooms. No children
under 10. No dogs in dining room or unattended in bedrooms.
Credit cards MasterCard, Visa.
Terms B&B: single £70–£130, double £80–£100, suite £140. Set dinner
£24.50. Off-season breaks, grouse-shooting parties. Christmas, New Year
packages. 1-night bookings sometimes refused Sat.

REIGATE Surrey *See SHORTLIST*   **Map 2**

RHYDYCROESAU Shropshire   **Map 3**

Pen-y-Dyffryn   *Tel* (01691) 653700
Rhydycroesau   *Fax* (01691) 650066
nr Oswestry SY10 7JD
                                         E-mail stay@peny.co.uk
                                         Website www.peny.co.uk

"A delightful haven; just the place to retreat to the silence of
Shropshire," says a visitor this year to this listed Georgian stone

rectory. The owners, Miles and Audrey Hunter, say it was once the home of an eccentric Celtic scholar. Despite the name, it is just in England; its grounds lead down to the River Cynllaith, which marks the Welsh border. Perched almost 1,000 feet up, it looks west towards the Welsh mountains. Lake Vyrnwy is nearby, and there are "wonderful sunsets". Visitors this year appreciated the setting – "one of the most beautiful of any inland hotel we know" – and the "relaxed atmosphere". "The visiting dogs thought it great" (there is a large field where they can be exercised). The new chef, David Morris, continues the tradition of "modern British cooking with a green touch", using organic local produce where possible. Braised shank of Welsh lamb is served with a purée of root vegetables; pan-fried pork has a Shropshire blue cheese sauce; there is always a vegetarian main course. But one visitor reported long delays at mealtimes this year. The decor is old-fashioned: vivid colours, inherited furniture, flowery fabrics, patterned carpets, and some bathrooms may need updating. The Hunters are continuing a rolling programme of redecoration. The bedrooms are not large, but most have a view. Two rooms, each with a private patio, are in a converted coach house. The atmosphere is informal, and children are welcomed.

Guests may fish for trout in pools in front of the house, and there is good walking from the door, including the Offa's Dyke circular path. Golf, climbing, and stately homes and Welsh castles are nearby. (*John Marland, Dr and Mrs PH Tattersall, Mrs ME Hartley, Pat Pells*)

Open 20 Jan–20 Dec.
Rooms 9 double, 1 single. 2, each with private walled courtyard, in coach house. 1 on ground floor.
Facilities 2 lounges, cocktail bar, restaurant; quiet classical background music evenings. 5-acre grounds: 3-acre exercise area for dogs; trout fishing. Golf nearby.
Location 3 miles W of Oswestry by B4580. Follow signs to Llansilin. Train: Oswestry.
Restrictions No smoking: restaurant, main lounge, bedrooms. No dogs in public rooms.
Credit cards Amex, MasterCard, Visa.
Terms B&B single £37–£64, D,B&B £55–£85. Set dinner £21; full alc £27. Child accommodated in parents' room: B&B £10–£20. 1-night bookings sometimes refused weekends.

"Set meals" indicates fixed-price meals, with ample, limited or no choice on the menu. "Full alc" is the hotel's estimated price per person of a 3-course *à la carte* meal, with a half bottle of house wine. "Alc" is the price of an *à la carte* meal excluding the cost of wine.

RINGLESTONE Kent

Map 2

The Ringlestone Inn
Ringlestone, nr Harrietsham
Maidstone ME17 1NX

Tel (01622) 859900
Fax (01622) 859966
E-mail bookings@ringlestone.com
Website www.ringlestone.com

"A very comfortable place to stay, with particularly good breakfasts."
"A happy atmosphere, fine choice of food, hard-working staff." Apart
from one couple who felt "not very welcome", most reports continue
enthusiastic for this old inn. Once a hospice for monks, it has been an
inn since about 1615. Many original features remain, including a
carved inscription on an oak sideboard: "A Ryghte Joyous and welcome greetynge to ye all." Also brick and flint walls, old beams, an
inglenook fireplace (with a small bread oven), carved settles and old
panelling. It is set amid farmland, in "beautifully landscaped" grounds
with lawns, shrubs, trees, rockeries, ponds, waterfalls and a fountain,
in a hamlet in the North Downs. The bedrooms are in an old farmhouse
opposite and a garden cottage. They are decorated to a high standard,
with rustic oak furniture, a large bed with good linen; well-designed,
spacious bathrooms have a separate shower cubicle. The food is enterprising: traditional country recipes are used, eg, game pie with redcurrant wine; Barbary duck marinated in damson wine; fish in
elderflower wine; fruit flans, tarts and trifle to end. Thirty-six varieties
of fruit wines and liqueurs are stocked. Lunch is a hot and cold buffet.
"We have no petty restrictions here," say the owner and the manager,
Michael Millington-Buck and Michelle Stanley. "Patrons may sit
where they like. Children, accompanied by an adult, are welcomed –
under gentle supervision." "Well-behaved dogs" are also welcomed.
Leeds Castle is three miles away; the M20 motorway is a five-minute
drive. (*Good Pub Guide, and others*)

Open All year, except 25 Dec.
Rooms 5 double, 3 in farmhouse, 2 in cottage.
Facilities Lounge, 3 bars (piped background music), restaurant; function/con-
ference facilities. 8-acre grounds: water garden, gardens, *pétanque,* paddock.
Unsuitable for &.
Location In hamlet 8 miles E of Maidstone. From M20, exit 8 (for Leeds
Castle), turn on to A20. At roundabout opposite *Great Danes* hotel, turn left to
Hollingbourne. Through village to top of hill; turn east at crossroads by water
tower, signposted Ringlestone.
Restrictions No smoking in bedrooms. Dogs in bars only.
Credit cards All major cards accepted.
Terms B&B £55.50–£100. Full alc £30. Special breaks: 3 nights for the price
of 2 if Sun included. *V*

****

Hotel in Devon. The owner's "unobtrusive solicitude" borders
on the uninterested. No unprompted conversations ever took
place. No "What plans have you for today?"; "Happy Easter".
Service is clinically precise and subservient – how we wished
for the occasional ice-breaking quip.

****

RIPLEY North Yorkshire

Map 4

The Boar's Head
Ripley Castle Estate
Harrogate HG3 3AY

Tel (01423) 771888
Fax (01423) 771509
E-mail boars@ripleycastle.co.uk
Website www.ripleycastle.co.uk

𝒬 *César award in 1999*

"A comfortable hotel, but it also has a well-liked bar and the feel of an upmarket village pub." It was converted from an earlier inn by Sir Thomas and Lady Ingilby – his family have lived in the castle on the estate for 650 years. The Ingilbys are not often seen in the inn, and though the food was thought "fabulous" this year, some reports came of disorganised service, particularly at breakfast. But Charles and Claire Edmondson-Jones, who twice won the *Good Pub Guide*'s Dining Pub of the Year award for Leicestershire, were appointed managers in early 2000, so we'd like more reports, please. The superior bedrooms are liked, with their fresh flowers, books, and daily carafe of sherry, but some other rooms are small and less well furnished, and some look over the beer garden, busy in fine weather. The lounges have antique and period furniture, portraits and paintings. In the candlelit restaurant, Steven Chestnutt serves modern dishes, eg, salad of pigeon with marinated artichokes; aniseed chicken with caramelised roots; plum pudding soufflé; but one couple disliked the accompanying piped music, and preferred to eat in the bar/bistro, where they found a more varied menu, a "stylish decor" and a "cheerful atmosphere". It serves good beers, including Crackshot, brewed to the inn's own 17th-century recipe. Ripley Castle is a popular tourist attraction, and can get busy in summer. Hotel guests have access to the grounds, its deerpark, lake, Victorian gardens and greenhouses, and the Super Sleuth weekend includes a black-tie banquet in the castle. Fountains Abbey is 15 minutes' drive away; York is 40 minutes; castles, stately homes and great gardens abound. (*Good Pub Guide, Geoffrey L Watson, SR, and others*)

Open All year.
Rooms 25 double. 10 in courtyard, 6 in *Birchwood House* opposite. Some on ground floor.
Facilities 2 drawing rooms, bar/bistro, restaurant; background music. 20-acre grounds: garden; access to 500-acre castle estate with deerpark, lake, fishing. Civil wedding licence.
Location 3 miles N of Harrogate on A61 Harrogate–Ripon. Bus from Ripon.
Restrictions No smoking in bedrooms. No dogs: restaurant, most bedrooms, castle grounds.
Credit cards All major cards accepted.
Terms [2000] (*Non-refundable deposit of £50 required*) B&B: single £95–£115, double £115–£135; D,B&B (min. 2 nights) £75–£95 per person. Set lunch £14, dinner £22.50–£35 (restaurant), £25 (bistro). Child accommodated in parents' room: under 15, B&B £20. Cookery demonstrations. Yorkshire breaks, Super Sleuth weekends. Christmas package. *V*

Report forms (Freepost in UK) are at the end of the *Guide*.

ROCK Cornwall   Map 1

St Enodoc   *Tel* (01208) 863394
Rock, nr Wadebridge   *Fax* (01208) 863970
PL27 6LA   *E-mail* enodoc@aol.com
                                                 Website www.enodoc-hotel.co.uk

ॐ *César award in 2000*

"A lovely hotel." "A find – confident, comfortable, in a lovely setting." So write visitors this year to this family-friendly seaside hotel,
owned by the Marler family, who also own the *Knightsbridge Green
Hotel,* London (*qv*). The manager, Mark Gregory, and his staff are
"young, sophisticated, helpful at all times". In an "old-fashioned
Cornish backwater" on the Camel estuary, the hotel stands amid a
cluster of houses along a small road running parallel to the beach. It
was given a light, Mediterranean-type decor by Emily Todhunter, and
the effect is "one of simple, modern comfort with an eye on tradition":
"marvellous paintings" on gleaming white walls; distressed-effect furniture in vivid turquoise or blue; furniture and fittings "of the highest
quality". Crisp bedlinen; fluffy towels and quality toiletries in bathrooms; "excellent lighting; stunning views". "Very much a summer
hotel." Meals are served at wooden tables in the large, split-level
Porthilly Bar, which has panoramic views, and a terrace for summer
eating. A new chef, Rupert Brown, arrived in April 2000, and we
would be grateful for reports on his "Pacific Rim" cooking on a short
menu, eg, spinach and red pepper soup; grilled swordfish with
Singapore seafood noodles; frozen macadamia praline mousse with
coffee bean sauce. Eating arrangements are flexible: the *à la carte* dinner is served from 6 to 10 pm. "The wine list is interesting." If you
wish to dine elsewhere (Padstow is a short ferry ride across the
estuary, for example), they will help with ferries, bookings, etc. "Very
good breakfast, with croissants and bread baked on the premises, and
daily papers." There is a gym, a sauna and a billiards room, and a
heated swimming pool in the large garden. The tiny church recovered
from the dunes, where John Betjeman is buried, is on the adjacent St
Enodoc golf course. Good walks in all directions and stunning beaches
(eg, Daymar Beach). (*Mark Tattersall and Scott Darby, Jenny Dawe,
and others*)

Open Feb–mid-Dec.
Rooms 4 family suites, 15 double.
Facilities Ramp. Drawing room, library, bar/grill (modern background music
12–2 pm, 6–11 pm); gym, sauna, squash, billiards. 2-acre grounds: swimming
pool (heated Apr–Sept). Sandy beach, water sports, 3 mins' walk. Only restau-
rant suitable for &.
Location NW of Wadebridge. Take A30 to Bodmin, A389 to Wadebridge,
B334 to Rock. Train to Bodmin.
Restrictions Smoking in bar/grill only. No dogs.
Credit cards All major cards accepted.
Terms B&B: single £50–£95, double £70–£145, suite £90–£195. English
breakfast £6. Full alc: lunch £25, dinner £35. Child accommodated in parents'
room: first child, £5 for breakfast; each child thereafter, B&B £15. Golf, mid-
week, off-season breaks (D,B&B £52.50–£85 per person). *V*

ROGATE Hampshire   Map 2

Mizzards Farm   `BUDGET`   *Tel* (01730) 821656
Rogate   *Fax* (01730) 821655
Petersfield GU31 5HS   *E-mail* julian.francis@hemscott.net

An upmarket B&B in a 16th-century farmhouse. "Comfortable and
elegant, without pretension", it is informally run by Julian and Harriet
Francis. "They encourage one to regard the place as a temporary
home," one visitor wrote, beguiled by the "restorative atmosphere". In
the landscaped gardens, bordered on one side by the River Rother,
there is a lake and a covered swimming pool. Beyond are woods and
meadows, and a designated area of outstanding natural beauty, with
good walking on the South Downs and in the Wealden country.
Breakfast, which includes eggs Rubens, kippers, and home-produced
honey and jam, is served in a vaulted dining room, from which a staircase rises to a gallery. Guests have their own drawing room. There is
much hewn woodwork. The "well-proportioned bedrooms" have a
good-size bathroom "with interesting exhortations to visitors". One
room has a four-poster. The owners are "welcoming, and sensitive to
each guest's individuality", and the whole place is "a reminder of how
rural life must have been". No evening meal, but plenty of pubs and
restaurants are nearby. (*AJM*)

Open All year, except Christmas, New Year.
Rooms 3 double. No telephone.
Facilities Lounge, breakfast room. No background music. 2-acre grounds:
covered swimming pool (open May–end Sept), croquet, chess, lake, river.
Golf, riding, polo nearby. Unsuitable for &.
Location From centre of Rogate go S ½ mile, cross river, take 1st turning on
right.
Restrictions No smoking. No children under 7. No dogs.
Credit cards None accepted.
Terms B&B: single £38–£45, double £58–£70. 1-night bookings refused
weekends in season.

ROMALDKIRK Co. Durham   Map 4

The Rose and Crown   *Tel* (01833) 650213
Romaldkirk   *Fax* (01833) 650828
nr Barnard Castle DL12 9EB   *E-mail* hotel@rose-and-crown.co.uk
                                   Website www.rose-and-crown.co.uk

In an unspoilt Dales village on the edge of Teesdale, this 18th-century
coaching inn faces an oak-shaded green, with stocks, a water pump,
cows grazing, and a Norman church (its bells strike the hour). There is
plenty of praise this year for the owners, Christopher and Alison Davy,
their "competent staff", and the "first-class food" (for the third year in
succession, this is one of the *Good Pub Guide*'s dining pubs of the
year). "The atmosphere is marvellous, warm, relaxed, yet efficient."
"We chose it for a 60th birthday gathering; and the way they entered
into the celebrations was heart-warming." The public rooms have log
fires, panelling, brass and copper, old farming implements, prints,

maps and etchings, fresh flowers; the small lounge is equipped with magazines. The beamed, traditional bar, where old-fashioned seats face a log fire, is popular with locals and provides good bar meals. The oak-panelled restaurant serves cooking that is a combination of modern and regional, eg, ratatouille tartlet with parmesan shavings and aubergine crisps; chargrilled calf's liver with grilled pancetta, red wine and balsamic jus; baked lemon cheesecake with lemon curd ice-cream. "Presentation is superb; linen and crockery are immaculate; the staff are impeccably dressed." One visitor thought the wine a bit expensive, "but breakfast was excellent – especially the sausages and black pudding". The purpose-built courtyard bedrooms, which open on to the carpark, are good for walkers, dog-owners and business people. Recent renovation in the main house has produced modern bathrooms and some smart suites, each with a hi-fi system. The Davys have written a guidebook to local attractions (these include Durham Cathedral and castle, the Bowes Museum, good birdwatching, and some of Britain's finest grouse moors), which is placed in each room. And they have done their best to remedy the problem of poor sound insulation – not easy, given the age of the building. (*Jacqueline and Ian Ross, Chris Hay*)

Open All year, except Christmas. Restaurant closed to non-residents Sun evening.
Rooms 2 suites, 10 double. 5 in rear courtyard annexe. Some on ground floor.
Facilities Residents' lounge, lounge bar, Crown Room (bar meals), restaurant. No background music. Fishing, grouse-shooting, birdwatching nearby.
Location Centre of village, 6 miles NW of Barnard Castle on B6277. Ample parking. Hourly bus from Barnard Castle. Rail services to Darlington.
Restrictions No smoking in restaurant. No dogs in main lounge, restaurant.
Credit cards MasterCard, Visa.
Terms [2000] B&B: single £62, double £86, suite £100. Bar lunches. Set lunch £13.75, dinner £25. Special breaks all year. Walking, wine weekends. *V*

ROSTHWAITE Cumbria   Map 4

Hazel Bank   BUDGET   *Tel* (017687) 77248
Rosthwaite   *Fax* (017687) 77373
nr Keswick CA12 5XB   *E-mail* enquiries@hazelbankhotel.demon.co.uk
                              Website www.hazelbankhotel.demon.co.uk

Set in four acres of landscaped grounds and woodland in Borrowdale – one of the loveliest valleys in the Lake District – this "excellent small hotel" is a Victorian-style house, with Gothic and Moorish influences. The site so impressed Hugh Walpole that he used it in two of his novels. It is well placed for exploring the surrounding countryside. The owners, Glen and Brenda Davies, offer "country house accommodation for non-smokers" (guests may not even smoke in the grounds), and visitors are full of praise: "Highly recommended" is a frequent plaudit. The "unobtrusive and prompt service" is admired; so are the new bedrooms – including one with a four-poster bed – and the recently decorated dining room: "It is elegant, tasteful and spacious." Mrs Davies cooks dinner, which has a daily-changing four-course menu. No choice for the first two courses – they might be celeriac soup flavoured with saffron and orange; tenderloin of pork stuffed with pistachio nuts and apricots. Then come traditional puddings and local cheeses. The welcome is "warm", the atmosphere is "just right – friendly and unpretentious". The pretty village of Rosthwaite is largely owned by the National Trust and this is an excellent area for walking and hiking. (*RJ Smith, Janine E Robinson*)

Open All year, except Christmas.
Rooms 1 suite (in cottage, can be self-catering), 8 double. 2 on ground floor. No telephone.
Facilities Sitting room, honesty bar, dining room; drying room. No background music. 4-acre grounds: croquet, woods, becks. Derwentwater 3 miles.
Location About 6 miles S of Keswick on B5289 to Borrowdale. Just before village turn left over small hump-backed bridge. Bus: 79 Keswick–Borrowdale.
Restrictions No smoking. No children under 10. Dogs by arrangement; accompanied in bedrooms, not in public rooms.
Credit cards MasterCard, Visa.
Terms D,B&B £43–£59.50. Set dinner £17.95. 1-night bookings sometimes refused, if far in advance.

ROUGHAM Suffolk   Map 2

Ravenwood Hall	*Tel* (01359) 270345
Rougham, nr Bury St Edmunds	*Fax* (01359) 270788
IP30 9JA	*Website* www.ravenwoodhall.co.uk

"It has style," agree all visitors to this old house. Set in a large park, yet only three miles from Bury St Edmunds, it dates back to Tudor times; 16th-century wall paintings, ornately carved oak woodwork, and inglenook fireplaces testify to its age. Cricketing gear, tennis rackets and a mixed collection of pictures and prints "add a country air". Bearded goats and Shetland ponies graze in a paddock, and the large grounds have an open-air swimming pool, tennis courts and a croquet lawn. The best bedrooms are in the main house (one was described this year as "having the air of an old-fashioned nursery"). Rooms in converted stables are good for wheelchair users and dog owners; some have a glass door leading on to an "immaculate garden". In the heavily beamed, pink-walled dining room (once the Great Hall), the cooking of Annette Beasant is "classical English, with a modern twist", eg, home-smoked venison with a spiced pear salad, or baked camembert croquettes with cranberry chutney; monkfish tail with garlic, green peas and lentils, or steamed beef and mushroom suet pudding with Guinness gravy. "Very good vegetarian main courses too." A blackboard menu of simpler dishes is served in the bar, and cream teas are available. At breakfast, the menu ranges from porridge to bacon *froize* (a kind of pancake). Owner Craig Jarvis is "highly professional", said inspectors; who found the place "delightful", a view "fully endorsed" by a *Guide* reader this year. Weddings and parties are often held in a pavilion, formerly used by the cricketers of a now-defunct public school nearby. (*IJ*)

Open All year.
Rooms 14 double. 7 in mews. Some on ground floor.
Facilities Ramps. Lounge, bar, restaurant; function suite; classical background music in public areas all day. 7-acre grounds: swimming pool, tennis, croquet, children's play area. Golf nearby; hunting, shooting available. Civil wedding licence.
Location Off A14, 3 miles SE of Bury St Edmunds. Bus to Rougham.
Restrictions No smoking: restaurant, bedrooms. No dogs in public rooms.
Credit cards All major cards accepted.
Terms B&B: single £69–£92, double £90–£125. Bar meals. Set lunch/dinner £21.95; full alc £41.90. Christmas package.

RUARDEAN Gloucestershire   Map 3

The Malt Shovel Inn   BUDGET   *Tel* (01594) 543028
Ruardean GL7 9TW   *E-mail* mark@maltshovel.u-net.com
                                        Website www.maltshovel.u-net.com

An ancient inn, dating back to 1100, in a quiet village in the Forest of Dean and the Wye valley. "It is rather shabby, but extremely popular with locals, with real ales, a surprisingly good small selection of wines, and good bar snacks," says a visitor this year. "We found out just how friendly the Malt Shovel is on Christmas Day, when we were the only guests. We had Christmas lunch with Paul, the manager, the bar staff and their families, and were charged nothing." The "brilliant rescuer", Mark Dew, has been renovating the bedrooms and they are now "rather smart, and very comfortable, apart from the curse of the single bedside light". Other visitors praised "the generous and unassuming host", the "marvellous bar", and the "excellent blackboard menu (delicious steak and chips)". "A fascinating building, with an amazing collection of antiques and memorabilia, and a skittle alley." But when the host is away "things can fall apart". A generous breakfast is served in the dining room, at a table that seats 20. Much traditional oak and stone in the decor. The dining room is supported by a 24-foot oak tree, and it has mahogany doors and windows from such places as No. 10 Downing Street. There is period furniture and a collection of enamel London Underground signs. James and William Horlick, of malted milk drink fame, were born in the village, which has a 12th-century church. You can walk straight out into the unspoilt forest. (*NJ Fletcher*)

Open All year. Restaurant open by arrangement, Mon, Tues, Wed.
Rooms 1 suite, 4 double.
Facilities 3 bars, restaurant; "non-offensive" background music sometimes; function facilities; skittle alley. Live entertainment in main bar once a week. Patio: giant chess set. River Wye 1 mile. Golf, cycling, canoeing, ballooning nearby. Civil wedding licence.
Location Near post office of village 5 miles S of Ross-on-Wye. Train: Gloucester; then bus.
Restriction No smoking: restaurant, most bedrooms.
Credit cards All major cards accepted.
Terms B&B £25–£39. 2-course meal: lunch £9, dinner £12. Christmas package. 1-night bookings sometimes refused weekends. ***V***

RUSHLAKE GREEN East Sussex   Map 2

Stone House   *Tel* (01435) 830553
Rushlake Green   *Fax* (01435) 830726
Heathfield TN21 9QJ   *Website* www.stonehousesussex.co.uk

Peacefully set in a vast estate in unspoilt countryside on the Kent/
Sussex border, this magnificent house has been the family home of the
Dunns since it was built in about 1495. Later additions include a
Georgian wing, a walled garden, an ornamental lake and a 100-foot
herbaceous border. The present owners, Jane and Peter Dunn, run it on
house-party lines, and it "came up to all expectations", says a visitor
this year, at *Stone House* for an anniversary celebration. "It was blissful sitting on the terrace, looking at the view." The septuagenarian host
greets guests "with old world charm and insists on carrying the bags".
His wife is a Master Chef of Great Britain, with a *Michelin Bib
Gourmand* for the quality of her traditional "French- and Thai-
influenced cooking". She is also an interior decorator, and the decor
was thought "faultless, especially in the drawing room and library".
These are filled with antiques, porcelain, family heirlooms, portraits.
There are log fires, and a mahogany-panelled billiard room with a full-
sized antique table. The two grandest bedrooms, up a sweeping staircase, have a four-poster and lavish furnishings. The rooms in the Tudor
wing are less spacious but full of character (with beams and sloping
ceilings). Dinner (for residents only) is served with "exquisite china
and silver" in the wood-panelled dining room with antique dressers.
Five choices for each course including, eg, yellow tomato soup with
basil pesto; griddled saddle of wild rabbit with a thyme and three-
mustard cream sauce; rustic pear and almond tart. Vegetables and herbs
are home grown and game comes from the estate. The wine list has
been extended to some 200 bottles and over 90 half bottles. A simple
continental breakfast can be brought to the bedroom; a traditional one,
with a "superb buffet", is served downstairs. Plenty of outdoor activities on the estate (see below); pheasant shoots and corporate entertainment activities are arranged. Picnics can be ordered, complete with a
table and chairs, and set up in advance at nearby Glyndebourne. Local
sights include Battle, Batemans, Sissinghurst and Leonardslee, a long
stretch of Sussex coast. Gatwick is 35 miles away. (*Mrs Blethyn Elliott*)

Open 6 Jan–23 Dec.
Rooms 1 suite, 2 junior suites, 3 double, 1 single.
Facilities Hall, drawing room, library, billiard room, dining room. No back-
ground music. 1,000-acre estate: 5½-acre garden, farm, woodland, croquet,
archery, off-road driving, shooting, ballooning, pheasant/clay-pigeon shoot-
ing, 2 lakes, rowing, fishing. Sea at Eastbourne 13 miles. Unsuitable for &.
Location 4 miles E of Heathfield. B2096 towards Battle; 4th right to Rushlake
Green. Left at green; keep green on right; entrance far left at crossroads. Train:
Stonegate; pre-booked taxi.
Restrictions No children under 9. No dogs in public rooms.
Credit cards MasterCard, Visa.
Terms B&B: single £65–£80, double £90–£215, suite £155–£215. Set
meals (advance booking for lunch necessary) £24.95; Glyndebourne hamper
£27.50. Weekend house parties, winter breaks. 1-night bookings sometimes
refused. *V* (1 Nov–31 Mar; not Fri, Sat)

RYDE Isle of Wight   **Map 2**

Biskra Beach Hotel   NEW   *Tel* (01983) 567913
17 St Thomas's Street   *Fax* (01983) 616976
Ryde PO33 2DL   *E-mail* info@biskra-hotel.com
                                            Website www.biskra-hotel.com

In a resort on the north-east coast of the island, this new hotel has a
"glorious location" close to the sea. Two run-down, if grand, Victorian
houses were made over by Barbara Newman, the energetic co-direc-
tor (with Hamish Kinghorn). She returned to England after many years
in Bahrain, "applied much decorating expertise", and the hotel opened
two years ago. "With its cool, calm and collected decor, it is not for
lovers of frills and furbelows," says an inspector. "Natural fabrics,
stripped pine and wrought iron have been used throughout. The high
ceilings and friezes of the old houses marry well with Scandinavian-
style austerity. We liked the effect a lot, though some flowers would
have softened the impact. Our superb bedroom, overlooking the sea,
had its own wooden deck and steamer chairs. But the bathroom was
minute and a bit stark. In the busy bar, pop music wailed, but they
turned it down without demur when we asked." The bistro-style
restaurant in the basement, popular with outside diners, has a new
chef, Lisa Roberts, since the inspection took place, so we'd like
reports on her modern cooking (eg, smoked chicken risotto with
rocket, shaved Parmesan and pumpkin oil; roasted cod wrapped in
pancetta with roasted aubergines and fried green tomatoes; warm
chocolate and banana pudding with praline ice). Snacks are available
in the bar; you can take a drink on the terrace, or sit in the outdoor hot
tub, overlooking the Solent. The style is informal; children are welcomed (intercoms are provided); and so are dogs. Osborne House is
nearby, and all the attractions of the island are easily reached by car.

Open All year, except 26 Dec.
Rooms 14 double. 5 in annexe.
Facilities Lounge, bar, 2 dining rooms; "easy listening" background music. ½-
acre grounds: Canadian hot tub, seafront patio, direct access to beach, with bar
and barbecue. Golf, sailing, water sports, etc, nearby. Unsuitable for &. Civil
wedding licence.
Location 5 mins' walk from esplanade, in resort on NE coast of island.
Hovercraft from Portsmouth.
Credit cards Amex, MasterCard, Visa.
Terms B&B double £57.50–£120. Full alc £30. Child accommodated in parents' room: under 3, free; 3–12, £10–£15. Special breaks; Christmas package. *V* (not May–Sept)

RYE East Sussex   **Map 2**

Cadborough Farm   BUDGET   *Tel* (01797) 225426
Udimore Road   *Fax* (01797) 224097
Rye TN31 6AA   *E-mail* cadfarm@marcomm.co.uk
                                      Website www.marcomm.co.uk/cadborough

"Jane Apperly's welcome is genuine, and she clearly enjoys meeting
people." "Just great – with style, quality, an excellent hostess. Very

GHG." Praise this year and last for this smart B&B. Standing in the middle of farmland, it was built in 1952 on the foundations of a 17th-century farmhouse; old oak and tile floors still survive. No residents' lounge, but guests may use the owner's drawing room. Most bedrooms are spacious and well equipped, with a big bathroom, flowers, chocolates and home-made biscuits, and they are generously heated in winter. "Excellent breakfasts" (continental, English or vegetarian) are served in a pleasant room with a panoramic view over the Romney Marshes: freshly squeezed juice, home-made marmalade, locally baked bread (you make your own toast). There is a railway line at the bottom of the adjacent field, but trains do not run at night. Rye can be reached by a private 15-minute cliff walk. Many famous houses, castles and gardens, including Batemans, Bodiam, Sissinghurst and Great Dixter, are within easy reach. (*PR, John Saunders*)

Open All year, except Christmas, New Year.
Rooms 1 suite, 2 double. No telephone. 5 self-catering cottages in converted outbuildings.
Facilities Use of owner's drawing room, breakfast room. No background music. 24-acre grounds. Beaches, river fishing nearby. Unsuitable for &.
Location 1 mile SW of Rye on B2089. Train to Rye; then taxi (or owner will sometimes meet).
Restrictions No smoking. No children under 8. Dogs by arrangement; not in public rooms.
Credit cards MasterCard, Visa.
Terms B&B £30. 1-night bookings sometimes refused.

Jeake's House　　BUDGET　　　　　　　*Tel* (01797) 222828
Mermaid Street　　　　　　　　　　　　　*Fax* (01797) 222623
Rye TN31 7ET
　　　　　　　　　　　　　　E-mail jeakeshouse@btinternet.com
　　　　　　　　Website www.s-h-systems.co.uk/hotels/jeakes

♛ *César award in 1992*

"Delightful as usual." "Quite superb: historic, homely, luxurious and friendly all at once; firmly stamped with the personality of the attentive hostess. We particularly appreciated the vegetarian breakfast, and Yum Yum, the Siamese cat." This year's praise for Jenny Hadfield's civilised B&B in one of Rye's picturesque cobbled streets. Composed of two old converted buildings (one was earlier a wool house, a Baptist school and then the home of the American poet Conrad Aiken), it is filled with books, antiques, old pictures and samplers. The bedrooms and bathrooms are "spotless and lovely", each with a different colour scheme and a brass or mahogany bed; some furniture is at odd angles, due to the sloping floors. Some rooms look over the courtyard garden (with a pond and fountain) across rooftops to fields beyond; others are above the street (not noisy, but the windows of the neighbouring houses are quite close). One room is small. Some bathrooms are shared (bathrobes are provided). The parlour has an upright piano with period sheet music; the sitting room has a bar and daily newspapers. Breakfast is served from 8 am in a large, galleried former Quaker meeting room with deep red walls, high windows, good paintings and china, plants, and a fire on cold days. There is a buffet with fresh fruit; well-cooked hot dishes, home-made marmalade, etc. Rye, a delightful town, perches above a plain between the rivers Rother and Tillingham. It has many literary connections: EF Benson immortalised it as "Tilling" in his Mapp and Lucia novels; both Henry James and Rumer Godden lived in Lamb House, now owned by the National Trust. (*Angela Evans, Alan Green*)

Open All year.
Rooms 1 suite, 10 double, 1 single. 10 with *en suite* facilities.
Facilities Parlour, bar/sitting room, breakfast room (background chamber music). Beaches, bird sanctuary nearby. Unsuitable for &.
Location Central. Private carpark (£3 daily). Train/bus station 5 mins' walk.
Restrictions No smoking in breakfast room. No children under 11. No dogs in breakfast room.
Credit cards MasterCard, Visa.
Terms B&B £26.50–£61. Child accommodated in parents' room: 50% of adult rate. Reductions for 4 days or more; 15% midweek reduction Nov–Feb, except Christmas, New Year. 1-night bookings refused weekends.

The Old Vicarage   BUDGET   *Tel* (01797) 222119
66 Church Square   *Fax* (01797) 227466
Rye TN31 7HF
                                     E-mail oldvicaragerye@tesco.net
                          Website www.homepages.tesco.net/~oldvicaragerye

A much-admired B&B – its owners, Paul and Julia Masters, "really care for their guests' well-being", one visitor wrote. Others thought it "a fantastic bargain" and wrote of "staggering attention to detail". The pink 18th-century ex-vicarage stands by the 15th-century church (gilt cherubs strike the clock bell on the quarter-hour) on a pretty, traffic-free square. "The house is delightful; breakfast was one of the best we have had," another guest wrote. Served in a small bay-windowed room overlooking the garden, it includes properly brewed tea, home-made scones, bread and jams, free-range eggs and award-winning sausages, but orange juice is not freshly squeezed. The owners dispense friendly advice about parking and eating places. The price includes tea on arrival, a wide range of sherries, available in the well-lit lounge at twilight, and a morning newspaper. The cheerful bedrooms (two are in the attic) have flowery fabrics, a drinks tray (with home-made biscuits and fudge), TV, magazines, "a wealth of local information", and views of the walled garden, the church, and Rye rooftops. The whole house is now a smoke-free zone. Henry James wrote *The Spoils of Poynton* here before moving to Lamb House. (*MR*)
Note: Not to be confused with *The Old Vicarage Hotel* in East Street. More reports, please.

Open All year, except Christmas.
Rooms 1 family, 4 double. No telephone.
Facilities Lounge, library/TV room, breakfast room. No background music. Small walled garden. Tennis, bowling, putting nearby; beach (safe bathing) 2 miles. Unsuitable for &.
Location By St Mary's church. Follow signs to town centre. Through Landgate Arch to High St, 3rd left into West St. Private parking nearby.
Restrictions No smoking. No children under 8. Guide dogs only.
Credit cards None accepted.
Terms B&B £18.50–£37. Winter breaks Nov–Feb; weekly discounts. 1-night booking refused weekends Mar–Oct.

ST AUSTELL Cornwall   Map 1

Boscundle Manor   NEW   *Tel* (01726) 813557
Tregrehan   *Fax* (01726) 814997
St Austell PL25 3RL   *E-mail* stay@boscundlemanor.co.uk
                                     Website boscundlemanor.co.uk

An 18th-century stone manor house, now a restaurant-with-rooms, set
in extensive grounds (with a disused tin mine). It is run in hands-on
style by Andrew and Mary Flint. "The cuisine was superb, the accommodation excellent," says a report this year, bringing *Boscundle* back
to the *Guide*. Other visitors wrote of the "charming house, hospitable
hosts, great breakfasts". Inspectors liked the "characterful place" and
its "domestic ambience". "The interior is cosy, done with taste: lovely
old china, antique bits, oil paintings by a local artist, beautiful old
Cornish watercolours. Our bedroom was simple but comfortable, with
William Morris textiles, frilly lampshades, knick-knacks, magazines,
fresh flowers, a compact bathroom. At dinner, the Flints ate at the
same time as their guests, and they joined them for conversation over
coffee. Service is by unobtrusive but pleasant staff." For the first time
the Flints have employed a chef, Thomas Bradbury. His menus offer
two choices of each course, with dishes like cream of cauliflower
soup; pan-fried chicken breast with a wild mushroom jus; creamed
rice with blackcurrant topping. One visitor thought the cheeseboard
disappointing, "but the wine list is fantastic, with over 40 clarets". In
the grounds are a well-equipped games room in a converted mine
building; a covered and an open-air swimming pool and a "spectacular two-hole golf course". There is, however, some noise from surrounding roads. The Eden 2000 project is "almost next door", and
other famous gardens are not far. Carlyon Bay is half a mile away.
(*Hugh J Maher, Ian Chapman, and others*)

Open Apr–Oct inclusive. Dining room closed to non-residents Sun.
Rooms 2 suites, 8 double, 2 single. 2 in cottage, 2 in garden.
Facilities Sitting room, conservatory, bar, dining room, private dining room.
No background music. 14-acre grounds: old mine shaft; games room (gym,
ping-pong, etc), 2 swimming pools (1 indoors); golf practice area. Riding, sail-
ing, fishing, golf nearby. Unsuitable for &.
Location 2 miles E of St Austell. From A390 to Truro follow signs to
Tregrehan.
Restrictions No smoking in dining room. No dogs in public rooms.
Credit cards Amex, MasterCard, Visa.
Terms B&B: single £65–£75, double £110–£130, suite £140–£160. Set din-
ner £22.50. 3-night rates.

ST BLAZEY Cornwall   Map 1

Nanscawen House   *Tel/Fax* (01726) 814488
Prideaux Road   *E-mail* keithmartin@compuserve.com
nr St Blazey PL24 2SR   *Website* www.nanscawen.currantbun.com

The 16th-century seat of the Nanscawen family, in the "bosky hillside
setting" of the Luxulyan valley, is now the spacious, wisteria-covered

home of Keith and Fiona Martin, which they run as a B&B. It has a
large secluded garden with a heated swimming pool, and a spa bath
heated to 97°. Hospitality is "unobtrusive and cordial", and they offer
"excellent value for money", say recent visitors. The three bedrooms
are large: Rashleigh "is delightful", with flowery fabrics, lots of pink
and blue, a garden view and a bathroom with a spa bath; Prideaux has
a four-poster bed. In the large drawing room, a small honesty bar has
a selection of wines, liqueurs and brandies. Breakfast, in a conservatory, includes freshly squeezed orange juice, local smoked salmon
with scrambled eggs; also fruit and yogurt. Cream teas are served. For
an evening meal, the Martins will advise about the many restaurants
nearby. For sightseeing, Lanhydrock is ten minutes' drive away; St
Austell is four miles, Fowey is five. Plenty of beaches are within easy
reach. (*J and EN, and others*)

Open All year, except 25/26 Dec.
Rooms 3 double.
Facilities Drawing room with honesty bar. Breakfast room. No background
music. 5-acre grounds: gardens, swimming pool (heated Apr–Sept), spa bath.
Golf, riding, beaches, fishing. Unsuitable for &.
Location 4 miles NE of St Austell. After level-crossing in St Blazey, from
A390, turn right opposite Texaco garage. *Nanscawen* ¾ mile on right (row of
trees marks foot of drive).
Restrictions No smoking. No children under 12. No pets.
Credit cards MasterCard, Visa (*3% surcharge, except on deposits*).
Terms B&B: single £40–£58.50, double £50–£84. Special breaks Oct–Mar.

ST HILARY Cornwall   **Map 1**

Ennys `BUDGET`   *Tel* (01736) 740262
Trewhella Lane, St Hilary   *Fax* (01736) 740055
nr Penzance TR20 9BZ
                                                    E-mail ennys@zetnet.co.uk
                                                    Website www.ipl.co.uk/ennys

A "gem of a 17th-century manor house", Grade II listed, owned and
run as a B&B by Gill Charlton, formerly travel editor of the *Daily
Telegraph*. It stands at the end of a mile-long single-track drive, surrounded by fields that lead down to the River Hayle (good for walks
and picnics). In the sheltered garden is a grass tennis court and a good-
sized heated swimming pool (not available to guests between 12.30
and 4.30 pm). Roses and creepers surround the front door. The large
sitting room has books, a log fire and a garden view. Souvenirs of the
owner's travels (eg, the odd Buddha and fertility symbol) pep up the
classic country decor. Three of the bedrooms (one is tiny) are in the
main house. They are furnished in sophisticated style, with an antique
bed, sprigged fabrics and matching wallpaper, a patchwork quilt, a
window seat overlooking the garden or countryside. Two family suites
are in a converted barn opening on to a courtyard. Three self-catering
apartments are in other converted outhouses; they are sometimes
offered on a B&B basis in low season. Guests can help themselves to
afternoon tea with home-baked scones and cakes (included in the
B&B rates) in the kitchen. An evening meal is not on offer, but Ms
Charlton can recommend the best pubs and restaurants in the area.

St Hilary is a hamlet in the narrow end of Cornwall where one can see the sea both to the north and the south. The setting is peaceful, but there is plenty to see and do nearby: sandy surfing beaches, the Land's End and Lizard peninsulas, famous gardens (Trelissick, Trebah, Trengwainton). More reports, please.

Open 10 Feb–1 Nov.
Rooms 2 family suites in converted barn, 3 double. Also 3 self-catering apartments (can be let for B&B off-season). No telephone.
Facilities Sitting room, breakfast room. No background music. 3-acre grounds: swimming pool (not available 12.30–4.30 pm), tennis. Sandy beach 3 miles; fishing, sailing, windsurfing, riding, golf nearby.
Location 5 miles E of Penzance. Train to Penzance; then taxi.
Restrictions No smoking: breakfast room, bedrooms. No children under 2. No dogs.
Credit cards (*5% surcharge*) MasterCard, Visa.
Terms B&B: single £40–£50, double £60–£70, suite £90–£110. 1-night bookings sometimes refused high season weekends.

ST IVES Cornwall   **Map 1**

The Garrack   *Tel* (01736) 796199
Burthallan Lane   *Fax* (01736) 798955
St Ives TR26 3AA   *E-mail* garrack@accuk.co.uk
                                         Website www.garrack.com

"Very homely, in a 1950s way, with most hospitable staff; excellent value for money," says a visitor this year to this traditional hotel which the Kilby family have run for over 30 years. High on a hill above Porthmeor beach (European Blue Flag for cleanness, popular with surfers), the creeper-clad stone building is a Relais du Silence. It has wide beach and sea views, and the town is a short but steep walk away. Good for a family holiday, *The Garrack* has rooms with bunk beds; also children's menus, baby-listening, etc. "Straightforward, good-quality meals" are served in the restaurant. With its conservatory extension, and storage tank for live lobsters, it is popular with outside diners. Local lamb, organic beef, venison and home-grown vegetables are also served; there is always a vegetarian option. The wine list numbers over 80 vintages and includes plenty of half bottles. The bedrooms are well appointed; some have a four-poster and a spa bath. Some are in the old house; "lovely ones, with good views" are in a modern extension. Two are in a cottage annexe, some way from the main building. The small leisure centre has a swimming pool ("small but adequate", with a counter-current swim jet), and an all-day snack bar. Loungers and palm trees on the lawn. Nearby are the Tate, the Barbara Hepworth museum and garden, numerous private art galleries. (*Peter Dell, JD*)

Open All year.
Rooms 16 double, 2 single. 1 designed for &. 2 in cottage.
Facilities 2 lounges, TV lounge, restaurant (mixed background music during dinner); conference facilities. 2-acre grounds: garden, leisure centre: small swimming pool, sauna, whirlpool, solarium, fitness room, coffee shop, bar. Beaches 5–10 mins' walk.

Location 1 mile from centre. From Penzance on B3311 turn right on to B3306 towards St Ives. Hotel off this, to left.
Restrictions No smoking: restaurant, leisure centre. Dogs in designated bedrooms; not in public rooms.
Credit cards All major cards accepted.
Terms B&B: single £58–£64, double £116–£148; D,B&B £75–£92 per person. Snack lunches. Set dinner £24.50; full alc £35. Child accommodated in parents' room: 5% to 20% of adult rate, according to age. Off-season breaks. Christmas programme. 1-night bookings occasionally refused.

ST MARTIN'S Isles of Scilly   **Map 1**

St Martin's on the Isle   *Tel* (01720) 422092
St Martin's, Isles of Scilly   *Fax* (01720) 422298
Cornwall TR25 0QW
                                                   E-mail stay@stmartinshotel.co.uk
                                                   Website www.stmartinshotel.co.uk

The only hotel on this unspoilt, car-free island, the third largest of the Scillies, is a cluster of stone cottages which was built in the 1980s under the supervision of the Prince of Wales (aka the Duke of Cornwall). It is a Pride of Britain member, set on the shore, in lawns dotted with tables, chairs and parasols. It looks across to Tresco and Teän ("stunning views; spectacular sunsets"), but the west-facing garden "sometimes gets the full force of prevailing winds". In school holidays, the hotel is busy with families (it supplies buckets and spades, games, videos and baby-listening); at other times it is a peaceful place to stay. The hands-on "charming managing director", Keith Bradford, meets arriving guests off the launch, the hotel is run with "constant attention to detail", and "everybody is addressed by name". "The staff are polished and professional; they did everything they could to make our stay a success," one admirer wrote. The public rooms are split level, with stone walls, and "beautiful, extravagant flowers everywhere". Bedrooms (all were redecorated this year) have a "good but plain" decor (modern pine furniture, striped fabrics); they vary in size (some are "by no means large"); many have a sea view. Sophisticated, "if sometimes a bit rich", French cooking by Patrick-Pierre Tweedie (ex-*Gavroche*, London) is served in the main restaurant (where modern paintings hang on yellow walls). From the *prix-fixe* menu you might choose: seared scallop and parmesan salad with balsamic vinegar dressing; red mullet fillets on an asparagus mousse with tapenade and potato galette; rum caramelised paw-paw Tatin with rum ice-cream. "The cooking was some of the best we have experienced anywhere," one couple wrote. "The high standard encouraged us to be adventurous and try, eg, ostrich." Tables are rotated "so everyone gets the view". Lighter meals are served in the bar/grill. Trips by launch, with a picnic, to other islands are arranged, and guests can go fishing on a Cornish crabber (their catch will be cooked for breakfast). Birdwatching walks are also organised. "A wonderful spot." "A gem, albeit an expensive one." But one visitor thought the indoor swimming pool "not very tempting". (*Ali and Peter Tomlinson, NH*)

Open Apr–Oct.
Rooms 2 suites, 28 double. Some on ground floor.

Facilities Ramps. Lounge, lounge bar/grill, restaurant; snooker room, indoor swimming pool. No background music. 1-acre garden adjoining sandy beach, jetty, boating, diving, water sports. Civil wedding licence.
Location North end of island. Boat or helicopter from St Mary's; hotel will arrange all-in travel package. No cars on island.
Restrictions No smoking in restaurant. No children under 12 at dinner. No dogs in public rooms.
Credit cards All major cards accepted.
Terms [2000] B&B £75–£125. Bar lunch £10, set dinner £30; full alc £40. Light meals available. Child accommodated in parents' room: under 16, up to 2 children free. 1-night bookings refused in season.

ST MARY'S Isles of Scilly   Map 1

Star Castle   *Tel* (01720) 422317
The Garrison, St Mary's   *Fax* (01720) 422343
Isles of Scilly   *E-mail* recept@starcastlescilly.demon.co.uk
Cornwall TR21 0JA   *Website* www.starcastlescilly.demon.co.uk

"An enormously enjoyable stay" was had by visitors this year to John and Mary Nicholls' "friendly and unostentatious" hotel (much smarter now than when they arrived five years ago). The old fortress was built in the form of an eight-pointed star, as a defence against the Spanish Armada. Surrounded by a dry moat and 18-foot ramparts, it stands above the town, with commanding views of sea and islands in all directions ("wonderful sunsets"). The Prince of Wales, later King Charles II, took refuge here before fleeing to France in 1646; another Prince of Wales, the future Edward VIII, inaugurated the hotel in 1933. Mr Nicholls is a "hands-on" host, greeting guests at mealtimes, and remembering names (he is also head of the lifeboat service, and a pilot for visiting ships). The dining room is in the former officers' mess, and there is a conservatory fish restaurant; the food in both was thought "excellent". In the former, you might order terrine of chicken breasts with leeks wrapped in Parma ham; pan-fried breast of guinea fowl on a mild spiced Puy lentil casserole; in the latter, king prawns on tomato and coriander jelly; pan-fried seabass with champagne sauce and mussels. A meat dish is always offered in the fish restaurant, and a vegetarian dish in both restaurants. Wines are reasonably priced, with a good selection of half bottles. The most characterful bedrooms are in the main house; three singles are in guard rooms on the battlements. Two modern blocks in the gardens have large bedrooms and suites, suitable for a family. Some have a private garden or a veranda. There is a small lounge, and a small, dark bar in the former dungeon, but most visitors take advantage of the sun-trap lawns, enclosed by high hedges, in the subtropical gardens (there is also a covered swimming pool). Guests can go island-hopping in the hotel's 32-foot launch (Tim the boatman is commended for his "wit and repartee"). (*Peter and Ali Tomlinson, and others*)

Open Mar–end Oct.
Rooms 4 suites, 25 double, 4 single (3 in ramparts). 22 in 2 garden annexes.
Facilities Lounge, games room, bar, 2 restaurants (classical background music in evening). 4½-acre grounds: covered swimming pool; private motor launch.

Beach nearby. Golf, cycle hire, riding, sailing, diving, fishing available. Unsuitable for ♿.
Location ¼ mile from town centre. Boat (2¾ hours), helicopter (20 mins) from Penzance; Skybus (15 mins) from Land's End (except Sun); hotel will meet.
Restrictions No smoking in restaurants. No children under 5 in restaurants at night. No dogs in public rooms, except bar.
Credit cards MasterCard, Visa (*surcharge*).
Terms B&B: single £62.50–£73, double £105–£180, suite £152–£190; D,B&B £62.50–£105 per person. Set dinner £25; full alc £35. Child accommodated in parents' room: 5–55% of adult rate. Inclusive breaks (including travel) Mar–Oct. *V* (low season only)

ST MAWES Cornwall   Map 1

Tresanton   *Tel* (01326) 270055
Lower Castle Road   *Fax* (01326) 270053
St Mawes TR2 5DR
                                                 E-mail info@tresanton.com
                                                 Website www.tresanton.com

"An absolute delight," says a visitor this year to this "smart, modern, yet unpretentious" hotel. Others enjoyed "the feeling of a club". With its wooden, tiled and mosaic floors, expensive, restrained fabrics, and Riviera-like views, it has a Mediterranean feel. The reception is also praised: "Despite the fact that you arrive two floors below, someone appears to whisk your luggage to your room and park your car." "No trouser-presses, mini-bars or dome-lifting," says the owner, Olga Polizzi of the Forte dynasty. She and her husband, the journalist William Shawcross, are often to be seen; her two daughters are also involved in the running. The manager, John Rogers, and the chef, Peter Robinson, are new this year. Service is "relaxed, informal, mainly young", if sometimes disorganised. The setting on the Roseland peninsula is "brilliant". The collection of white buildings stands in terraced subtropical gardens above a fishing village, overlooking the Fal estuary. Nearby is a castle built by Henry VIII. The best bedrooms are "most comfortable, with superb views, *objets d'art*, antiques", but one visitor this year wrote of a small and poorly finished room at the top. They have a large bed, a CD-player and video; some have a private terrace; bathrooms are equipped with a huge bathtub. In the "stunning restaurant" with its white marble floor, white-clothed tables in rows, and huge white plates, tables are closely packed, "good, unusual food is beautifully presented in modern 'tower style', but meal service can be erratic". There is a short, no-choice *menu du jour*, and a longer *prix-fixe* with, eg, confit duck cakes and foie gras with grapes and orange; seabass with pea and broad bean risotto; pear and almond tart. The wine list, with stiff mark-ups, is "reasonably good but a bit eccentric". Children are welcomed: boxes of toys and games are available in the lounge. There is also a children's menu. There is a small cinema and a film library. A small sand/rock beach is close by; the hotel owns an eight-metre racing yacht, the *Pinuccia*, which was commissioned by an Italian publisher for the 1939 World Cup. Nearby are coastal walks, Cornish gardens, St Ives, St Michael's Mount.
(*Edwin Prince, HH Bayntun-Coward, JT, and others*)

Open All year, except Jan.
Rooms 2 suites, 24 double. In 3 buildings.
Facilities Lounge, bar, restaurant; cinema, conference facilities. No background music. Terraced garden. Near sea, sand, rock beaches, safe bathing; 8-metre yacht, boats. Unsuitable for &. Civil wedding licence.
Location On cliff road, near castle. From A3078, follow signs to St Mawes. *Do not take road to castle.* Carry on along Polvarth Rd, into village, along seafront. Hotel on right. Train: Truro; bus or taxi.
Restriction No dogs.
Credit cards Amex, MasterCard, Visa.
Terms B&B: single £170–£187, double £200–£220, suite £300–£350. Extra bed £30. Set lunch (2 to 3 courses) £15–£20; dinner £24.50–£33. Christmas packages.

SALISBURY Wiltshire *See SHORTLIST*   **Map 2**

SANDGATE Kent   **Map 2**

| **Sandgate Hotel and** | *Tel* (01303) 220444 |
| **Restaurant La Terrasse** | *Fax* (01303) 220496 |

The Esplanade
Sandgate, Folkestone CT20 3DY

♧ *César award in 1999*

"The food and dining room are superb." "Rates highly in our hymn-book of praise. The operation runs without blemish. The food is expensive, but there is no doubt about its quality." This serious French restaurant-with-rooms is in a Victorian building across the road (which can be noisy at night) from the wide beach of a village on the smart side of Folkestone. Front-of-house is Zara Gicqueau, a local; her husband, Samuel (from the Loire), is the chef of the *Michelin*-starred restaurant, *La Terrasse*. He and the restaurant manager, Joël Fricoteaux, have both worked at *Le Manoir aux Quat'Saisons*, Great Milton (*qv*). Most of the "young and enthusiastic" staff are French. The smart public rooms have floor-to-ceiling windows overlooking the sea; in the lounge there are antique mirrors, and an open fire in winter. The small restaurant is yellow and blue with silver candelabra and paintings of Loire vineyards. It opens on to a terrace that has sun-shades in summer. You must book well in advance for a meal (residents are not guaranteed a table in the restaurant). Freshly caught fish and shellfish are served, and typical dishes include terrine of hare and duck foie gras; roast turbot with girolle mushrooms; roast William pear with a ginger-scented caramel sauce. The "beautiful continental breakfast" includes freshly squeezed orange juice, home-made croissants and jams; an English fry-up is also available. The small bedrooms are decorated in pastel colours; the best have a balcony with a sea view. Day-trips by Sea-Cat and hovercraft to France and Belgium are organised, including a visit to the restaurant's cheese supplier in Boulogne. Sandgate has many antique shops and a well-restored Tudor castle. The Channel Tunnel is ten minutes' drive; Dover is eight miles away. (*HS, and others*)

Open All year, except 1 week Oct, 4 weeks Jan. Restaurant closed Sun evening/Mon/Tues midday, except bank holidays.
Rooms 12 double, 2 single.
Facilities Lift. Lounge/bar, restaurant (classical background music); terrace. Pebble beach, safe bathing, opposite.
Location On seafront. 3 miles W of centre of Folkestone, on A259 coastal road to Hythe (some traffic noise). Train: Folkestone; then bus/taxi.
Restrictions No smoking in restaurant. No dogs.
Credit cards All major cards accepted.
Terms B&B: single £45, double £58–£76. Set lunch/dinner £22–£35; full alc £48. Weekend, midweek, Christmas breaks.

SCARBOROUGH North Yorkshire *See SHORTLIST*   Map 4

SCOTSDYKE Cumbria   Map 4

March Bank   BUDGET   *Tel* (01228) 791325
Scotsdyke
nr Longtown CA6 5XP

With salmon and sea trout fishing in the nearby Esk, this simple establishment is popular with fishing folk (freezer and drying facilities are available). Run by Mr and Mrs Moore, it has won a Les Routiers Casserole award for good value combined with a warm welcome, and *Guide* readers appreciate the "cheery feel" and unpretentious cooking. It is on the main road from Carlisle to Galashiels and Edinburgh, in what was once known as the "Debatable Land", between Longtown and the Scottish border. Double glazing keeps out traffic noise. The bar, adorned with sporting trophies, looks over the river. The intimate dining room, which seats only 20, is popular with locals. It specialises in local fish and game, eg, locally smoked salmon; Poacher's Pie with flaky crust and a moist mélange of game in gravy. Traditional desserts include syrup pudding and custard. Most main courses cost less than £10. The wine list is "more than adequate". Food is served promptly. The bedrooms (some are large) are decorated with Sanderson fabrics. Room 3 has a four-poster. At busy times, guests find themselves in the Bothy, reached up a steep flight of steps in a field, some 50 yards away. Packed lunches are available. More reports, please.

Open All year, except Feb.
Rooms 2 suites, 2 double, 1 in Bothy, 50 yds.
Facilities Lounge, bar, restaurant ("easy listening" background music during meals). 3-acre grounds. River Esk, fishing close by. Sea 10 miles away. Unsuitable for &.
Location On main A7 Galashiels road, 3 miles N of Longtown. Bus from Carlisle.
Restrictions No smoking: restaurant, lounge. No dogs in public rooms.
Credit cards Amex, MasterCard, Visa.
Terms B&B: single £35, double £50, suite £55. Set lunch/dinner £18.95; full alc £20.

SEATON CAREW Co. Durham   Map 4

The Staincliffe Hotel   NEW/BUDGET   *Tel* (01429) 264301
The Cliff   *Fax* (01429) 421366
Seaton Carew TS25 1AB

In an old holiday resort on the North Sea coast, still with a substantial day-trip trade, this old hotel recently underwent "the mother of all make-overs", says its nominator. "Everywhere has been hit by a style blitz." The owners, Jeff and Lynn Hind, bought it two years ago in a run-down state, and they have employed two local designers with "astounding results". Each room is hand-decorated in a different style, with much use of stencils. The Gothic Turret has stippled red walls with gold motifs; the Napoleon Campaign Tent suite has a four-poster bed; in Wisteria you might wake up to the scent of orange groves. The Charters Bar is nautical in style. "The function room could be described as Art Deco massive, and the restaurant/bistro as Art Nouveau Baroque. The menu, if not entirely original, was interesting: Thai-style fish-cakes and nicely succulent medallions of beef made for a more exciting meal than expected. Fried fish, chips and mushy peas, the traditional northern seaside fare, is also available, and a note in the bedroom says that if you specify in advance what sort of fish you want, the chef will get it from the morning market and cook it to order. Seaton Carew was founded by Quakers from Darlington, whose influence on the local architecture is clearly visible; unfortunately, Teesside's chemical works is also rather visible. Once inside the hotel, however, you quickly forget them, such is the effort that has been put into the decor. Good value." (*Peter Jones*)

Open All year.
Rooms 5 suites, 13 double, 2 single.
Facilities Foyer, lounge (background swing/jazz), bar, cocktail bar, restaurant; ballroom (various entertainments: murder and mystery, etc); conference facilities. 2-acre garden overlooking sea. Unsuitable for &. Civil wedding licence.
Location On A178, overlooking sea, W of Hartlepool marina, in resort 2 miles S of Hartlepool. From Hartlepool, on A689, turn right at *Owton Lodge* pub and roundabout. Follow road to sea; turn left; hotel ½ mile on left.
Restrictions No smoking: restaurant, bedrooms. No dogs.
Credit cards All major cards accepted.
Terms [2000] B&B: single £48–£58, double £58–£68. Full alc £20. Christmas package.

SEAVIEW Isle of Wight   Map 2

The Priory Bay Hotel   *Tel* (01983) 613146
Priory Drive   *Fax* (01983) 616539
Seaview PO34 5BU   *E-mail* enquiries@priorybay.co.uk
                                      Website www.priorybay.co.uk

An architectural mix: this is a Tudor farmhouse on the site of a Cluniac priory, with Georgian, Victorian and modern additions. The setting "is idyllic", says a visitor this year. The huge grounds contain a nine-hole par three golf course, and a track leads through bluebell woods to a lovely (but sometimes crowded) beach, with sand, rock pools, safe bathing, and a café that serves "delicious, if expensive, food". The building was renovated in 1998 by Andrew Palmer, founder of the New Covent Garden Soup Company, and his brother James; they created an informal hotel that is both child- and dog-friendly. The "magnificent public rooms" are admired, in particular the huge salon with its octagonal window over the fireplace, luxurious sofas, coffee-table books and magazines. In the restaurant (with elaborate plaster-work and giant murals of local views of yesteryear) the menus are much improved this year, with main courses like John Dory with lemon sauce; grilled local lobster with saffron sauce. The wine list is "short but well put together, with mark-ups lower than the norm". The bedrooms vary: No. 6, above the restaurant, is "spacious and lovely"; others are "pleasant, simply but adequately furnished, with good lighting"; and a room in the eaves was thought "delightful" this year. Cottages in the grounds, some "attractive and thatched", some "hideous", provide suites that are good for families and dog-owners (some are self-catering) "but these rooms are not of the same standard as the rest". Apart from a few minor hiccoughs with reception, service is generally thought "fine", but the check-out time is not: "10 am is ridiculous." (*Mrs L Elliott, Nigel Fletcher*)

Open All year.
Rooms 18 double in main hotel. Also cottages (including family suites and self-catering facilities). 2 ground-floor rooms.
Facilities Drawing room, lounge, bar (classical background music early evening), restaurant, function facilities. 70-acre grounds: unheated outdoor pool; 9-hole par 3 golf course, tennis, beach: café, sailing, fishing, windsurf-ing. Riding, gliding nearby. Unsuitable for &. Civil wedding licence.
Location S of Seaview, between St Helens and Nettlestone. Bus/taxi from Ryde, 3 miles.
Restriction No dogs in main hotel.
Credit cards Amex, MasterCard, Visa.
Terms [2000] B&B: single £50–£94, double £88–£138, suite £148–£188. D,B&B £64–£114 per person. Weekend supplement. Bar meals. Set dinner £25; full alc £40. 3-day break. Christmas package. 1-night bookings some-times refused. *V*

Seaview Hotel & Restaurant
High Street
Seaview PO34 5EX

Tel (01983) 612711
Fax (01983) 613729
E-mail reception@seaviewhotel.co.uk
Website www.seaviewhotel.co.uk

ꙭ *César award in 1988*

"A fine example of an owner-managed hotel," wrote a visitor this year of Nicholas and Nicola Hayward's small hotel/restaurant "of charac-ter". Standing on the main road, leading down to the sea, of an old sailing village on the north-east shore of the island, it houses a "fasci-nating collection" of naval photographs, prints and things nautical. "The service is excellent, the staff are genuinely accommodating, and our children were welcomed rather than merely tolerated. The owners are omnipresent; even in Cowes week they appeared totally relaxed." With its two restaurants, pub and lounge bar on the ground floor, and in summer a pavement café as well, it caters for all comers. At busy times, particularly summer weekends, it gets very crowded (food is sometimes also served in the residents' lounge). In low season, when things are calmer, it is popular with retired people. The hotel is too small to offer many facilities for children, but the adjacent two-bedroomed cottage is good for a family. The bedrooms vary in size; rear ones are quietest. Some rooms overlook the carpark, and one above the kitchens can be noisy until late. One visitor enjoyed a "large and pleasant" front room, with bay window, sea view and a "traditional style". Reports on the food range from "good, but not exceptional", to "excellent – especially the lobster and crab". Plenty of choice on the menus of quite traditional dishes, eg, salmon with an anchovy and pink peppercorn sauce; duck with plum and ginger sauce. Puddings are "high on cholesterol and slightly less good". One visitor enjoyed "a starter of singularly good bubble and squeak which impressed so much that I asked if I could have it for breakfast – which they managed". "Admirable choice at breakfast; no horrid little packets; you are waited on from start to finish." Dogs are welcomed. Priory Bay, with its wide sandy beach, is a 20-minute low-tide walk away. (*Tessa Stuart, NM Mackintosh, Iain Elliott, and others*)

Open All year, except 3 days over Christmas. Main restaurant closed Sun evening, except bank holidays.
Rooms 2 suites, 14 double. 2 in annexe, with balcony. 2 on ground floor.
Facilities Lounge, 2 bars, restaurant; function room; patio. No background music. Sea, sandy beach 50 yds: sailing, fishing, windsurfing.
Location Village centre. Follow signs for seafront. Small carpark. Bus/taxi from Ryde 3 miles, Cowes 10 miles.
Restrictions No smoking: 1 dining room, lounge, 2 bedrooms. No children under 5 in restaurant after 7.30 pm. No dogs in public rooms.
Credit cards All major cards accepted.
Terms [2000] B&B: single £55–£100, double £70–£125, suite £120–£180. Set Sun lunch £13.95; full alc £28. Child accommodated in parents' room: under 12, £2.50–£10.50; in own room, 50% of adult rate. Weekend, midweek, painting breaks. 1-night bookings refused weekends. ***V***

SHEFFIELD South Yorkshire *See SHORTLIST*   **Map 4**

SHEPTON MALLET Somerset   **Map 1**

Bowlish House   *Tel/Fax* (01749) 342022
Coombe Lane, off Wells Road
Shepton Mallet BA4 5JD

In 1999 new owners, John and Dierdré Forde, took over this restaurant-with-rooms on the edge of an old market town near the Mendip Hills. "They are starting, gently, to restore those parts of the interior that need attention," say visitors this year. "We could not have enjoyed our stay more." Not grand, but elegant, the Grade II* listed Palladian-style house has a flagstoned entrance hall, a handsome wooden staircase and some good antique furniture. It is on a main road, but its rear garden is peaceful. Only three bedrooms: they are spacious, "with excellent beds, TV, large bathroom". But the accent is on the meals served in the dining room and its conservatory extension. Mrs Forde, who trained in Switzerland and later worked at *The Savoy* and *The Dorchester* in London, is the chef, and her "mouth-watering cooking" was appreciated: "A light cheese and chive soufflé; roast fillet of monkfish with a rich red wine sauce, done as well as we could imagine; crisp lemon tart. The petits fours were plentiful and good." Breakfast included freshly squeezed orange juice, excellent muesli, warm granary toast and croissants; cooked dishes if wanted. Will *Bowlish House* retain the *Michelin* red "Meals" awarded to the previous owners for the quality and good value of its food? The Fordes are hoping to add two or three bedrooms. Bath and Wells, Stourhead, Glastonbury, Cheddar and Longleat are all nearby. (*James and Eleanor Stewart; also Michael and Ann Cole*)

Open All year, except 2 weeks in winter. Restaurant closed for lunch, and Sun/Mon except by arrangement.
Rooms 3 double. No telephone.
Facilities Lounge, bar, restaurant, conservatory (occasional classical background music during dinner). ¼-acre garden. Unsuitable for &.
Location ¼ mile W of Shepton Mallet, on A371 to Wells. Train to Castle Cary, 4 miles.
Restrictions No smoking: restaurant, bedrooms. No dogs in public rooms.
Credit cards MasterCard, Visa.
Terms B&B: single £48–£58, double £68. English breakfast £5. Set dinner £24.95.

Charlton House and Mulberry Restaurant   *Tel* (01749) 342008
Charlton Road   *Fax* (01749) 346362
Shepton Mallet BA4 4PR   *E-mail* reservations-charltonhouse@btinternet.com
                          Website www.mulberry-england.co.uk

"An absolute delight – friendly, informal but highly professional." Praise this year for this Domesday-old manor house that was turned into a small hotel in 1997 by Roger and Monty Saul, founders of the Mulberry label. The interior is a showcase for their products, and the decor is lavish and theatrical, with silks and velvets, bright colours, prints and paintings, knick-knacks, fresh flowers. Wellington boots, lacrosse sticks and fishing tackle are displayed at the entrance to give a country house feel. Each bedroom has its own character: one is a converted chapel; some are light and airy, others are opulent, with a carved oak four-poster bed (one has a headboard depicting a naked Adam and Eve with the serpent and a docile lion); some bathrooms are "palatial". The restaurant, as opulent as the rest, with its hooded kaftan chairs, has a *Michelin* star for Adam Fellows' modern cooking, eg, steamed scallops with lemon balm and coriander, caramelised apple and light curry sauce; red mullet on a bed of couscous with piperade; citrus fruit terrine with blood orange sorbet and thyme-scented brandy snap. The wine list is "well compiled, with good-value and particularly interesting dessert wines". Service is by "young, intelligent and impeccably dressed staff". Children are welcomed. The River Sheppey, with fishing rights, runs through the grounds, which get some noise from the busy road nearby. Wells is six miles away; Bath is 19 miles: other local sights include Glastonbury, Longleat, the Cheddar Gorge. (*Iain Elliott, and others*)

Open All year.
Rooms 3 suites, 13 double. 3 in lodge, 1 in coach house.
Facilities Ramps. Drawing room, conservatory, restaurant (light jazz/classical background music all day); conference/function facilities; sauna, plunge pool. 8-acre grounds: gardens, tennis, croquet, trout lake, river (fishing), helipad. Riding, golf nearby. Civil wedding licence.
Location On A361, 1 mile E of Shepton Mallet, towards Frome (on right). Train: Castle Cary (4 miles).
Restrictions No smoking in restaurant. Dogs in 1 bedroom only, not in public rooms.
Credit cards All major cards accepted.
Terms B&B: single £100–£135, double £140–£200, suite £235–£300. English breakfast £7.50. Set lunch £17.50, dinner £37; full alc £48. Autumn/ winter weekend and midweek breaks. Christmas package. 1-night bookings refused Sat.

SHIPHAM Somerset   **Map 1**

Daneswood House   NEW   *Tel* (01934) 843145
Cuck Hill, Shipham,   *Fax* (01934) 843824
nr Winscombe BS25 1RD   *E-mail* info@daneswoodhotel.co uk
                                   Website www.daneswoodhotel.co.uk

Strange-looking, much windowed building (formerly an Edwardian homeopathic health hydro) in 7-acre grounds on wooded Mendip hillside. "Magnificent views, good bedrooms (our bathroom had a window), good value," says nominator. Owners David and Elise Hodges have presided for 25 years. Good, unfussy modern cooking (eg, steamed seabass on spinach and ricotta mousse; roast duck breast with mashed potatoes) on menus with lots of choice in no-smoking restaurant; alfresco meals in summer. Breakfasts in conservatory. 3 cottage suites (with private lounge), 14 double rooms. Lounge with bar (permanent background music). Unsuitable for &. Guide dogs only. Good facilities for children (high chairs, cots, etc). B&B: single £79.50, double £95. Set lunch £15.95–£29.95, dinner £29.95. Conference/business/function trade courted, so perhaps not a true Guide hotel; we'd like your views, please. *V*

SHIPTON GORGE Dorset   **Map 1**

Innsacre Farmhouse   BUDGET   *Tel/Fax* (01308) 456137
Shipton Gorge
nr Bridport DT6 4LJ

"It would be hard to imagine a more peaceful place; only birdsong disturbs the peace," a correspondent wrote in 1999 of this 17th-century farm guest house. "Caring atmosphere; meticulous attention to detail; small touches of personal kindness. Wonderful value." All this is endorsed by visitors this year. Only caveat: "Our shower was feeble and, though I am medium to small in size, the bathtowels left much of my body uncovered." Others, too, thought staying here "a delightful experience". The informal hosts, Sydney and Jayne Davies, are "most welcoming", the position "is wonderful, under a hill on which sheep graze and bunnies hop". Complimentary tea and home-made biscuits are provided for arriving guests, and Mrs Davies is an "enthusiastic and imaginative" cook. A three-course no-choice supper is served by arrangement (you must order the night before). Specialities include roast wild boar; ham hock and beans; baked pears with hot toffee sauce; apple tart. Set amid lovely countryside, *Innsacre* is reached up a cobbled drive through large grounds, with a flowery terrace, gardens, an orchard, goats and sheep. The large downstairs room is divided by screens to form a lounge with a huge inglenook fireplace, and a beamed, stone-walled dining area with oak tables and chairs. "Unusual antiques, interesting paintings and prints, good fabrics, fresh flowers, strong colours, all reflect the owners' taste." The bedrooms are furnished in French country style: oak beds, cotton sheets, blue-and-white duvets. They have fresh milk for tea-making, "ravishing views". The hayloft is suitable for a family. For breakfast there is locally smoked fish, spiced apple compote, home-made jam, cafetière coffee served in large French cups; cooked dishes to order. Dogs are welcomed (there is a charge of £5 whatever the length of stay). House parties are catered for. The sea and the National Trust coastal path are three miles away. (*DG Randall, and others*)

Open All year, except 24 Dec–1 Jan. Dining room closed midday, and Sat evening Easter–Oct.
Rooms 4 double, all with bath with shower attachment. No telephone.
Facilities Lounge/bar, dining area. No background music. 10-acre grounds. Fishing, shingle/sand beach nearby. Unsuitable for &.
Location 2½ miles SE of Bridport. Take A35 west from Dorchester. After *c.* 12 miles, 2nd left to Shipton Gorge; go round hill; entrance on left after *c.* ⅓ mile. Train: Dorchester; then taxi.
Restrictions Smoking in bar only, not at breakfast. No children under 9.
Credit cards MasterCard, Visa.
Terms B&B: single £45, double £65–£75. Evening meal (by arrangement) £16.50. 10% reduction for 5 nights or more. 1-night bookings refused weekends, bank holidays.

SHURDINGTON Gloucestershire   **Map 3**

The Greenway   *Tel* (01242) 862352
Shurdington,   *Fax* (01242) 862780
nr Cheltenham GL51 5UG   *E-mail* relax@greenway-hotel.demon.co.uk

A creeper-clad mansion just outside Cheltenham. "The gardens are lovely and peaceful," says a regular *Guide* correspondent this year. It is set well back from the A46, and is named for the pre-Roman path which runs beside it to the hills beyond, a safe way in an area inhabited by wild animals. Elizabethan in origin, it has a flagstoned hall, antique furniture, formal flower arrangements. Now run by manager Shaune Ayers, the hotel changed hands in December 1999, but a visitor in April 2000 was "very impressed". "The staff were cheerful; there is good attention to detail. The decor in the bedrooms is unimaginative, but the public rooms are confidently furnished. Dinner was elaborately presented and very good; the wine list was predictable but adequate. But the best meal was breakfast, with a good selection of cooked options, including smoked haddock, kippers and an outstanding English plateful." The restaurant is formal ("smart casual" dress is required), and it does a busy outside trade; you need to reserve a table when booking your room. Its conservatory overlooks a sunken garden with a lily pond and opens on to a pretty terrace where drinks and lunches are served in summer. Chef Peter Fairclough, who has stayed on from the previous regime, serves a fixed-price, three-course dinner with plenty of choice, eg, risotto of Cornish crab with a saffron sauce; pavé of Cotswold venison with oxtail faggots and a vinegar-scented jus; iced apricot parfait with a compote of apricots. "The standard is high, but we couldn't manage dessert by day three," one couple said. Lunch is simpler and you can take just one or two courses. The large bedrooms are furnished in country house style; most have a kingsize bed. We'd like to know if the lighting, much criticised in the past in both bedrooms and public rooms, has been improved. Good walking all around, as well as Cotswold sightseeing (villages, towns, stately homes, notably Blenheim Palace, Sudeley and Warwick castles, churches, gardens). (*Stephen Edwards, and others*)

Open All year.
Rooms 3 suites, 14 double, 2 single. 8 in coach house. 1 equipped for ♿.
Facilities Hall, drawing room, bar, restaurant (occasional classical background music); function facilities. 10-acre grounds: croquet. Golf, riding, tennis, swimming, clay-pigeon shooting available. Civil wedding licence.
Location 2½ miles SW of Cheltenham, on A46. Train: Cheltenham; then bus or taxi.
Restrictions No smoking: restaurant, 8 bedrooms. No children under 7. Guide dogs only.
Credit cards All major cards accepted.
Terms B&B: single £99, double £165–£215, suite £230–£240; D,B&B (min. 2 nights): single £129, double £215–£265, suite £280–£290. Lunch from £6.50, set dinner £35. Christmas package. *V*

SIDMOUTH Devon *See SHORTLIST*   **Map 1**

SOAR MILL COVE Devon   **Map 1**

Soar Mill Cove Hotel   *Tel* (01548) 561566
Soar Mill Cove   *Fax* (01548) 561223
nr Salcombe TQ7 3DS   *E-mail* info@makepeacehotels.co.uk
                                   Website www.makepeacehotels.co.uk

The setting is "stunning", everyone agrees: the Makepeace family's purpose-built hotel stands at the head of an isolated cove near Salcombe. National Trust land is all around and a beautiful bay, with a wide sandy beach, is a short walk away down a hill. The Makepeace parents have retired, and the hotel is now run by Keith Makepeace junior, backed by a "helpful, very friendly staff". All the bedrooms are on the ground floor, and all have patio doors opening directly on to their own private terrace and the gardens. They are well equipped, but their intensely floral decor and their bathrooms have been thought "dated" by some visitors. Opinions vary on the cooking (orders are taken in the early evening): some think it "wonderful": "delicious lobster"; "exceptional fish, memorable scallops; lovely light chocolate bavaroise"; but others wrote of "fussy food that does not deliver" (the menu includes dishes like poached fillet of freshest plaice, stuffed with grapes and served with a delicate saffron stamen sauce; pan-fried breaded escalope of veal, glazed with a melting topping of Cornish Yarg and English mustard). The hotel bills itself as child-friendly, and parents appreciate the safe, small outdoor and indoor swimming pools, the play areas and acres of grass, but one visitor found the baby-listening arrangements inadequate; and was unhappy about the "restrictive dinner times" (7.30 to 8.30 pm). Several visitors found the hotel expensive for what is offered. Beauty treatments, aromatherapy and cooking lessons are available. A car is essential if you want to explore, but be warned of "very narrow lanes". The Makepeaces also own the *Rosevine Hotel*, Portscatho, Cornwall. (*S Carlisle, NM Mackintosh, Mrs M Box, and others*)

Open Feb–end Dec.
Rooms 3 family suites, 18 double. All on ground floor.
Facilities Lounge (pianist and "a duo of lady singers" twice weekly), bar, restaurant; small indoor swimming pool; beauty salon. 10-acre grounds: small swimming pool, tennis, putting, pet donkey, miniature pony, children's play area. Sea, sandy beach, 600 yds.
Location 3 miles W of Salcombe. From A381 turn right through Marlborough; follow signs for Soar, then Soar Mill Cove. Train: Totnes; bus: Malborough (3½ miles); hotel will meet.
Restrictions No smoking: restaurant, bedrooms. Dogs by arrangement; not in public rooms.
Credit cards Amex, MasterCard, Visa.
Terms B&B £70–£148; D,B&B £70–£189. Alc lunch £20–£30; set dinner £34. 3-day packages all year; Christmas package.

SOMERTON Somerset   **Map 1**

The Lynch BUDGET   *Tel* (01458) 272316
4 Behind Berry   *Fax* (01458) 272590
Somerton TA11 7PD   *E-mail* the_lynch@talk21.com
                                Website www.thelynchcountryhouse.co.uk

A Grade II* listed Georgian building with oatmeal walls and a grey slate roof. It stands well back from a road, among 2,800 trees that have been planted to attract and accommodate wildlife. Owner Roy Copeland runs it as an upmarket B&B. He and his poodle Lotti are "warmly welcoming", and visitors in 2000 appreciated the courtesies offered: bags carried, advice about dinner, etc. The staff are "unobtrusive and friendly", and the cosy bedrooms are well supplied with local information. The best rooms are on the first floor; the honeymoon suite overlooks herbaceous borders in front of the house, and has "a wonderful Georgian four-poster". Simpler, but still pretty, rooms are on the top floor. A glass lantern on the roof provides a panoramic view of the surroundings. No residents' lounge; an adequate breakfast (the muesli was thought "excellent") is served in a room that overlooks a lake with black swans, exotic ducks and fish. Somerton has a lovely church and plenty of eating places: a fireside dinner in *The Grove* pub, in the market place, was enjoyed this year. Glastonbury and the Cheddar Gorge are nearby. (*CR, Trevor Lockwood*)

Open All year, except Christmas/New Year.
Rooms 5 double. Also 2-bedroomed cottage.
Facilities Breakfast room. No background music. 2½-acre grounds: lake. Unsuitable for &.
Location N edge of village (5 mins' walk to centre). Train: Castle Cary.
Restrictions No smoking. No dogs in public rooms.
Credit cards All major cards accepted.
Terms [2000] B&B: single £45–£53, double £49–£85.

SOURTON Devon   **Map 1**

Collaven Manor   *Tel* (01837) 861522
Sourton   *Fax* (01837) 861614
nr Okehampton EX20 4HH   *Website* www.trevean.com/collaven

On the north-west edge of Dartmoor, with scenic views, this creeper-covered 15th-century manor house has connections with the family of Emma, Lady Hamilton. Its short drive leads off a busy road, but inside it is "a homely place", say reporters this year. "We found the seclusion we wanted, and pleasant bedrooms. Owners Jeff and Jacqui Mitchell made us feel cosseted but not swamped by attention." The airy building has a beamed and stone-walled lounge with an inglenook fireplace (with bread ovens). Behind are green lawns with tables and chairs, and a path opposite the hotel leads on to the moors. "Good uncomplicated home cooking" is served on menus with plenty of choice, eg, seafood salad; breast of chicken stuffed with garlic butter and wrapped in bacon. "As vegetarians we particularly appreciated the effort made on our behalf" (dishes like garlic mushroom roulade; goat's cheese and caramelised red onion tart). Some bedrooms are beamed, with a four-poster. The Lydford Gorge is five miles away, and other National Trust properties are nearby. (*Mrs S Hotchkin, Jackie Shaw*)

Open All year.
Rooms 7 double, 2 single.
Facilities Lounge, bar lounge, breakfast room, restaurant (jazz/blues background music "if guests wish"). 4-acre grounds: croquet, bowls. Golf, riding, pony-trekking, fishing nearby. Unsuitable for &. Civil wedding licence applied for.
Location On A386, ½ mile S of Sourton.
Restrictions No smoking: dining room, breakfast room, lounge. No dogs in public rooms.
Credit cards Amex, MasterCard, Visa
Terms B&B £45–£53; D,B&B £59–£72. Set Sun lunch £12, dinner £22.50. Off-season breaks. Christmas package. 1-night bookings refused bank holiday weekends. *V*

SOUTHWOLD Suffolk   **Map 2**

The Swan   *Tel* (01502) 722186
Market Place   *Fax* (01502) 724800
Southwold IP18 6EG   *E-mail* swan.hotel@adnams.co.uk

Everyone agrees about the charms of Southwold: "It is like stepping back into the 1920s or '30s." "It has the feel of a real community, rather than a seaside resort." This 300-year-old building (owned, like most of the hotels in the area, by Adnams the brewer and wine merchant, and managed by Carole Ladd) is the town's premier hotel. With white-framed windows, iron balconies, Union flag flying, it stands in the market place by the town hall. Again, apart from one visitor who thought the place "impersonal", most reports have been enthusiastic: "A good, old-fashioned hotel." "Stylish, comfortable, unspoilt; staff young, friendly, helpful. Good food." The public areas are smart and traditional: a flagstoned hall, a spacious lounge with deep chairs and an open fire, a staircase with wrought iron banisters. The place is busy most of the year with outside guests calling for tea and meals, so service can be pressed at times. The chef, David Smith, supervises meals in both the bar and the restaurant. There is now one fixed-price dinner menu, and also an *à la carte* menu with main courses like poached lemon sole with a seafood mousseline and pak choi; breast of duck with lime marmalade; calf's liver with haggis mash and bacon and a whisky sauce. Breakfast includes "wonderful bacon and sausages", haddock and kippers. The best bedrooms are in the main house. The four-poster suite "is luxurious"; a spacious double has "an interesting curved window on one side with a view of the sea, and a large main window overlooking the square". A room under the eaves has "a feeling of faded gentility". The purpose-built bedrooms at the rear, round what was once a bowling green, are good for dog-owners. They "lack privacy", but they were increased in size this year, and "the lovely gardens compensate (the gardener is a genius)". Southwold's long shingle beach is a short walk away. A special break, with tours of local gardens, is sometimes offered. (*Anne and Denis Tate, Simon Small, Barbara Blake, and others*)

Open All year. Restaurant closed midday Nov–Mar, except Christmas.
Rooms 2 suites, 39 double, 4 single. 17 in garden annexe (all on ground floor).
Facilities Lift. Drawing room, reading room (residents only), bar, restaurant; function facilities. No background music. ½-acre garden: croquet. Sea close by.
Location Central. Rear parking. Train: Halesworth 9 miles, Darsham 11 miles; then taxi.
Restrictions No smoking in restaurant. No children under 5 in restaurant after 7 pm. Dogs at management's discretion in annexe only; not in public rooms.
Credit cards All major cards accepted.
Terms [2000] B&B: single £65–£80, double £99–£135, suite £165; D,B&B (winter midweek) £70–£80 per person. Bar lunches. Set lunch £20 and £22, dinner £25.50; full alc £38. Christmas package.

Don't keep your favourite hotel to yourself. The *Guide* supports; it doesn't spoil.

---

256   ENGLAND

STADDLEBRIDGE North Yorkshire   Map 4

McCoy's   *Tel* (01609) 882671
The Cleveland Tontine   *Fax* (01609) 882660
Staddlebridge
Northallerton DL6 3JB

♔ *César award in 1989*

For 18 years the McCoy brothers, Peter, Tom and Eugene, have run
their quirky restaurant-with-rooms with "laid-back professionalism".
They pride themselves on their lack of formality, and describe the
decor as "a comfortable mismatch of colour, a pastiche of style and
accent, born more out of penury than design". The place may be
slightly less eccentric these days, and they now employ a chef, Marcus
Bennett, but *Guide* readers continue to relish its exuberant style and
the "technically proficient, stylishly presented cooking that concen-
trates on flavour". The Victorian stone house stands at the Cleveland
Tontine, where two busy roads converge on the edge of the North
Yorkshire moors. The furniture is a higgledy piggledy mix: "Comfy
sofas and chairs from junk shops", potted plants and the odd cat, set
the tone in the lounges, while the bedrooms are cheerful, with con-
trasting wallpapers, good lighting, effective double glazing, plenty of
storage space and a straightforward bathroom. The restaurant, dimly
lit and with bare floorboards, potted palms, good napery and cutlery,
opens for dinner on Friday and Saturday. Its eclectic fixed-price
menus include dishes like ravioli of chicken with Thai curried sauce;
nut-roasted turbot with red onion and basil; custard tart with rhubarb
ice-cream. The downstairs bistro, open all week, serves similar dishes
from a blackboard menu to loud '40s music; tables are closely packed.
The 70-item wine list is as cosmopolitan as the food, and has plenty of
half bottles. "Breakfast, served until late in a lovely bright room,
includes anything you want, even a newspaper. We had a gorgeous
plate of exotic fruits, excellent scrambled eggs on toast made from
home-made bread. The friendly young staff are efficient." (*P and JT*)

Open All year, except 25/26 Dec, 1 Jan. Restaurant open Fri, Sat; bistro daily.
Rooms 6 double.
Facilities 2 lounges (residents only), breakfast room, bar, bistro, restaurant
(background music during meals). Medium-sized garden. Unsuitable for &.
Location 6 miles NE of Northallerton, at junction of A19/A172 (rooms
double-glazed); enter via southbound lane of A172. Staddlebridge not on map.
Restriction No dogs in public rooms.
Credit cards All major cards accepted.
Terms [2000] B&B: single £75, double £90. Set lunch £9.95–£11.95, dinner
(restaurant) £28; full alc (bistro) £35.

Many people are upset when they cancel a booking and discover that they have lost a deposit or been charged the full rate
of the room. Do remember that when making a booking you are
entering into a contract with the hotel. Always make sure you
know what the hotel's policy about cancellations is.

STAMFORD Lincolnshire   **Map 2**

The George   *Tel* (01780) 750750
71 St Martin's   *Fax* (01780) 750701
Stamford PE9 2LB   *E-mail* reservations@georgehotelofstamford.com
                            Website www.georgehotelofstamford.com

♀ *César award in 1986*

A "classic coaching inn and charming hotel, with an array of attractive
public rooms and bars", and a "lovely cobbled courtyard" where
drinks are served in summer. Built in 1597, it has had many famous
guests: Charles I (1641) and William III (1696) stayed here, as did the
Duke of Cumberland returning from victory at Culloden in 1745. The
London Room and the York Bar (which serves "excellent Ruddles
County direct from the barrel") were once waiting rooms for travellers
on the south- or north-bound stagecoach. With its mullioned windows,
flagstoned entrance hall, old panelling and creaking floorboards, it is
full of character. A report in 2000: "Extremely comfortable. Often
busy but service does not suffer. The staff are exceptionally skilled;
food, service and decor are of high quality. My husband had good
memories of a steak-and-kidney pudding from a previous visit.
Although it was not on the menu, the pudding was prepared for the following evening, and found excellent." Meals in the handsome dining
room, candlelit at night, are traditional, with roasts on a silver carving
wagon, cheeses and puddings on trolleys. "One of the few places
where we regularly order good wine, due to their excellent pricing policy." On busy Saturdays, dinner is sometimes served in two shifts.
Bedrooms vary greatly, and some are quite a walk from reception. The
best ones are stylishly decorated; some have a four-poster, some have
antiques. Roadside rooms get traffic noise. Some courtyard ones are "a
bit basic", and can be hot in summer. Unusually, a cooked breakfast
can be delivered to the bedroom, otherwise it is served among tropical
plants in the garden room, where light meals and teas are also
taken. There is an ancient crypt under the cocktail bar, and a walled,
monastic rear garden with a sunken lawn for croquet. Stamford is an
unspoilt old stone-built market town. On its outskirts is Burghley
House, a magnificent stately home with a 300-acre deerpark.
(*Paul Sellars, Good Pub Guide, Lynn Wildgoose, Mr and Mrs M
Firth, Mr and Mrs PJ Hall*)

Open All year.
Rooms 1 suite, 36 double, 10 single.
Facilities Ramps. 2 lounges, 2 bars, 2 restaurants; 4 private dining rooms,
business centre. No background music. 2-acre grounds: courtyard, monastery
garden, croquet, Rutland Water 6 miles. Civil wedding licence.
Location ½ mile from centre (front rooms double-glazed; quietest overlook
courtyard). From A1, turn at roundabout signposted Stamford B1081. Hotel at
bottom of hill by traffic lights. Large carpark. Railway station 100 yds.
Restriction No dogs in restaurants.
Credit cards All major cards accepted.
Terms [2000] B&B: single £78–£105, double £103–£220, suite £140–£150.
Light meals available. Set lunch £14.50–£16.50; full alc £37. Weekend rates;
special breaks Easter, Aug.

See also SHORTLIST

STAVERTON Devon							**Map 1**

Kingston House					*Tel* (01803) 762235
Staverton						*Fax* (01803) 762444
nr Totnes TQ9 6AR				*E-mail* info@kingston-estate.net
								Website www.kingston-estate.net

In the lovely countryside of the South Hams near the Tudor town of
Totnes, this 18th-century wool merchant's house has been restored
"with great care and attention" by the owners, Mr and Mrs Corfield.
"Fine features are to be found at every turn", including ancient panelling, partially exposed murals and a magnificent marquetry staircase.
"Entering the house is like stepping back into another century," wrote
a visitor in 2000. Each of the three large bedrooms has been meticulously restored (one bathroom is not *en suite*). "Magnificent antique
four-poster beds, drapes, lovely rugs, valuable knick-knacks trustingly
displayed, quality white linen, comfortable, non-creaky beds. No TV
– hurrah!" The Blue Bathroom has faux marble wall paintings, a huge
1830s bath, a view over the walled garden, the sound of rooks. Guests
in 2000 appreciated the welcome by the "kind hostess", the fires burning in the hall and lounge, the Great Danes, Apollo and Juno, dozing
on the carpet. The public rooms are "lovely, large and comfortable",
but the piped classical music ("repetitive Pachelbel, and Dido's
lament") was less appreciated. The restaurant, with only three tables,
"is lovely", and the no-choice dinner is based on 18th-century menus,
eg, fillet of beef in red wine with oranges and mace, or chicken
supreme cooked in fruit juices with ginger and marmalade. But several
visitors thought it overpriced, and found the breakfast only "adequate". When the house is full, guests can be accommodated in
cottages which are otherwise let on a self-catering basis. (*Jaime
Ribeiro dos Santos, and others*)

Open All year, except Christmas; dining room closed New Year, and to non-
residents.
Rooms 3 double (1 bathroom is not *en suite*). Also 18 in 9 cottages (can be
self-catering; 2 suitable for &). No TV.
Facilities Hall (classical background music), drawing room, sitting room with
TV, dining room. 13-acre grounds. Golf, fishing nearby; Dartmoor 15 mins'
drive; coast 25 mins. Civil wedding licence.
Location 4 miles N of Totnes. From A38 at Buckfastleigh, 22 miles S of
Exeter, take A384 towards Totnes for 2½ miles. At Staverton, bear left at *Sea
Trout* inn; follow Kingston signs 1 mile. Train: Totnes; then taxi.
Restrictions No smoking: dining room, main house bedrooms. Children and
dogs in cottages only.
Credit cards All major cards accepted.
Terms [2000] B&B: single £80–£90, double £120–£140; D,B&B: single
£114.50–£124.50, double £154.50–£174.50. Set dinner £34.50. *V*

Please make a habit of sending a report if you stay at a *Guide*
hotel, even if it's only to endorse the existing entry.

STOCKCROSS Berkshire   Map 2

The Vineyard   `NEW`   *Tel* (01635) 528770
Stockcross, Newbury   *Fax* (01635) 528398
RG20 8JU
                                      E-mail general@the-vineyard.co.uk
                                       Website www.the-vineyard.co.uk

Owned by Sir Peter Michael, founder of Classic FM, and named in
honour of his Californian winery, this old hunting lodge in a moneyed,
if not particularly attractive area, recently underwent a massive refurbishment. In front, tongues of flame leap from the surface of a large
pool; tall metal sculptures welcome visitors to the carpark. Some
might think it OTT, say inspectors. "The decor is stunning, in lush
country house style, based on good antiques and Sir Peter's eclectic art
collection: colourful and expensive Oriental rugs, sofas piled with
large buttoned cushions, chess sets, artistic flower arrangements,
plants, magazines, newspapers and books give a welcoming air. Our
bedroom, designed by Emily Todhunter, was huge, with views of the
garden, bouffant drapes, antiques, paintings (mostly of naked
women), a four-poster, poor reading lights, a well-designed bathroom.
But we heard the traffic on the busy road that runs alongside the hotel,
and also the noise of a pump." There is a spa with a specially commissioned water sculpture, and a gym. In the *Michelin*-starred restaurant, a pianist gently plays; the wine list is "a dream", with 1,400 wines
(500 are Californian). "The dishes were all beautifully presented and
well executed. Sweetcorn and chorizo soup had a satiny texture; sirloin of Scottish beef was full of flavour; fillet of brill was moist and
fresh, with tiny truffle slices; desserts (vanilla brûlée and lemon tart)
arrived under canopies of spun sugar. As with so many posh hotels,
things fell apart at breakfast: service was disorganised, cooked dishes
were good, toast and orange juice were poor. The staff were sweet
natured, but in need of a guiding hand."

Open All year.
Rooms 13 suites, 9 double, 11 single. Some on ground floor.
Facilities Lift, ramps. Lounge, conservatory, restaurant (pianist); meeting
rooms, private dining room; spa: swimming pool, whirlpool, gym. Garden.
Golf nearby. Civil wedding licence.
Location 3 miles NW of Newbury. Take A4 to Hungerford; join B4000 at
bypass junction; *Vineyard* is signposted. Train: Newbury.
Restrictions No smoking in some bedrooms. No dogs.
Credit cards All major cards accepted.
Terms [2000] (*Excluding VAT*) B&B: single £139, double £165–£245, suite
£245–£445; D,B&B (Fri–Sun only): £125–£295 per person. Set lunch £25,
dinner £45; Full alc £60. Spa, golf weekends.

STOKE GABRIEL Devon   Map 1

Gabriel Court   *Tel* (01803) 782206
Stoke Gabriel   *Fax* (01803) 782333
nr Totnes TQ9 6SF   *E-mail* beacom@aol.com

In a delightful old village with a fine church, on an inlet of the River
Dart, this white-painted manor house with a modern extension is the

Beacom family's unpretentious hotel. With its tower topped with a weather vane, it dates back to the 14th century (it was the home of a single family from 1487 until 1928). It stands in terraced Elizabethan-style gardens with clipped yew arches, box hedges and magnolia trees, and it has a swimming pool and a grass tennis court. "It either suits you or it doesn't, but for sheer reliability it is difficult to beat," says one regular visitor. It is "very well run", all agree, and it offers "good, old-fashioned hospitality". "The owner or his son always come out to greet arriving guests and carry their luggage along the brightly carpeted corridor to their well-maintained room" (most of the bedrooms face south). Redecoration is constantly in progress. The food ("served properly hot") is English traditional, with main courses like roast rack of lamb with onion sauce; roast pheasant with bread sauce and redcurrant jelly. Vegetables are plainly cooked. The puddings are often old-time favourites, eg, apple crumble with Devon clotted cream; steamed chocolate sponge, and there is a generous cheeseboard. "The food has improved markedly – same style, just better," is one verdict this year. But several guests would have liked a lighter option to the £27 set dinner menu. Breakfast includes cooked dishes, lots of toast, fruit in season. Afternoon tea is included in the half-board price. Children are welcomed, and so are dogs. Trips on the Dart can be organised. Paignton and the coast (safe beaches) are within easy reach; Dartmoor is 14 miles inland. Greenway House, the home of Agatha Christie, is 3 miles away. (*A and CR, Richard Creed, and others*)

Open All year. Dining room closed midday, except Sun.
Rooms 3 family, 14 double, 2 single. 1 chalet.
Facilities Lounge, bar lounge, TV/meeting room, dining room. No background music. 2½-acre garden: heated swimming pool, tennis, children's playground. River Dart, fishing 300 yds. Golf, riding nearby. Beach 3 miles. Unsuitable for &.
Location In village 3 miles SW of Paignton; turn S off A385 to Totnes. Train: Totnes; hotel will meet.
Restrictions No smoking in dining room. Dogs must be on a lead in public rooms.
Credit cards All major cards accepted.
Terms B&B: single £55–£59, double £80; D,B&B: single £80–£85, double £130–£135. Packed lunches available. Set Sun lunch £13, dinner £27. Christmas package.

STOKE-ON-TRENT Staffordshire *See SHORTLIST*   Map 3

STONOR Oxfordshire   Map 2

The Stonor Arms	*Tel* (01491) 638866
Stonor	*Fax* (01491) 638863
nr Henley-on-Thames	*E-mail* stonorarms.hotel@virgin.net
RG9 6HE	*Website* www.stonor-arms.co.uk

18th-century inn in centre of village on B480, 4 miles NW of Henley. Now a smart restaurant/hotel, managed by Sophia Williams. Cosy lounge with open fire; popular bar with "very Henley decor". Formal

*restaurant (no smoking) and small conservatory serve modern
English cooking. Good breakfast. No background music. Civil wedding licence. 1-acre walled garden. Carpark. 10 bedrooms (with
antiques, good fabrics; 4 no-smoking, 1 adapted for &) in converted
barn at rear, well away from road. Amex, MasterCard, Visa accepted.
B&B: single £99, double £125; D,B&B (2 nights min.): single from
£115, double from £145. Bar meals; full alc £45.* "Not cheap, but
lovely setting, obliging staff," said last year's report. This year's comments less enthusiastic: "Cool welcome; disappointing dinner – presentation took precedence over content." So we'd like more reports,
please. *V*

STRATFIELD TURGIS Hampshire   Map 2

The Wellington Arms   *Tel* (01256) 882214
Stratfield Turgis   *Fax* (01256) 882934
Hook RG27 0AS

*Above-average coaching inn, managed by Moira Cunningham, on
A33, on Duke of Wellington Estate, close to his home at Stratfield Saye
(halfway between Reading and Basingstoke). 35 bedrooms: some face
road, most are in modern annexe at rear: quiet, comfortable and
spacious, some on ground floor. One 2-roomed family suite, 1 suitable
for &. Good snacks in "delightful" bar lounge (patterned wallpaper,
matching sofas, paintings, ornaments, open fire), more ambitious
meals, but also grilled steaks, in restaurant (closed Sat midday, Sun
evening). "Very pleasant young staff." No background music.
Functions, conferences, wedding receptions held. 1-acre garden.
Near river (fishing), Wellington riding school, racecourses at Ascot
and Newbury. Closed Christmas. All major credit cards accepted. No
dogs in public rooms. B&B: single £60–£110, double £95–£125, suite
£110–£140. Full alc £30. Weekend reductions.*

STRATFORD-UPON-AVON Warwickshire   Map 3

Caterham House   *Tel* (01789) 267309
58/59 Rother Street   *Fax* (01789) 414836
Stratford-upon-Avon CV37 6LT

🎗 *César award in 1998*

A coral-pink Georgian house, popular with theatre-goers and actors
alike: it is a short walk away from the Royal Shakespeare theatre. One
pair of frequent visitors enjoy discussing the plays, and much else,
with the Anglo-French owners, Dominique and Olive Maury, who
have run this small B&B for over 20 years. "It is as comfortable and
as professionally run as ever," they write this year. The house has a
"bright continental atmosphere", and the housekeeping is "of a
notably high standard". "The cooked breakfasts are superb, and the
croissants, needless to say, are the best. Very good value." Dominique
Maury presides over the bar in the lounge, which opens on to a small
flowery patio. His wife is responsible for the idiosyncratic decor:

"beautiful hall, landings and stairs; gleaming paintwork; unusual pictures, painted furniture, English and French antiques". Each bedroom has its own character; all have a brass bedstead (some are narrow), plants and flowers. Plenty of restaurants nearby. (*Sarah and Tony Thomas, JB*)

Open All year, except Christmas Day.
Rooms 14 double (1 with bath, 13 with shower). 2 in annexe, 2 in cottage. No telephone (pay-phone available).
Facilities Lounge with TV, bar, breakfast room; no background music; small patio. Unsuitable for &.
Location Central, *c.* 200 yds from river, opposite police station (some traffic noise). Carpark.
Restriction Dogs by arrangement; not in public rooms or unattended in bedrooms.
Credit cards MasterCard, Visa.
Terms B&B: single £54–£68, double £76–£84. Child accommodated in parents' room: babies free; under 10, 50% of adult rate.

STRETTON Rutland   Map 2

Ram Jam Inn BUDGET	*Tel* (01780) 410776
Great North Road	*Fax* (01780) 410361
Stretton LE15 7QX	*E-mail* rji@rutnet.co.uk
	Website www.ramjaminn.co.uk

A godsend for travellers on the Great North Road (A1M) – Mike Littlemore and Margaret Cox's motel with a difference (its odd name is thought to refer to an 18th-century drink). Inside are wooden floors, terracotta tiles, cheerful colours, an open-plan kitchen, a bar, café and bistro, decorated with old copper pans, stone cider jars and the like. Eating arrangements are flexible (no fixed menus); in the bar area, visitors perch on stools; tables are dotted around; food is "simple and good": salads, fish and chips, chargrilled steaks and sausages, always a dish of the day; calorific puddings, eg, lime and basil cheesecake; apricot sponge. Bread and teatime scones are home baked. Drinks range from tea, coffee, freshly squeezed orange juice to beers and a serviceable list of wines. The bedrooms are bright, with patterned wallpaper, wicker chairs, an efficient bathroom; all but one overlook the garden and orchard, so traffic noise is not too much of a problem. Breakfast includes hearty cooked dishes and the morning newspapers. (*JFH*)

Open All year, except 25 Dec, 1 Jan.
Rooms 1 family, 6 double.
Facilities Ramp. Open-plan bar/café/bistro; light background music all day; conference room. 1-acre grounds: patio, sunken garden. Only eating/sitting areas suitable for &.
Location W side of A1 9 miles NW of Stamford. Travelling S leave A1 on B668 to Oakham; travelling N leave A1 through Texaco garage just past B668 turn-off. Large carpark.
Restrictions No smoking in eating areas. Dogs in bedrooms only, by prior arrangement.
Credit cards Amex, MasterCard, Visa.
Terms [2000] Room: single £45, double £55, family £70. Breakfast £6.50. Full alc £23.

STURMINSTER NEWTON Dorset   Map 2

Plumber Manor   *Tel* (01258) 472507
Sturminster Newton DT10 2AF   *Fax* (01258) 473370
                                     E-mail book@plumbermanor.com

◊ *César award in 1987*

"An absolute delight." "A unique mixture of relaxation and efficiency.
It's so peaceful." "Richard and Alison Prideaux-Brune wear this place
like an old and favourite tweed jacket, and the welcome and comfort
generated bear that indefinable stamp of polished reality without
swank." With one exception, praise continues for this Jacobean house,
which has been the Prideaux-Brune family home since the early 17th
century. It was turned into a restaurant-with-rooms in 1973. Two
black labradors "add a special charm". The kitchen, where Brian
Prideaux-Brune, Richard's brother, presides, turns out English/French
dishes with rich sauces. The result is "imaginative and traditional",
"stylish but unpretentious; like the very best of home cooking", with
"most generous helpings", eg, duck liver pâté with plum relish; guinea
fowl with Thai curry sauce. The dessert trolley, not for the faint-
hearted, is laden with dishes like chocolate truffle torte, and lemon and
ginger crunch. "Service is relaxed and confident, born of long experience, no hint of pretentiousness, as reflected in a reasonable and practical house wine list." Some bedrooms in the main house may be in
need of refurbishment (they lead off a gallery hung with family portraits). The best rooms, in a converted barn, are spacious and well
equipped, though their bathrooms are "rather dated". Two marked
walks lead from the grounds. Local attractions include the lovely old
town of Sherborne; the sights of Hardy country; Old Wardour Castle
and Kingston Lacy. Hunting with the Portman can be arranged, and
shooting parties are accommodated. (*Hazel Pennington, Brian and
Eve Webb, JP Marland, Sarah Curtis, and others*)

Open All year, except Feb. Restaurant closed midday, except Sun.
Rooms 16 double. 10 in stable courtyard (2 on ground floor).
Facilities 2 lounges (1 with bar), gallery, restaurant. No background music.
5-acre grounds: garden, tennis, croquet, trout stream; stabling for visiting
horses. Golf, swimming, fishing, clay-pigeon shooting, hunting nearby.
Location 2 miles SW of Sturminster Newton; turn off A357 towards
Hazelbury Bryan. Train: Gillingham, Dorset; then taxi.
Restrictions Children and dogs by prior arrangement. No dogs (except
owners') in public rooms.
Credit cards All major cards accepted.
Terms B&B: single £80–£90, double £95–£145. Set lunch (Sun) £17.50, din-
ner £21.50–£30. Child accommodated in parents' room: £10. Short breaks
Nov–Mar. 10% discount on 2-night stay Oct–Apr.

If you agree with our dislike of piped music, do contact
Pipedown, the International Campaign for Freedom from
Piped Music. PO Box 1722, Salisbury SP4 7US, *e-mail*
pipedown@btinternet.com

Stourcastle Lodge   BUDGET   *Tel* (01258) 472320
Gough's Close   *Fax* (01258) 473381
Sturminster Newton DT10 1BU   *E-mail* enquiries@stourcastle-lodge.co.uk
                               Website www.stourcastle-lodge.co.uk

"Good value for money, with welcoming and hardworking hosts.
Dinners were imaginative, and of a consistently high standard." A
report this year on Ken and Jill Hookham-Bassett's 300-year-old
house. With its slate roof and tall white chimneys, it stands in a traffic-free close off the high street of this small market town. Works by
local artists hang on the walls; in the cottage-style garden, humorous
sculptures, eg, Henrietta and her seven piglets, are scattered around.
The bedrooms are named after members of the Dashwood family, who
owned the lodge in the 18th century. They are decorated with stencils,
and all but one have an antique brass bed; all overlook the garden; two
have a whirlpool bath. The "well-equipped family room" was liked
this year, apart from the lack of "a decent towel rail" in the *en suite*
shower room. A collection of antique kitchen implements is displayed
in the dining room, where Mrs Hookham-Bassett's Aga-cooked meals
are served. Dorset lamb roasted with rosemary and garlic; local trout
with lemon dressing; queen of puddings, or whisky and lemon bread
and butter pudding are some of the traditional dishes on her menus (no
choice until dessert). Herbs and vegetables come from the garden. No
licence; bring your own wine. One visitor thought the standard of the
cutlery was not up to the quality of the cooking. "Good breakfasts",
with home-made muesli, bread and preserves, and free-range eggs.
The River Stour, with fishing, is 300 yards away. Stourhead is nearby.
Bath, Glastonbury, Salisbury and Dorchester all within striking distance. (*Mrs E A Mudford, and others*)

Open All year. Lunch not served.
Rooms 5 double.
Facilities Lounge, dining room. No background music. ¼-acre garden. River
with coarse fishing 100 yds. Unsuitable for &.
Location 25 yds from centre.
Restrictions No smoking: restaurant, bedrooms. No dogs.
Credit cards MasterCard, Visa.
Terms B&B: single £37–£46, double £60–£74; D,B&B £49–£65 per person.
Set dinner £19. Child accommodated in parents' room: 50% of adult rate.
Reductions for long stays. Christmas package.

SUTTON COLDFIELD West Midlands   **Map 3**

New Hall   *Tel* (0121) 378 2442
Walmley Rd   *Fax* (0121) 378 4637
Walmley, Sutton Coldfield   *E-mail* newhall@thistle.co.uk
B76 1QX   *Website* www.slh.com/NewHallc

"It remains excellent," says a returning visitor to this magnificent
building, 12th-century in origin, with mullioned windows, stained
glass, much oak panelling and carved oak. It is said to be the oldest
inhabited moated manor house in England. Terraced gardens,
designed in the 16th and 17th centuries, lead to shrubs, wooded areas,

and outdoor entertainments (see below). Some of the impressive public rooms are given over to functions and conferences: "The Great
Chamber is quite stunning." The hotel belongs to a chain (the Thistle
group), something the *Guide* normally avoids, but "the general set-up
and attention to detail are atypical of a chain hotel", says a regular visitor. "The manager, Caroline Parkes, remains clearly in charge, setting
high personal standards and demanding equally high standards of the
staff." The meals served in the formal dining room (with stained-glass
windows and dark panelling) are thought as good as everything else.
The new chef, Simon Brough, cooks ambitious modern dishes, eg,
velouté of garlic and potato soup with cèpes and snails; steamed sea
trout with pak choi and shellfish consommé; warm apple and walnut
tart with rum and raisin caramel. A light breakfast can be served in the
bedrooms. Breakfast in the restaurant is served by waitresses wearing
long yellow dresses with aprons, and a large choice of cooked dishes
is available. The best bedrooms, in the main house, are "sumptuous",
with heavily festooned curtains, a four-poster bed, a decanter of
sherry, home-made biscuits. Each is named after a type of lily
(Lucinda, Dawn, etc). The rooms in a purpose-built wing are good
too, "if less interesting". The
hotel is currently building a
leisure spa, including swimming pool, due for com-
pletion in summer 2000. The
Snow Dome indoor ski slope
at Tamworth is 10 minutes'
drive away; Birmingham's
airport is nearby; the city
centre is 20 minutes' drive
away. (*Dr Peter Richardson*)

Open All year.
Rooms 10 suites, 46 double, 4 single. Some on ground floor, 1 adapted for &.
Facilities 2 drawing rooms, cocktail bar, restaurant, function facilities. No back-
ground music. 26-acre grounds: gardens, woodland walks, putting green, 9-hole
par 3 golf course, croquet, floodlit tennis, trout lake; spa. Civil wedding licence.
Location On B4148, near Walmley village; close to M42 and M6 motorways
(hotel will send directions).
Restrictions No smoking: restaurant, most bedrooms, some public rooms. No
children under 8. No dogs.
Credit cards All major cards accepted.
Terms [2000] B&B: single from £110, double from £130, suite from £205.
D,B&B: single from £136, double from £182, suite from £241. Weekend,
champagne, theatre breaks. Christmas, New Year packages.

SWAFFHAM Norfolk   **Map 2**

Strattons   *Tel* (01760) 723845
4 Ash Close   *Fax* (01760) 720458
Swaffham PE37 7NH   *Website* www.strattons-hotel.co.uk

"Fantastic hosts, truly welcoming." "A singular place, run by a
couple who care." "Both romantic and child-friendly." Continuing

admiration for Les and Vanessa Scott's informally run, ecologically correct, Grade II listed Palladian-style villa. Though only a few yards from the centre of the old market town, it has a rural feel, with bantams, guinea fowl and ducks under old trees in the garden. It is the Scotts' family home, inhabited also by their two children and family pets. The decor is found "cluttered" by some, but "inspiring, invigorating" by others, and the "mildly eccentric" style is generally enjoyed. In the downstairs rooms "every surface is covered: some items are quite odd, eg, an old sewing machine, a marble phrenological bust", also paintings, patchwork and cats – both real and artificial. The bedrooms, all different, are equally distinctive. The Venetian Room, in vivid blue, has a mural of Botticelli's "Venus" in the bathroom; the Tuscan Room has a Mediterranean decor. The Moroccan-style Red Room is "mind blowing", painted red throughout, with "red plush, splendid quirky details, a bathroom like the king's tent at Agincourt, a bath long enough for tall people to stretch out in". Vanessa Scott is considered "an exceptional cook". Her menus are based on local produce, organic when possible. Home-grown vegetables are brought to the door; herbs and edible flowers are also home grown. The daily-changing four-course dinner menu includes, eg, duck and wild boar rillettes with crostini; roasted salmon on sweet pepper arame; always an original vegetarian main course; "ripe farmhouse cheeses of the British Isles"; desserts such as Bramley bread-and-butter pudding. Les Scott is knowledgeable about wines, and his hand-written list offers plenty by the glass. "Great breakfasts", served in relaxed style, include the Scotts' own blended muesli, kedgeree, oyster mushrooms on toast, goat's cheese omelette. Dogs are welcomed. Swaffham has elegant 18th-century buildings, and a traditional market on Saturday. The National Trust village of Houghton and many medieval churches are nearby; the North Norfolk Heritage Coast is 30 minutes' drive. (*Joanne Hoddy, G and A Smeed, JC*)

Open All year, except Christmas. Lunch by arrangement.
Rooms 1 suite, 5 double.
Facilities Drawing room, restaurant (occasional jazz/folk/classical background music); terrace. 1-acre garden. Unsuitable for &.
Location Enter Ash Close at N end of Market Place, between estate agent and Express Cleaners. Ample private parking. Train/bus: King's Lynn/Downham Market; then taxi or coach.
Restrictions No smoking. No dogs unaccompanied in bedrooms.
Credit cards Amex, MasterCard, Visa.
Terms [2000] B&B: single £70, double £95, suite £150. Set dinner £30. 3-night midweek rates. 1-night bookings sometimes refused.

SWINBURNE Northumberland   Map 4

The Hermitage   `BUDGET`   *Tel* (01434) 681248
Swinburne   *Fax* (01434) 681110
nr Hexham NE48 4D9   *E-mail* stewart@thehermitagenow.freeserve.co.uk

A B&B in a country house set in large grounds in a hamlet near Hexham. It is the family home of Katie Stewart; she and her husband, Simon, "warm-hearted, no-nonsense hosts", have returned after many years abroad. No signs proclaim its existence, but careful instructions are given. You approach through a grand arch and up a long private drive, bordered by daffodils in spring. Old family portraits hang in the public rooms, and there are some lovely antiques. The nominators admired their bedroom: "Reached up a staircase, round corners and along halls, it was large and comfortable, with views over the garden and woodland beyond from one window, and the large vegetable patch from the other. All was quiet except for birdsong and the occasional squawk of a pheasant. Period furniture and appropriate decor combined with practicalities like two suitcase stands. This epitomised the welcome, the stay, and the breakfast, a hearty affair with lots of thick toast" (but orange juice is preserved). In fine weather, it is served on a terrace. Several good pubs are within 15 minutes' drive. One visitor this year reported: "Guests are expected to be out between 10.30 am and 5 pm." But he admired the "superb public rooms, with a true country house atmosphere". Swinburne has a large reservoir and a 17th-century house on the site of an old castle. The Roman Wall is a four-mile drive away; many of Northumberland's castles, mansions and gardens are within easy reach. (*LC and RP, Robin Oaten*)

Open Mar–Sept inclusive.
Rooms 2 suites, 1 double. No telephone, TV.
Facilities Drawing room with TV, breakfast room. 2-acre gardens: tennis. Unsuitable for &.
Location A68 for 7 miles N of Corbridge; turn left on to A6079. Lodge gates 1 mile on right. Follow drive for ½ mile.
Restrictions No smoking upstairs. No children under 10. No dogs.
Credit cards None accepted.
Terms [2000] B&B £30–£45.

TALLAND-BY-LOOE Cornwall   Map 1

Talland Bay Hotel   *Tel* (01503) 272667
Talland-by-Looe PL13 2JB   *Fax* (01503) 272940
                                           E-mail tallandbay@aol.com

A traditional hotel with a country house atmosphere, set 150 feet above a wide bay (a stiffish walk up) in well-nurtured and sheltered subtropical gardens. The building is 16th-century in origin, but it was much altered in the 1930s and 1940s, when it was converted into a hotel. It is now owned by Barry and Annie Rosier and managed by Maureen Le Page. Recent visitors found it "delightful" and wrote of "glorious views from both bedroom and bathroom, complemented by golden silence" and "friendly service" (though some have found it "aloof"). The bedrooms vary greatly; the best are "pleasant and well equipped". Some in the oldest part have walls three feet thick. Some are quite small. One room has a large tiled fireplace and balcony overlooking the gardens and sea. Some have a private garden. Five rooms are in cottages. One of these, near the carpark and the kitchen, suffers from noise and overheating, but two others are good for a family, having a bunk-bedded room as well as a double. Three sea-facing rooms were added in late 1999. Light lunches are informally served, in the bar or on the terrace. In the restaurant the best tables, at the front, have good views, but those at the back can be "pretty gloomy". The chef, Serge Puyal, cooks in a "classical European" style on menus with plenty of choice, eg, venison with a parsley and truffle coating garnished with poached figs; roasted whole John Dory with cumin and lemon; chocolate, brandy and pecan nut cake. There is always a vegetarian main course, and local lobster and crab can be ordered, given 24 hours' notice. Breakfasts are praised – fresh orange juice, "scrambled eggs cooked to perfection", and "tasty sausages" – and a "superb afternoon tea" is included in the room rate. There is easy access to the coastal path. The Heligan Gardens, and several National Trust properties, are nearby. (*Stephen Parish, LW, RWB, and others*)

Open Feb–end Dec.
Rooms 1 suite, 2 family, 14 double, 3 single. 5 in cottages in grounds.
Facilities Sitting room, library, cocktail bar, restaurant; patio. No background music. 2½-acre garden: swimming pool, sauna, badminton, putting, croquet. Beach 5 mins' walk. Golf nearby. Unsuitable for &.
Location 2½ miles SW of Looe. Left at hotel sign on Looe–Polperro road. Train: Liskeard, 8 miles; then taxi/branch line to Looe.
Restrictions No smoking: restaurant, 1 lounge. No children under 5 at dinner. Dogs by arrangement; not in public rooms.
Credit cards All major cards accepted.
Terms [2000] B&B: single £47–£76, double £94–£152, suite £114–£132; D,B&B: single £67–£96, double £134–£192, suite £154–£172. Snack lunches. Set lunch £12.50, dinner £22; full alc £38.50. Reductions for children, according to age. Off-season breaks, painting holidays. Christmas, New Year packages.

TAPLOW Buckinghamshire   Map 2

Cliveden   *Tel* (01628) 668561 (*in UK* 0800 454063)
Taplow SL6 0JF   *Fax* (01628) 661837 (*in UK* 0800 454064)
                         Website www.clivedenhouse.co.uk

This magnificent stately home stands above the Thames in huge National Trust grounds. It has a colourful past: three dukes lived here; so did the Astor family, for four generations, when they entertained politicians, royalty and others. It is now an expensive hotel, which our inspectors liked with reservations this year. "*Cliveden* gets most of the big things right, and it has many of the trappings of a grand country house, but it is let down by small details. The staff are friendly, the house is superb, the swimming pool where Christine Keeler once frolicked is delightful, and the food is delicious. Dining and breakfasting in the restaurant overlooking the grounds is a real pleasure. But at the prices charged (£290 upwards a night for a double room, with everything else on top), perfection is expected. And that is not always delivered." During their visit, admittedly on a busy Saturday, glasses were not cleared away, drink orders went astray, room clocks were not set at the right time, and some of the carpets needed a clean. But one of the pleasures of staying here is that you can enjoy the magnificent grounds (which are open to the public) when they are not crowded with sightseers, and the spectacular public rooms (with their tapestries, suits of armour, fine paintings), which can be crowded with functions during the day. Many sporting facilities (see below) are included in the room price, and the hotel makes a point of welcoming children. The bedrooms are named for previous owners and visitors. Those in the main house (Nancy Astor, Buckingham, etc) are as splendid as the public rooms; the ones in the garden wing (eg, Gladstone, Grenfell) are attractive but less characterful. One suite is a cottage in the grounds, by the Thames, formerly used by Stephen Ward. The place aims for the atmosphere of an Edwardian house party: guests' names on hand-written cards on bedroom doors, butlers and footmen at the ready, maids in pinafores. Since the parent company was taken over by an American consortium which includes Bill Gates, there has been a shake-up of the management: Stephen Carter is now in charge, and there is a new head chef, John Wood (ex-*Savoy*, London). He supervises the two restaurants: *Waldo's* (*Michelin* star) (where fixed-price menus include dishes like ravioli of langoustine, mussels and leeks; vanilla-roasted monkfish with foie gras and lobster risotto), and the *Terrace Restaurant* where you could order grilled Dover sole; steak and French fries, or more elaborate dishes like sautéed guinea fowl with a vin jaune cream sauce; duck scented with five spices and vanilla. Three vintage boats are available for river trips. The *Royal Crescent Hotel*, Bath (*qv*), is under the same management. More reports, please.

Open All year.
Rooms 17 suites, 22 double. 12 in wings, 1 in cottage. 9 on ground floor. 13 air-conditioned.
Facilities Lift, ramps. Great Hall (pianist sometimes), library, boudoir, billiard room, breakfast room, 2 restaurants, conservatory; function facilities; crèche; club: indoor and outdoor swimming pools, sauna, spa bath, gym, health/beauty treatments. In 376-acre National Trust grounds (open to the public) on River Thames; tennis, squash, riding, practice golf, fishing, jogging; 3 boats. Civil wedding licence.
Location 10 miles NW of Windsor. M4 exit 7. On B476 opposite *Feathers* pub. Train: Burnham, 2 miles.
Restriction No smoking: restaurants, 7 bedrooms. No dogs in restaurants.
Credit cards All major cards accepted.
Terms [2000] (*Excluding £2.50 donation to National Trust*) Room: double £290–£430, suite £465–£830. Breakfast: continental £12, English £17. *Terrace Restaurant*: set lunch from £26, full alc dinner from £65; *Waldo's*: set dinner £58 and £84. Fitness, Christmas, New Year packages. 1-night bookings sometimes refused weekends.

TAUNTON Somerset　　　　　　　　　　　　　　　　　　　**Map 1**

The Castle　　　　　　　　　　　　　　*Tel* (01823) 272671
Castle Green　　　　　　　　　　　　　　*Fax* (01823) 336066
Taunton TA1 1NF　　　　　*E-mail* reception@the-castle-hotel.com
　　　　　　　　　　　　　Website www.the-castle-hotel.com

🌣 *César award in 1987*

For the last 50 years of its 300-year history, the Chapman family have been custodians of this wisteria-covered and castellated hotel. It has welcomed royalty, from Queen Victoria to the present monarch, and the moated rear garden is a reminder of the old castle that once stood on the site. Kit Chapman now presides, with a new manager this year, Kevin McCarthy. He runs a "very special place", say visitors this year. "Standards are even better than when we first visited 20 years ago." Others wrote: "Absolutely no pretentiousness – just first class." The public rooms are elegant, with old oak furniture, tapestries, paintings, elaborate flower arrangements, and there is a fine wrought iron staircase. The bedrooms vary in size and style, and most have a good-sized bathroom. Front ones can get noise of pubs and traffic, but they are triple-glazed; the quietest ones overlook the garden. The penthouse suite and roof garden have views of the Quantock and Blackdown hills. Renovation is in progress: redecoration of bedrooms, and installation of air-conditioning in some bedrooms and public rooms. The new head chef, Richard Guest, has worked in London with Anton Edelmann at *The Savoy*, and with Jean Christophe Novelli at *Maison Novelli* in Clerkenwell, where he earned a *Michelin* star. He is continuing the hotel's British style of cooking, using local fresh produce when possible (suppliers get a credit on the menu). Lots of choice including, eg, spiced beef jelly with beetroot chutney; partridge on braised celery and cabbage with a liver sauce; steamed ginger pudding with lemon curd ice-cream. "Dinner was of the highest quality," says a visitor this year. Lighter meals are available in the more informal *Brazz*, the café/restaurant, adjacent (a branch has just opened in Exeter). A continental breakfast can be brought to the bedroom; a substantial cooked one is served in the dining room. In low season, musical weekends are held. Exmoor, the Quantocks and the gardens at Stourhead are nearby. (*David and Karin Taylor, Iain Ure, Stephen Edwards*)

Open All year.
Rooms 5 suites, 27 double, 12 single.
Facilities Lift, ramps. Lounge, lounge bar, restaurant, brasserie; no background music; private dining/meeting rooms; roof garden. ¼-acre garden.
Location Central (follow signs for castle). Garages (£10), parking. Bus station 2 mins; railway station 5 mins.
Restrictions No smoking: restaurant, some bedrooms. Small dogs only; not in public rooms.
Credit cards All major cards accepted.
Terms [2000] B&B: single £95, double £145–£160, suite £230–£560. Set lunch/dinner £26; full alc £40. West Country breaks (2 nights min.) D,B&B from £95 per person; musical weekends. Christmas, New Year packages. Special rates for honeymooners, old boys/parents from local schools.

TEFFONT EVIAS Wiltshire   **Map 2**

Howard's House   *Tel* (01722) 716392
Teffont Evias   *Fax* (01722) 716820
nr Salisbury SP3 5RJ   *E-mail* paul.firmin@virgin.net
                      Website www.howardshousehotel.co.uk

♥ *César award in 1993*

"One of our absolute favourites," a couple of seasoned travellers write this year, of this "extremely civilised place". Set in the picture-postcard village of Teffont Evias, near Salisbury, it stands near the little River Teff. It was built in 1623, and extended and renovated in 1837, following the then owner's visit to Switzerland during his Grand Tour – hence the steeply pitched, broad-eaved roof. The "courteous owner and staff, excellent food, lovely rooms" are all admired; so are the romantic garden and the relaxed style: children and dogs are welcomed; there is no dress code. The smallish bedrooms, decorated in pastel shades, have "exquisite biscuits and real milk in a chilled thermos for early morning tea". The newly refurbished lounge is done in warm yellows that complement an old stone fireplace and exposed beams. It can get busy in peak periods, thanks to the popularity of the green-and-white restaurant (it has a *Michelin Bib Gourmand*). Owner/chef Paul Firmin, with Boyd McIntosh, serves modern British cooking, eg, marinated fillets of red mullet with lime and lavender oil; roast rack of lamb with garlic confit, sweet onion tartlet, rosemary and thyme gravy; glazed lemon tart with a vodka and white chocolate sorbet. The "excellent wine list" includes some reasonably priced bottles. Freshly squeezed orange and "beautifully presented" dishes for breakfast. "The village is now the home and headquarters of William Daniels, who runs Famous Fishing, which provides high-class fly-fishing on famous chalk streams," we are told. Stonehenge and Wilton House are within 20 minutes' drive. (*John and Thérèse Hall, and others*)

Open All year, except Christmas. Restaurant closed midday, except Sun.
Rooms 9 double.
Facilities Lounge, restaurant (occasional classical background music). 2-acre grounds: croquet. River, fishing, shooting nearby. Unsuitable for &.
Location On B3089, 9½ miles W of Salisbury. In Teffont Magna, follow signs to hotel. Train: Tisbury, 3½ miles; then taxi.
Restrictions No smoking in restaurant. No dogs in restaurant.
Credit cards All major cards accepted.
Terms B&B: single £70–£75, double £95–£145. Set lunch (Sun) £18.50, dinner £19.95; full alc £41. 2-night breaks. ***V***

TEIGNMOUTH Devon   Map 1

Thomas Luny House   NEW   Tel (01626) 772976
Teign Street   *E-mail* alisonandjohn@thomas-luny-house.co.uk
Teignmouth TQ14 8EG   *Website* www.thomas-luny-house.co.uk

"An excellent small B&B. John and Alison Allan are charming and friendly, and really good hosts." A regular correspondent's report restores this small Georgian house to the *Guide* after a time with no reports. Named for the marine artist who built it, it is near the fish quay, in the old part of town. You enter through an archway in a high whitewashed wall. The double drawing room and breakfast room, both with an open fire, lead through French windows on to a small garden. Three bedrooms are spacious, the fourth is small; all have fresh flowers, Malvern water, books and magazines. The communal breakfast includes freshly squeezed orange juice, home-made yogurt, "excellent scrambled eggs", "lovely home-baked fruit bread" and leaf tea. Earlier visitors praised the "pretty house", the "most attractive" bedrooms, and the "welcoming, yet discreet" owners. Tea (early morning and afternoon) and a newspaper are included in the rates. Teignmouth's days as an elegant bathing resort are long gone, but "the countryside around is full of delights", including good birdwatching on the Exe estuary. (*Marilyn Frampton*)

Open All year.
Rooms 4 double.
Facilities 2 lounges, breakfast room. No background music. Small walled garden. Sea, sandy beach 5 mins' walk. Unsuitable for &.
Location Central. From A380 take B3192 to Teignmouth. Left at traffic lights; right at next lights; 1st left into Teign St. Courtyard parking.
Restrictions No smoking. No children under 12. No dogs.
Credit cards MasterCard, Visa.
Terms (*Not VAT-rated*) B&B: single £40, double £75.

TETBURY Gloucestershire   **Map 3**

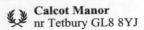 **Calcot Manor**   *Tel* (01666) 890391
nr Tetbury GL8 8YJ   *Fax* (01666) 890394
                                        E-mail reception@calcotmanor.co.uk
                                        Website www.calcotmanor.co.uk

César award: Family hotel of the year

Originally a large Cotswold farmstead (its 14th-century tithe barn, once used by Cistercian monks, is one of the oldest in England), this Pride of Britain member has been turned by Richard Ball into a thriving, flexibly run family hotel, while also catering for adults wanting something sophisticated. Family rooms are in a barn at some distance from the main house. They have a double bedroom, a sitting room with bunk beds or sofa beds, TV with video, baby-listening, etc. There is a small heated outdoor pool, a supervised playroom for children over three, a collection of toys and games. Adults on their own are assigned a bedroom in the main house or converted stables ("we loved the privacy"). Some rooms have a six-foot bed; some have a whirlpool bath; all are stocked with shortbread, fruit, toiletries, etc. "Our bedroom was large, well furnished and comfortable. Service was good. Very good food at good value," writes one guest this year, who "would happily return". The restaurants are run by Michael Croft. The more sophisticated *Conservatory* serves dishes such as chargrilled tuna with couscous; osso bucco; caramelised white chocolate rice pudding. The *Gumstool* bar/brasserie, which serves local ales, is "well laid out to allow intimacy without losing an overall sense of contented bustle". Its "good, interesting" dishes include, eg, devilled lamb's kidneys in pastry; Thai spiced crab cakes; braised lamb shank with tomatoes and herbs. You can order "ample" or "generous" portions. The *Gumstool* also serves grilled steaks, chips and salads, and will produce peanut-butter sandwiches on demand (young children get their supper here). Breakfasts include fresh orange juice and local sausages. Conferences and functions are held. Tetbury has a market place with lovely old houses, and the 600-acre Westonbirt Arboretum. On Woolsack Day in the spring, locals race up the steep Gumstool Hill carrying heavy sacks of wool. A good base for exploring Laurie Lee country. (*KJ Barnes, Good Pub Guide; also Val Hennessy*)

Open All year.
Rooms 4 suites, 24 double. 19 in barns and stables. 11 on ground floor.
Facilities Ramps. 2 lounges, restaurant, bistro (background light jazz); private dining room, conference facilities; children's playroom with nanny (open 4 hrs daily). 9-acre grounds: heated swimming pool, tennis, children's play area, croquet; bicycles. Golf, fishing, riding nearby. Bicycles provided. Civil wedding licence.
Location 4 miles W of Tetbury, on intersection of A4135/A46. Train: Kemble, 6 miles; then taxi.
Restrictions No smoking in *Conservatory* restaurant. No dogs.
Credit cards All major cards accepted.
Terms B&B: single £115, double £130–£175, suite £180–£185. Set lunch £14; full alc £30. Child accommodated in family suite: under 1, free; 1–12, £15; over 12, £25 (incl. English breakfast and high tea). 2-day breaks. Christmas package. 1-night bookings refused peak season Sat.

The Close NEW
8 Long Street
Tetbury GL8 8AQ

Tel (01666) 502272
Fax (01666) 504401
Website www.oldenglish.co.uk

In the middle of this mellow old Cotswold market town, this fine 15th-century house has been a hotel since 1974. It was sold by Virgin in 1998 to a group called Old English Inns plc, and it returns to the *Guide* this year with enthusiastic praise for the managers, Louise and Daren Bale (he is the chef): "They work so hard; they deserve a fanfare." The "relaxed atmosphere" is admired – "nothing OTT", and so is the personal attention – cases carried, etc. The bedrooms vary in size and style, but all are "comfortable in every way", furnished with antiques, and stocked with Madeira, plastic ducks and "a personal cuddly guard dog". Most look on to the walled garden at the rear. In the public rooms there are open fires, polished furniture and floorboards, fresh flowers, board games. The ambitious cooking is admired too: "Excellent seabass with vanilla-scented lobster and cucumber; superb roast fillet of lamb with marinated couscous, truffled beans and red pepper reduction; delicious banoffee parfait and white chocolate tart." Weddings and other functions are extensively catered for. Christmas is an "ideal adult occasion". (*June Marsden, and others*)

Open All year.
Rooms 15 double. Some on ground floor.
Facilities Ramps. 2 lounges, restaurant; background music; 3 function rooms. Civil wedding licence.
Location Centre of Tetbury (rear rooms quietest). Carpark.
Restrictions No smoking in restaurant. No children under 12 in restaurant at night. No dogs.
Credit cards Amex, MasterCard, Visa.
Terms B&B: single £65–£85, double £80–£120; D,B&B: single £90–£110, double £120–£165. Set lunch £16.50, dinner £29; full alc £42. Midweek breaks. Christmas package. 1-night bookings occasionally refused Sat.

THIRSK North Yorkshire   Map 4

Sheppard's NEW/BUDGET   *Tel* (01845) 523655
Front Street, Sowerby   *Fax* (01845) 524720
Thirsk YO7 1JF   *E-mail* sheppards@thirskny.freeserve.co.uk

In suburb of Thirsk, Mrs Sheppard's restaurant- and bistro-with-rooms in converted farm buildings round cobbled courtyard. "A gem," say nominators. Modern cooking; background music. Closed 1st week Jan. 8 bedrooms (3 above restaurant). No smoking: restaurant, bedrooms. MasterCard, Visa accepted. B&B £42–£62. Set lunch/dinner £9.95; full alc £27.15. More reports, please. *V*

THORNBURY Gloucestershire   Map 3

Thornbury Castle   *Tel* (01454) 281182
Castle Street   *Fax* (01454) 416188
Thornbury   *E-mail* thornburycastle@compuserve.com
Bristol BS35 1HH   *Website* www.thornburycastle.co.uk

An imposing early 16th-century castle on the northern edge of the busy modern world of Thornbury. It was visited in 1535 by Henry VIII and Anne Boleyn; later, Mary Tudor lived here before coming to the throne. In 1966, it became a luxurious hotel. It is now a Pride of Britain member, and it has been owned for the past 14 years by Maurice and Carol Taylor (aka the Baron and Baroness of Porthlethen); their son, Justin, is managing director. Many visitors are Americans who relish the combination of modern comforts with grandeur both inside and out: towers, crenellations, winding stone staircases, arrow slits and oriel windows; baronial public rooms, huge fireplaces, antique furniture, tapestries and Tudor portraits. Some of the bedrooms (they are called "bedchambers" here) are huge; some have views of the oldest Tudor garden in England, surrounded by the castle wall. A seven-sided room in a tower, with a four-poster bed, and a gas log fire in its vast fireplace, "was large enough for my morning run", said one reporter. The singles are small, and medieval windows mean that some rooms are quite dark. Some rooms get traffic noise from a busy road. The restaurant, much patronised by outside diners, has a new chef, Colin Woodward, and a regular visitor writes in 2000: "He is inventive, artistic and good. He takes old favourites and presents them with style and panache." Main courses include, eg, breast of Gressingham duck with a parsnip mousse, crisp apple millefeuille and Calvados jus; rack of lamb with herb crust, basil mash and ratatouille-stuffed tomato. There is a separate vegetarian menu. The wide-ranging wine list includes wine grown in the castle's vineyard. The staff are praised again this year: "They are the best I've seen anywhere – attentive but not obsequious or intrusive. I always feel as though I am coming home when I return to *Thornbury Castle*." But more than one visitor disliked the "omnipresent piped music . . . To wake to rooks cawing, and look over ancient walls is magical, but the spell was broken by the background Verdi at breakfast." Thornbury is a good base for visiting Bristol, and for touring South Wales and the Cotswolds. (*Tessa Stuart, Mrs Francis V Viola III, and others*)

Open All year, except 4 days Jan.
Rooms 2 suites, 16 double, 2 single. Some across small courtyard. 3 on ground floor.
Facilities Lounge, library, 3 dining rooms. Background music all day in public areas. 15-acre grounds: garden, croquet, small farm, vineyard. Leisure centre (with swimming pool), golf nearby. Civil marriage licence.
Location 12 miles N of Bristol. From Thornbury on B4061 continue downhill to monumental water pump; bear left. Follow brown "historic castle" signs. Entrance to left of parish church 300 yds. Train: Bristol Parkway; then taxi.
Restrictions No smoking in dining rooms. Guide dogs only.
Credit cards All major cards accepted.
Terms B&B: single £85–£105, double £105–£260, suite £195–£350. Set lunch (2 to 3 courses) £16.50–£19.50; dinner (3 courses) £39.50. 2-night winter breaks. Christmas package. *V*

THORPE MARKET Norfolk   Map 2

Elderton Lodge   NEW   *Tel* (01263) 833547
Gunton Park, Cromer Road   *Fax* (01263) 834673
Thorpe Market NR11 8TZ   *E-mail* enquiries@eldertonlodge.co.uk
                                Website www.eldertonlodge.co.uk

*In large deerpark, 3 miles from the coast, Christine ("a charming, hard-working hostess") and Martin Worby's Grade II listed former shooting lodge (reportedly once visited by Edward VII and Lillie Langtry). Good public rooms (original panelling, sporting prints); good breakfasts; restaurant specialises in local seafood and game; occasional classical background music; mature garden. Shooting parties and small conferences catered for. Closed 8–25 Jan. Ten bedrooms (2 on ground floor; 5 no-smoking). Dogs allowed; no children under 10. 1-night bookings sometimes refused. B&B £45–£65; D,B&B £64.50–£84.50 [2000]. *V*

TINTAGEL Cornwall   Map 1

Trebrea Lodge   *Tel* (01840) 770410
Trenale   *Fax* (01840) 770092
Tintagel PL34 0HR

"A perfect place to explore North Cornwall, and to unwind and enjoy each hour of the day," said one visitor this year to this 14th-century, grey stone manor house with an 18th-century façade. Others wrote of the "courtesy and professionalism" of the "caring owners", and of the welcome extended to their young dog. Run in relaxed style by John Charlick, Sean Devlin (the chef) and Fergus Cochrane, the house stands on a wooded hillside with uninterrupted views across open fields to the Atlantic. Because it is only one room deep, the rooms have windows on both sides. "Lying in bed looking towards the sea must be the nearest one gets to heaven on earth." There is a smart upstairs drawing room with antique furniture, and a cosier sitting/smoking room, with an honesty bar and a log fire, on the ground floor. The bed-rooms vary in shape and size; they have antiques, interesting pictures, "and everything you could want" (sherry, fresh milk, mineral water, etc). One room has a carved wooden four-poster; a small one with beamed ceiling is reached up a steep stairway; one, in the old wash-house, has a separate entrance (an umbrella is provided for inclement weather). The oak-panelled restaurant can be busy serving non-residents – you should reserve your table when booking a bedroom. Dinner is served at 8 pm. The menu appears at breakfast; it is a no-choice meal, but "they will willingly provide an alternative if asked". "Dinner, by candlelight, with a view of the sunset, consists of top quality ingredients, carefully cooked and presented, with home-made soda bread." It might consist of grilled goat's cheese salad; chicken breasts with pesto cream sauce; sticky toffee pudding with fudge sauce; local cheeses (Cornish Yarg, Devon Sharpham). There's a small, well-chosen wine list. After dinner, over coffee and camomile tea, the chef sometimes mingles with the guests, "happy to discuss his recipes". The breakfast with fresh orange juice, and a buffet on a side-board, is thought excellent: "We were impressed by the 'bangers' and the perfectly poached eggs." Standards of housekeeping are high. *Trebrea* is well away from Tintagel, which is a touristy village, thanks to its Arthurian connections, but is worth visiting for the romantic ruined castle spectacularly set on a cliff. Its old post office, in a 14th-century building, is owned by the National Trust. Excellent walking nearby, along National Trust coastline or on Bodmin Moor. (*Jan and Alan Codd, John and Nicky Davies, Suzanne Lyons, Sir John Hall*)

Open Feb–Dec. Dining room closed midday.
Rooms 7 double. 1 in annexe.
Facilities 2 lounges, dining room. Jazz/classical music in kitchen during meals. 4½-acre grounds. Sand/rock beach ¾ mile. Unsuitable for &.
Location ½ mile SE of Tintagel. From Boscastle road, right by modern RC church, right at top of lane. Hotel 300 yds on left. Train: Bodmin Parkway; then taxi.
Restrictions Smoking in lounge bar only. No children under 12. "Well-behaved dogs" by prior arrangement (£3.75 daily).
Credit cards MasterCard, Amex, Visa.
Terms B&B: single £55.80–£67.50, double £77.40–£96; D,B&B: single £77.35–£91.50, double £120.60–£144. Set dinner £24. 2- to 7-day breaks. 1-night bookings sometimes refused.

TITCHWELL Norfolk   **Map 2**

Titchwell Manor   `NEW`   *Tel* (01485) 210221
Titchwell, nr Brancaster   *Fax* (01485) 210104
PE31 8BB   *E-mail* margaret@titchwellmanor.co.uk
                                  Website www.titchwellmanor.co.uk

Titchwell is famous for its RSPB bird reserve, and Margaret and Ian Snaith's small hotel offers special packages to RSPB members in winter. Two readers have recommended it this year: "It is a substantial Victorian building with additions. The lounge is welcoming, with a huge open fire. The staff are enthusiastic. Our well-equipped bedroom looked over a neat garden. The food was excellent, with a good selection at dinner, and generous breakfasts." "Good attention to detail. Very welcoming owners." The decor is simple and colourful, with stencilled walls and patterned fabrics. Two restaurants: a semi-formal dining room and a seafood bar. The set three-course menu includes, eg, dressed crab on warm samphire; local seabass with a coriander crust; butterscotch baked cheesecake. The house is on a main road, but this did not bother winter visitors, and it has "wonderful views over salt marshes to the sea". "In this beautiful part of the world, the sky seems to take on an extra dimension." Two championship golf courses are nearby. (*David and Patricia Hawkins, G Wiseman; also Good Pub Guide*)

Open All year, except last 2 weeks Jan.
Rooms 8 suites, 8 double. 4 in stable annexe. Some on ground floor.
Facilities Lounge, bar, restaurant, seafood bistro (occasional jazz/country/classical background music). 1½-acre garden. Beaches, golf nearby.
Location 5 miles E of Hunstanton. On A149 coast road between Brancaster and Thornham. Nearest station: King's Lynn.
Restrictions No smoking: restaurants, 5 bedrooms. No children in restaurant after 7 pm. No dogs in public rooms.
Credit cards All major cards accepted.
Terms B&B: single £35–£60, double £70–£90, suite £70–£100. Set lunch £15, dinner £23; full alc £35. 2-day breaks: D,B&B from £50 per person. 1-night bookings sometimes refused Sat. ***V***

TORQUAY Devon   Map 1

Mulberry House   BUDGET   *Tel* (01803) 213639
1 Scarborough Road
Torquay TQ2 5UJ

At corner of quiet street with many guest houses, 5 mins' walk from seafront: restaurant-with-rooms in Victorian listed white stucco villa. Three "calm, beautifully furnished" bedrooms, with marble fireplace, pine furniture, no telephone; 2 with power shower, 1 with large mirrored bathroom. No lounge, flowery terrace. Help-yourself drinks, tea and coffee; excellent dinners (modern cooking) and breakfasts; dedicated hostess Lesley Cooper; remarkable value. Restaurant closed to non-residents Mon/Tues. Checkout time 10 am. No smoking. Only restaurant suitable for ♿. Street parking. Credit cards not accepted. B&B £25–£35; D,B&B £42.50–£50. Set lunch £7.95; full alc £25 [2000]. More reports, please.

TREBARWITH STRAND Cornwall   Map 1

The Old Millfloor   BUDGET   *Tel/Fax* (01840) 770234
Trebarwith Strand
Tintagel PL34 0HB

A small white 16th-century guest house in a large garden with a millstream. The beach is a ten-minute stroll away, and there is good cliff walking in this beautiful area of north Cornwall. The "slightly eccentric" owner, Janice Waddon-Martyn, runs the place in relaxed style – "she is a little laid-back, but pleasantly efficient," says a visitor this year. She serves breakfast between 8 and 10 am, and she encourages guests to ask for tea and coffee whenever they please. The "hospitable feel", with log fires, even in summer if it is cold, and the child-friendliness are appreciated, and also the lack of TV and piped music in public rooms. The interior is airy with plenty of colour, gleaming wood, fresh flowers and cleverly used fabrics. Bedrooms have white walls, pure white linen, lots of lace, big feather pillows and a wash-basin and TV. There is one large shared bathroom, which can lead to queues in peak periods. The home-cooked supper, with limited choice, is served by candlelight between 7 and 8 pm in the small beamed dining room. No licence; bring your own wine. "The very simple cooking is good, and portions are generous" – the menu might include carrot and ginger soup; chicken fillet baked with herbs, leeks, carrots and orange; chocolate truffle slice with cream. Soups and ice-creams are home made; organic meat is used when possible. Rolls are freshly baked, as are the scones for tea (no charge). Breakfasts are "especially good and lavish". Not for the disabled or infirm, as the house is reached by a steep path down from the road: "You have to cling to a piece of rope and clutch at any bit of tree." Best take the minimum of luggage. Tintagel is two miles away. (*EW*)

Open Easter–Nov.
Rooms 3 double, with wash-basin. TV; no telephone.
Facilities Lounge/dining room. No background music. 10-acre grounds: garden, orchard, paddocks, stream. Beach 10 mins' walk down, 20 mins up. Riding centre 2½ miles. Unsuitable for &.
Location 2 miles S of Tintagel by B3263. Train Bodmin Parkway; then taxi/bus.
Restrictions No smoking. No dogs.
Credit cards None accepted.
Terms [2000] (*Not VAT-rated*) B&B £18–£20. Set dinner £13.50. Unlicensed: bring your own wine. Child accommodated in parents' room free; in separate room 50% of adult rate.

TRESCO Isles of Scilly	**Map 1**

The Island Hotel	*Tel* (01720) 422883
Tresco, Isles of Scilly	*Fax* (01720) 423008
Cornwall TR24 0PU	*E-mail* islandhotel@tresco.co.uk
	Website www.tresco.co.uk

The private island of Tresco is leased by Robert Dorrien Smith from the Duchy of Cornwall. Only two miles by one, it is warmed by the Gulf Stream, and famed for its subtropical Abbey Gardens. The native wildlife is supplemented in October by rare migrant birds from Asia and America. There are ruined castles, civil war battle sites and prehistoric burial sites to be explored on the heath. No cars; but bicycles can be hired (they should be booked in advance). A tractor and trailer convey guests from the quay or heliport to this modern hotel, now managed by Philip Callan – the helpfulness of his staff is said to be "a little variable" this year. The decor may be conventional, but public areas are spacious and comfortable. A floor-to-ceiling glass wall in the sitting room gives dramatic views of the rocky coastline and other islands. Many visitors are regulars, drawn by the "idyllic setting", the peacefulness in term time, and the child-friendliness during the school holidays – it gets booked up months ahead, though there are no family suites, and rates for children are not low. "Our high-spirited grand-children were well cared for," says one member of a three-generation family of visitors. "They were given high tea, and the child-sitting ser-vice enabled the adults to have a civilised dinner. The food was varied and well cooked" (the chef, Peter Hingston, serves main courses like curried cod with chardonnay butter sauce; roast noisettes of lamb on rosti potato with Puy lentils). Tables are rotated to give everyone a turn at a window table. Suites have a balcony, and the best bedrooms, in the Flower wing, have picture windows opening on to a private patio. Bar lunches are "expensive but substantial"; snacks, tea, coffee and drinks are served all day. Breakfast includes plenty of fruit "and scrummy Abbey Platter (the works), but packet orange juice and rather dreary toast", and service can be haphazard. There is a collec-tion of buckets, spades and pushchairs by the front door for general use. (*Sir Timothy Harford, and others*)

Open Mar–end Oct.
Rooms 3 suites, 40 double, 5 single. Some in 2 annexes. 2 on ground floor.
Facilities Lounge/bar, Quiet Room (residents only), restaurant, games room. No background music. 2¾-acre grounds: tennis, croquet, bowls, swimming pool (open 1 May–30 Sept), beach: safe bathing, diving, snorkelling. Tresco not suitable for &.
Location NE side of island. Boat or helicopter from Penzance. Hotel will make travel arrangements; guests met on arrival.
Restrictions No smoking in restaurant; no dogs allowed on Tresco.
Credit cards MasterCard, Visa.
Terms [2000] D,B&B: single £90–£120, double £95–£175, suite £120–£230. Snack/packed lunches. Set lunch £17.50, dinner £33; full alc £43. Child accommodated in parents' room: £32.50. Reductions for 5 days or more. Gardening, painting, writing, birdwatching holidays.

See also SHORTLIST

TUNBRIDGE WELLS Kent   **Map 2**

Hotel du Vin & Bistro   *Tel* (01892) 526455
Crescent Road   *Fax* (01892) 512044
Tunbridge Wells   *E-mail* reception@tunbridgewells.hotelduvin.co.uk
TN1 2LY   *Website* www.hotelduvin.co.uk

A handsome 18th-century Grade II listed sandstone building over-looking Claverley Park. Queen Victoria, then a princess, frequently stayed here during the "season". The building was extended in the 1830s by Decimus Burton, known for the Palm House at Kew Gardens. Now part of Gerard Basset and Robin Hutson's Alternative Hotel Group (see also Bristol and Winchester), it is managed by Matthew Callard, maintaining the group's aim of serving superior wines with informal food at reasonable prices. "An attractive atmosphere, with lofty rooms, bare board floors and dark painted walls," wrote a visitor in 2000. "A charming young staff." Reception may be "a little eccentric". The busy bistro (you need to reserve a table) serves modern dishes, eg, monkfish and skate terrine with crispy whitebait; baked cod with artichokes, clams and chorizo; fig tart with honey ice-cream. "It was delightful, with great food, great service, a knowledgeable and unimposing *sommelier*," one visitor wrote, but another thought that her dinner "lacked a certain 'edge'". One visitor found the breakfasts "unremarkable", but another wrote of "really good croissants and coffee". The bedrooms and bathrooms ("large and light, minimally but well furnished") are sponsored by wine and champagne companies; Veuve Cliquot is much admired. "The sheets are fantastic and the bath brilliant; CD-players mean you can bring your favourite music with you." Some bathrooms have a freestanding Edwardian-style bath and a cubicle with a power shower. The quietest rooms are at the back, overlooking the park (at the front is a busy road on a steep hill). The public rooms, decorated with copies of paintings by Modigliani, Picasso, etc, are candlelit at night, but dimmer switches enable you to turn up the lighting if you wish to read. The snooker room is dedicated to Havana cigars. The Burgundy Bar, "full of comfy sofas and chairs", offers a good selection of wines by the glass. (*Patricia Darby, Sue Davies, Joanne Hoddy*)

Open All year.
Rooms 1 suite, 31 double.
Facilities Lift. Lounge, bar lounge, snooker lounge, bistro. No background music. 1-acre grounds.
Location Central, by intersection of Mount Pleasant Rd and Crescent Rd/Church Rd (opposite Assembly Hall, police station). Private carpark.
Restriction No dogs.
Credit cards All major cards accepted.
Terms [2000] Room: single/double £75–£139, suite £109–£139. Extra bed £10. Breakfast: continental £7.50, English £11.50. Full alc £30.

TWO BRIDGES Devon   **Map 1**

Prince Hall   *Tel* (01822) 890403
Two Bridges   *Fax* (01822) 890676
Yelverton PL20 6SA   *E-mail* bookings@princehall.co.uk
                                     Website www.princehall.co.uk

The hamlet, at a road junction in the middle of Dartmoor, is named for its bridges across the West Dart River, one of which dates back to 1780. And this late 18th-century house was built as a private home for Sir Francis Buller, at 32 the youngest-ever British High Court judge. Set well back from a small road, in large grounds, it has panoramic views across the river valley. It is now a small hotel, informally run by Carrie and Adam Southwell. He is the chef, and most reporters found the food "very good" this year. "The owners are well in evidence and very welcoming; their staff are particularly thoughtful. The house dogs, Harvey and Rosie, know their place but are also friendly." (This is not a place to visit if you dislike dogs.) Other guests wrote of "a glorious location; atmosphere of a private house party". The decor is "that of a comfortable country home, not over-fancy". Many bedrooms are spacious; the best ones have a four-poster bed, a fireplace, and views of the moors; standard ones overlook a courtyard. The menus (with choice) are based on local meat and game and locally caught fish, eg, chargrilled scallops with a vermouth and saffron sauce; seabass on a bed of pickled red cabbage; roast lamb with minted apricots. "Excellent home-baked rolls; portions adequate to large; everything properly hot." The wine list is strong on New World bottles, and reasonably priced. But several visitors this year found the piped music annoying. "Breakfast is served with a smile between 8.30 and 9.30 am, after that you just get the smile," say the Southwells. Special dishes such as haddock, kippers and black pudding must be ordered the night before. Cream teas are served, in the garden in summer. "Well-behaved" visiting dogs are welcomed – no charge. Maggie the pig, the geese and the horses "all add to the fun". You can walk from the grounds straight on to the moor. The dramatic landscape is said to have inspired Sir Arthur Conan Doyle, a visitor in the late 19th century, to write *The Hound of the Baskervilles*. A nearby Stone Age wood of dwarf oaks is worth a visit. (*Brian and Rosalind Keen, and others*)

Open Mid-Feb–mid-Dec. Restaurant closed midday (packed lunch available).
Rooms 8 double, 1 single.
Facilities Sitting room, lounge/bar, restaurant; jazz/classical background music at night. 6-acre grounds. River Dart, fishing 3 mins' walk; riding, shooting, golf nearby. Only restaurant and bar suitable for ⅋.
Location 1 mile SE of Two Bridges, on B3357 to Ashburton. Train: Plymouth (17 miles); then taxi.
Restrictions No smoking in restaurant. No children under 10 in restaurant at night.
Credit cards All major cards accepted.
Terms [2000] B&B £45–£60; D,B&B £70–£85. Set dinner £29. 1-night bookings refused bank holidays. Reductions for 3 nights or more.

ULLSWATER Cumbria   **Map 4**

Howtown Hotel   BUDGET   *Tel* (017684) 86514
Ullswater, nr Penrith CA10 2ND

♔ *César award in 1991*

"The situation is outstanding," says one aficionado of this unsophisticated, inexpensive guest house, 101 years old this year. Another visitor called it "a very nice old country house, with super furniture and paintings, good dinners and a good wine list". Set back from the road on the eastern shore of the second-largest lake in the Lake District, *Howtown* is well placed for yachting, windsurfing and other water sports, and it is a favourite of walkers and climbers. Such is its popularity that it is often fully booked (first-time visitors can feel a bit "out of the club"). The owner, Jacquie Baldry, and her son, David, are the third and fourth generation to be involved, but service is by young women, many from the south of England (one visitor this year thought it "could have been more willing"). With its solid furniture, comfortable lounges, "remarkable collection of pewter, well-nurtured gardens, and magnificent flowers in the entrance lounge" this is a "marvellous retreat", according to a regular visitor. But some bedrooms are "poky", and few have private facilities (queues can build up outside the bathroom). The large best room, to the right of the upstairs sitting room, has a view on to the lake. Rooms in the annexe and the self-catering cottages have an *en suite* bathroom. In the main house, early morning tea is brought to the room, and beds are turned down during dinner. Breakfasts are generous, with stewed and fresh fruit, eggs as you wish. The dining room has tables close together, and a fixed dinner menu served at 7 pm. It consists of home-made soups, roast meats, traditional puddings such as fruit crumbles. Vegetables "are not a strong point". "The cooking hasn't changed, but the coffee is better," Mrs Baldry assures us. The bar carries "an admirable selection of malt whiskies". A cold lunch is served on weekdays; on Sunday there is a *table d'hôte* lunch and a cold supper. Substantial, if not gourmet, packed lunches are provided. Cream teas ("amazingly cheap at £2.50") come with fresh-baked scones, good jams and a silver teapot. The two dogs: Tad, something of a mongrel, and Zingara, a Rhodesian Ridgeback, "are still going strong". (*JC, and others*)

Open End Mar–1 Nov.
Rooms 10 double, 2 single. 4 with bath, 1 with shower. 2 in annexe. 4 self-catering cottages. No telephone.
Facilities 4 lounges, TV room, 2 bars, dining room. No background music. 2-acre grounds. 200 yds from lake: private foreshore, fishing. Walking, sailing, climbing, riding, golf nearby. Unsuitable for &.
Location E shore of lake, 4 miles S of Pooley Bridge. Bus from Penrith station (9 miles).
Restrictions No children under 7. Dogs by arrangement; not in public rooms.
Credit cards None accepted.
Terms [2000] D,B&B £43–£48. Set lunch: weekday £7.50, Sun £9.25, packed £3.75. Set dinner £14.50; cold Sun supper £9.75. 1-night bookings sometimes refused.

Sharrow Bay	*Tel* (017684) 86301
Ullswater	*Fax* (017684) 86349
nr Penrith CA10 2LZ	*E-mail* enquiries@sharrow-bay.com
	Website www.sharrow-bay.com

César award in 1999

"A marvellous weekend. Spoiling in fantastic surroundings. The staff make you feel that you are the only guest. Expensive, but compared with some of the five-star chain hotels, a bargain." "*Sharrow* continues in its own inimitable way." "The food is wonderful. Our delightful bedroom, Marion, with lake views, was reminiscent of a room in an old-fashioned play." Some of this year's comments on the original English country house hotel (Relais & Châteaux), now 52 years old. It stands on the eastern shore of Ullswater, looking to jagged Lakeland fells. This stark beauty contrasts with the now rather dated style of the pink-and-gold public rooms, where antiques and ornaments fill every corner, and cherubs peek out from curtains and hang from ceilings. The founder, Brian Sack, still much in evidence, runs the place with managing director, Nigel Lightburn, and a long-serving staff. It is something of a shrine to Mr Sack's late partner, Francis Coulson. His large tombstone stands in the garden; his name is on the bedroom welcoming cards and on the menus; his Regency syllabub is often served at dinner. The food (*Michelin* star) "is a little lighter now", one regular visitor thought. Dinner at 8 pm is a six-course affair, with starters like mulligatawny soup or terrine of duck foie gras; substantial main courses, eg, venison with braised red cabbage, fried polenta, sweetcorn pancake, juniper and rosemary sauce; fillet of lamb in a herb brioche crust with couscous and a leek and potato galette. Every dish is elaborately garnished. A queue builds up to choose from the desserts. Teas are lavish, and at breakfast "the waiters seem to compete to see how much they can persuade you to eat". The opulence continues in the bedrooms, which have a fridge, Scrabble, backgammon, glossy books on the Lake District; and countless ornaments – one couple counted 28 vases, figurines, dishes, etc. Some rooms in the main building are small; larger ones are in *Bank House*, a mile away (a "people carrier" takes guests to the main house). Fittings everywhere are "of high quality", and housekeeping and maintenance are "impeccable". At times the public areas are crowded, delays can occur in the restaurant, and

the whole experience is too much for some tastes (and one visitor found the staff "slightly severe"). But those in favour lap up the "superlative comfort". Five new suites are due to open in June 2000. (*Sue Davies, Heather Sharland, Conrad and Marilyn Dehn; also Pat and Jeremy Temple, and others*)

Open Early Mar–early Dec.
Rooms 5 suites, 19 double, 2 single. 16 in cottage, lodge, *Bank House* (1 mile). 4 on ground floor. 5 more suites planned for June 2000.
Facilities Main house: 2 lounges, conservatory, 2 dining rooms; *Bank House*: 2 lounges, breakfast room. No background music. 6-acre grounds: gardens, woodland; ½-mile lake shore, safe (cold) bathing, private jetty, boathouse. Civil wedding licence.
Location E shore of Ullswater, 2 miles S of Pooley Bridge. M6 exit 40. Turn on to Howtown Lane by small church in Pooley Bridge.
Restrictions No smoking in restaurant. No children under 13. No dogs in house (kennels nearby).
Credit cards MasterCard, Visa.
Terms D,B&B £120–£145. Set lunch £36.25, dinner £47.25. 20% midweek reduction off-season. 1-night bookings sometimes refused weekends.

****

Hotel in Scotland. In almost all respects this is a very nice hotel, but the downside was very hard beds. Why do hotels persist in treating guests like fakirs?

****

ULVERSTON Cumbria   **Map 4**

The Bay Horse   *Tel* (01229) 583972
Canal Foot   *Fax* (01229) 588044
Ulverston LA12 9EL   *E-mail* reservations@bayhorse.furness.co.uk
                                   Website www.furness.co.uk/bayhorse

The approach to this old inn is unappealing, through an industrial
estate and past a huge Glaxo-Wellcome factory, but it has a "stunning"
waterside setting at the end of the Ulverston canal, where once
coaches crossed the sands of Morecambe Bay to Lancaster. A huge
stone horse's head adorns the bar. Robert Lyons, the chef and co-
owner (with John Tovey, now retired to South Africa), presides with
manager Peter McKinnon. They run it informally (too much so, for
one visitor, who was put out to find that the "smart dress" code was
ignored by many day-trippers in the busy bar). Reports are mixed this
year: another visitor was critical of the housekeeping, and thought the
accommodation overpriced, and a third found the inn "highly professional". But everyone appreciates the view from the bedrooms with
ducks, swans and cygnets on the water, and all manner of birds on the
mud flats (bird books and a bird feeder are provided). It is "amazingly
peaceful" at night – you are lulled to sleep by the sounds of gulls, and
lapping water if the tide is in. Rooms tend to be small, with a narrow
bed, but they have French windows opening on to a terrace. More
ambitious meals are served in the conservatory restaurant that overlooks the Leven estuary (everyone goes in to dine at 7.30 pm). One
visitor this year thought the food disappointing, but most have enjoyed
the cooking on a long weekly-changing menu: "excellent and innovative"; "as good as ever", they say, remembering dishes like monkfish
and king prawns in a lemon and fresh herb butter; quail stuffed with
apricot, prune and fresh sage, with a juniper and fresh thyme sauce. If
you want something simpler you can choose a steak from a separate
menu (it comes with a baked potato and salad). Bread, pickles and
chocolates are home made. There is a good selection of New World
wines. "The staff are good-natured and efficient," says a visitor this
year. "Very good breakfasts: freshly squeezed orange juice, good marmalade, perfectly poached eggs." Nearby is Holker Hall, a stately
home with fine gardens and a motor museum. (*PF, Good Pub Guide,
HS, and others*)

Open All year.
Rooms 9 double.
Facilities Bar lounge, conservatory restaurant; mixed/classical background
music during meals. Unsuitable for &.
Location 8 miles NE of Barrow-in-Furness. From M6, exit 36, take A590
towards Barrow-in-Furness. On entering Ulverston, go straight through 1st
roundabout; turn left after 200 yds on to Canal Foot road. Continue to end; turn
left. Branch railway line from Lancaster.
Restrictions No smoking in restaurant. No children under 12.
Credit cards MasterCard, Visa.
Terms (*Excluding 10% service charge on meals*) B&B £60–£65; D,B&B
£85–£90. Set lunch £17.75; full alc £35. Christmas package.

UPPER SLAUGHTER Gloucestershire   Map 3

Lords of the Manor [NEW]   *Tel* (01451) 820243
Upper Slaughter, nr Bourton-on-the-Water   *Fax* (01451) 820696
GL54 2JD   *E-mail* lordsofthe manor@btinternet.com
                                  Website www.lordsofthemanor.com

Once the home of the rector of this tiny, picture-postcard village, this
lovely 17th-century house stands in a large park. It has been "seam-
lessly extended" and turned into a smart hotel with a *Michelin*-starred
restaurant. "It still maintains high standards," says a visitor who knew
it under its earlier ownership (it changed hands two years ago, and is
now managed by Iain Shelton). "Bedrooms in the main house are
excellent, and there are good ones in converted stables. The situation
is charming, with views down the lawns to a willow-flanked lake.
Service is first class; food is excellent – the chef's little extra courses
add interest to the meal. Ideal for a real spoil." John Campbell cooks
modern dishes, eg, velouté of wild mushrooms with truffle tortellini;
roast John Dory, with haricot blanc and saffron emulsion; mandarin
brûlée with cappuccino ice-cream. "Portions are not enormous; everything is excellently cooked, and beautifully presented." With open
fires, strong colours, fresh flowers, antiques and family portraits, the
public rooms have a country house air. The restaurant overlooks the
walled garden. Some bedrooms look on to the old courtyard, where the
village dining hall once stood; some have sloping ceilings. Popular
with American and Japanese visitors. (*John Knott, and others*)

Open All year.
Rooms 1 suite, 24 double, 2 single.
Facilities Drawing room, library, writing room, bar, restaurant. No back-
ground music. 8-acre grounds: carp lake. Unsuitable for &.
Location Edge of village, 3 miles SW of Stow-on-the-Wold.
Restrictions No smoking in restaurant. No young children at dinner. No dogs.
Credit cards All major cards accepted.
Terms (*Excluding VAT*) B&B: single £99, double from £145, suite £295. Set
lunch £21, dinner £75. Summer and winter breaks. Christmas, New Year rates.

UPPINGHAM Rutland   Map 2

The Lake Isle   *Tel/Fax* (01572) 822951
16 High Street East
Uppingham LE15 9PZ

"Within two minutes we were delighted, and we remained so throughout our brief stay," say visitors this year to this "very French" restaurant-with-rooms. Others wrote: "Hospitality is first class, very
friendly." The 18th-century building stands on the main street of a
charming market town; entrance, through the back, is via a "neat and
flower-filled yard, with the feeling of a mews". The bedrooms are
named after French wine regions and the cooking of the owner/chef,
David Whitfield, is French influenced. His wife, Claire, is front-of-
house. Their staff are "uniformly friendly"; even in the owners'
absence, "the place seemed to run like clockwork, the atmosphere

remained relaxed". The restaurant, with pine-panelled walls and pine furniture, has a weekly-changing menu for which you pay according to the number of courses taken. "Particularly good were cod with a mildly spicy Thai sauce, and summer pudding; other dishes include, eg, prawn ravioli with a lobster sauce; roulade of duck and chicken on a red onion marmalade; bread-and-butter pudding with a passion fruit and pineapple sauce" (but one reader was disappointed with her treacle tart). Emphasis is on fresh ingredients, and a small loaf of freshly baked bread is placed on each table. The wine list is "amazing, in two parts: wines and fine wines. There is a good selection of half bottles." When the restaurant is closed, simple meals are provided for residents. The bar was once a barber's shop, known as "Sweeney Todd's", where boys from the public school had their hair cut. There's a pretty pink-walled lounge above the restaurant, and a small garden. The "immaculately clean" bedrooms are provided with sherry, fresh fruit, good biscuits. Some rooms are small, but Dom Pérignon is large, with a whirlpool bath; Bordeaux has a power shower. The suites, on two floors, with a spacious living area, are in mews houses. "Generous breakfasts" have freshly squeezed orange juice, cereals, "delicious home-made jams", a good choice of hot dishes, excellent coffee. One couple with a child reported a misunderstanding over the hotel's "pricing policy" which was not satisfactorily resolved. "The guided tour of Uppingham School is interesting" and there is some lovely countryside around, in an area often neglected by tourists. (*Peter and Moira Smith, ID, Sarah and Tony Thomas, and others*)

Open All year. Restaurant closed Mon midday; to non-residents Sun evening.
Rooms 2 suites (in mews), 9 double, 1 single.
Facilities Lounge, bar, restaurant; meeting room. Small walled garden. Unsuitable for &.
Location Town centre. Entrance at rear of hotel. On foot approach via Reeves Yard. By car: travelling N on A6003, turn right into High St East at 1st lights (travelling S, turn left at 2nd lights). Go past hotel; right into Queen St. Just before bottom sharp right into No Through Road, right again at Private Parking sign – this small road leads to entrance. Carpark. Train: Oakham, 6 miles; Kettering, 14 miles.
Restriction No smoking: restaurant, bedrooms. No dogs in public rooms.
Credit cards All major cards accepted.
Terms B&B: single £45–£52, double £65–£69, suite £75–£80. D,B&B £54–£75 per person. Set lunch £13.50, dinner £23.50. Special breaks (champagne, etc). Christmas package. *V*

VERYAN Cornwall   **Map 1**

The Nare   *Tel* (01872) 501111
Carne Beach   *Fax* (01872) 501856
Veryan-in-Roseland   *E-mail* office@narehotel.co.uk
nr Truro TR2 5PF   *Website* www.narehotel.co.uk

"Probably the nicest in Devon and Cornwall" is how one couple described this traditional family hotel. Returning after nearly a year, they were "greeted as old friends", and their preference for duvets over blankets was remembered. Other visitors wrote of the "courteous

staff; excellent breakfast and afternoon tea; good and varied dinner
menu (delicious fresh lobsters)". "They are unusual in that they actually take notice of requests for small portions." The owner, Mrs Bettye
Gray, and her grandson, Toby Ashworth, who represents the fourth
generation of a hotel-keeping family, run *The Nare* with manager
Richard Young. Set in extensive grounds above Carne Beach, it is surrounded by National Trust land on the Roseland peninsula. In its subtropical gardens are a swimming pool, a tennis court, secluded corners
for sunbathing. There is direct access to the beach and safe bathing.
The interior has a country house feel, with antiques, oriental rugs,
ornaments and flowers, but the absence of any no-smoking areas is
regretted. The bedrooms vary in size; the best-designed ones have a
sea view; many have a balcony. Deluxe double rooms have a large
bedroom-cum-lounge with a full-length patio, a huge bathroom, a
walk-in wardrobe. There are inter-communicating rooms for families.
Old-fashioned services such as shoe-cleaning, evening room-tidying,
hot-water bottles in beds, etc, are appreciated. The varied menu
includes vegetarian options and local fish and seafood, and ends with
a dessert trolley. Guests help themselves to coffee and petits fours in
the lounge. Light suppers and lunches, and a nursery tea for under-
sevens, are served in the Gwendra Room. The hotel's 22-foot boat, the
Maggie O'Nare, is available for charter. Veryan's name is a corrup-
tion of St Symphorien, to whom the village church is dedicated. Its
Regency round houses were so constructed to give the Devil no corners in which to hide. (*GK Clarke, John and Ann Smith, and others*)

Open All year.
Rooms 3 suites, 28 double, 5 single. Some on ground floor. Self-catering
cottage.
Facilities Lift. 2 lounges, bar lounge, billiard room, light lunch/supper room,
restaurant, conservatory; drying room; indoor swimming pool, spa bath, sauna,
gym. No background music. 5-acre grounds: gardens, heated indoor and outdoor swimming pools, tennis, children's play area, safe sandy beach, sail-
boarding, fishing. Concessionary golf at Truro Golf Club.
Location From A390 take B3287 towards Tregony; then A3078 towards St
Mawes *c.* 1½ miles. 1st left to Veryan; through village, leaving *New Inn* on
left; 1 mile straight towards sea. Signposted from main road.
Restriction No dogs in public rooms.
Credit cards MasterCard, Visa.
Terms B&B £75–£150; D,B&B (min. 3 nights) £80–£250. Set lunch £16.50,
dinner £33; full alc £45. Special breaks: bridge, etc. Christmas package.

WAREHAM Dorset   **Map 2**

The Priory   *Tel* (01929) 551666
Church Green   *Fax* (01929) 554519
Wareham BH20 4ND   *E-mail* reception@theprioryhotel.co.uk
                                        Website www.theprioryhotel.co.uk

Q *César award in 1996*

"Remains one of the best hotels we know." "On our third visit, we
enjoyed it more than ever, from the moment we stepped over the
threshold to a personal welcome." "Service is attentive at all times, but

never overpowering." One visitor this year wrote of an impersonal reception, but most have written enthusiastically again about John and Stuart Turner's luxurious hotel. Formerly the Priory of Lady St Mary, it is approached across a green, "a coloured oasis of Georgian houses", to the flagstoned courtyard, filled in summer with busy lizzies, petunias and geraniums. The "immaculately maintained gardens, full of hidden corners and interesting plants", and with views of the Purbeck Hills, slope down to the River Frome. The "country house atmosphere" is admired (though some visitors could have done without the discreet classical background music), and so is the food. Breakfast ("with excellent toast and real orange juice") and lunch are served in a cream-and-green room overlooking the grounds; dinner is in the stone-vaulted cellars. The chef, Stephen Astley, cooks modern dishes, eg, salad of duck confit and Parma ham, flavoured with oranges, on a raspberry vinegar dressing; baked halibut with asparagus on a mussel, leek and saffron broth. In the beamed drawing room, a pianist plays on Saturday. The bedrooms vary greatly, but all have fruit and books; most are spacious. A single was thought "tiny, and basically furnished" this year, but a double was "charming and peaceful, with a lovely view downriver". The best bedrooms are in the Boathouse, a converted 16th-century clay barn on the riverbank; some have a four-poster bed and a balcony overlooking the garden. There can be noise from the main road out of Wareham. The Turners also own the *Casterbridge Hotel*, Dorchester (*qv*). Corfe Castle is close by; so is good walking in the Purbeck countryside and on the South West Coast Path. (*Nigel and Jennifer Jee, HJM Tucker, and others*)

Open All year.
Rooms 2 suites, 14 double, 3 single. 4 in boathouse. Some on ground floor.
Facilities 2 lounges (1 with pianist Sat evenings), bar, 2 dining rooms; "discreet" classical background music. 4-acre gardens: croquet, river frontage, mooring, fishing, bicycle hire. Sea 4 miles. Unsuitable for &.
Location From A351 bypass at station roundabout, take North Causeway/North St to centre. At traffic lights, left into East St, 1st right into Church St; hotel between church and river.
Restrictions No smoking in dining rooms. No children under 8. Guide dogs only.
Credit cards All major cards accepted.
Terms [2000] B&B: single £80, double £100–£240, suite £240. Light lunches. Set lunch (2 to 3 courses) £12–£25.50, dinner (4 to 5 courses) £26.50–£31.50; full alc £49.15. Off-season breaks. Christmas package.

WARMINSTER Wiltshire   Map 2

Bishopstrow House   *Tel* (01985) 212312
Boreham Road   *Fax* (01985) 216769
Warminster BA12 9HH   *E-mail* reservations@bishopstrow.co.uk

With "the feel of a family hotel such as you would find in southern France or Italy", this late Georgian country house "is a good place to spoil yourself", says a visitor this year. Others had a "very enjoyable three-generation bank holiday weekend". The manager, David Dowden, heads an "enthusiastic and charming staff", who provide "excellent service". A returning visitor wrote of "an enchanting stay", and the "easy feel" of the place is liked. There is plenty to see and do in the large grounds (most of which are reached through a tunnel under a road): gardens with ancient trees and temples, a lovely stretch of the River Wylye, quiet spots for "soaking up the sun". The "state of the art" spa, with a good-sized swimming pool, beauty treatments, etc, attracts a "real mix of guests: families with children, young and old romantics as well as celebrities". Dogs are welcomed too, and allowed in the public rooms. These are dramatic, with vibrant colours, tartan carpets, mirrors of gargantuan proportions, heraldic motifs. The bedrooms vary greatly. Some suites and bedrooms are spacious and luxurious; smaller ones at the top of steep stairs are comfortable, but less interesting. Front rooms can get noise from cars and delivery trucks. The modern cooking of Chris Suter is thought "simply delicious". Plenty of choice, including, eg, crostini of roast scallops and grilled asparagus; confit of Quantock duck; soft chocolate fondant and peanut tart with almond milk ice-cream. "The wine list is interesting and the French *sommelier*, Armand, very helpful." The dining room is formal; some tables have "lovely views of the garden"; but one reader this year experienced "the odour of chlorine from the pool next door which did not enhance the delicious food". Light meals and sandwiches are available all day. Local sightseeing includes Longleat, Stourhead, Stonehenge, Bath and Salisbury. (*Debbie Peers-Smith, Victoria Maltby, JS Rutter, NR*)

Open All year.
Rooms 5 suites, 27 double.
Facilities Hall, drawing room, library, bar, conservatory, restaurant (pianist or jazz/classical background music during meals); children's games room; function/conference facilities; health spa (gym, hairdresser, swimming pool, sauna, solarium). 28-acre grounds: outdoor swimming pool, indoor/outdoor tennis; river, fishing rights (15 Apr–15 Oct), shooting. Golf nearby. Unsuitable for &. Civil wedding licence.
Location On B3414, 1½ miles E of Warminster. Train: Westbury, 8 miles; then taxi.
Restrictions No smoking in restaurant.
Credit cards All major cards accepted.
Terms [2000] B&B: single £90–£99, double £185–£195, suite £290–£325. Bar meals available all day. Set lunch/dinner £35; full alc £35. Child accommodated in parents' room: B&B £25. Fly-fishing, golf, spa, country breaks. Christmas package. 1-night bookings refused Sat. *V*

WASDALE HEAD Cumbria   Map 4

Wasdale Head Inn   *Tel* (019467) 26229 and 26333
Wasdale Head   *Fax* (019467) 26334
nr Gosforth CA20 1EX   *E-mail* wasdaleheadinn@msn.com
                                        Website www.wasdale.com

One *Guide* reader, who recently toured the Lakes "walking from pub to pub/hotel", wrote that this was "one of the best places on the trip – simple yet very comfortable, in a stunning setting". The old gabled building has an isolated position at the head of Wasdale, England's deepest lake. Owned, and run in humorous style, by Howard and Kate

Christie and their border collie Froach, it is a "super place, with a helpful, hard-working staff" and an informal atmosphere. The bedrooms are gradually being upgraded. The decor is traditional, with solid old furniture, wood panelling, and climbing mementos; the "comfortably old-fashioned" residents' lounge has books and games. The main bar, which has an open fire, is named after the inn's first landlord, Will Ritson, reputed to be the world's biggest liar – lying competitions are held in the village once a year in his memory. The inn holds beer festivals and mountaineering-related courses, including women's courses with female instructors, and it has a "Bah Humbug" Christmas package – "no crackers, no silly hats". Howard Christie is co-chef with Mike Nixon, using local produce, such as Herdwick lamb, when possible; calorific puddings include Granny Christie's Cranachan (ie, cream, raspberries, whisky and roasted porridge oats). Portions are "designed for people who have been on the fells all day". Breakfasts are equally hearty, with a buffet of fruit, cheeses, etc, and porridge, local bacon, free-range eggs; devilled kidneys or kedgeree by arrangement. Bar meals, packed lunches and cream teas are available. There is a large drying room, and a full laundry service. (*Peter Wilson; also Good Pub Guide*)

Open All year. Restaurant closed Sun–Wed Nov–March.
Rooms 1 family, 3 suites in annexe 20 yds; 8 double, 2 single. Some on ground floor. Also self-catering apartments. No TV (poor reception).
Facilities Lounge, residents' bar, public bar, restaurant; steam room; drying room; beer garden. No background music. 3-acre grounds: stream, pond. Wastwater 1 mile, sea 12 miles. Canadian canoes available. Unsuitable for &.
Location 10 miles from Gosforth, Holmrook. Follow signs from A595. Train: Seascale; hotel will meet.
Restrictions No smoking: restaurant, lounge, 6 bedrooms. "Well-behaved dogs accepted subject to Froach's approval."
Credit cards Amex, MasterCard, Visa.
Terms B&B £35–£54.50. Bar lunches. Set dinner £22. Special breaks. Courses: rock-climbing, fell walking, cooking, etc, all year. Christmas package.

WATER YEAT Cumbria   **Map 4**

Water Yeat Guest House NEW/BUDGET *Tel/Fax* (01229) 885306
Water Yeat
nr Coniston LA12 8DJ

17th-century farmhouse ½ mile from S tip of Coniston Water, (Arthur Ransome country). On A5084, 2½ miles N of Lowick. Now an "excellent", inexpensive country guest house. New owner, Ursula Walsh, has redecorated. 5 simple bedrooms (1 family), with floral fabrics, lovely views. 4-acre garden/woodlands. "Good and varied dinners", with some choice, communally served in beamed dining room. Hearty Cumbrian breakfasts with home-made preserves. No background music. Open mid-Feb–mid-Nov; dining room closed Sun except bank holidays. Unsuitable for &. No smoking. No children under 4 except when whole house is taken. No dogs. Credit cards not accepted. B&B £25–£30. Set dinner £18.50 [2000]. "Generous hosts, good food and excellent value," say visitors this year. *V*

WATERHOUSES Staffordshire	Map 3

The Old Beams
Leek Road
Waterhouses ST10 3HW

Tel (01538) 308254
Fax (01538) 308157

"Expensive but very good" is a verdict this year on this restaurant-with-rooms, in a hamlet on the edge of the Peak District. It has a *Michelin* star for owner/chef Nigel Wallis's modern cooking; his wife, Ann, is "wonderful at front-of-house", "full of warmth". Their son is the "rather serious" wine waiter – the house wines are "reasonably priced", and there is a good selection of half bottles on the carefully annotated wine list. Specialities on the *à la carte* menu include warm scallop mousse with a ravioli of langoustine on a spicy sauce; roast noisette of lamb with a herb crust and brunoise of vegetables; hot pistachio soufflé with chocolate sauce. Meals are served in the beamed, low-ceilinged dining room or a conservatory with Italian-style frescoes and luxuriant plants, which overlooks the sloping garden. On weekdays, a two-course option is available as an alternative to the five-course lunch. Coffee comes with "excellent petits fours". The large reception lounge has a bar. The small bedrooms, each named after a local pottery, are across a major road, in an old smithy; you should ask for one on the quieter side, by a millstream. They have brightly flowered fabrics, hand-embroidered sheets, fruit, flowers, home-made biscuits and fudge, books and glossy magazines, a marble bathroom, with thick towels, and an umbrella for rainy days. Most are liked, but one recent visitor thought the four-poster room overpriced: "It was undeniably elegant, but gloomy and cold; the bathroom was positively sepulchral and poorly lit." A simple continental breakfast, with home-made croissants, brioches and jam, is included in the room rate. A cooked breakfast costs extra. Alton Towers is nearby. (*John Townsend, and others*)

Open All year, except Jan. Restaurant closed midday Tues and Sat, Sun evening/Mon.
Rooms 5 double. All in annexe across road. 1 on ground floor.
Facilities Reception lounge/bar, restaurant (varied background music sometimes). ½-acre garden.
Location On A523 Ashbourne–Leek (all rooms double-glazed). Bus from Derby/Manchester.
Restrictions No smoking: restaurant, bedrooms. Dogs in bedrooms only in special circumstances.
Credit cards All major cards accepted.
Terms B&B: single £65, double £75–£120. English breakfast £6.50. Set lunch £16.95 (weekdays)–£23; full alc £45.

Hotels often book you into their most expensive rooms or suites unless you specify otherwise. Even if all room prices are the same, hotels may give you a less good room in the hope of selling their better rooms to late customers. It always pays to discuss accommodation in detail when making a reservation, and to ask for a free upgrade on arrival if the hotel isn't full.

WATERMILLOCK Cumbria   Map 4

Leeming House   *Tel* (0870) 400 8131
Watermillock   *Fax* (017684) 86443
Penrith CA11 0JJ   *E-mail* heritagehotels_ullswater.leeming house@forte-hotels.com
                                Website www.heritage-hotels.com

"Beautiful and serene, with extensions that have mellowed well, it stands in a lovely *jardin à l'anglaise* that slopes gently towards Ullswater. The trees in the grounds are handsome and varied, and a well-documented tree trail makes for an interesting walk. The view to the lake from the public rooms is over steep steps, a fountain, a meadow. Red squirrels and all sorts of birds come to raid the wooden feeding boxes opposite the dining room windows." A regular *Guide* correspondent is moved to lyricism by this Regency house, now a luxury hotel owned by a division of Forte hotels. Christopher Curry, the "hands-on manager", much admired when he ran the hotel under an earlier regime, is now at the helm once more, "energetically taking it back upmarket". Service throughout was thought "competent, charming and full of goodwill" this year. Much refurbishment has taken place: new carpets and furniture, good fabrics, handsome oil paintings in the public rooms. "Superb fresh flowers grace the public rooms, and posies of fresh rosebuds sit in clear vases on the dining room tables." Housekeeping remains "fastidious". In the elegant restaurant, Adam Marks serves "a blend of traditional and modern dishes", eg, duck liver pâté with damson compote, or onion bahji with avocado, mango and tomato salsa; local venison with red cabbage, dates and Cointreau sauce, or broccoli and feta cheese rice-paper parcels with saffron cream sauce. Puddings include "original ticky tacky toffee pudding"; apricot and almond torte. Some upstairs bedrooms in the original house have "spectacular views" from their balcony; all are attractively decorated, with good pictures, a spacious bathroom; "the attention to comfort makes them a pleasure to sit in". Newer bedrooms "have less character, but are equally well equipped". Breakfast, "a feast", offers everything from fresh fruit salad and porridge to a traditional Cumberland platter ("no need for lunch"). A good base for visiting the pastoral Eden valley, Hadrian's Wall, etc. (*Francine and Ian Walsh*)

Open All year.
Rooms 35 double, 5 single. 10 on ground floor. 1 designed for ♿.
Facilities Ramp. Drawing room, sitting room, library, bar, conservatory, restaurant, private dining room; function/conference facilities. No background music. 22-acre grounds on lake shore: garden, tree trail. Civil wedding licence.
Location W shore of Ullswater, on A592. 8 miles from M6 exit 40. Train: Penrith; then bus, taxi.
Restrictions No smoking: restaurant, library, 11 bedrooms. No dogs in public rooms.
Credit cards All major cards accepted.
Terms B&B £49–£109; D,B&B £74–£134. Lunch alc. Set dinner £27.50. Christmas package. *V* (Nov–Mar inclusive)

The *Guide* takes no free hospitality and no advertisements.

Old Church Hotel   *Tel* (017684) 86204
Old Church Bay   *Fax* (017684) 86368
Watermillock   *E-mail* info@oldchurch.co.uk
Penrith CA11 0JN   *Website* www.oldchurch.co.uk

Kevin Whitemore is now running this small hotel with his daughters. Well protected from the nearby narrow and busy road, it stands on the site of a 12th-century church, in peaceful grounds on the shores of Ullswater, England's second largest lake. Decorated in warm colours, the house is filled with lavish soft furnishings, flowers, pot plants, books and magazines. The hall has a carved oak Victorian Gothic fireplace; the lounge has pink wallpaper, pink built-in dressers, pink-upholstered chairs. The bedrooms, with lake or fell views, vary in size and style. Some tables in the dining room look over the lake. The home-cooked dinner is modern English, eg, carrot and coriander soup; fillet of salmon with Cumberland mustard glaze; breast of Gressingham duckling with sweet and sour sauce. Rich desserts include clotted cream fudge torte; white chocolate, rum and raisin truffle cake. Breakfasts are generous, but the full English variety is available only after 9 am. Children are welcomed (games, etc, are provided). Good walking in the area, but a car is needed. More reports, please.

Open Mar–Nov. Restaurant closed midday, Sun evening.
Rooms 10 double.
Facilities 2 lounges, bar, dining room (mixed background music). 4-acre grounds on lake: mooring, fishing, rowing boat. Unsuitable for &.
Location Off A592, 3 miles S of Pooley Bridge; 7 miles from M6 exit 40. Train: Penrith; then bus.
Restrictions No smoking: dining room, 1 lounge. No dogs in house.
Credit cards Amex, MasterCard, Visa.
Terms B&B £45–£99; D,B&B £75–£125. Full alc £30. 1-night bookings sometimes refused Sat, bank holidays. 3-night breaks.

Rampsbeck   *Tel* (017684) 86442
Watermillock   *Fax* (017684) 86688
Penrith CA11 0LP   *E-mail* enquiries@rampsbeck.fsnet.co.uk
                          Website www.rampsbeck.fsnet.co.uk

With "breathtaking views" over Ullswater and the surrounding fells, this white walled 18th/19th-century "rich Victorian's show-off home" is set in large grounds. It has manicured gardens, in which rabbits gambol, and paths that lead down to the lake shore. A huge entrance opens on to a sweeping staircase and rooms with large bay windows, high ceilings and elaborate mouldings. The lounge has a large marble fireplace, patterned wallpaper, patterned carpet, Victorian furniture, current newspapers, plants and flowers. One visitor this year thought the place was "resting on its laurels", but generally there is praise for the "homely welcome by the indefatigable Marion Gibb and her smartly attired staff of friendly girls". She runs the hotel with her husband, Thomas, and her mother, Marguerite MacDowall. The bedrooms are "splendidly spacious", with an old-fashioned decor; some have lake views and a balcony with table and chairs where afternoon tea or continental breakfast can be taken. Andrew McGeorge's cooking, served in the spacious, candlelit dining room, is mostly liked. His daily-changing *table d'hôte* menu has expanded this year, giving three or four choices of each course, with such dishes as terrine of potato and goat's cheese; pan-fried mignons of beef; poached plums with vanilla ice-cream. There is also an *à la carte* menu. The comprehensive wine list is wide ranging and moderately priced. Special mention was made this year of the "tasty canapés and petits fours – the finest we have ever had" – and the breakfasts, "which were out of this world, particularly the scrambled eggs". The market town of Penrith is nearby, and so is the remote valley of Martindale with its 1,300-year-old yew tree. (*JH Bell, Peter Clowes, GF Garsten, and others*)

Open Early Feb–early Jan.
Rooms 1 suite, 18 double, 1 single.
Facilities Hall, 2 lounges, bar, restaurant. No background music. 18-acre grounds: croquet, lake frontage: fishing, sailing, windsurfing, etc. Golf, clay-pigeon shooting, archery nearby. Unsuitable for &.
Location 5½ miles SW of Penrith. From M6 exit 40, follow signs for A592 to Ullswater. At T-junction on lake shore turn right. Hotel 1¼ miles. Train: Penrith; then bus/taxi.
Restrictions No smoking: restaurant, 1 lounge, 2 bedrooms. No small children in restaurant at night. Dogs by prior arrangement.
Credit cards MasterCard, Visa.
Terms [2000] B&B £50–£100; D,B&B £79–£129. Set lunch £25, dinner £29–£39.50. Special breaks. Christmas package. 1-night bookings occasionally refused.

WATH-IN-NIDDERDALE North Yorkshire   Map 4

The Sportsman's Arms   BUDGET   *Tel* (01423) 711306
Wath-in-Nidderdale, Pateley Bridge   *Fax* (01423) 712524
nr Harrogate HG3 5PP

In peaceful conservation village, 2¼ miles NW of Pateley Bridge: Ray and Jane Carter's "civilised restaurant-with-rooms" (says Good Pub Guide*) in 17th-century sandstone building reached by old pack-horse bridge across River Nidd. "High standards, agreeable staff"; good English/French meals (Mr Carter has worked in France) in bar and dining room. "Sensible, extensive" wine list, with some reasonably priced bottles. Good breakfasts. 2 lounges. Open fires in public rooms. Occasional background music in bar. Functions catered for. Ramp. 1-acre garden. River 50 yds (fishing rights). Birdwatching, abbeys, castles nearby. Closed Christmas. 13 bedrooms, some large and newly refurbished; some in converted barn and stables around courtyard, 25 yds; 1 on ground floor. No smoking: restaurant, bedrooms. No dogs in public rooms, except bar. MasterCard, Visa accepted. B&B £40–£50; D,B&B £45-£70; full alc £28.*

WELWYN GARDEN CITY Hertfordshire
See SHORTLIST   Map 2

WENLOCK EDGE Shropshire   Map 3

Wenlock Edge Inn `BUDGET`   *Tel* (01746) 785678
Hilltop, Wenlock Edge   *Fax* (01746) 785285
nr Much Wenlock TF13 6DJ   *E-mail* info@wenlockedgeinn.co.uk
                                Website www.wenlockedgeinn.co.uk

Run by two generations of the Waring family, Harry, Joan, Diane, Jonathan and Stephen, this "fine example of an honest, old-fashioned inn" stands on a minor road near one of the highest points of the dramatic wooded ridge made famous by AE Housman and Mary Webb. There are "stunning views" to the west and south in this designated area of outstanding natural beauty, largely owned by the National Trust. There is praise again this year for the owners, "all fully in attendance" – "their affability and warmth pervade the atmosphere". "As a stranger on my own, I was made genuinely at home; after a convivial evening, all was quiet by midnight; I enjoyed a good night's sleep." An evening meal (steak and mushroom pie; "chocolate chimney") was found "very good"; the large menu of home-cooked dishes also includes warm pasta and spring vegetable salad; roast free-range pork with Bramley apple sauce; a wide choice of tarts, sponges and crumbles. The inn also offers "a decent wine list, well-kept local ales and interesting whiskies". One bar has wooden pews, an old oak counter and an open fire; the other has an inglenook fireplace with a wood-burning stove. Tables on the terrace are set amid tubs of colourful flowers. "The extremely chatty barman may be persuaded to tell your Chinese horoscope," say the Warings. The locals are equally "chatty and friendly", especially on the second Monday of the month, when the story-telling club meets. A residents' lounge is upstairs. The three "cosy and well-equipped" bedrooms have beams, a sloping ceiling, smallish windows with a padded window seat, TV, books, magazines, knick-knacks, "lots of goodies", and a shower room with water from the inn's own well. "Breakfast was copious and tasty, with some of the best bacon I've encountered." There is a wildlife pond in the small side garden. (*Trevor Lockwood, Good Pub Guide, and others*)

Open All year, except Christmas, New Year. Dining room closed to non-residents Mon.
Rooms 3 double. 1, on ground floor, in adjacent cottage. No telephone.
Facilities Residents' lounge, lounge bar, public bar, dining room. No background music. Patio; small garden; paddock opposite. Walking, riding, fishing, mountain biking nearby; gliding, hang-gliding 9 miles.
Location On B4371, 4 miles W of Much Wenlock.
Restrictions No smoking in dining room. Children under 8 not accommodated (no under-14s in bar). Guide dogs allowed in all areas; other dogs in cottage room, bar area only.
Credit cards Amex, MasterCard, Visa.
Terms B&B: single £45–£49, double £70–£75. Full alc £18. 10% discount for 3 nights or more. *V*

Please make a habit of sending in a report as soon as possible after a visit, when details are still fresh in your mind.

WEOBLEY Herefordshire   Map 3

The Salutation Inn	*Tel* (01544) 318443
Market Pitch	*Fax* (01544) 318216
Weobley HR4 8SJ	*E-mail* info@salutationinn.com
	Website www.aitch.net/salutation

"Excellent: warm, clean, with good food, pleasant staff and hard-working, hands-on owners." "It combines the tranquillity of the countryside with the welcoming atmosphere of a working village inn. Recommended for quality, value, and location in a delectable part of the country." More praise this year for Chris and Frances Anthony's 14th-century black-and-white inn. It serves "above average" pub meals (eg, steak and stout pie; fillet of salmon in a ginger and orange cream; supreme of pheasant). In the beamed restaurant, which has a conservatory extension, there is a choice of more ambitious dishes, such as braised guinea fowl with bacon, thyme and red wine jus; seafood brochette with wild rice and roast pepper risotto, but you can also order grilled steak with mushrooms. There is a separate vegetarian menu. The wine list includes a good selection of New World bottles as well as French and Italian wines. "Food and service in the restaurant were first rate, but service was a bit slow in the lounge bar" (this has two sections – one for smokers – and a log fire in a large stone fireplace). The pretty bedrooms upstairs have antique beds and flowery fabrics. The best one is spacious, with a "very comfortable" four-poster and a smart bathroom. The others have an *en suite* shower only, but there is a bath in a communal bathroom. The room above the oak-beamed bar is to be avoided because of the jukebox below. "Very good breakfasts", in a conservatory, include fresh orange juice, nothing packaged, smoked haddock. Weobley is full of listed Grade I and Grade II medieval and Tudor buildings, and it has a tall-spired 900-year-old church. (*JK Lunn, Davis and Andrea Dassori; also Good Pub Guide*)

Open All year.
Rooms 5 double. No telephone.
Facilities Residents' lounge with TV, lounge bar, public bar (jukebox), restaurant (no background music); fitness room; patio garden. River Wye 7 miles: fishing. Only restaurant suitable for &.
Location Top of main street of village 12 miles NW of Hereford. Carpark. Local buses.
Restrictions No smoking: restaurant, conservatory, bedrooms. Children accommodated in cottage only. Dogs by arrangement; not in public rooms, except public bar.
Credit cards All major cards accepted.
Terms B&B: single £44–£50, double £70–£75. Full alc £30. Reductions for long stays.

British hotels nowadays have private facilities in most bedrooms. And many have TV, baby-listening and tea-making facilities. To save space we do not list all of these; if any is particularly important to you, please discuss with the hotel.

## WEST CLIFFE Kent								Map 2

Wallett's Court
West Cliffe
St Margaret's at Cliffe
Dover CT15 6EW

Tel (01304) 852424
Fax (01304) 853430
E-mail wallettscourt@compuserve.com
Website www.wallettscourt.com

"We love it; it is always wonderful," says one visitor to this Grade II* listed Jacobean manor house, which stands high above the sea in a designated area of outstanding natural beauty. The owners, Chris and Lea Oakley (their son Gavin is manager) have developed the Domesday-old house over the years (its restaurant is popular with well-heeled local diners). It has many interesting features: an ancient staircase, a carved wood porch, a 17th-century wall painting, a priest hole in the roof, exposed brickwork, moulded plaster fireplaces. There are black wood-burning stoves, antiques and leather sofas in the large lounge. "All the staff are friendly. Even in summer the candles in the bar were lit, creating a lovely atmosphere." The bedrooms vary greatly. The three in the main house have the most character: a large room with an oak-panelled four-poster bed is named for Queen Eleanor of Castile, a former visitor. Other rooms are in converted barns; some are small, with a tiny shower (one was thought to be "in need of an overhaul"). Four rooms above the leisure centre in a converted barn are well kitted out, but one couple found theirs over-heated, with noise from the spa. The newly installed swim-trainer jet in the small swimming pool "is great – you can swim on the spot, fighting the current". Though Chris Oakley is still in the kitchens, he is handing over the reins to Stephen Harvey, whose cooking was thought "outstanding" this year: "Superb meals. The restaurant is lovely." "Almost all the dishes were excellently prepared, well presented." The long *prix-fixe* menu includes, eg, wild boar rissoles or sausages; jugged hare; pan-fried haunch of venison; gingered crème brûlée with rhubarb compote. There are also a five-course no-choice Kentish gourmet menu at £40, a vegetarian menu and a short bar/room-service menu. Breakfast, in a conservatory, includes eggs from the family's farm nearby, toasted granary bread, home-made preserves. "You can have virtually what you want." Many visitors stay only one night on their way to the Continent; an early breakfast is available from 6.30 am. "The walk to St Margaret's at Cliffe is pleasant and pastoral. A short wander on, and one can gaze out over the white chalk cliffs across the channel." Canterbury is 15 miles away. (*Nancy Wood, Linda Brook, NW, and others*)

Open All year.
Rooms 4 suites, 12 double. 13 in converted barns, stables, cottages.
Facilities 2 lounges, bar, restaurant (classical background music on quiet evenings), conservatory. 7-acre grounds: spa (swimming pool, sauna, steam room), tennis, croquet, jogging trail, treehouse. Sea 1 mile (reached by footpath). Golf nearby. Unsuitable for &.
Location 3 miles N of Dover. From A2 take A258 to Deal. 1st right to West Cliffe; hotel ½ mile on right, opposite church. Train: Dover Priory; then bus 90.

Restrictions No smoking: restaurant, pool barn, 8 bedrooms. No children under 8 in restaurant after 8 pm. No dogs.
Credit cards All major cards accepted.
Terms B&B: single £70–£110, double £80–£130, suite £130–£150. Set lunch £17.50, dinner £27.50–£40.Christmas packages. *V*

WESTDEAN East Sussex   Map 2

The Old Parsonage   *Tel/Fax* (01323) 870432
Westdean
nr Seaford BN25 4AL

"Can there be a more delightful, better-value place to stay in the UK?" wonders a regular *Guide* correspondent. Aided and abetted by its owner, Raymond Woodhams, he gave his wife a two-day stay here for Christmas, and concluded: "Perfection is hard to attain in any sphere, but this comes close to it. It feels like a smaller version of an Oxford senior common room." With thick stone walls, mullioned windows, old timbers, a sympathetic Victorian extension, the atmospheric medieval building stands by a 12th-century church in a conservation village by Friston Forest. Mr Woodhams, who is studying part-time for the priesthood, appears as "head waiter" at breakfast; his wife, Angela, "is equally hospitable". "Walking shoes in hand up an immaculately cream-carpeted staircase, you arrive at the ancient baronial hall, now a bedroom with a four-poster bed, tiny casement windows (looking over gravestones), great beams, medieval works of art, even a processional cross propped up in one corner. The private bathroom, across the hallway, has all manner of herbal and visual delights, including botanical prints." Two further bedrooms are located in the Victorian wing. The breakfast room, reached via a spiral stone staircase, has "superb antique furniture" and orchids, and breakfast is "a feast, with fresh fruit juice, home-made preserves and muesli, an enormous traditional English breakfast, like a mixed grill, designed to last until dinner time". No restaurant; *The Hungry Monk* at Jevington is warmly recommended, or you could try *The Tiger*, an old pub at Eastdean. Beautiful gardens and old stone walls surround the house; sheep graze in a pasture opposite. The sea is reached by a country path through a designated area of outstanding natural beauty. Beachy Head is some 20 minutes' drive away. (*Michael Bourdeaux*)

Open All year, except Christmas, New Year.
Rooms 3 double. No telephone/TV, etc.
Facilities Sitting room, breakfast room. No background music. 2-acre grounds surrounded by forest. Sea, safe bathing, fishing 1 mile; golf, racing nearby. Unsuitable for &.
Location 5 miles W of Eastbourne. Off A259 Brighton–Hastings coast road, E of Seaford. Train: Seaford; then taxi (5 mins).
Restrictions No smoking. No children under 12. No dogs.
Credit cards None accepted.
Terms B&B double £65–£80. 1-night bookings sometimes refused weekends.

For details of the Voucher scheme see page xxx.

WEST PORLOCK Somerset   Map 1

Bales Mead   *Tel* (01643) 862565
West Porlock TA24 8NX   *Fax* (01643) 862544

"The owners are charming; the house and garden are extremely pretty," says a visitor this year to Stephen Blue and Peter Clover's small B&B. Situated in a hamlet between Porlock and Porlock Weir in the Exmoor National Park, it looks over the "stunning coastline" and is surrounded by wild moors and rolling hills. The "courteous hosts" have given the Edwardian house a "retro" decor, influenced by the 1920s and 1930s, "with enough quirks to make it feel homely". "The attention to detail and the thoughtful touches make you feel very spoilt," another guest wrote. The bedrooms are decorated with hand-stencilled wall borders and good fabrics, and supplied with a hot-water bottle, biscuits, fruit, sherry, a teddy bear and much else besides. Two have sea views and a private bathroom (with Spanish tiles, and crystal decanters containing bath oils and salts). A third room is available if guests are willing to share a bathroom. Breakfast, served communally or at separate tables, includes freshly squeezed orange juice, fresh fruit salad, yogurt, cooked dishes garnished with flowers, all on Royal Doulton china with silver cutlery, lace tablecloths, proper table napkins. It is sometimes served by candlelight, with a piano accompaniment by one of the hosts. "Rather a lot of do and don't notices," is one comment this year, "but they do their best to make you welcome, and we thoroughly enjoyed our stay." Porlock Weir has a picturesque, tiny harbour. Local attractions include Dunster Castle, Arlington Court, National Trust villages, gardens, etc. (*Maxine Turner, DR*)

Open All year, except Christmas/New Year.
Rooms 3 double, 2 with private facilities. No telephone.
Facilities Lounge, breakfast room (classical background music). ½-acre garden. Shingle beach, harbour ½ mile; bathing, fishing, boating. Unsuitable for &.
Location Off A39, between Porlock village and harbour at Porlock Weir.
Restrictions No smoking. No children under 14. No dogs.
Credit cards None accepted.
Terms B&B: single £46–£66, double £66. 1-night bookings refused bank holiday weekends, high season.

WHEELOCK Cheshire   Map 3

The Grove House   BUDGET   *Tel* (01270) 762582
Mill Lane, Wheelock   *Fax* (01270) 759465
nr Sandbach CW11 4RD

"A lovely spot and very useful for walkers of the Cheshire canal ring," said a visitor this year to this restaurant-with-rooms. With "the feeling of a private home" (flowers, potted plants, knick-knacks, books and family photographs), it is a Georgian house in what was an old village on the Trent and Mersey Canal and is now a continuation of Sandbach. Brenda Curtis owns it with her daughter and son-in-law, Katherine and Richard Shaw. He is the chef, providing ambitious modern cooking on a long daily-changing menu. Visitors this year write of "superb food, fresh ingredients and fresh ideas"; "imaginative dishes, presented with an original touch", eg, tomato bubble and squeak deep fried in a lager batter, served on a sweet and sour vegetable stew; pan-fried pork fillet rolled in blue poppy seeds, on black pudding with a kiwi, apple and cucumber pickle. "Crème brûlée one of the best I have had." The wine list "demonstrates genuine expertise". Vegetarians are well catered for. The background music can be obtrusive, especially at breakfast (which has "rather boring toast", but good, unpackaged butter and jams). The bedrooms are spacious, "light and airy", with "a good bathroom" and "real attention to detail". "Decor slightly OTT but fun." One visitor was pleased to find that his complimentary bottle of wine was, unusually, replaced each day. Jodrell Bank, Little Moreton Hall and Crewe railway station are nearby. (*S and TT, and others*)

Open All year. Only restaurant open 27–30 Dec.
Rooms 1 suite, 6 double, 1 single.
Facilities Lounge, bar, restaurant, private dining/meeting room, patio restaurant; jazz/classical background music. ½-acre garden. Golf, fishing, riding nearby. Only restaurant suitable for &.
Location Off A534 2 miles S of Sandbach; near M6 exit 17. Straight across roundabout with Safeway supermarket on right. Left at next roundabout; follow signs to Wheelock. Hotel is on left, immediately after *Nag's Head*. Train: Crewe; local bus.
Restrictions No smoking: restaurant, 2 bedrooms. Dogs by arrangement; not in public rooms.
Credit cards Amex, MasterCard, Visa.
Terms B&B: single £30–£50, double £60–£75, suite £70–£85. Set Sun lunch £13, dinner £14.50; full alc £20. Weekend rates.

WHITBY North Yorkshire *See SHORTLIST*   **Map 4**

WHITEWELL Lancashire   **Map 4**

The Inn at Whitewell   NEW   *Tel* (01200) 448222
Forest of Bowland   *Fax* (01200) 448298
nr Clitheroe BB7 3AT   *Website* www.greatinns.co.uk

A civilised inn run in jokey style by Richard Bowman, who leases it from the Duchy of Lancaster. Set deep in the forest and reached via narrow lanes, it is "small, quirky, comfortable, in a beautiful area", says a report this year, restoring it to the *Guide*. "The willing, helpful and informal staff provide relaxing hospitality." Food is "excellent", and the wine list is "remarkable in quality, value and length" (Mr Bowman is also a wine merchant). Antiques and old paintings abound (there is also an art gallery), and log fires warm the public rooms. Bedrooms are "fabulous", with a CD-player, a luxurious bathroom. Some (at the back) look over "a beautiful wilderness"; some have a peat fire. "The bar, very attractive, if a bit huntin', shootin' and fishin', buzzes with young folk." The *Good Pub Guide 2000* names the inn Lancashire dining pub of the year, praising the sandwiches, grills, etc, in the bar, and the "very polite service". The restaurant serves starters

THE 2001 GOOD HOTEL GUIDE

Use this voucher to claim a 25% discount off the normal price for bed and breakfast at hotels with a ***V*** sign at the end of their entry. **You must request a voucher discount at the time of booking and present this voucher on arrival. Further details and conditions overleaf.** Valid to 6th September, 2001.

THE 2001 GOOD HOTEL GUIDE

Use this voucher to claim a 25% discount off the normal price for bed and breakfast at hotels with a ***V*** sign at the end of their entry. **You must request a voucher discount at the time of booking and present this voucher on arrival. Further details and conditions overleaf.** Valid to 6th September, 2001.

THE 2001 GOOD HOTEL GUIDE

Use this voucher to claim a 25% discount off the normal price for bed and breakfast at hotels with a ***V*** sign at the end of their entry. **You must request a voucher discount at the time of booking and present this voucher on arrival. Further details and conditions overleaf.** Valid to 6th September, 2001.

THE 2001 GOOD HOTEL GUIDE

Use this voucher to claim a 25% discount off the normal price for bed and breakfast at hotels with a ***V*** sign at the end of their entry. **You must request a voucher discount at the time of booking and present this voucher on arrival. Further details and conditions overleaf.** Valid to 6th September, 2001.

THE 2001 GOOD HOTEL GUIDE

Use this voucher to claim a 25% discount off the normal price for bed and breakfast at hotels with a ***V*** sign at the end of their entry. **You must request a voucher discount at the time of booking and present this voucher on arrival. Further details and conditions overleaf.** Valid to 6th September, 2001.

THE 2001 GOOD HOTEL GUIDE

Use this voucher to claim a 25% discount off the normal price for bed and breakfast at hotels with a ***V*** sign at the end of their entry. **You must request a voucher discount at the time of booking and present this voucher on arrival. Further details and conditions overleaf.** Valid to 6th September, 2001.

1. Hotels with a ***V*** have undertaken to give readers a discount of 25% off their normal bed-and-breakfast rate (or their room rate if breakfast is charged separately). You will be expected to pay full prices for other meals and all other services.
2. You may use one voucher for a single-night stay or for a longer visit, and for yourself alone or for a partner sharing your room. But you will need two vouchers if you are booking more than one room.
3. Participating hotels may refuse a voucher reservation if they expect to be fully booked at the full room price nearer the time, or accept a voucher for one night only.

CONDITIONS

- - ✂ -

1. Hotels with a ***V*** have undertaken to give readers a discount of 25% off their normal bed-and-breakfast rate (or their room rate if breakfast is charged separately). You will be expected to pay full prices for other meals and all other services.
2. You may use one voucher for a single-night stay or for a longer visit, and for yourself alone or for a partner sharing your room. But you will need two vouchers if you are booking more than one room.
3. Participating hotels may refuse a voucher reservation if they expect to be fully booked at the full room price nearer the time, or accept a voucher for one night only.

CONDITIONS

- - ✂ -

1. Hotels with a ***V*** have undertaken to give readers a discount of 25% off their normal bed-and-breakfast rate (or their room rate if breakfast is charged separately). You will be expected to pay full prices for other meals and all other services.
2. You may use one voucher for a single-night stay or for a longer visit, and for yourself alone or for a partner sharing your room. But you will need two vouchers if you are booking more than one room.
3. Participating hotels may refuse a voucher reservation if they expect to be fully booked at the full room price nearer the time, or accept a voucher for one night only.

CONDITIONS

- - ✂ -

1. Hotels with a ***V*** have undertaken to give readers a discount of 25% off their normal bed-and-breakfast rate (or their room rate if breakfast is charged separately). You will be expected to pay full prices for other meals and all other services.
2. You may use one voucher for a single-night stay or for a longer visit, and for yourself alone or for a partner sharing your room. But you will need two vouchers if you are booking more than one room.
3. Participating hotels may refuse a voucher reservation if they expect to be fully booked at the full room price nearer the time, or accept a voucher for one night only.

CONDITIONS

- - ✂ -

1. Hotels with a ***V*** have undertaken to give readers a discount of 25% off their normal bed-and-breakfast rate (or their room rate if breakfast is charged separately). You will be expected to pay full prices for other meals and all other services.
2. You may use one voucher for a single-night stay or for a longer visit, and for yourself alone or for a partner sharing your room. But you will need two vouchers if you are booking more than one room.
3. Participating hotels may refuse a voucher reservation if they expect to be fully booked at the full room price nearer the time, or accept a voucher for one night only.

CONDITIONS

- - ✂ -

1. Hotels with a ***V*** have undertaken to give readers a discount of 25% off their normal bed-and-breakfast rate (or their room rate if breakfast is charged separately). You will be expected to pay full prices for other meals and all other services.
2. You may use one voucher for a single-night stay or for a longer visit, and for yourself alone or for a partner sharing your room. But you will need two vouchers if you are booking more than one room.
3. Participating hotels may refuse a voucher reservation if they expect to be fully booked at the full room price nearer the time, or accept a voucher for one night only.

CONDITIONS

like kedgeree, or pressed fish terrine, and main dishes include loin of Bowland lamb filled with apricot and herbs; roast venison with a hot-pot of parsnip, and celeriac. Set on the River Hodder, the inn offers fishing for salmon, trout, grayling, etc. "Many dogs are regular customers," says Mr Bowman. (*Peter L Dell, Peter Wilson*)

Open All year.
Rooms 1 suite, 16 double. 4 (2 on ground floor) in coach house 150 yds.
Facilities Hall, bar, dining room, 2 private dining rooms. No background music. 1-acre garden, riverside lawn, 7 miles fishing.
Location 6 miles NW of Clitheroe. Take B6246 from Whalley, or road through Dunsop Bridge from B64778.
Restriction Only "frightening dogs" banned from public rooms.
Credit cards All major cards accepted.
Terms B&B: single from £59, double from £84, suite £94–£120. Bar meals. Full alc £32.

WHITSTABLE Kent   **Map 2**

Hotel Continental   `BUDGET`   *Tel* (01227) 280280
29 Beach Walk   *Fax* (01227) 280257
Whitstable CT5 2BP   *Website* www.oysterfishery.co.uk

The Romans came to Whitstable to eat the oysters from its vast oyster beds. Nowadays, it is a busy town with some small-scale boat building and an annual oyster festival. The Whitstable Oyster Fishery Company has long been one of the town's most popular seafood restaurants, offering some basic accommodation in fishermen's huts on the shingle beach. It also owns this 1930s hotel, decorated in simple Art Deco style and set across the road from the beach at the end of the seafront – "a marvellous position". It has a large sitting area, and a bar (with a "lovely tiled floor", newspapers, Monopoly and Scrabble) which serves brasserie-type dishes like moules and frites, or char-grilled sardines. The restaurant, "very French in feel", has sea views ("lovely to watch the sun set"); it offers "good value", and "very good cooking", eg, moules marinière; roast seabass with red pepper, tomato and anchovy; "rather original" puddings, such as fruit jellies, panna cotta with raspberry sauce. Children's menus and vegetarian dishes are offered too. The accommodation is not luxurious; a large bedroom was found cold this year; some rooms are extremely small, with no storage space, others good-sized, with a balcony overlooking the sea. But the place "has a strange charm", one visitor thought. It also has modern bathrooms, "a wonderful view across the estuary", and good walking from the door. Breakfast, accompanied by newspapers, has freshly squeezed orange juice, kippers, smoked haddock, vegetarian dishes and DIY toast. Nearby are the Imperial Oyster Cinema (under the same ownership), ten-pin bowling and water sports. (*JCF, and others*)

Open All year. Bar meals served 12 noon–9 pm except Sat night.
Rooms 3 suites, 20 double. Also 6 huts.
Facilities Lounge, bar, restaurant; background jazz noon–midnight; live jazz monthly. Shingle beach opposite; windsurfing, etc. Unsuitable for &.
Location Central, on waterfront. 2 carparks.

Restrictions No smoking: restaurant, bedrooms. No dogs.
Credit cards All major cards accepted.
Terms B&B: single £43–£65, double £45–£65, suite £85–£125. Set lunch £14.95, dinner £17.50; full alc £23. Stay Fri/Sat, get Sun free. Christmas, New Year packages.

WILLESLEY Gloucestershire   Map 3

Tavern House   *Tel* (01666) 880444
Willesley   *Fax* (01666) 880254
nr Tetbury GL8 8QU

"A most attractive, rambling 17th-century house, run with high standards," say inspectors this year of this Grade II listed former coaching inn, in a Cotswold hamlet on the Tetbury to Bath road. You enter by a gate in the stone wall of an "immaculately kept" small front garden. The interior, "similarly immaculate", has a pretty country decor, a square stone-flagged hall, antiques and old furniture, flowers and magazines. The decent-size lounge overlooks the flowery rear garden (where loungers and wooden benches stand on a lawn). The four bedrooms have floral fabrics, comfortable beds. The largest, at the top, reached via a narrow staircase with a red rope "handrail", has exposed beams, good lighting, a spacious pink-and-green bathroom. Breakfast, in a bright room with books, pictures, a Dutch coat of arms above its inglenook fireplace, "was adequate and substantial: very good smoked haddock, but the juice was tinned". The owners, Janet and Tim Tremellen, who single-handedly run this "most pleasant place", are "courteous and full of local know-how". Recommended eating places include the *Rattlebone Inn* in the nearby village of Sherston, "which for sheer beauty warrants a visit". The Westonbirt Arboretum is a mile away, Badminton three, and Berkeley Castle and the Wildfowl and Wetlands Trust at Slimbridge are not far. The road is quiet at night, the Tremellens tell us, and rooms are double-glazed.

Open All year, except late Jan–early Feb.
Rooms 4 double.
Facilities Lounge, breakfast room. No background music. ¾-acre garden. Golf, hunting, horse- and motor-racing nearby. Unsuitable for &.
Location 4 miles SW of Tetbury on A433 (quiet at night; rooms double-glazed).
Restrictions Smoking in lounge only. No children under 10. No dogs.
Credit cards MasterCard, Visa.
Terms B&B: single £47.50–£70, double £65–£70. 2- to 3-day breaks. 1-night bookings sometimes refused.

WILLITON Somerset   Map 1

The White House   *Tel* (01984) 632306 and 632777
Williton TA4 4QW

❦ *Cesar award in 1988*

Dick and Kay Smith have been running this modest Georgian town house as a highly personal restaurant-with-rooms for more than 31 years (they always take a long winter break to re-charge their batteries). They continue to garner praise. "We were sad to leave," wrote one guest, who was touched to have been advised by the Smiths to use one of the *Guide*'s vouchers – "with the money saved, we chose better wine". And a regular visitor said: "In 21 years the standards have never slipped." What impresses is the Smiths' "attention to small details" and the care that they show towards their guests. The house stands on a busy road, but it has a courtyard garden, with shingle, palms, fig trees and trailing geraniums, and it is filled with antiques, paintings, prints and ceramics, all chosen with taste. Old wine auction prints hang on the cork walls in the bar. Bedrooms in the main house are spacious, and thoughtfully equipped; the smaller rooms in converted stables and a coach house are also thought "excellent" (they are the quieter ones). The Smiths work as a team, unaided, in the kitchen, and produce "unfussy dishes, based on good local ingredients, and cooked with skill and care". The four-course dinner, with choice, might consist of smoked haddock and yellow pepper soup; steamed asparagus with hollandaise sauce; lightly roasted loin of spring lamb; hazelnut meringue cake with apricots, or West Country cheeses with home-made oatcakes. The Smiths take wine seriously, and are proud of their eclectic cellar; they have won a "house wine of the year" award on several occasions. Breakfast has fresh Aga-baked rolls, freshly squeezed orange juice, "splendid poached eggs", good coffee. Williton is well placed for visiting Exmoor and the Quantock Hills. Dunster Castle and Cleeve Abbey – an impressive monastic site – are within striking distance. (*Gillian Comins*)

Open Mid-May–Nov. Restaurant closed midday.
Rooms 10 double. 4 in annexe around courtyard. 1 on ground floor
Facilities Lounge, bar, restaurant. No background music. Sea, shingle beaches 2 miles; sandy beach 8 miles.
Location On A39 in centre of village (rear rooms quietest). Forecourt parking. Train: Taunton, 15½ miles; then bus/taxi.
Restrictions No smoking: restaurant, lounge. Dogs in annexe rooms only.
Credit cards None accepted.
Terms B&B: single £52, double £90. Set dinner £33.50. D,B&B breaks (2 days or more) *V*

WILMINGTON East Sussex   **Map 2**

Crossways Hotel   *Tel* (01323) 482455
Lewes Road   *Fax* (01323) 487811
Wilmington BN26 5SG   *E-mail* crossways@fastnet.co.uk

A restaurant-with-rooms in a handsome rectangular house, white-painted and green-shuttered, in a large garden with duck pond, rabbits and a herb garden. A large collection of cheese dishes decorates the dining and breakfast rooms. No guest lounge, but the bedrooms contain "every appliance imaginable – fridge, TV, clock, etc, knick-knacks galore, an expression of the owners' exuberant personalities"; some rooms have a sofa; one has a balcony. "The proprietors, David Stott and Clive James, and their staff were competent, helpful and friendly," says a visitor this year. "Our small bedroom had a pleasant view over the garden; the shower room was small and narrow but it worked well." The meals "are generous and rich without being sophisticated". "The feel is of eating in a dining room rather than a restaurant: an intimate atmosphere." Plenty of choice on the four-course menu. Starters such as smoked duck and mango salad, or curried prawn and banana basket, are followed by home-made soup. Main courses might be guinea fowl with sun-dried tomato sauce, or steak au poivre. "Exceedingly good desserts", eg, strawberries in Muscat wine; lemon and gooseberry sorbet. The wine list includes several English bottles, among them Breaky Bottom and Sussex Sunset. "Breakfast had good marmalade, but the coffee was somewhat weak." The house is on the Eastbourne to Lewes main road, but windows are double-glazed, and the garden provides a buffer zone. Wilmington is an affluent village in the Cuckmere valley, under the gaze of the "Long Man of Wilmington" (said to be the largest chalk-cut figure in Europe). It has a ruined 13th-century Benedictine priory, and a string of old cottages along its main street. Handy for Glyndebourne, 15 minutes' drive away, and for walkers – the South Down Way and the Weald Way are close by. (*CJ Daintree, and others*)

Open 24 Jan–23 Dec. Restaurant closed midday, Sun, Mon.
Rooms 5 double, 2 single.
Facilities Breakfast room, restaurant (occasional classical background music). 2-acre grounds. Beach 4 miles. Unsuitable for &.
Location 6 miles N of Eastbourne on A27 (some rooms double-glazed). Large carpark. Train: Polegate, 2 miles; then taxi.
Restrictions No smoking in restaurant. No children under 12. No dogs.
Credit cards Amex, MasterCard, Visa.
Terms B&B: single £50, double £75–£80; D,B&B (min. 2 nights) £64 per person. Set dinner £29.95. Gourmet, Glyndebourne breaks.

WIMBORNE MINSTER Dorset   Map 2

Beechleas   *Tel* (01202) 841684
17 Poole Road   *Fax* (01202) 849344
Wimborne Minster BH21 1QA   *E-mail* hotelbeechleas@hotmail.com

"Unstuffy and unpretentious," writes a visitor this year of Josephine McQuillan's small hotel/restaurant, a Grade II listed red brick Georgian town house on the road to Poole. Another correspondent wrote that she and her seriously ill partner "were treated with the utmost kindness and genuine understanding", and many others also praised the "friendly staff". "Attention to small details sets *Beechleas* apart." A first-floor bedroom was admired: "It was pretty, large and comfortable, with good-quality furnishings." But some rooms have been thought "poky", with over-heavy duvets. One couple "loved the open fire in the small drawing room, and in the restaurant, busy with non-residents dining, where we had a lovely corner table". There is one report this year of a disappointing meal, with poor service and "ugly and intrusive background music", but the Aga-cooked meals, using local, naturally reared or grown produce, are mostly enjoyed: "Though they were busy, service was unhurried and unobtrusive. Every aspect of the dinner was delicious: a rich double-baked cheese soufflé, and seabass with leeks and an anchovy and caper sauce were highlights. The accompanying vegetables were a delight. Breakfast, in the conservatory overlooking the garden, was pleasant. Good coffee, warm rolls, but the jams were indifferent." There is traffic noise by day, but it subsides at night; the annexe rooms are probably quietest. Wimborne is a delightful market town, with an impressive minster, "lots of proper shops, little alleys, and a feeling of space". The surrounding countryside is "gentle and varied". A local guide will take hotel guests on a Thomas Hardy tour. Kingston Lacy, a National Trust house with an outstanding collection of paintings, is just west of town. (*Anne and Dawson Walker, H Pennington, Mrs Ellin Osmond, AD Lloyd, and others*)

Open All year, except Christmas, New Year. Lunch by arrangement.
Rooms 9 double. 2 in coach house, 2 in lodge. 2 on ground floor.
Facilities Drawing room, restaurant (background music "when it seems appropriate" during meals). Small walled garden. Coast 6 miles.
Location 5 mins from centre, on road (some rooms get traffic noise). Small carpark.
Restrictions No smoking: restaurant, bedrooms. Dogs by arrangement in ground floor bedroom.
Credit cards All major cards accepted.
Terms B&B: single £69–£89, double £79–£99. Lunch (by arrangement) £18.75. Set dinner (2 to 3 courses) £18.50–£22.75. Child accommodated in parents' room from £10. Weekend breaks from £60 per person D,B&B.

WINCHCOMBE Gloucestershire   Map 3

Wesley House   *Tel* (01242) 602366
High Street   *Fax* (01242) 609046
Winchcombe GL54 5LJ
                                          E-mail enquiries@wesleyhouse.co.uk
                                          Website www.wesleyhouse.co.uk

"A warm welcome; pleasant service," says a visitor this year to this 15th-century half-timbered restaurant-with-rooms (named for Methodist preacher John Wesley, who is believed to have stayed in the building in 1779). "Small, inviting, higgledy-piggledy", it stands on the busy main street of this ancient Saxon town. "You step inside to a lounge with a welcoming log fire; beyond is the two-tier restaurant." Owner Matthew Brown is "a natural host, with a mischievous manner"; his staff "are friendly", and service "is pleasant, though sometimes slow". We'd be grateful for reports on the work of the new chef, James Lovatt: he cooks modern dishes, eg, galantine of quail on toasted brioche with grape chutney; duck breast on apple and sage rosti with bramble sauce; steamed butterscotch sponge pudding on English sauce. A cheaper and simpler "early bird menu" (salads, pasta, etc) is served between 6.45 and 7.45 pm on weekdays. A steep beamed staircase leads to the bedrooms. All but one are very small, but they are stylish, with black beams, rich fabrics, antiques, *objets d'art*; some get street noise; most bathrooms are minute, "but fresh fruit on a landing, and milk in a thermos flask make all the difference". The best bedroom, The Terrace, has panoramic views across the North Cotswold edge and the fields surrounding Sudeley Castle (once the home

of Henry VIII's last wife, Catherine Parr). Breakfast has freshly
squeezed orange juice, warm rolls and croissants, butter and jams in
little bowls, "excellent cooked dishes ranging from smoked haddock
to home-made sausages". Winchcombe, in the Isbourne valley, a designated area of outstanding natural beauty, was a prosperous wool
trading centre in the Middle Ages; its grand church and fine old half-
timbered buildings recall this period. (*RJ Barratt, and others*)

Open All year, except 10–28 Jan.
Rooms 5 double (1 with terrace), 1 single.
Facilities Lounge/bar, restaurant with terrace (classical background music at
night); function facilities. Horse-racing, riding, golf nearby. Unsuitable for &.
Location High street of town 6 miles NE of Cheltenham (4 rear/side rooms
quietest). Street parking. Bus from Cheltenham.
Restrictions No smoking: restaurant, bedrooms. Unsuitable for toddlers. No
dogs.
Credit cards Amex, MasterCard, Visa.
Terms B&B: single £35–£45, double £65–£80. Set lunch £10.50, dinner
£28.50. D,B&B (min 2 nights) from £59 per person. 1-night bookings sometimes refused. *V*

WINCHESTER Hampshire   **Map 2**

Hotel du Vin & Bistro   *Tel* (01962) 841414
14 Southgate Street   *Fax* (01962) 842458
Winchester SO23 9EF   *E-mail* admin@winchester.hotelduvin.co.uk
                                 Website www.hotelduvin.com

Q *César award in 1998*

This was the first hotel of a small group owned by Gerald Basset and
Robin Hutson. There are now sister hotels of the same name in
Tunbridge Wells and Bristol (*qqv*). All are run with the aim of encouraging good drinking by offering a wide range of wines with a modest
mark-up, accompanied by affordable food. They are liked for their
unpretentious air (no dress code, etc), and their child-friendly attitude.
The Winchester operation, managed by Michael Worren, is in a
Georgian red brick town house near the cathedral. The decor is dedicated to wine: walls are densely hung with vinous pictures, labels,
menus and old photographs. The high-ceilinged sitting room has a
trompe l'oeil painting, huge sofas and squashy armchairs. In the lively
bistro, pale yellow, softly lit and music-free, with wooden floors and
small polished mahogany tables, the chef, Andy Clark, serves modern
English/French food on a short menu. Roast veal sweetbreads
wrapped in Parma ham, and smoked haddock with chive tagliatelle
and poached egg were enjoyed this year. Portions are generous.
Service is willing, but it can be slow: after a 30-minute wait, one guest
retired to bed dessert-less; it was finally delivered to his room by the
maître d' with a complimentary glass of champagne – "a nice touch".
The bedrooms are stylish and uncluttered, with CD-player, Egyptian
cotton sheets, an efficient bathroom with a power shower. Each is
sponsored by a wine company, and decorated in its colours. Some
rooms are in the main house; others in a purpose-built building in the
walled garden. Those that face the garden are quietest. There is one

report of a room that was small and dark, but Courvoisier (cream and white) is large and quiet, and Durney Vineyards is a "sensuous" suite, with a four-poster draped in maroon velvet and murals that reproduce celebrated nudes. (*Jack F Hall, and others*)

Open All year.
Rooms 1 suite, 22 double. 4 in garden. 1 on ground floor with &. access.
Facilities Drawing room, bar, restaurant. No background music. Small walled garden.
Location Central (back rooms quietest). Hotel will send directions. Carpark. Station 10 mins' walk.
Restriction Guide dogs only.
Credit cards All major cards accepted.
Terms Room: single £89, double £89–£125, suite £185. Breakfast: £8.50. Full alc £40. Extra bed for child: £10. Christmas package.

The Wykeham Arms   *Tel* (01962) 853834
75 Kingsgate Street   *Fax* (01962) 854411
Winchester SO23 9PE

♲ *César award in 1996*

"We were impressed with the building, location, accommodation, and the quality and quantity of the food," says a visitor this year to this "classic town pub". Graeme Jameson, who built up its reputation during 14 years, is no longer the tenant, though he is still around in an advisory capacity, and "all is now well under the management of Tim Manktelow-Gray" – "he is lovely, very welcoming", and his staff are "most helpful". The 250-year-old building stands between the cathedral and the college (it is named for the college's founder, William of Wykeham). Inside, a series of rooms and eating areas radiate from a central bar. Log fires burn, and there is an extraordinary collection of memorabilia: cigarette cards, hats, pictures of royalty, walking sticks arranged in rows, about 1,600 tankards. Schoolboys' oak desks, passed on from the college, are used as tables here and there. The lunchtime menu ranges from toasted sandwiches to smoked haddock and bacon chowder; confit of duck on roasted vegetables. A more ambitious repertoire appears in the evening, when dishes might include pigeon breast on a warm salad of garlic potatoes and asparagus; grilled fillet of red bream with watercress and anchovy butter; panna cotta with pineapple and apricot compote. *The Wyke*, as it is known locally, takes wine seriously and many wines on its "wonderful list" are available by the glass. The bedrooms all have a mini-bar, fridge, TV. The smallish rooms above the pub are to have a refit this year. Smarter rooms are in the annexe, the *St George*, a 16th-century building opposite – it has a suite on two floors, a courtyard garden, a residents' sitting room (also a post office/store and a wine merchant). Frequent concerts in the college and Evensong in the cathedral provide entertainment on the doorstep. Difficult to find if you arrive by car, but detailed instructions accompany booking confirmations. (*Mrs PM Glover, MG, Good Pub Guide*)

Open All year, except 25 Dec.
Rooms Pub: 7 double; *St George*: 1 suite, 4 double, 1 single.

Facilities Pub: 2 bars, 6 eating areas, breakfast room; sauna; small garden. *St George*: sitting room, kitchen; garden. No background music. Unsuitable for ♿.
Location By Kingsgate arch, between college and cathedral; hotel will send directions. Carpark.
Restrictions No smoking: 3 eating areas, breakfast room, *St George* bedrooms. No children under 14. No dogs in *St George* bedrooms.
Credit cards All major cards accepted.
Terms B&B: single £45–£99, double £79.50–£97.50. Alc lunch £19.95, dinner £25.95.

WINDERMERE Cumbria   **Map 4**

The Archway   NEW/BUDGET   *Tel* (015394) 45613
13 College Road   *Fax* (015394) 45328
Windermere LA23 1BU   *E-mail* archway@btinternet.com
                            Website www.lakedistrictguesthouses.co.uk

Victorian stone-built guest house in quiet road close to centre. Recently extensively refurbished by new owner, Vanessa Price: antiques, fresh flowers, family photos, pictures of owner's dogs. "Superb" breakfasts include local sausages, American pancakes. No background music. Small front garden. No smoking. No children under 10. No dogs. Unsuitable for ♿. Limited parking. Closed 2 weeks Jan. 4 bedrooms (no telephone) – 2 have views of mountain and lake, 1 overlooks a carpark. The "caring hostess" is praised this year, but we'd like fuller reports, please. B&B £25–£48. Evening meal by arrangement: £13.50.

Gilpin Lodge   *Tel* (015394) 88818
Crook Road   *Fax* (015394) 88058
nr Windermere LA23 3NE   *E-mail* hotel@gilpin-lodge.co.uk
                                 Website www.gilpin-lodge.co.uk

♦ *César award in 2000*

A white house, dating from 1901 and with carefully grafted extensions. Fronted by a flagstaff and a dovecote, it is set well back from a road in large grounds with gardens, ponds, woodlands and moor. The owners, John and Christine Cunliffe ("they cannot do enough for their visitors," says a report this year) run it on country house lines: no reception, no formal bar. With one exception (a visit during the owners' absence), reports continue strongly favourable: "A lovely place. The staff take a pride in their work." "Neither grand nor stylish, it has a comfortable feel. There is a palpable flexibility towards guests' needs. Service is friendly without formality, and also efficient. Housekeeping is impeccable." In winter, fires blaze in the large sitting rooms, decorated with bright colours, good-quality fabrics, antiques, china ornaments, fresh flowers. Many bedrooms are spacious and have a sitting area and lovely views. A "magnificent bathroom" was admired this year. The dinner menu "is always interesting". The chef, Grant Tomkins, serves modern dishes, eg, shrimp and fennel risotto with a lemon and dill butter dressing; monkfish with a spaghetti of vegetables and wilted spinach.

Portions may be a bit large for some tastes. Lunches are flexible, ranging from a full meal in the restaurant to a light one served in the lounge. Afternoon teas are "a work of art". The lengthy breakfast menu includes freshly squeezed orange juice, home-baked breads, home-made jams, strawberry sorbet in pink champagne, all manner of cooked dishes. Local attractions include places associated with Beatrix Potter, William Wordsworth and John Ruskin, and two stately homes: Levens Hall and Sizergh Castle. (*Heather Sharland, Prof. Wolfgang Stroebe, David Wooff, Tessa Royal; also Ian and Crispina McDonald, Alan Greenwood, and others*)

Open All year.
Rooms 14 double. Some on ground floor.
Facilities Ramps, 2 lounges, 3 dining rooms ("discreet" background music during lunch and dinner). 20-acre grounds: gardens, ponds, croquet. Lake Windermere, fishing, boating, etc, 2 miles. Free access to Parklands country club nearby: swimming pool, sauna, squash, badminton, snooker.
Location On B5284 Kendal–Bowness. M6 exit 36. Train: Windermere (2 miles); then taxi.
Restrictions No smoking in restaurant. No children under 7. No dogs.
Credit cards All major cards accepted.
Terms D,B&B £60–£125; B&B £15 reduction. Light lunches; set Sun lunch £17.50, dinner £35; full alc lunch (Mon–Sat) £27. Off-season reductions; reductions for longer stays. Christmas, New Year packages. 1-night bookings sometimes refused weekends.

Holbeck Ghyll
Holbeck Lane
Windermere LA23 1LU

Tel (015394) 32375
Fax (01534) 34743
E-mail accommodation@holbeck-ghyll.co.uk
Website www.holbeck-ghyll.co.uk

Lord Lonsdale, the first president of the Automobile Association and donor of the Lonsdale Belt for boxing, built this Lakeland mansion as a hunting lodge in 1888. These days it is a luxurious hotel (Pride of Britain), owned by David and Patricia Nicholson. They run it with a "keen young international staff", and *Guide* readers think it "expensive, but excellent". Reached up a steep drive off the road to Ambleside, it has "stunning views" across Lake Windermere to Langdale Falls. In the large grounds there are streams, good walks, all kinds of wildlife, tennis, croquet and a jogging trail. A small spa provides health and beauty treatments. The public rooms have stained glass in the style of Charles Rennie Mackintosh, high ceilings, wood panelling, large pieces of antique furniture, mirrors, luxurious fabrics. Bedrooms in the main building are well appointed, but the best rooms are the newer ones in the lodge; all of these have a balcony or patio area with views of the lake; four also have a kitchenette. There are two dining rooms: the older oak-panelled one is the more opulent; the *Terrace Restaurant* has French windows leading on to a patio for alfresco lunches and early evening meals in summer. The young chef, Stephen Smith, earned a *Michelin* star in 2000 for his sophisticated modern cooking, eg, tian of crab and tomato with langoustines and shellfish vinaigrette; braised pig's trotter stuffed with ham hock and pork knuckle, with morel jus. Simpler dishes and vegetarian options can be provided. The extensive wine list provides a good choice from around the world. "Good breakfasts, especially the croissants on Sunday." Children are welcomed, although there are few special facilities for them. The homes of Wordsworth and Beatrix Potter are nearby. (*A and RS*)

Open All year.
Rooms 5 suites, 15 double. 6 (4 with kitchenette) in lodge in grounds. Some on ground floor.
Facilities Ramps. Hall with inglenook, 2 lounges, bar area, 2 dining rooms; function facilities; small health spa: sauna, steam room, exercise equipment, etc. No background music. 7-acre grounds: streams, ponds, woods to lake shore (800 yds), tennis, putting, croquet, jogging track. Golf, water sports nearby. Civil wedding licence.
Location 3 miles N of Windermere off road towards Ambleside. Pass Brockhole Visitor Centre on left, right turn (Holbeck La) towards Troutbeck. Drive ½ mile on left. Station 3 miles.
Restrictions No smoking: restaurant, lodge bedrooms. No dogs in public rooms.
Credit cards All major cards accepted.
Terms B&B: single £85–£140, double £160–£220, suite £180–£230; D,B&B: single £95–£175, double £170–£300, suite £200–£300. Set Sun lunch £19.50, dinner £42.50. 10% reduction for 5 or more nights. Off-season, Christmas, New Year, luxury breaks. 1-night bookings sometimes refused Sat off-season. *V*

Storrs Hall   *Tel* (015394) 47111
Windermere LA23 3LG   *Fax* (015394) 47555
                                    E-mail reception@storrshall.co.uk
                                    Website www.storrshall.co.uk

"It's just beautiful, and the personal attention you receive is never ending, never flagging. The manager shimmers round from morning to night, like Jeeves. Our bedroom had everything you could want, including the view: two white swans drifted across the still water." "The location is perfect, in wooded grounds leading to a jetty with boats bobbing in a small bay. Another wooded pathway leads to a second jetty and a small temple rising from the water." Two reports this year on this Grade II listed Georgian mansion, built by John Gandy, an associate of Sir John Soane, in the style of a villa at Bellagio on Lake Como. A "rather institutional" extension has now been added. It sits in large wooded grounds on a peninsula, with views to the south down the lake (not another building in sight) and to the north towards Bowness. Owned by Richard Livock and Les Hindle, it is managed by Nigel Lawrence, "a gem of the old school, assiduously deferential". Mr Livock is an antiques dealer, and the house is "a treasure trove of antique furniture and art". In the large entrance hall, lit by a cupola, huge flower arrangements stand on tables and pedestals. The large, high-ceilinged drawing room has an open fire, rare books and a grand piano: a smaller library contains "every imaginable board game". The bar is sporty, with stuffed fish and animals, and antlers. Some find the whole atmosphere "a bit stuffy" and the Victorian furniture "rather heavy". But the best bedrooms are "large with a magnificent bed, huge wardrobe, spacious bathroom with a freestanding, clawfoot bath and separate shower". The restaurant/conservatory looks over lawns that are sometimes visited by fawns. A new chef, Michael Dodds, arrived in October 1999. One visitor thought all the food – including the home-baked cakes at tea – "lovely", but a Sunday night meal (chef's night off) was said to "lack finesse", apart from very good pastry work. "Despite this, the service was attentive and good-humoured, and breakfast was very good indeed, with fresh orange juice, excellent porridge, fruit, etc." (*Ruth West, Kate and David Wooff*)

Open Feb–Dec.
Rooms 3 suites, 15 double.
Facilities Hall lounge, drawing room, library, bar, restaurant; light classical background music most of the day. 17-acre grounds with lake frontage: jetty, fishing, boating, etc. Unsuitable for &.
Location 4 miles S of Windermere, on A592. Train: Windermere, Oxenholme; then taxi.
Restrictions Smoking banned in restaurant, discouraged in bedrooms. No children under 12. Dogs by arrangement, not in public rooms.
Credit cards Amex, MasterCard, Visa.
Terms B&B: single £90–£125, double £155–£190, suite £235–£300; D,B&B: single £122–£155, double £215–£250, suite £295–£360. Set lunch £17.50–£22.50, dinner £35; full alc £48.50. Special breaks; Christmas package. ***V***

WINDSOR Berkshire *See SHORTLIST* **Map 2**

WINSTONE Gloucestershire **Map 3**

Winstone Glebe `BUDGET`
Winstone
nr Cirencester GL7 7JU

Tel/Fax (01285) 821451
E-mail sparsons@cableinet.co.uk

"The setting is quiet; the views gorgeous, the bedrooms comfortable." In a Domesday-old village in a designated area of outstanding natural beauty, this Georgian ex-rectory stands amid gardens and paddocks by a Saxon church. It is the family home of Susanna (an ex-restaurateur) and Shaun Parsons, and furnished in "genuine country house style". They run it on house-party lines, combining informality with "a high standard of service and individual attention", say *Guide* readers. Mrs Parsons' cooking is admired too. Dinner (no choice until dessert) might consist of sun-dried tomato and mozzarella galette; loin of pork slowly cooked on fennel and milk; cherry frangipane or lemon syllabub, then cheese. Mr Parsons "genially dispenses pre-prandial drinks and appropriate table wines by the glass". "We appreciated the fire in the drawing room on a chilly May evening." Breakfast includes cereals on a side table and make-it-yourself toast, which "involves a bit of getting up and down, making it a slightly disturbed meal". The bedrooms in the main house are "pretty and comfortable", but the one above the coach house, reached up steep stone steps, is thought less attractive. All have a private bathroom, but only one is *en suite*. "Winstone is unexciting, but the Duntisbournes, just down the valley, are some of the loveliest, most unspoilt villages in the Cotswolds."

Nearby are polo at Cirencester; medieval castles, old churches, stately homes and gardens. (*GW, and others*)

Open All year, except Christmas.
Rooms 3 double. 1 in coach house 30 yds. No telephone; TV in coach house room.
Facilities Drawing room, dining room. No background music. 3-acre grounds: garden, tennis, paddocks. Unsuitable for &.
Location Off A417 between Cirencester and Gloucester. House is 300 yds short of church, by public footpath sign.
Restrictions No smoking: dining room, bedrooms. No dogs in bedrooms; by arrangement in public rooms.
Credit cards MasterCard, Visa.
Terms B&B £30–£36. Single supplement £8. Set dinner £20.

WINTERINGHAM Lincolnshire   Map 4

Winteringham Fields   *Tel* (01724) 733096
Winteringham DN15 9PF   *Fax* (01724) 733898
                                        E-mail wintfields@aol.com
                                        Website www.winteringhamfields.com

Ⓠ *Cesar award in 1996*

"What a joy! The most perfect 'French restaurant-with-rooms' I've ever encountered in this country. It is the perfect excuse to journey north via the Humber Bridge," enthused one correspondent from London. "We were met in the courtyard at 5 pm on a bleak November night, and were made to feel cosseted and welcome from that moment on." Germain and Annie Schwab's 16th-century farmhouse stands at the crossroads in a quiet village on the southern bank of the Humber estuary, an unlikely setting for a place with two *Michelin* stars. Returning devotees again found the meals "superb – Germain is always at the stoves. If he cannot be there, they close the restaurant." "Expensive, but worth every penny," is another comment. Meals begin with an array of appetisers and are punctuated by "all sorts of interesting titbits". The *à la carte* menu might include tournedos of monkfish tail with purée of fennel and an orange and aubergine jus; peppered rump of venison with apricot cracked wheat cake and a juniper and thyme reduction. Desserts such as a hot pyramid of chocolate, nougatine and honey are equally spectacular, and the cheese trolley "is a revelation". A simpler, three-course no-choice *menu du jour* is also available. The house has exposed beams, low doorways and ceilings, oak panelling, narrow corridors and Victorian furniture. In the bedrooms "no detail has been overlooked: good lighting, fresh flowers, up-to-date magazines, etc". The rooms in the main building have uneven floors and chintzy fabrics (one has a four-poster and a bathroom down a tiny flight of steps). More spacious ones are in converted stables across the courtyard, and this year there are two "beautifully designed" new rooms in a renovated dovecote (with a kitchen) two minutes' walk away. "Unsurpassed breakfasts with lovely marmalade, ambrosial lemon curd in swan-shaped dishes, fresh orange juice on the table, lightest-ever brioche, croissants, breads, etc, and the immediate arrival of coffee." Annie Schwab (who has an MBE for services to tourism) runs the place with a "marvellous staff". They are "efficient and enthusiastic, yet also informal and friendly". Walks along the estuary are "particularly attractive", and there is a marked path to a hide for birdwatchers. (*Ann Thornton, John and Joan Wyatt, Pat and Jeremy Temple, Kate and David Wooff*)

Open All year, except Sun, Mon, 2 weeks Christmas/New Year, last week Mar, 1st week Aug.
Rooms 2 suites, 8 double, 3 in courtyard, 2 in dovecote, 1 in cottage, 200 yds. 3 on ground floor.
Facilities Lounge, bar, restaurant, conservatory; private dining room. No background music. ¼-acre grounds; pond. Unsuitable for &.
Location Centre of village 4 miles SW of Humber Bridge. Train: Scunthorpe; bus: Winteringham.
Restrictions No smoking: restaurant, all bedrooms. Dogs at proprietors' discretion, not in public rooms.
Credit cards Amex, MasterCard, Visa.
Terms B&B: single £75–£115, double £90–£160, suite £160. English breakfast £10. Set lunch £25 and £28, dinner £32 and £60; full alc £67.

WOLVERHAMPTON West Midlands *See SHORTLIST*   **Map 3**

WOOLACOMBE Devon   **Map 1**

Watersmeet   *Tel* (01271) 870333
Mortehoe   *Fax* (01271) 870890
Woolacombe EX34 7EB   *E-mail* watersmeethotel@compuserve.com
                                Website www.watersmeethotel.co.uk

The setting of this traditional hotel is "fantastic", everyone agrees, on a cliff above the rocky coast, with views from Woolacombe Bay past Hartland Point to Lundy Island. National Trust land is all around, and there is good walking at Morte Point close by. New owners, Mr and Mrs Wickman, took over in February 2000, but manager Neil Bradley has stayed on from the previous regime, and many of the staff have been here for years. Very good for a family holiday, *Watersmeet* has a heated outdoor pool and an indoor one with a wave machine; a wide beach with sand and rock pools is a short walk down steps from the large garden; many other activities are available (see below). Children's teas "are appealing to them, and also healthy". Breakfasts were thought "good and promptly served" this year; opinions on the dinners varied from "excellent" to "a bit variable", but the dining room is "very elegant, with well-trained and speedy service", and there is plenty of choice on the dinner menu, eg, scallops with white wine sauce; turbot with basil hollandaise sauce; lemon and cream torte with honey ice-cream. The best bedrooms overlook the sea; they are well appointed, but housekeeping may be "a bit mixed". Inter-connecting lounges in the front overlook the views. In low season there are bridge, golfing and painting holidays. (*KS, Richard Creed, Gordon Hands*)

Open 10 Feb–4 Jan.
Rooms 1 suite, 20 double, 1 single. Some on ground floor.
Facilities Lounge, 2 bars, restaurant (classical background music; pianist twice weekly); indoor swimming pool, games room. 3-acre grounds: tennis,

swimming pool, croquet, golf practice; by sandy beach: sea bathing, rock pools, surfing. Golf, clay-pigeon shooting, riding arranged.
Location On coast. Mortehoe is 4 miles SW of Ilfracombe. Train: Barnstaple (16 miles).
Restrictions No smoking in restaurant. No children under 8 at dinner. No dogs.
Credit cards All major cards accepted.
Terms B&B: single £58–£110, double £116–£194; D,B&B (min. 2 nights): single £71–£125, double £142–£220. Light lunch from £2.95; set dinner £26.50; full alc £28.50. Christmas package.

WORCESTER Worcestershire *See SHORTLIST*   **Map 3**

WORFIELD Shropshire   **Map 3**

The Old Vicarage   *Tel* (01746) 716497
Worfield   *Freephone* 0800 0968010
Bridgnorth WV15 5JZ   *Fax* (01746) 716552
                          E-mail admin@the-old-vicarage.demon.co.uk
                          Website www.oldvicarageworfield.com

"For us, this is rather like coming home," writes a loyal supporter after another "splendid stay" in Peter and Christine Iles's converted red brick vicarage (Pride of Britain). It has a "lovely setting" with views of distant hills sloping down towards the River Worfe. Public rooms have a mixture of antique and repro furniture, a remarkable collection of clocks, original prints and watercolours on pale yellow walls. The bedrooms vary in style (some small ones have been thought over-priced, and the family suite, under the eaves, is said to have a "cramped bathroom"). Rooms in the coach house are probably the best, but all are well-appointed, and provided with sherry, biscuits, cut-glass tumblers, ice, etc, while bathrooms have "soft white towels, good soaps and oils". "Housekeeping is immaculate." The restaurant, under Richard Arnold, has a *Michelin Bib Gourmand* for, eg, risotto of white crab with Parmesan wafers, dill and sun-dried tomato relish; chargrilled fillet of Longhorn beef with a cassoulet of Puy lentils, chorizo, wild mushrooms and vegetable pearls; iced coconut parfait with kiwi sorbet and mango sauce. *Guide* readers this year found the food "wonderful and good value"; "outstanding in quality"; "beautiful local produce cooked with love and restraint, with well-judged accompaniments"; "the patisserie chef is brilliant". Also admired: the pre-dinner appetisers, home-baked walnut rolls, tapenade and oil dressing on the tables, and the trolley of English cheeses. Guests who visit on a two-day leisure break are now able to dine from the whole of the menu, rather than part of it as previously. The wine list is "full of delights and extensive" (it includes organic and vegan wines, and over 40 half bottles). "Service by young local women is willing and knowledgeable" but it can be slow at breakfast (this includes home-made black pudding, free-range eggs). Worfield is a good base for visiting the Severn Valley Railway and the Cosford Aerospace Museum; special breaks include a trip to the Ironbridge Gorge and its recently restored bridge, close by. (*Ann Thornton, Brian Pearce*)

Open All year.
Rooms 3 suites, 11 double, 4 in coach house, 2 on ground floor.
Facilities Ramps. Lounge, conservatory, bar, 3 dining rooms; small conference facilities. No background music. 2-acre grounds: croquet. Golf nearby.
Location 4 miles NE of Bridgnorth. 1 mile from A454, by cricket ground. Regular buses from Bridgnorth.
Restrictions Smoking in conservatory only. No dogs in public rooms.
Credit cards Amex, MasterCard, Visa.
Terms [2000] B&B: single £75–£110, double £115–£175, suite £175; D,B&B: single £100–£135, double £150–£215, suite £215. Set lunch £18.50, dinner £22.50–£36. Special breaks; golfing breaks. Christmas package. ***V***

YARMOUTH Isle of Wight Map 2

The George   *Tel* (01983) 760331
Quay Street   *Fax* (01983) 760425
Yarmouth PO41 0PE   *E-mail* res@thegeorge.co.uk

Built as a residence for Admiral Sir Robert Holmes, the then Governor of the island, and visited by Charles II in 1651, this is now a stylish hotel, owned by Jeremy and Amy Willcock and John Illsley, and managed by Jacki Everest. It stands between the pier and a fortress, built by Henry VIII as a defence against the French. Reports are mixed this year: everyone admires the building, with its magnificent flagstoned hall, spectacular wooden staircase, panelled residents' lounge with an open fire, and "beautiful bedrooms" on the two upper floors – many have their original wood panelling; two lead on to a balcony. "No 20 was one of the best hotel rooms we have ever experienced: It overlooked the small, immaculate garden, the minute shingle beach, the sails in the Solent and the constant movement of the ferries; the bathroom was particularly nice, with a 'loo with a view'." The total absence of piped music is applauded. The brasserie is popular with locals and yachties. The formal red-walled restaurant has a *Michelin* star for the cooking of Kevin Mangeolles, eg, seabass tartare with brandade and carrot mayonnaise; millefeuille of red mullet and pork skin with lime and artichoke; pistachio parfait with coconut milk sorbet. One couple admired the cooking in both the restaurant and brasserie, but other visitors thought the meals "pretentious and unbalanced" (even the admirers complained of a scarcity of vegetables). And whereas some found the "ample" staff "friendly"; others thought them "snooty", and the owners "aloof". The hotel can be taken over for a house party; its yacht, the *Master George*, is available for hire. The ferry from Lymington docks close by; unless you want to drive round the island, you should park on the mainland and travel as a foot passenger, thereby halving the exorbitant price of the crossing (the hotel has no carpark). (*Nigel and Jennifer Jee, and others*)

Open All year; restaurant open Tues–Sat dinner only.
Rooms 1 suite, 14 double, 2 single.
Facilities Lounge, bar, brasserie, restaurant; conference room. No background music. ¼-acre garden on pebble beach (no bathing). Sailing, riding, golf, clay-pigeon shooting, walking nearby. Unsuitable for &. Civil wedding licence.
Location Waterfront, by ferry port. Train/car: Lymington Pier; then ferry.

Restrictions No smoking in 4 bedrooms. No children under 10. Dogs by arrangement; not in public rooms, except bar.
Credit cards Amex, MasterCard, Visa.
Terms [2000] B&B: single £85–£95, double £145–£192.50, suite £165; D,B&B (min. 2 nights) £92.50–£116 per person. Set lunch £17.95, dinner £39.50; full alc £30. 1-night bookings refused weekends. Christmas package, 2-night rates: D,B&B (1 dinner free each night).

YORK North Yorkshire   **Map 4**

The Grange   *Tel* (01904) 644744
1 Clifton   *Fax* (01904) 612453
York YO30 6AA   *E-mail* info@grangehotel.co.uk
                                   Website www.grangehotel.co.uk

"The weekend was made special by our choice of hotel. The four-poster bedroom was well equipped, very romantic; the staff were courteous and helpful." So runs one tribute this year to Jeremy Cassel's Regency town house, close to the ancient city walls and within walking distance of the minster. Returning visitors found the staff as friendly as ever. "Our 'superior kingsize' bedroom, though not very large, and with limited drawer/shelving space, was very comfortable." All bedrooms have fine fabrics, antiques, good lighting and a smart bathroom. The public rooms are striking, with panelling, smart wallpapers, family portraits, open fires in the large drawing room and morning room, and a grand staircase. We'd like reports on the cooking of the new chef, Michael Whiteley (he arrived in April 2000). The red-walled *Ivy Restaurant* serves modern dishes such as rolled duck foie gras and rabbit terrine; roast partridge with parsnip purée; pear and cinnamon tarte Tatin. The brasserie, in a vaulted cellar (open at midday and in the early evening) serves dishes like curried parsnip soup; oxtail braised in red wine; rice pudding with plum compote. In the seafood bar, fish dishes (grilled sea bream with aubergine caviar; salmon fish-cakes with spinach, etc) can be accompanied by a glass of Dom Ruinart champagne. The hotel is on a busy road, but front rooms are double-glazed. (*James O'Connor, Philip and Eileen Hall; also John Morgan*)

Open All year.
Rooms 1 suite, 26 double, 3 single. Some on ground floor, 1 adapted for &.
Facilities Ramps. Drawing room, morning room, library, restaurant, brasserie, seafood bar (jazz/popular background music during meals); conference facilities. Civil wedding licence.
Location 500 yds from city wall, on A19 N to Thirsk (front rooms double-glazed). Carpark.
Restrictions Smoking discouraged in restaurant. Small dogs only, not in public rooms.
Credit cards All major cards accepted.
Terms [2000] B&B: single £99, double £125–£185, suite £215; D,B&B £89–£112. Set lunch £11.50, dinner £25; full alc: restaurant £24–£32; brasserie £22. Special breaks (2 or more nights) all year. Christmas, New Year packages. 1-night bookings sometimes refused.

Middlethorpe Hall   *Tel* (01904) 641241
Bishopthorpe Road   *Fax* (01904) 620176
York YO23 2GB   *E-mail* info@middlethorpe.com
                                           Website www.middlethorpe.com

Once the home of the diarist Lady Mary Wortley Montagu, this magnificent Grade II listed William and Mary mansion (Relais &
Châteaux) has been restored by Historic House Hotels Ltd (see also
Hartwell House, Aylesbury, *The Cadogan*, London, *Bodysgallen
Hall*, Llandudno, Wales). Stuart McPherson was promoted to manager
this year. The house stands near York racecourse, in a large park with
a small lake, a ha-ha, a white garden, a walled garden and expanses of
lawn (but the hum of traffic from the nearby busy road is audible). The
impressive façade is matched by an equally imposing interior: a black-
and-white marble-floored hall, an intricately carved staircase;
antiques, oil paintings, *objets d'art*, chandeliers in the "extremely
comfortable" public rooms (the ban on mobile phones and laptop
computers was applauded this year). Despite the grandeur of the building, there is praise for the "friendly staff" and "relaxed atmosphere".
The best bedrooms, in the main house, are enormous and grand. Some
have a large sitting room and a walk-in wardrobe. Some have two
bathrooms. The cheaper rooms, in converted stables, are also enjoyed
– they are "pretty, and well provided with pampering extras" (but one
visitor this year reported poor sound insulation of his room's ceiling,
and another was severely critical of the housekeeping). The traditional
English cooking was thought "excellent". The mussel minestrone is
"highly recommended", and other dishes include, eg, ravioli of quail;
braised pig's trotters stuffed with sweetbreads; chilled rice pudding
with poached pear. There is also a vegetarian menu. The chef, Martin
Barker, will offer alternatives to the set menu to visitors on a long stay.
The "very professional young *sommelier* and helpful restaurant staff"
were admired this year. The panelled dining room overlooking the
garden is formal (men are asked to wear a jacket and tie at dinner), but
there is also a simpler grill room. The new health spa has an
"excellent" pool – "good for a proper swim". Castle Howard, Newby
Hall and the Harlow Carr Botanical Gardens are nearby. (*Robert
Scourfield, and others*)

Open All year. Closed to non-residents Christmas Day, 31 Dec.
Rooms 7 suites, 19 double, 4 single. 19 in courtyard.
Facilities Drawing room, sitting room, library, bar, restaurant, grill room, pri-
vate dining rooms, function facilities. No background music. 20-acre grounds:
walled garden, croquet, lake, spa: health and beauty facilities, swimming pool.
Golf nearby. Unsuitable for &.
Location 1½ miles S of centre, by racecourse. From A64 follow signs to York,
then A1036 and signs to Bishopthorpe, then Middlethorpe. Train: York;
then taxi.
Restrictions No smoking in restaurant. No children under 8. No dogs.
Credit cards MasterCard, Visa.
Terms [2000] Room: single £105–£130, double £145–£215, suite £195–£260.
Breakfast: continental £10.50, English £14.50. Set lunch £18.50, dinner £34.
Winter, spring champagne, summer historic house, spa breaks. Christmas,
New Year packages.

Mount Royale   *Tel* (01904) 628856
The Mount   *Fax* (01904) 611171
York YO24 1GU   *E-mail* reservations@mountroyale.co.uk
                                Website www.mountroyale.co.uk

"An excellent place, and excellent value. A wonderful huge room. A massive menu; huge servings of food. Very '70s. Very Yorkshire." This year's tribute to this "dependable, traditional" hotel near the racecourse and Micklegate Bar, and three-quarters of a mile from the minster. An earlier visitor wrote: "The friendly staff are always ready to help. We always feel at home." The building, mainly William IV, with modern extensions, is owned by two generations of the Oxtoby family, and managed by Stuart Oxtoby with a long-serving staff. In the mature garden at the back there is a heated swimming pool. The best bedrooms, with a sitting area and a private veranda, are in the garden annexe, connected to the main building by a covered walkway filled with orange, lemon and fig trees, bougainvillea and subtropical plants. Some rooms in the main house are quite small and old-fashioned; front ones have double glazing to cut out the noise from the busy road outside. Bathrooms are "stocked with useful goodies". Plenty of public rooms: a small bar, a lounge with antiques, and a conservatory; also a beauty centre, and a full-sized snooker table. A pianist plays in the evening in the restaurant (it consists of several rooms, most of which overlook the garden). A brasserie, *Oxo's,* opened this year. The food is traditional, eg, pan-fried calf's liver and roast duckling as a main course; desserts include Eton mess and Grand Marnier crème brûlée. There is a vegetarian menu, and "plenty of bargains" are to be found on the wine list. Breakfast has a buffet with lots of choice, and cooked dishes such as kedgeree. (*H Willbourn, GM*)

Open All year. Brasserie open Sun–Fri; restaurant open Mon–Sat.
Rooms 6 suites (4 in garden annexe), 16 double, 1 single. 6 on ground floor.
Facilities 2 lounges, bar, conservatory, brasserie, restaurant (pianist in restaurant; background CDs in public rooms at night; function/meeting room; beauty centre. ½-acre grounds: swimming pool (heated May–Sept), children's play house.
Location Past racecourse on A1036 from Tadcaster, at junction with Albemarle Rd (front rooms double-glazed). Parking. 10 mins' walk or bus from centre.
Restrictions No smoking in restaurant. No dogs unattended in bedrooms.
Credit cards All major cards accepted.
Terms [2000] B&B: single from £85, double from £95, suite £140. Full alc: brasserie £28, restaurant £37. 2-day breaks; Christmas package.

See also SHORTLIST

****

Hotel in the Midlands. Despite its promise of rustic authenticity, the interior of this pub was a great disappointment. The food was watery and insipid and the music intrusive to the point of distraction. Endless repeats of Phil Collins's greatest hits must be on a par with Chinese water torture.

****

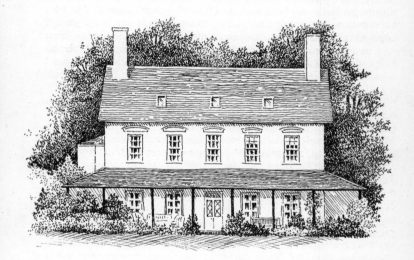

Plas Bodegroes, Pwllheli

ABERGAVENNY Monmouthshire   Map 3

Llanwenarth House   *Tel* (01873) 830289
Govilon, nr Abergavenny NP7 9SF   *Fax* (01873) 832199

"Bruce and Amanda Weatherill made us feel very welcome"; "we liked the trusting atmosphere", runs renewed praise this year. Their family home, "not grand, but cosy", with just five guest bedrooms, is a 16th-century manor house, built of warm grey limestone, above the Usk valley in the Brecon Beacons National Park. Most rooms are "large and comfortable, with views of lovely countryside", though there is one report of a "dingy bathroom". The house is filled with "decades worth of personal belongings, lovingly acquired" and dogs ("well behaved and beautiful"). Mrs Weatherill "will cook you an out-standing meal, served in sophisticated surroundings"; her husband, waiting at table, "gives a lengthy description of each ingredient" – most soft fruits and many vegetables are home grown, as is the lamb.

Vegetarians are well catered for. Oeufs en cocotte; halibut "with a divine sauce", and "the pingiest late summer pudding and rhubarb crumble ice-cream" were enjoyed this year. Wines are "carefully chosen and served". Eating arrangements are flexible: guests often dine together at one large table, but there are smaller tables too, for those who prefer to eat *à deux*. "The house is well maintained, the location is lovely" (but one reader disliked "the pylons which mar the otherwise spectacular view"). Many guests are walkers. Before and after dinner they tend to socialise by the log fire in the Georgian drawing room. "Superb breakfasts" include kippers, home-made jams, home-laid eggs. Honey comes from hives in the orchard. The large grounds, with two huge copper beeches, horses and chickens, are bordered by the Brecon and Monmouthshire Canal, where boats may be hired by the day. There is good walking nearby in the Welsh hills, where you can climb Sugar Loaf Mountain; or you can explore the castles and archaeological sites of the Welsh Marches. Aberglasney, "a garden lost in time" featured on BBC TV, is an hour's drive away, easily reached by the A40 which is not far off. Plenty of sporting activities are available, too (see below). (*Judith Hasko, and others; also Mr and Mrs Eubank*)

Open Mar–mid-Jan; Christmas, New Year by arrangement. No lunches. Dining room opened 5 nights a week, to suit guests' requirements.
Rooms 5 double, 1 on ground floor. No telephone.
Facilities Drawing room, dining room. No background music. 2-acre gardens in 10-acre small farm: croquet, canal (boat hire); stabling for visiting horses. Fishing, golf, pony-trekking, shooting nearby.
Location From junction of A40/A465/A4042, take A465 towards Merthyr Tydfil for 3½ miles. At roundabout take 1st exit to Govilon; the hotel's ½-mile drive is 150 yards on right. Train: Abergavenny 4½ miles; then local bus/taxi.
Restrictions No smoking: dining room, bedrooms. No children under 10. No dogs in public rooms.
Credit cards None accepted.
Terms B&B: double £80–£84; single occupancy: £20 discount. Reductions for longer stays. Set dinner £25. 1-night bookings sometimes refused bank holidays.

ABERSOCH Gwynedd   **Map 3**

Porth Tocyn Hotel   *Tel* (01758) 713303
Abersoch LL53 7BU   *Fax* (01758) 713538
                                  E-mail porthtocyn.hotel@virgin.net
                                  Website www.porth-tocyn-hotel.co.uk

𝒬 *César award in 1984*

"Splendid, with a beautiful restaurant, fine views." Praise came again this year for this old *Guide* favourite, a family-friendly hotel that has been owned and run by the Fletcher-Brewer family for more than 50 years. It is set quietly above a popular yachting village, with glorious vistas of Snowdonia and Cardigan Bay. The "exuberant" Nick Fletcher-Brewer "has his eye on every detail", and "the friendly atmosphere created by the staff soon affects the guests, who gather in the comfortable chintz-covered armchairs by the fire". Lounges are traditional, with country antiques and fresh flowers, and there's a small children's sitting room with games, TV, video, etc. The bedrooms are cottagey rather than luxurious; many are inter-connected for use by a family group. Some walls are thin. Children under seven have high tea, to avoid a "summer camp" atmosphere at dinner. The restaurant has had a *Good Food Guide* entry for over 40 years, and the cooking, with Louise Fletcher-Brewer and Guy Lamble as chefs, continues to be praised: "A very good lunch with lots of choice on a little terrace with a fabulous view." "The food is varied, imaginative and served in generous quantities; the fish dishes are particularly good." The hotel writes to us this year that menus this year have been shortened and lightened: "The old five-course menu was too much for most guests." Homemade soups, and poached halibut on a tomato and basil sauce, have been particularly enjoyed; so have desserts such as rum bread-and-butter pudding, and hazelnut and strawberry roulade. Light weekday lunches are informally served; there is a "gargantuan" Sunday buffet lunch. Refurbishment this year includes recarpeting of main rooms, and installation of new showers. "Though our ground-floor bedrooms were never designed for wheelchair users, we do attract quite a few disabled guests, who by and large cope well," Mr Fletcher-Brewer tells us. (*Bridget Bentley, JC, and others*)

Open Shortly before Easter–mid-Nov.
Rooms 14 double, 3 single. 3 on ground floor.
Facilities 5 sitting rooms, children's room, bar, restaurant. No background music. 25-acre grounds: gardens, swimming pool (heated May–Sept), tennis. Beach, safe bathing, sailing, fishing, golf, riding, clay-pigeon shooting nearby.
Location 2 miles S of Abersoch, through hamlets of Sarnbach and Bwlch Tocyn. Follow 4 brown signposts: Porth Tocyn.
Restrictions No smoking: restaurant, bedrooms. No children under 7 in restaurant at night (high teas until 6.15 pm). No dogs in public rooms.
Credit cards MasterCard, Visa.
Terms [2000] B&B: single £49–£64, double £65.50–£119. Cooked breakfast £5. Set lunch (Sun) £18, dinner (2 to 5 courses) £23.50–£30. Child accommodated free in parents' room free. Reductions for long stays. 1-night bookings occasionally refused.

ABERYSTWYTH Ceredigion *See SHORTLIST*   **Map 3**

BETTWS GWERFYL GOCH Denbighshire   **Map 3**

The Old Rectory `BUDGET`   *Tel* (01490) 460387
Bettws Gwerfyl Goch
nr Corwen LL21 9PU

"Wonderful breakfasts, outstanding dinners, inglenook firelit evenings with our dear and caring hosts, always interesting" – one of three plaudits this year for Frank and Lesley Hart. Their 18th-century rectory with modern additions, "a homely old house in a big garden", is on the edge of the Snowdonia National Park, and their idiosyncratic style is liked by many readers: no television in the house ("we can provide a wireless for Archers fanatics"); no smoking anywhere. The

Harts are ex-teachers, "knowledgeable about all things", and they create an ambience of "great peace". "We find the quiet disturbs some people," they write. Mrs Hart makes her own bread, preserves and ice-cream. Guests this year again loved the food, notably the vegetables accompanying the "ample and delicious" main dishes. Dinner, which must be booked the day before, is generally served round one long table, but anyone wishing to eat alone can do so in the conservatory, which also serves as a breakfast room. No licence; guests bring their own drink (no corkage is charged). The menu is simple: "I do not decorate the food with silly bits that people do not eat," writes Mrs Hart. A light supper is also available. There are open fires in the dining room and lounge, lots of books, a grand piano which guests may play. The snug bedrooms are provided with flowers and home-made biscuits. The grounds are home to owls, badgers and Britain's rarest mammal, the pine marten. Frank Hart, an experienced hill-walker, can suggest suitable walks in the area. Caernarvon and Conwy castles are within easy reach. (*Karin and Jörg Wöhrwag, Sallie D Kay, S and JF*)

Open 23 Mar–7 Jan.
Rooms 3 double.
Facilities Lounge (classical music, if requested), dining room, conservatory/breakfast room. 1¼-acre garden. Fishing nearby, river, walks. Unsuitable for &.
Location NW of Corwen. A5 to Maerdy (4½ miles). Right after *Goat Inn*. After 1½ miles left at crossroads in centre of Bettws Gwerfyl Goch. *Old Rectory* 400 yds on left, behind high wall.
Restrictions No smoking. No dogs in house.
Credit cards None accepted.
Terms (*Not VAT-rated*) B&B £29–£34; D,B&B £46.50–£51.50. Supper £9, dinner £17.50. Packed lunches available. Child accommodated in parents' room: under 3, free; 3–10, 50% of adult rate. Christmas package. *V*

BODUAN Gwynedd   Map 3

The Old Rectory BUDGET   *Tel/Fax* (01758) 721519
Boduan, nr Pwllheli LL53 6DT

"Gabrielle and Roger Pollard made us very welcome in their beautiful home, which offers every comfort. The public rooms are elegantly furnished with antiques and paintings, the bedrooms are well equipped." More admiration this year for this guest house in a yellow 18th-century ex-rectory. It has a "lovely setting" – a big garden with lawns, mature trees and paddock, near the church of a village in a wooded area of the Lleyn peninsula. "Many of our guests leave us as friends," write the Pollards. Family antiques and photographs fill the house; there's a tall carved pine fireplace, reputedly designed by Sir Clough Williams-Ellis, in the drawing room. An evening meal, with "good home cooking" by Mrs Pollard, is served by arrangement, using local fish, meat, game and vegetables: dishes include, eg, local smoked salmon with pickled cucumbers; pork with cider and mushroom sauce; braised beef in red wine; New Orleans bread-and-butter pudding with whiskey cream sauce. There is a short wine list. All bedrooms have just been redecorated. Nearby are three golf courses, and miles of footpaths; also splendid beaches. Well placed for exploring the beautiful Lleyn peninsula. The mountains of Snowdonia and several castles, including Harlech and Caernarfon, are within an hour's drive. (*Alison Elliott, and others*)

Open All year, except Christmas week.
Rooms 4 double. No telephone. Also self-catering cottage.
Facilities Drawing room (classical background music "when appropriate"), dining room. 2½-acre grounds. Off-road driving, clay-pigeon shooting, archery, golf, go-karting, sailing, riding, sandy beaches nearby. Unsuitable for &.
Location 4 miles NW of Pwllheli off A497, opposite church. Train: Pwllheli; then bus/taxi.
Restrictions No smoking. Small dogs by arrangement; not in public rooms.
Credit cards None accepted.
Terms B&B £30–£40; D,B&B £50–£60. Set dinner £20–£25. Reduced rates for children accommodated in parents' room. 10% reduction for 3 nights or more. 1-night bookings refused bank holidays. *V*

BRECHFA Carmarthenshire   Map 3

Tŷ Mawr   *Tel* (01267) 202332
Brechfa SA32 7RA   *Fax* (01267) 202437
                                   E-mail tymawr@tymawrcountryhotel.co.uk
                                   Website www.tymawrcountryhotel.co.uk

Inspectors praise owners Roger and Veronica Weston for the "genuinely warm welcome, in an overall spirit of generosity" at their small restaurant-with-rooms. It is a 15th/16th-century white-fronted Welsh farmhouse in a lovely setting by the River Marlais on the edge of Brechfa forest. Features include low ceilings and stone walls, oak beams, tiled floors, deep floral armchairs, outsize fabric daffodils and a log fire in the large sitting room. There is a flowery terrace, with tables and chairs, looking over the garden and orchard. The bedrooms are not large, but are well lit, with good storage space. "Pretty flowered wallpaper gives a mid-Victorian feel; tea-making facilities came with scrumptious big biscuits; comfortable beds, plenty of hot water, but the central heating wheezed a bit in the morning." *Tŷ Mawr* has its own bakehouse, and "delicious home-made organic bread" is a feature of every meal. Mrs Weston is the chef, and the dinner, served in the Gothic-style candlelit restaurant, has been enjoyed: plenty of choice, eg, prawns in garlic; sirloin of Welsh beef with a mustard sauce; strawberry cream meringue – and a vodka-laced sorbet between courses. "Perfectly cooked vegetables, an excellent selection of Welsh cheeses, a good range of reasonably priced wines." Breakfast has a lavish buffet: cereals, fruit, etc, and also the Full Monty, with free-range eggs. Sunday lunch is a speciality. Nearby are the

nature reserve at Dinas, the new National Botanic Gardens of Wales, and Kidwelly, Carreg Cennen and Llansteffan castles. "The roads around us are all virtually traffic-free," say the Westons.

Open All year. Restaurant closed midday, except Sun.
Rooms 5 double. No telephone.
Facilities Lounge, bar/reception, 2 dining rooms (varied background music). 1-acre garden: small river. Golf, fishing, riding, walking nearby; beach 12 miles. Unsuitable for &.
Location Centre of village (quiet road). 14 miles NE of Carmarthen.
Restrictions No smoking: restaurant, bedrooms. Dogs by arrangement; not in public rooms.
Credit cards MasterCard, Visa.
Terms B&B £42–£52; D,B&B £60–£75. Set Sun lunch £13, dinner £23. 2-night breaks. Christmas, winter packages. *V*

BRECON Powys   Map 3

Penpont   BUDGET   *Tel* (01874) 636202
nr Brecon LD3 8EU   *E-mail* penpont@globalnomad.co.uk
                                        Website www.penpont.com

A mellow stone house with a "warmly informal atmosphere", *Penpont* stands gloriously below the Brecon Beacons by the fast-flowing River Usk, in an area rich in wildlife. It was built in 1666 by Daniel Williams, an ancestor of present owners Gavin and Davina Hogg. Recently much renovated externally, it is reached by a long drive; new planting (including a maze in the shape of a green man) helps keep out road noises. Around is a working estate, with 40 acres of parkland and some unusual old buildings, including a chapel, a dovecote and stables. The four large bedrooms, not all with facilities *en suite*, are furnished simply "and with great charm", says an inspector, "taking one back to an earlier era". The Tapestry Room has the original 17th-century wall hangings. Guests have the use of a large oak-panelled sitting room lined with books and furnished with "welcoming old sofas and easy chairs". The room features works by local artist Robert Macdonald, a member of the Welsh Group. Children are welcomed. Breakfast, served in a large room, is "adequate", with a good choice of hot items. Dinner for a group can be provided by arrangement, otherwise there are several good pubs within easy driving distance. An excellent base for walkers and birdwatchers, Penpont is quite close to Dan-yr-Ogof caves and Big Pit; historic Tretower Court and Caerphilly Castle are within easy reach.

Open All year, except Christmas, New Year.
Rooms 1 suite, 3 double, 2 with facilities *en suite*. 2 with radio; no telephone/TV. 5-bedroomed flat, sleeps 14.
Facilities Drawing room, breakfast/dining room. No background music. 40-acre grounds: tennis, swings, river: 2 miles of fly-fishing. Walking, climbing nearby. Unsuitable for &.
Location 4 miles W of Brecon, on A40 between Brecon and Llandovery. Look out for hanging sign.
Restrictions No smoking in bedrooms. No dogs.
Credit cards None accepted.
Terms B&B £30. Set dinner (by arrangement, groups only) £20. Child accom-

modated in parents' room: 50% of adult rate. 1-night bookings sometimes refused.

CAERSWS Powys   **Map 3**

Maesmawr Hall   *Tel* (01686) 688255
Caersws SY17 5SF   *Fax* (01686) 688410
                                    E-mail reception@maesmawr.co.uk
                                        Website www.maesmawr.co.uk

The lounge at this Grade II listed 16th-century half-timbered hunting lodge has wood panelling, oak beams, an open log fire and garden views. Reached up a long tree-lined drive through mature gardens, it is set amid the hills of mid-Wales, near a village in the Severn valley. The owners, Isabel and Alan Hunt and Marilyn and John Pemberton (he is the chef), have carefully modernised and refurbished (but some curtains and carpets "may have seen better days"). A recent visitor was delighted: "It epitomises the best kind of owner-run small establishment; it is proud of what it does. I was welcomed by name, and given an excellent large bedroom in the main house (a luxury not often granted to the single traveller). It had generous towels, good linens. One of the proprietors was always visible and friendly in the restaurant and bar area." The flexibility over food is also liked: dishes are available as bar snacks or room-service meals, and the "excellent and nicely presented dinners, with plenty of fresh vegetables", are enjoyed. The set-price menu offers plenty of choice, eg, a medley of smoked fish as a starter; roast duck with orange and Cointreau sauce; lemon mousse torte. There's an extensive and fairly priced wine list. The best bedrooms are in the main house; some have a sloping ceiling and a four-poster: sloping floors, too, and many steps, "which might be a challenge to the less able". Newer rooms are in the coach house across the lawn (some are a bit small). Breakfast includes fresh fruit salad, hot dishes cooked to order; no portion control. "With Carno and Newtown nearby, this is something of a staff hotel for Laura Ashley, and many of the fabrics hail from those factories." The hotel also courts the function/conference trade. It has fishing rights on the River Severn, and can arrange rough shooting nearby. There is good walking in the Montgomeryshire hills and the Shropshire Mynd. Powis and Montgomery castles are nearby. (*DP, HW*)

Open All year, except 25–29 Dec.
Rooms 16 double, 1 single. 6 in coach house, some on ground floor.
Facilities Lounge, bar, restaurant; "easy listening" background music at night; function room with bar and dance floor. 4-acre gardens. River Severn, fishing 250 yds; pony-trekking, shooting, golf nearby. Unsuitable for &. Civil wedding licence.
Location 6 miles W of Newtown. Off A489 1 mile before Caersws (300-yd drive on right). Train: Caersws, 1 mile.
Restrictions No smoking: restaurant, bedrooms. Dogs in annexe only, not in public rooms.
Credit cards Amex, MasterCard, Visa.
Terms [2000] B&B: single £56, double £75; D,B&B (min 2 nights): £57.50–£65. Set lunch £13.50, dinner £25. Child accommodated in parents' room: B&B £5–£15. Weekly rates.

CAPEL GARMON Gwynedd   Map 3

Tan-y-Foel   *Tel* (01690) 710507
Capel Garmon   *Fax* (01690) 710681
nr Betws-y-Coed LL26 0RE   *E-mail* tanyfoel@wiss.co.uk
                                                  Website www.tyfhotel.co.uk

Secluded in eight acres of wooded grounds above the lush Conwy valley in the Snowdonia National Park, this old stone house enjoys
superb views north towards the sea and west towards the mountains.
It is stylishly decorated, and its owners, Peter and Janet Pitman, provide "a consistently high standard of hospitality and service". Her
much-admired cooking is "definitely *nouvelle*, beautifully cooked and
presented", with Oriental influences and use of organic vegetables,
and such enterprising dishes as confit of Welsh belly pork on stir-fried
pak choi; steamed fillet of seabass on washabi mash, served with griddled scallops. The menu is short, but there is enough choice to suit
most tastes over several days. There is a wide-ranging wine list. The
bedrooms are decorated in vibrant colours and lavish fabrics. Some
have a kingsize or four-poster bed; they are supplied with chocolates
and other extras, and have a good-sized bathroom. One sitting room
has just been revamped in contemporary style; another is now a break-
fast/light lunch room. Breakfast is "every bit as good as dinner".
Guests are asked not to arrive before 3.30 pm or later than 9.30 pm.
Conwy Castle and the gardens at Bodnant are not far off. Newer
reports much needed.

Open Feb–Nov, New Year.
Rooms 7 double. 2, with own entrance, adjoining main house.
Facilities Lounge, breakfast/lunch room, restaurant. No background music. 8-
acre grounds. Unsuitable for &.
Location 1½ miles NE of Betws-y-Coed towards Llanrwst. Take 2nd right to
Capel Garmon/Nebo off A470. 1½ miles up hill; sign on left.
Restrictions No smoking. No children under 7. No dogs.
Credit cards All major cards accepted.
Terms [2000] B&B: single £70–£90, double £80–£150. Set dinner (2 to 3
courses) £25–£30. Winter, summer breaks. 1-night bookings often refused,
especially bank holidays.

CARDIFF *See SHORTLIST*   Map 3

CLYTHA Monmouthshire   Map 3

Clytha Arms   **NEW**   *Tel/Fax* (01873) 840206
Clytha, nr Abergavenny
NP7 9BW

Owned and run by Andrew and Beverley Canning as informal country
pub, very lively: converted dower house amid lawns and gardens. 6
miles SE of Abergavenny, off A40, on B4598 (old road to Raglan).
4 bedrooms. Enthusiastic service by cheerful young staff (sometimes
slow). Very good breakfasts, using local ingredients (including wild

boar sausages). Good dinners in no-smoking restaurant (eg, venison in ale, with herb dumplings; wild mushroom and chestnut pancake); wide range of bar snacks. No background music. Pleasant bedrooms, some large (one with four-poster), all with own bathroom, no telephone. Fishing in River Usk 2 miles. Closed Christmas; restaurant closed Sun night/Mon. Unsuitable for &. *No dogs. All major credit cards accepted. B&B £45–£70. Set Sun lunch £14.95; full alc £25. More reports, please.*

CRICKHOWELL Powys   Map 3

The Bear   *Tel* (01873) 810408
High St, Crickhowell   *Fax* (01873) 811696
NP8 1BW   *E-mail* bearhotel@aol.com
                                                  Website www.bear-hotel.co.uk

Named for its "all-round appeal" as "Pub of the Year in Great Britain for 2000" by the *Good Pub Guide*, this big creeper-clad, white-fronted coaching inn is enthusiastically owned and "faultlessly run" by Judith Hindmarsh and her son Stephen. "They and their staff are consistently courteous, friendly and efficient." Dating back to 1432, it stands in the centre of a charming market town below the Brecon Beacons. It has a cobbled forecourt and, through an archway, an inner courtyard; in summer the whole place is colourful with flowery hanging baskets and tubs. They have recently refurbished the bedrooms; "ours was spacious, with a simple decor of no special character," say inspectors in 2000. But another couple had a room that was "very Welsh" with a huge bed, but poor lighting, and they thought the bathwater dangerously hot. Some rooms have a four-poster, some a spa bath. Some are in a new building designed in the style of a Tudor manor house, in the courtyard; each room leads off a balcony. One suite is in a cottage at the bottom of the garden. "The imaginative food is beautifully served." The bar, popular with locals, and often very busy, serves soups, salads, pies and pasta. One of the dining rooms, in the oldest part of the building, has oak beams, stone walls and a flagstone floor; another is intimate, with candles, fresh flowers and lace tablecloths. The menus include, eg, potted duck with orange and thyme; local venison with roast parsnips and chestnut risotto; apple and blackberry pie. There is a good selection of Welsh cheeses. The "calmly civilised lounge" is heavily beamed, with bentwood armchairs and cushioned settles, a log fire, an antique dresser, lots of interesting prints, and a view of the market square. In summer, meals are served under a pergola in the "very pretty" small garden. "Breakfast was excellent, if politically incorrect (lots of fried offerings)." "Well-behaved dogs are welcomed, much to the dismay of the resident dogs," write the owners. There are many outdoor activities in the Brecon Beacons (see below), and Langorse Lake is nearby, with sailing, water sports and wildlife. (*CV, Michael Forrest, Lynn Wildgoose, and others*)

Open All year. Restaurant closed Sun evening.
Rooms 2 suites, 30 double. 13 in courtyard. 4 on ground floor.
Facilities 2 lounges, 2 bars, 2 dining rooms. Courtyard, small garden. Climbing, gliding, golf, fishing, caving, pony-trekking nearby.

Location Centre of town (quietest bedrooms at rear). Train: Abergavenny (6 miles).
Restrictions No smoking in family bar. No dogs in restaurants.
Credit cards Amex, MasterCard, Visa.
Terms B&B: single £47–£78, double £61–£115. Full alc: bar £21, restaurant £31.

Gliffaes NEW   *Tel* (01874) 730 371
Crickhowell   *Fax* (01874) 730 463
NP8 1RH   *E-mail* calls@gliffaeshotel.com
                      Website www.gliffaeshotel.com

In a glorious setting above the Usk valley just west of Crickhowell, this imposing Italianate mansion, complete with campanile, has been owned and run since 1948 by the Brabner family. It is a sporting hotel *par excellence*, with two and a half miles of fishing on the Usk. It has a pretty conservatory, a terrace with a superb view over the valley below, and large, lovely grounds, with 2,000 trees just planted for the millennium. It fell from the *Guide* after some reports of gruff welcomes, indifferent housekeeping, variable food. But many earlier visitors have enjoyed the place (one couple have spent 157 nights here since 1982), and latest reports in 1999–2000 speak of improvements: "A warm welcome. Housekeeping has been smartened up, most bedrooms have been redecorated in admirable taste, and the food gets even better. After a morning's walking, it was a joy to return to open log fires, comfortable chairs, spacious lounges." "We had a marvellous time. An idyllic location, excellent walking, good food and wine, friendly and efficient service." One factor may be that the older generation of Brabners have now been joined in management by a daughter and son-in-law, Susie and James Suter. The staff are mainly local, "with a heady mix of South Africans; their enthusiasm and good manners make up for the odd slip". Justin Howe's cooking is traditional with inventive touches, eg, local venison with chestnut purée; fillet of brill with mushroom purée. Bedrooms are simple, priced according to view; some are small. At breakfast there is a wide selection of fruit compotes, cereals, etc, as well as cooked dishes, but coffee stands in vacuum jugs – ordering a pot of tea is probably a better bet. (*Col. and Mrs AJW Harvey, Nicholas Jefcoat; also JR Sargent, Major-Gen. Brian Davis*)

Open All year.
Rooms 16 double, 6 single. 3 in annexe, 100 yds.
Facilities Ramps. Sitting room, drawing room, conservatory, bar, dining room (classical/jazz background music at quiet times). 33-acre grounds: tennis, croquet, golf practice net, putting, fishing (ghillie available). Civil wedding licence.
Location 2½ miles W of Crickhowell, 1 mile off A40; follow Gliffaes sign. Train: Abergavenny (6 miles); taxi.
Restrictions No smoking in dining room. No dogs in house.
Credit cards All major cards accepted.
Terms B&B: single £52.40–£123, double £63.40–£134.55; D,B&B £56–£147.30 per person. Set dinner £24.30; full alc £36.95. Special rates for 2–5 nights.

EGLWYSFACH Powys **Map 3**

Ynyshir Hall
Eglwysfach
nr Machynlleth SY20 8TA

Tel (01654) 781209
Fax (01654) 781366
E-mail info@ynyshir-hall.co.uk
Website www.ynyshir-hall.co.uk

César award in 1997

"A really charming and welcoming hotel." "A treat." Plenty more praise came this year for Rob and Joan Reen's white Georgian longhouse, very smart and newly repainted. It is set in wide landscaped gardens on the shore of the Dyfi estuary, surrounded by the RSPB's large and "fantastic" Ynyshir bird reserve. "It is a stunning house, luxurious, wonderfully restored, in superb grounds. Our bedroom and bathroom, with clouds on the ceiling, made us feel like royalty. The food was out of this world, though its quantity was almost too much. Prices are high, but worth it." Rob Reen's professional artist's eye has created a "stunning decor": bedrooms glow with vibrant colours, lots of blues and apricots, coordinated with Welsh pottery, antiques, rich fabrics and bright rugs (but rooms vary in size and outlook). "The owners enjoy looking after their guests, and it shows. The whole hotel smells fresh, of expensive pot-pourri. Our bedroom had good pillows and reading lights, a decanter of sherry, lots of extras, dramatic paintings on the walls. The large marble-floored bathroom had huge bathrobes. The cooking is multi-faceted and ambitious, with a menu changing daily – confit of salmon, daube of Welsh black beef with crisp pancetta, were superb; the hot lemon soufflé with wild raspberry sorbet is the stuff that dreams are made of. Welsh and French cheeses come with a large glass of port." The award-winning chef Chris Colmer provides modern British cooking with much use of local produce. Dishes are "technically complex", and there is great emphasis on presentation. Ingredients are rich, "but you can ask for simpler dishes". Lavish breakfasts include home-made marmalade and jams, crisp bacon, local sausages, fresh fruit. The new two-roomed studio suite, with a tiny kitchen, "would be ideal for a family". Oscar, the Bernese hound, "is a gentle giant". You can visit the Centre for Alternative Technology ("very green") just north of Machynlleth. Harlech, Powys and Chirk castles, Bodnant, Portmeirion and Snowdonia are not far off. There are plenty of sporting activities (see below). (*Padi and John Howard, Brian Pullee, John RC West*)

Open All year, except 5–23 Jan.
Rooms 4 suites (1 on ground floor), 6 double. 2 more planned for 2001.
Facilities Drawing room, bar lounge, breakfast room, restaurant (piped harp/classical music sometimes played at night). 14-acre gardens in 365-acre bird reserve: croquet, putting. Beaches, sailing, river and sea fishing, riding, pony-trekking, golf nearby. Unsuitable for ♿.
Location Just W of A487, 6 miles SW of Machynlleth, 11 miles NE of Aberystwyth. Train: Machynlleth; then taxi.
Restrictions Smoking in bar lounge only. No children under 9. Dogs by arrangement; in 1 bedroom only, not in public areas.
Credit cards All major cards accepted.
Terms B&B: single £75–£135, double £120–£170, suite £150–£200. Set

lunch £22, dinner £36. Christmas, New Year packages. 1-night bookings
sometimes refused high-season weekends.

GARTHMYL Powys   Map 3

Garthmyl Hall　　**BUDGET**   *Tel* 01686) 640550
Garthmyl   *Fax* (01686) 640609
nr Montgomery SY15 6RS

♀ *César award in 2000*

In the rolling countryside of the Welsh Marches, this lovely late-
Georgian house stands amid a mixture of wild and formal gardens and
fields. "The grounds are lovely and the house is delightful – elegant,
beautifully furnished. But the food is even better." That is one recent
plaudit, endorsed this year: "We had one of the luxury rooms, simple
and tasteful, large, light and airy, very quiet, with a huge bathroom.
Dinner was excellent and breakfast fresh and plentiful." Other visitors
enjoyed the place's "unintimidating charm". "The "hard-working and
enthusiastic" owners, Nancy and Tim Morrow, "are always around if
you want something, but are not intrusive". They write: "We aim to
offer the comfort of a top-quality hotel (luxurious towels, bathrobes,
etc) with the relaxed informality of a country home," and they have
put a lot of thought into making the place child-friendly. Our inspectors admired the "marvellous" stone-floored hallway and sandstone
staircase; the effective lighting, and their bedroom: "Everything well
thought out: a beautiful antique French painted bed, a Victorian writing table, flowers, chocolates, bottled water, a lovely bathroom." Pre-
dinner drinks are in the huge main reception room, with an ornate
gilded ceiling and a log fire; there is a cosy library. The "lovely dining
room" has green walls, intricate carvings, and plants and flowers
giving a country feel (but its lighting may be a bit dim for some). Local
ingredients are used in the four-course dinner menu (no choice,
preferences discussed in advance), eg, roast pepper timbale with a
mousse of Welsh goat's cheese; fillet of local lamb with Mediterranean vegetables; Snowdon pudding; Welsh cheeses. At breakfast,
the dining room has checked tablecloths, giving a café feel: "We had
wonderful scrambled eggs from the hens that scratch about outside."
The prices "are very reasonable for such quality". The interesting old
town of Montgomery is close by; other local attractions include Powis
Castle, Berriew village with black-and-white houses and peacock
topiary. (*Peter Williams, John and Joan Wyatt, and others*)

Open All year. Dining room closed midday and Sun.
Rooms 8 double, 1 single. TV on request.
Facilities Drawing room, morning room with informal bar, library with TV,
dining (background music if requested); function facilities. 14-acre grounds:
5-acre gardens, croquet, 9-acre fields. River Severn ½ mile, fishing. Civil wed-
ding licence. Unsuitable for ♿.
Location On A483 halfway between Welshpool and Newtown. Train:
Welshpool; then bus to village.
Restrictions Smoking in library only. No dogs.
Credit cards Amex, MasterCard, Visa.

Terms B&B: single £40–£70, double £55–£95. Picnic lunch by arrangement. Set dinner £19.50.

KNIGHTON Powys   Map 3

Milebrook House   *Tel* (01547) 528632
Milebrook   *Fax* (01547) 520509
Knighton LD7 1LT   *E-mail* hotel@milebrook.kc3ltd.co.uk

Beryl and Rodney Marsden are the "hard-working and genial hosts" at this tiny hotel, a grey 18th-century stone house near the English border, on the River Teme outside Knighton. The main snag is the busy road in front: rear rooms are quietest, including four luxurious new ones with thick carpets, a blue-tiled bathroom. The restaurant is popular with locals, and a reader this year found the dinner "beautifully cooked and presented", adding: "The tables are a bit close, but the company was good, so why worry?" Dishes are unpretentious: the *prix-fixe* menu might include salad of smoked chicken; rack of Welsh lamb with rosemary. Many vegetables are from the garden. "Mrs Marsden is always pleasant, and the outlook is beautiful." A disabled guest found the hotel very comfortable, too. "I appreciated the ground-floor bedroom and its well-equipped bathroom." In the grounds are a formal garden, a croquet lawn, a pond, and meadows with wild flowers and a riverside walk. The hotel has a mile-long stretch of the Teme for trout-fishing and Rodney Marsden is happy to advise on birdwatching. Some of the best stretches of Offa's Dyke path are nearby, and Knighton has a heritage centre for the dyke. The border towns of Ludlow, Clun, Presteigne and Kington are worth visiting. (*John Marland, DG*)

Open All year. Restaurant closed Mon midday.
Rooms 10 double. 2 on ground floor. 1 suitable for &.
Facilities Ramps. Lounge, bar, 2 dining rooms. No background music. 3-acre grounds on river: croquet, fishing. Golf nearby.
Location 2 miles E of Knighton on A4113 (rooms double-glazed). Train: Knighton.
Restrictions No smoking: dining room, lounge, bedrooms. No children under 8. No dogs.
Credit cards All major cards accepted.
Terms B&B: single £51–£55, double £75.50–£83.50. D,B&B: single £70.50–£74.50, double £114.50–£122.50. Set lunch £12.50, dinner £19.95; full alc £32.50. Special breaks. Christmas, New Year packages. 1-night bookings sometimes refused high season weekends. *V*

LLANDDEINIOLEN Gwynedd   Map 3

Ty'n Rhos   *Tel* (01248) 670489
Seion, Llanddeiniolen   *Fax* (01248) 670079
nr Caernarfon LL55 3AE   *E-mail* enquiries@tynrhos.co.uk
                                    Website www.tynrhos.co.uk

"A very nice place with good food," says a visitor this year to Nigel and Lynda Kettle's converted farmhouse, noted for its cooking, on the

plain between Snowdonia and the coast (good views). It has a large
lounge, with antiques, books and games, where drinks are served. The
bedrooms have pine furniture and fresh flowers. One on the ground
floor is "large and lovely, with pretty blue wallpaper, picture windows
with sliding door on to the patio, large comfortable armchairs, good
beds, an excellent bathroom". Many have good views; three are in
converted farm buildings. There is a new manager this year, Nigel
Hughes, but Carys Davies remains chef, cooking "traditional dishes
with a modern Welsh twist". Residents are encouraged to take the no-
choice dinner menu at £19.50, which is included in the half-board rate.
This has been found "excellent value": it could be salmon fish-cakes,
then chicken breast on couscous, then a dessert or cheese. The more
expensive *à la carte* has more variety and ambitious dishes, eg, fried
pigeon with sherry essence; venison on caramelised red cabbage;
cheesecake with red and black fruits, Welsh cheeses or Welsh rarebit.
Service can be disorganised at busy times, say recent guests.
Breakfasts are "excellent value and well varied": they include freshly
squeezed orange juice, kedgeree and kippers; preserves are home
made; nothing is packaged. "The staff are helpful, the house is cosy
and warm", but one reader would have liked better drying facilities in
this area of good walking. Moss, the sheepdog, will accompany guests
on a stroll. Beyond the garden are fields with sheep and cattle, and two
small lakes with ducks, coots and moorhens, and pleasant views
towards the beaches of Anglesey and the Menai Strait. Nearby attractions: Caernarfon and Penrhyn castles, Bodnant gardens, narrow-
gauge railways. (*Virginia Day, JW*)

Open All year, except 23–28 Dec. Restaurant closed Sun evening to non-
residents.
Rooms 1 suite, 10 double, 3 single. 3 in cottage annexe. 1 on ground floor.
Facilities Ramp. Lounge, bar, restaurant, conservatory; classical background
music on quiet evenings; conference/meeting room planned. 72-acre farm: 1-
acre garden: croquet, carp lake. Sea 9 miles.
Location 6 miles NE of Caernarfon, in hamlet of Seion. From Llandudno, take
road to Conwy, first turning to Caernarfon, right by *Little Chef*: hotel is then
signposted. Bus from Bangor.
Restrictions Smoking in lounge only. No children under 6. No dogs in house.
Credit cards Amex, MasterCard, Visa.
Terms B&B: single £55, double £80–£110, suite £100–£160; D,B&B £60–
£100 per person. Set lunch £12.95, dinner £21; full alc £30.

LLANDEILO Carmarthenshire   **Map 3**

The Cawdor Arms   NEW/BUDGET   *Tel* (01558) 823500
Rhosmaen Street   *Fax* (01558) 822399
Llandeilo SA19 6EN   *E-mail* cawdor.arms@btinternet.com
                                     Website www.cawdor-arms.co.uk

"It has the feel of a large country house hotel, but is in the main street
of a small market town." This Georgian coaching inn has new English
owners, John Silver, former nuclear engineer, and his wife Sylvia, former teacher. An inspector now restores it to the *Guide*, quirks and all:
"A very agreeable hotel, with a friendly atmosphere. The Silvers have

recreated the aura of late-Victorian Britain: warm wallpaper, large fireplaces and substantial furniture mark the public rooms. And if they have shown restraint on Victorian clutter, they have let themselves go on Victorian sentimentality: teddy bears in pinafores and bonnets outside bedroom doors, a rocking sheep on the landing, cabinet displays of twee china cups. Bedrooms too have a late Victorian feel: ours, called Charlotte's Room, with dusky blue wallpaper, was comfortably furnished and looked over a garden. Bedside lighting was good. Our welcome, and the service at dinner, by Mrs Silver and her staff, was friendly and efficient. In the large, handsome dining room, the food was superbly cooked, beautifully presented." Rod Peterson is chef and dishes on offer may include, eg, leek soufflé; duck breast with red cabbage; cheesecake, etc; always a vegetarian option. "Mr Silver, in an attractive vari-coloured waistcoat, served us a good merlot from his mainly French wine list. Dinner, and breakfast too, came with a selection of delicious home-made breads. Our only criticism: background music, a sort of bluesy jazz, in the evenings. The hotel welcomes children, and has plenty of books for them. Imaginative special events include 'Murder Mystery' evenings and weekend painting courses." Other visitors, too, have enjoyed the friendly and expert service, and have found the food "excellent". Public areas have been "boldly decorated". One report criticised the exterior's upkeep, and summed up: "An interesting experience, very Welsh despite the owners being very English." (*AP Wiltshire, MF, and others*)

Open All year, restaurant closed 1st week Jan.
Rooms 16 double, 1 single.
Facilities Lounge, bar, restaurant (piped music in evening). Courtyard. Unsuitable for &.
Location Centre of town (front rooms double-glazed). Parking.
Restrictions No smoking: restaurant, some bedrooms.
Credit cards Amex, MasterCard, Visa.
Terms [2000] B&B: single £45, double £60–£75; D,B&B: single £65, double £100–£115. Set lunch £11.95–£14.95, dinner £21. Child accommodated in parents' room: £15; babies free. Weekend programmes: painting, "Murder Mysteries", etc. Christmas package. *V*

LLANDRILLO Denbighshire   **Map 3**

Tyddyn Llan   *Tel* (01490) 440264
Llandrillo   *Fax* (01490) 440414
nr Corwen LL21 0ST   *E-mail* tyddynllanhotel@compuserve.com
                                                   Website tyddynllan.co.uk

Ω *César award in 1989*

Peacefully set in the Vale of Edeyrnion, Peter and Bridget Kindred's grey stone Georgian country house has again been judged "excellent" this year. "It is a beautifully restored house in a wonderful quiet location. Our bedroom and bathroom were large, very comfortable, outstandingly decorated, with delightful furniture. The food and service were first class." "The Kindreds know how to create the atmosphere of a family home," said another reader, though one found the welcome "slightly cool", and did not care for the repetitive background music at dinner. But others wrote of the "very capable" and "friendly" staff. The public rooms are "strikingly and pleasantly decorated", with antique and period furniture, and clever use of colour. The bedrooms are pretty and well lit. The high-ceilinged restaurant is popular with outside diners for the modern cooking of the new chef, Sean Ballington (his wife Monica is front-of-house): "We loved the starter of millefeuille pastry with seafood." Other dishes, using local produce, might include smoked fillet of Welsh black beef; honey-glazed Hereford duck breast. There is also a vegetarian menu. Wines are "interesting and fairly priced". Imaginative light lunches are available. Salads are picked from the neo-Elizabethan herb garden, and jellies are made from the owners' quinces and crab apples. Peter Kindred, whose own work hangs in the dining room, runs painting weekends in November and March. Wine tastings and gourmet dinners are held.

There's good walking in the nearby Berwyn mountains; Chirk Castle and Erddig House are within a half-hour's drive; Bala Lake, popular with windsurfers, is even nearer. The hotel has a four-mile stretch of the River Dee, with fishing, mostly for grayling. (*Lesley Brown, John RC West, and others*)

Open All year.
Rooms 10 double.
Facilities 3 lounges, bar, restaurant (classical background music). 3½-acre grounds: water garden, croquet. River fishing (ghillie available), riding, golf, sailing, walking nearby. Unsuitable for &. Civil wedding licence.
Location From A5 W of Corwen take B4401 to Llandrillo. Train: Wrexham; then taxi or bus.
Restrictions No smoking in restaurant. No dogs in public rooms.
Credit cards All major cards accepted.
Terms B&B: single £67.50–£85, double £105–£140; D,B&B: single £95–£112.50, double £160–£195. Set lunch £15.50, dinner £27. Special interest weekends, painting courses, in low season. Christmas, New Year house parties. *V*

LLANDUDNO Conwy   **Map 3**

Bodysgallen Hall   *Tel* (01492) 584466
Llanrhos   *Fax* (01492) 582519
Llandudno LL30 1RS   *E-mail* info@bodysgallen.com
                                      Website www.bodysgallen.com

𝒬 *César award in 1988*

"It was truly excellent, we had a delightful stay," runs this year's praise for a classy hotel (Relais & Châteaux), well managed by Matthew Johnson. It is a 17th-century Grade 1 listed mansion, set in a large park on a hillside outside this pleasant Victorian seaside resort, and it has been restored to its original splendour by Historic House

Hotels Ltd (see also *The Cadogan*, London, *Hartwell House*, Aylesbury, and *Middlethorpe Hall*, York). Visitors have written of its "cosseting embrace" and "efficient staff". You should ask about table position when booking your dinner (best ones have a garden view, and you might not want to sit too near the weekend pianist. Others have admired the spa (with a 54-foot swimming pool, gymnasium and three beauty salons), in a converted farmhouse. The "lovely grounds" include a 17th-century knot garden and an 18th-century walled rose garden. The interior is impressive; panelled rooms, ancestral portraits, splendid fireplaces and stone mullioned windows, and the cooking, by the new chef, David Thompson, is "elaborate" and fairly traditional, eg, cream of ham and haricot bean soup; braised shank of lamb; strawberry soufflé or Welsh rarebit. Most bedrooms are large and elegant. The cottage suites, close to the spa, are good for a family (as long as the children are over eight). Attractions in the area include the splendid gardens of Bodnant, and the castles of Conwy, Caernarfon and Beaumaris. (*Terry Bond, and others*)

Open All year.
Rooms 16 cottage suites, 17 double, 3 single. Some on ground floor.
Facilities Hall, drawing room, library, bar, dining room (pianist Fri, Sat); conference centre. 200-acre parkland: gardens, tennis, croquet; spa: swimming pool, gym, sauna, beauty treatment, club room (light meals and drinks). Riding, shooting, fishing, sandy beaches nearby.
Location Follow A55 towards Llandudno. Take A470 exit; hotel 2 miles on right. Train: Llandudno, 2 miles.
Restrictions No smoking: dining room, 3 bedrooms. No children under 8. Dogs in cottages/parkland only (not in gardens).
Credit cards MasterCard, Visa.
Terms Room: single £99–£104, double £140–£235, suite £165–£180. Breakfast £13.50. D,B&B (2 nights min.) £110–£130 per person. Set lunch £17.50, dinner £33.90. Special breaks. Christmas package.

St Tudno Hotel   *Tel* (01492) 874411
The Promenade   *Fax* (01492) 860407
Llandudno LL30 2LP   *E-mail* sttudnohotel@btinternet.com
                                      Website www.st-tudno.co.uk

Ⓠ *César award in 1987*

Front lounges have "lovely views of the sea and the promenade" at Janette and Martin Bland's fairly luxurious hotel, with excellent food. Liked again this year, it is a Grade II listed house, facing the ornate Victorian pier, and it has a Victorian-style decor: lounges with much drapery, potted plants, and patterned wallpaper; bedrooms (some are small) with lots of frills, pastel colours and fresh milk for tea; some bathrooms have a spa bath. The best bedrooms are front ones, facing the promenade. The suite, good for a family, is named after Lewis Carroll's Alice Liddell, who holidayed here in 1861. Visitors this year liked their family room, and added: "Our welcome was impressive, and all staff were keen to please. Housekeeping was of a high standard. Breakfast was very good, with excellent coffee. At dinner, we liked the smoked chicken and apple salad; main courses of seabass, salmon, guinea fowl; strawberry cheesecake, and coconut parfait with pears and honey." David Harding's modern British cooking, artistically presented and using plenty of local produce, is served in the garden-style restaurant. "It gets better and better," says one recent visitor. Guests can choose between a daily and a "gourmet" menu that has such dishes as fricassee of chicken with baby carrots, champagne and mustard. "The wine list is excellent, too." Children are welcomed, but in the evenings it is preferred that they eat with their parents in the coffee lounge, rather than the restaurant. There is a small indoor swimming pool and a new "secret garden". Parking can be difficult, but the staff will help. Bodnant garden, Conwy, Caernarfon and Penrhyn castles are nearby. So are three championship golf courses. (*Alex and Beryl Williams, WK, and others*)

Open All year.
Rooms 2 suites, 16 double, 1 single. 1 on ground floor.
Facilities Lift. Sitting room, coffee lounge, lounge bar; restaurant; harpist Sat evening; small indoor swimming pool; front and rear patios, rear "secret garden". Sandy beach 60 yds. Unsuitable for severely &.
Location Central, opposite pier. Secure carpark, garaging.
Restrictions No smoking: dining room, sitting room, some bedrooms. No very young children in restaurant at night. "Small quiet dogs by arrangement only"; not in public rooms, unattended in bedrooms.
Credit cards All major cards accepted.
Terms B&B: single £65–£78, double £95–£190, suite £270–£280. Set lunch £17.50, dinner £35; full alc £39.45. Bar lunches. Midweek, weekend, off-season, Christmas, New Year breaks. 1-night bookings occasionally refused bank holidays.

LLANFACHRETH Gwynedd   **Map 3**

Tŷ Isaf Farmhouse   BUDGET   *Tel/Fax* (01341) 423261
Llanfachreth   *E-mail* raygear@tyisaf.freeserve.co.uk
Nr Dolgellau LL40 2EA   *Website* www.tyisaf78.freeserve.co.uk

Much liked again in 2000 ("excellent, our favourite in this class"), Ray and Lorna Gear's small guest house stands in a hamlet on a quiet road in the Snowdonia National Park, with views of green fields and hills. Built in 1624, it is a longhouse, with thick stone walls, oak rafters, an inglenook fireplace and a country decor. It offers simple comforts along with "most imaginative food", say *Guide* readers. The setting is "idyllic", with a garden running down to a stream, two llamas, Math and Mathonwy (named after Celtic heroes), in a meadow, and hens which supply free-range eggs. Substantial no-choice dinners have a Welsh emphasis, eg, Welsh lamb and puréed leeks; Brythill y Cig Moch (trout fillet and parsley wrapped in bacon) and Welsh cheeses. Unlicensed; bring your own wine. The three comfortable bedrooms have pine furniture. Central heating has been added this year, and the lounge refurbished. The Gears write: "There's a pretty study with an ancient butter churn, lovely views and books to inspire the heart." In the lounge are TV, video, books and games, and background music if wanted. One reader wrote of "a house-party atmosphere", but a couple on their third visit retorted this year: "That sounds too yuppy. We'd say, a relaxed family occasion." There are plenty of outdoor activities locally: walking, climbing, birdwatching, fishing and sailing, etc. "The Coed y Brenin forest has one of the best cycling tracks in Europe," say the Gears. "We provide secure facilities for bicycles." Packed lunches are available. (*Mr and Mrs FF Farnham-Flower*)

Open Feb–Nov. Possibly closed at other times; please check.
Rooms 3 double. No telephone/TV.
Facilities Lounge with TV (classical or Welsh music if requested, early evening), study, dining room. 3-acre grounds: garden, paddock, stream. Walking, cycling, climbing, riding, fishing, sailing, beaches, castles nearby. Unsuitable for &.
Location 3½ miles NE of Dolgellau. On A470 Dolgellau bypass, take 1st right after *Little Chef,* signposted Bala, 1st left, signposted Dolgellau, 1st right signposted Llanfachreth. Continue to village; *Tŷ Isaf* 1st house on right. Train: Machynlleth, 12 miles; then taxi.
Restrictions No smoking. No children under 13. Dogs by arrangement (only 1 at a time).
Credit cards None accepted.
Terms B&B £27; D,B&B £42. Set dinner £17.50. £10 single supplement sometimes levied. 3-night breaks. *V*

LLANGAMMARCH WELLS Powys   Map 3

The Lake   *Tel* (01591) 620202
Llangammarch Wells LD4 4BS   *Fax* (01591) 620457
                                     E-mail lakehotel@ndirect.co.uk
                            Website www.ndirect.co.uk/~lakehotel

❧ *César award in 1992*

"Lovely grounds, good food, spacious bedrooms and public rooms." There is approval again this year (plus some caveats) for Jean-Pierre and Jan Mifsud's imposing half-timbered turn-of-the-century hotel (Pride of Britain). It has "a beautiful setting" amid unspoilt country-side, above lawns that slope down to the River Irfon. The service and the "warm welcome" are also admired: "The staff are all so friendly, helpful and happy. We were upgraded from a standard room to a suite at no extra cost." "This wonderful hotel is dog-friendly too, and the hotel dogs will accompany you on walks if you wish." The bedrooms vary in size; some suites are large, with a canopied or a four-poster bed; sherry and fruit are provided, and early morning tea is brought up. A generous afternoon tea is served in a huge lounge with deep sofas and armchairs, a log fire, family photographs on a grand piano, and magazines. The big dining room, with candlelit tables at night, serves modern English/French food, eg, terrine of ham knuckle and foie gras; brill with a salmon and truffle mousse; caramel mousse wrapped in chocolate with caramelised apples. Some ingredients are local and organically produced. The wines and the cheeseboard are much admired. The vast breakfast includes Welsh laverbread, and is accompanied by practical details about the weather and local sightseeing (excellent fishing rivers are nearby). Some complaints came this year: about room upkeep (eg, a faulty spa bath), a run-down tennis court, and slow meal service. And: "The hotel's blurb requests gentlemen to wear a jacket at dinner, but my husband was the only man to do so –

the others were all in shirtsleeves." Most bedrooms have been renovated. (*Sue Davies, AP, and others*)

Open All year.
Rooms 11 suites, 8 double. 2 on ground floor.
Facilities Ramp. 2 lounges, bar, billiard room, restaurant. No background
music. 50-acre grounds: lake (fishing), river, tennis, croquet, 9-hole par 3 golf
course, clay-pigeon shooting, archery. Riding, pony-trekking, golf, rivers,
fishing (tuition available) nearby. Civil wedding licence.
Location 8 miles SW of Builth Wells. From A483 Builth–Llandovery follow
signs to Llangammarch Wells, then to hotel. Train: Swansea/Shrewsbury, then
scenic Heart of Wales line to Llangammarch Wells; guests will be met.
Restrictions No smoking: restaurant, bedrooms. No children under 7 in dining
room after 7 pm (high tea provided). No dogs in public rooms, except guide
dogs.
Credit cards All major cards accepted.
Terms B&B £65.50–£107.50; D,B&B (min. 2 nights) £115–£152. Set lunch
£18.50, dinner £32.50. Winter breaks; Christmas, New Year packages. *V*

LLANSANFFRAID GLAN CONWY Gwynedd   Map 3

The Old Rectory Country House   *Tel* (01492) 580611
Llanrwst Road   *Fax* (01492) 584555
Llansanffraid Glan Conwy   *E-mail* info@oldrectorycountryhouse.co.uk
nr Conwy LL28 5LF   *Website* www.oldrectorycountryhouse.co.uk

� *César award in 1994*

Wendy Vaughan, chef and co-owner with her husband Michael, this
year became the first woman in Wales to receive a *Michelin* star for
cooking. Our readers also found the food at this ochre Georgian guest
house "excellent" this year. Menus offer no choice, but the food "is
interesting", eg, spiced monkfish in red wine sauce; roast chicken with
wild mushrooms; Welsh lamb with spinach parcels. Dinner is served
at separate tables at 8 pm, after drinks and *amuse-gueules* in the "most
attractive" panelled drawing room (a harpist sometimes plays). The
eclectic wine list has plenty of half bottles. The house stands up a steep
drive, with fine views over the Conwy estuary towards Snowdonia. In
front, descending in terraces to the road, are gardens partly formal,
partly wilder. "Comfortable, and good value," said a visitor this year,
echoing earlier praise: "They provide many of the elegances of a grand
country hotel." The house is full of antiques, ornaments and bric-à-
brac; board games, books and a piano in the drawing room; soft yellow
walls and elegant table settings in the dining room. The bedrooms
(some are small) are "lavishly decorated, with lots of cushions, easy
chairs or a sofa, and masses of goodies: fresh fruit, etc." Bathrooms
are mostly large (one was described as "way over the top"). Front
rooms now have double-glazed windows. Breakfasts include freshly
squeezed orange juice, Welsh rarebit made with ale, kippers, etc. The
Vaughans are knowledgeable about Welsh history and culture.
Bodnant gardens are just down the road; Conwy, Caernarfon and
Beaumaris castles are within 25 miles; so is the Snowdon Mountain
Railway. The Conwy Estuary Bird Sanctuary and three championship
golf courses are close by. One party in 1999 reported an unhelpful

reception, but most visitors regard Mr Vaughan as "an indefatigable host". (*Sir Timothy Harford, and others*)

Open 1 Feb–20 Dec, except 2 Nov. Dining room closed for lunch, occasionally for dinner (guests warned when booking).
Rooms 6 double. 2 on ground floor in coach house.
Facilities Lounge (harpist twice-weekly pre-dinner), restaurant. 2½-acre grounds. Sea, safe bathing 3 miles; fishing, golf, riding, sailing, dry ski-slope nearby.
Location On A470, ½ mile S of junction with A55. Train: Conwy, 2 miles.
Restrictions No children under 5, except babies under 9 months. Smoking/dogs in coach house only.
Credit cards MasterCard, Visa.
Terms B&B: single £79–£129, double £99–£149. Set dinner £29.50. 2-day breaks. 1-night bookings refused high-season weekends, bank holidays ***V*** (Nov, Dec, Feb, Mar)

LLANWRTYD WELLS Powys   Map 3

Carlton House   BUDGET   *Tel* (01591) 610248
Dol-y-Coed Road   *Fax* (01591) 610242
Llanwrtyd Wells LD5 4RA
                            E-mail alan@carlhouse.fsnet.co.uk
                            Website www.carltonrestaurant.co.uk

"Alan and Mary Ann Gilchrist are warm, attentive hosts, their staff are cheerful and willing, and the food is superb," say readers this year who came to celebrate their silver wedding and had a "spacious, well-heated suite". They also praised the "good value for money". This "mildly eccentric" small restaurant-with-rooms is in an Edwardian villa, distinctively painted bright red. The restaurant is in the bright front room, the lounge is a cosy, darker room at the back. Both were completely refurnished in April 2000. "We had far and away the best food on our trip," said recent American visitors. Others agree, including *Michelin*, which awards a Bib Gourmand (one of only four in Wales) for Mrs Gilchrist's "modern British" (and other) cooking, based on fresh, free-range and organic ingredients. Both the *à la carte* and the fixed-price menu change daily. They include, eg, Thai seafood salad; Welsh black beef with tapenade; roast marinated poussin; "Celtic promise" with a celery and apple salad. Special dietary needs are "sympathetically catered for". The wine list is varied and fairly priced. Breakfast is enjoyed too: "They really know how to scramble eggs"; these come with a rasher of thick bacon, fresh orange juice, and "good and plentiful coffee". The Gilchrists' daughter, Emma, and Cecily, the basset hound, are in attendance. As for bedrooms, one reader had a "beautiful large corner room", but another found the lighting poor. Some can suffer traffic noise; and stairs to upper floors are steep. Llanwrtyd Wells is a small spa town below the Cambrian mountains, in Wales's red kite country; they can be seen feeding at Gigrin, to the north, or at the RSPB's Dinas Reserve. (*Andrew and Rosemary Reeves, HRL, and others*)

Open All year, except 10–28 Dec.
Rooms 6 double, 1 single. No telephone.
Facilities Lounge, restaurant. No background music. Tiny garden. Fishing on Canmarch and Irfon rivers. Unsuitable for &.

Location Town centre. No private parking. Llanwrtyd Wells is on the scenic Heart of Wales railway line (Shrewsbury to Swansea).
Restrictions No smoking in restaurant. No dogs in public rooms.
Credit cards MasterCard, Visa.
Terms B&B: single £30, double £60–£75. Set dinner (2 to 3 courses) £18–£24. £25–£32. Special breaks.

LLYSWEN Powys   Map 3

Llangoed Hall   *Tel* (01874) 754525
Llyswen   *Fax* (01874) 754545
Brecon LD3 0YP   *E-mail* llangoed_hall_co_wales_uk@compuserve.com
                                     Website www.llangoedhall.com

"A delightful setting," says one guest this year. "Our rooms were wonderful, huge, spacious and quiet, with beautiful views. One of the most peaceful hotels I have stayed in," says another, despite having visited during the Hay-on-Wye book festival, when the place becomes "a hothouse of literati-glitterati – you crash into Martin Amis on the stairs, nod casually to Gerald Scarfe in the library, ogle Norman Mailer, and are in danger of greeting Gore Vidal like a long-lost friend on the way to dinner". The 17th-century mansion (redesigned in the 20th century by Sir Clough Williams-Ellis) stands back from a main road, in formal gardens, with a maze and views across the River Wye to the Black Mountains. Its owner, Sir Bernard Ashley, aims to create "the atmosphere of an Edwardian house party" (eg, no reception desk). His magnificent collection of pictures is distributed throughout. The public rooms are impressive: great hall with deep sofas and stone fireplace, morning room with piano, library with snooker table. "Fascinating antiques" and Oriental rugs abound. Bedrooms have Laura Ashley chintzes, period furniture (some four-posters). A new manager, John Robson, has arrived, and a new chef (the second since last year), Daniel James, and reports this year are very mixed. "Reception could not have been more helpful, and the young porter gave us a smiling welcome," said one visitor, but many wrote of an "excessively formal" atmosphere. The food was thought "beautifully cooked", but served in portions "that would scarcely satisfy an anorexic fairy", and the meal service "was either unbelievably frosty, or by willing young staff who spoke little English". Several returning visitors found evidence of "cost-cutting": "Afternoon tea has shrunk; the canapés before dinner have been replaced by olives; no more kedgeree or fish-cakes at breakfast." Some bedrooms are said to need redecoration, "and housekeeping wants watching". The "very pretty" yellow-walled restaurant has a *Michelin* star (one of only two in Wales) for main courses like sirloin of beef, with caramelised shallots, forest mushrooms, sauce bordelaise; risotto of wild mushrooms with parmesan, basil vinaigrette. But one visitor would have liked "some plainer alternatives to the designer food", and another thought there should be a ban on mobile phones at mealtimes. There is fishing on the Wye, good walking nearby in the Black Mountains and the Brecon Beacons, and other country pursuits are available (see below). Chepstow and Raglan castles are within easy reach (*D Fisher, Susan Hill, Brian Pullee, and others*)

Open All year.
Rooms 3 suites, 19 double, 1 single.
Facilities Hall, 3 lounges, restaurant, billiard room; private dining room, function room. No background music. 17-acre grounds: tennis, croquet, maze. River Wye 200 yds: fishing (ghillie). Riding, golf, gliding, clay-pigeon shooting, canoeing nearby. Only ground floor suitable for &. Civil wedding licence.
Location 11 miles N of Brecon, on A470, 1 mile N of Llyswen. Train: Cardiff or Newport; regular bus service or hotel will meet.
Restrictions No smoking in restaurant. No children under 8. No dogs in house (heated kennels in grounds).
Credit cards All major cards accepted.
Terms B&B: single £125, double £155–£260, suite £295–£315; D,B&B: single £135, double £195–£300, suite £355. Set lunch £15.50, dinner £35; full alc £53. 2-day breaks; Christmas, New Year house parties. 1-night bookings refused weekends 1 May–1 Oct.

NANTGWYNANT Gwynedd   Map 3

Pen-y-Gwryd Hotel   BUDGET   *Tel* (01286) 870211
Nantgwynant
Llanberis LL55 4NT

❦ *César award in 1995*

Many of the guests are mountaineers at Brian and Jane Pullee's "unique old inn", set in magnificent isolation near the foot of the Llanberis Pass in the heart of the Snowdonia National Park. Readers love the place, as attested by this year's accounts: "Not posh or sophisticated, but run on house-party lines. Wonderful evenings in the residents' bar, other guests always interesting: climbers, walkers, botanists, etc. A great social mix. Brian and Jane are great characters. A place for walking boots, not high heels." "Very good value." In 1953, Hunt and Hillary and most of the Everest team used the inn (which doubles as a mountain rescue post) as a training base before flying to Nepal; their signatures are scrawled on a ceiling. The slate-floored bar is filled with climbing memorabilia – well-worn boots, ice picks, etc. "Substantial breakfasts, packed lunches and excellent dinners intersperse periods of vigorous activity, leading to a general feeling of physical well-being." Bedrooms are simple, but "warm and comfortable": five have facilities *en suite*, and there are five public bathrooms, some with a massive old bath. There is a panelled lounge for residents, simply furnished, but with a blazing log fire. The large games room has bar billiards, etc. Outside, among the trees, is a natural spring-fed pool, fringed with ferns, and a sauna. Bar meals are ordered through a hatch. The chef, Lena Jensen from Jutland, produces five-course dinners with limited choice – "wholesome, tasty, plentiful and hot", eg, bacon and brie quiche; leek and onion soup; Welsh lamb with Provençal sauce; hot fudge surprise pudding; Welsh cheeses. The meal is announced by a gong at 7.30 pm, and everyone sits down together. Breakfasts include kippers, haddock and porridge. There is a new private chapel, "dedicated, not consecrated"; and the Pullees write this year: "New public lavatories at last." (*Sheelagh Innes, Roger Morgan-Grenville; also Good Pub Guide*)

Open Mar–Nov, New Year, weekends Jan/Feb.
Rooms 15 double, 1 single. 4 with bath, 1 with shower. No telephone, TV, etc.
1 ground-floor room in annexe (with 4-poster).
Facilities Lounge, bar, smoking room, games room, dining room; private
chapel. No background music. 2-acre grounds: natural swimming pool, sauna.
River/lake fishing nearby.
Location On A498 Beddgelert–Capel Curig, at junction with A4086. Local
buses, frequent in summer. Train: Bangor or Betws-y-Coed.
Restriction Smoking banned in dining room, discouraged in bedrooms.
Credit cards None accepted.
Terms B&B: single £23, double £56; D,B&B: single £40, double £90. Bar
lunch £4–£6, set dinner £17. 1-night bookings usually refused weekends.

NEWPORT Pembrokeshire   **Map 3**

Cnapan   BUDGET   *Tel* (01239) 820575
East Street   *Fax* (01239) 820878
Newport, nr Fishguard   *E-mail* cnapan@online-holidays.net
SA42 0SY   *Website* www.online-holidays.net/cnapan

"It has generosity of spirit," an inspector wrote of this small restaurant-with-rooms, a family affair run by John and Eluned Lloyd and
their daughter and son-in-law, Judith and Michael Cooper (mother and
daughter are the chefs). "They get the balance between friendliness
and reserve just right." The bright pink listed building, "almost French
in feel", is in the middle of an attractive old seaside town, and all agree
that it offers "excellent value for money", and "comfort of a homely
kind". A traditional Welsh dresser, crowded with family treasures,
stands in the hall; a wood-burning stove warms the guests' sitting
room; books, current magazines and local information are everywhere. The restaurant is large and cheerful, with flowers and candles
on lace-covered tables, plates, pictures and pieces of armour on walls,
a large stone fireplace. For a set price, residents choose items from the
extensive *carte*, which might include pan-fried scallops and prawns on
cardamom rice; fillet of pork stuffed with herbs, bacon and dried
fruits, with a light mustard sauce; brandy and ginger ice-cream. There
is always a vegetarian main course. At lunchtime there is a choice of
dishes like "fluffy fishermen's pie" with salad, puddings such as
"Piggy's delight" (a chocolate sponge with black cherries, chocolate
and cream). The small bedrooms are "ingeniously designed, if rather
cluttered", with pine furniture, bright colours, knick-knacks and a tiny
shower (there is also a massive bath along the corridor). Families can
use a two-roomed suite. Huge breakfasts include home-made marmalade, warm croissants, free-range eggs. In summer, drinks and tea
are served in the sheltered garden. Nearby are the Pembrokeshire Coast
Path, lovely countryside, beautiful beaches. More reports, please.

Note: There is also a Newport in Gwent, but you won't find *Cnapan*
there.

Open Mar–Dec. Restaurant only open at weekends Nov, Dec and Mar; closed
Tues Apr–Oct, also Christmas.
Rooms 5 double. No telephone.
Facilities Lounge, bar, restaurant; occasional jazz/classical background

music. Small garden. 10 mins' walk to sea; fishing, birdwatching, pony-trekking, golf, boating nearby. Unsuitable for &.
Location Centre of small town (quiet at night; rooms double-glazed). Private parking. Train: Fishguard; bus to Newport.
Restrictions No smoking: restaurant, bedrooms. Guide dogs only.
Credit cards MasterCard, Visa.
Terms B&B £30–£37; D,B&B £49–£56. Full alc £26. 1-night bookings occasionally refused.

PENMAENPOOL Gwynedd   Map 3

Penmaenuchaf Hall   *Tel* (01341) 422129
Penmaenpool   *Fax* (01341) 422787
Gwynedd LL40 1YB   *E-mail* relax@penhall.co.uk
                                         Website www.penhall.co.uk

Reached up a steep drive bordered by lofty cedars, this grey manor house stands within the Snowdonia National Park, outside Penmaenpool. Built by a Bolton cotton millionaire as his summer home, it has large grounds with gardens, lawns and woodlands over-looking the Mawddach estuary. "Beautiful location, stunning renovation of a Victorian mansion," says one reader this year, though another felt that prices were high. The staff and the owners, Mark Watson and Lorraine Fielding, are friendly: "It has a real country house feel; peaceful and pampering." The public rooms, elegant and spacious, have parquet floors, Oriental rugs, log fires, fresh flowers, and are "cleverly designed to facilitate conversation or allow you to retreat with a book". There is a Victorian billiard room and a pretty conservatory. The "beautifully decorated" bedrooms vary in size; many have splendid views. Breakfasts are "excellent", with "very good kippers". After two recent changes of chef, the modern British country house cooking of Laurence Rissel, with much use of Welsh beef and lamb, has been admired this year. The house has a large bat roost. There is good walking all around, as well as fishing, golf, birdwatching, castles. (*Dr John RC West, and others*)

Open All year, except 7–18 Jan.
Rooms 14 double.
Facilities Hall, morning room, library, billiards room, bar, restaurant (classical background music). 21-acre grounds: croquet, woodland walks. Free trout- and salmon-fishing on Mawddach estuary; golf, riding, white-water rafting, sailing, pony trekking nearby. Only public rooms suitable for &. Civil wedding licence.
Location From Dolgellau bypass (A470) A493 towards Tywyn and Fairbourne. Entrance drive to hotel ½ mile on left. Train: Morfa Mawddach; then taxi.
Restrictions No smoking: restaurant, morning room, library, 5 bedrooms. No children under 6, except babes in arms. Dogs by arrangement.

Credit cards All major cards accepted.
Terms [2000] B&B: single £70–£110, double £100–£160; D,B&B: single £96.50–£136.50, double £153–£213. Set lunch £15.75, dinner £26.50; full alc £38. Weekend, midweek, long and short special breaks. Christmas package. *V*

PORTHKERRY Vale of Glamorgan   Map 3

Egerton Grey   *Tel* (01446) 711666
Porthkerry, nr Cardiff CF62 3BZ   *Fax* (01446) 711690
                                             E-mail info@egertongrey.co.uk
                                             Website www.egertongrey.co.uk

"Excellent, with good food, welcoming staff, lovely atmosphere" – recent praise for this small, luxurious hotel, a former 19th-century rectory. Set in its own broad gardens, it stands near the Bristol Channel in a wooded valley, looking towards the Somerset coast over Porthkerry Park. The house is "full of country charm", with ornate mouldings, acres of beautiful panelling, antiques, porcelain, paintings, and a collection of old clocks. Owner Anthony Pitkin has taken on a new manager, Darren Munt, this year, and Nigel Roberts has been promoted to the head chef, so we'd welcome further reports. The spacious bedrooms, in Victorian or Edwardian style, have bold colour schemes, antiques, thick carpets, and carefully restored bathrooms (some have an enormous tub). Guests' names are placed on their door, house-party style. Dinner, elegantly served by candlelight, is in the former billiard room, with lovely panelling. If you take the "country house menu" you can opt for two or three courses, choosing perhaps sautéed mushrooms or warm quail salad; baked cod with an onion crust or wild mushroom risotto with toasted almonds and stilton cream; steamed fig pudding. Good wine list. Lots of interesting choices for breakfast. Small children are "warmly welcomed", and special food is cooked for them. Places to see nearby include the Welsh Folk Museum at St Fagans, and Caerphilly and Cardiff castles. The hotel is quite close to the airport, and some aircraft noise was reported this year.

Open All year.
Rooms 2 suites, 7 double, 1 single.
Facilities Drawing room, library, loggia, restaurant (classical background music), private dining room; function facilities. 3½-acre garden: croquet. Beach 200 yds; golf nearby. Only restaurant suitable for &. Civil wedding licence.
Location 10 miles SW of Cardiff. From M4 exit 33 follow signs to airport, bypassing Barry. Left at small roundabout by airport, signposted Porthkerry; after 500 yds left again, down lane between thatched cottages. Train: Barry, 4 miles, or bus from Cardiff centre.
Restrictions No smoking in restaurant. No dogs in public rooms.
Credit cards All major cards accepted.
Terms B&B: single £70–£89.50, double £95–£105, suite £110–£130; D,B&B: £55–£95 per person. Set lunch/dinner from £13.50; full alc £25. Special break: D,B&B £60; Christmas package. *V*

We need detailed fresh reports to keep our entries up to date.

PORTMEIRION Gwynedd   **Map 3**

Portmeirion Hotel   *Tel* (01766) 770000
Portmeirion LL48 6ET   *Fax* (01766) 771331
                              E-mail hotel@portmeirion-village.com
                              Website www.portmeirion.com

♲ *César award in 1990*

"A truly magical oasis, the most incredible resort in Britain," writes
one visitor this year to the late Sir Clough Williams-Ellis's famous
fantasy village, "a stunning stage set of an Italian village". It stands on
the steep hillside of a wooded peninsula, above a wide estuary; and
though tourists throng it by day, the hotel's guests are well protected
in Mediterranean-style gardens with peacocks and a swimming pool,
and they have the place to themselves in the evening. Behind its unpretentious early-Victorian exterior, the hotel is exuberantly decorated
with bright fabrics, carved panels, and furniture and ornaments
imported from Rajasthan. The atmosphere is very Welsh, however:
the "delightful and unobtrusively helpful" staff are all bilingual, and
so are the menus. There is even a Welsh harpist and a resident bard.
The bedrooms in the main house are thought "stunning": the Peacock
Room has "a magnificent four-poster bed and a lovely sitting room
facing the estuary". Bedrooms in the village, and the self-catering cottages, are simpler, "but all are unusual". Eleven new suites are due to
open in spring 2001 at Castell Oeudraeth. In the handsome, curved
dining room, Billy Taylor's cooking is modern Welsh, eg, Brecon
venison with a casserole of baby apples, apricots and walnuts; roast
Welsh lamb with leeks and lentils in a rosemary jus. "The food is the
best and most innovative I have tasted outside London," says one
reader this year, though another was quite critical, particularly of the
vegetables, and a third thought the dishes did not live up to their
descriptions. "But the wine was very good, with plenty of choice
under £20." Breakfast includes "wonderful fresh fruit salad" and
plenty of cooked dishes. "Palm trees and exotic shrubs thrive in the
gardens", where miles of paths lead along the headland and through
the woods to secret sandy beaches. Williams-Ellis's other life-work,
the garden at nearby Plas Brondanw, is open every day, and
Snowdonia is within easy reach, as are the castles of Caernarfon,
Harlech, Criccieth and Dolwyddelan. (*Chloe Macdonald, A Gradon;
also Brian Pullee, and others*)

Open All year. Restaurant closed Mon midday.
Rooms 14 suites, 26 double. 25 in village. Also self-catering cottages. 11
more rooms planned for 2001.
Facilities Hall, 3 lounges, 2 bars, restaurant, children's supper room; function
room. No background music. 70-acre grounds: garden, swimming pool
(heated May–Sept), tennis, lakes, sandy beach. Free golf at Porthmadog Golf
Club. Not really suitable for ♿.
Location SW of Penrhyndeudraeth, SE of Porthmadog, off A487 at
Minffordd. Street parking.
Restrictions No smoking in restaurant. No dogs in village.
Credit cards All major cards accepted.
Terms Room: single £90–£200, double £110–£220, suite £135–£220.
Breakfast £10. Set lunch £13.50, dinner £34. D,B&B (min 2 nights) £88–£230

per person. Christmas, New Year packages. 3 days for the price of 2, 31 Oct–13 Apr.

PWLLHELI Gwynedd   Map 3

Plas Bodegroes   *Tel* (01758) 612363
Nefyn Road   *Fax* (01758) 701247
Pwllheli LL53 5TH   *E-mail* gunna@bodegroes.co.uk
                                               Website www.bodegroes.co.uk

♀ *César award in 1992*

"A very special hotel experience. The grounds are beautiful, the owners are friendly, the food was stunning" (*Michelin Bib Gourmand*). "An oasis of tranquillity. Very relaxing, with a pleasant atmosphere and personal service." Reports this year and last on Chris and Gunna Chown's well-known restaurant-with-rooms, a small and pretty white Georgian house up an avenue of ancient beeches in wooded grounds. The "attractively understated" Scandinavian interior has been designed by the elegant Mrs Chown, who is Faroese. The restaurant, with "inspired decor" in shades of green, is hung with paintings by Welsh artists, including Kyffyn Williams and Gwilym Pritchard. Service "is exemplary". Chris Chown's "modern British" cooking has been highly praised. The menu does not change often enough for some, but it is varied. Dishes include hotpot of local seafood with chilli and coriander; warm salad of monkfish, ham and mushrooms; roast duck with cabbage and bacon; apple strudel. "The soft jazz music was just the right background sound" (but not all may agree). The bedrooms vary in size and price: some, simple but comfortable, are in the attic; larger ones, "sensitively appointed", are "relaxing in the extreme" – they have a four-poster and tall windows. Two are in a cottage at the rear, facing a courtyard garden. The lounge is quite small, and it can get crowded with non-resident diners, but the veranda, draped with wisteria and roses, is a pleasant place for sitting in fine weather. Breakfast is "excellent, with plenty of choice, delicious Greek yogurt and apricots, properly cooked hot dishes". Pwllheli is in a popular sailing area, near rocky shores, cliffs and beaches. (*John RC West, EJJ*)

Open 1 Mar–end Nov. Closed Mon, except bank holidays.
Rooms 10 double (2 in cottage), 1 single. Some on ground floor.
Facilities Lounge, bar, breakfast room, restaurant (occasional piped jazz/classical music). 5½-acre grounds. Safe, sandy beach 1 mile. Golf, sailing nearby. Unsuitable for &.
Location 1 mile W of Pwllheli, on A497 to Nefyn. Train: Pwllheli; then taxi.
Restrictions No smoking: restaurant, bedrooms. No dogs in public rooms.
Credit cards MasterCard, Visa.
Terms B&B £35–£60; D,B&B £55–£85. Set Sun lunch £14.50, dinner £28.50. 1-night bookings sometimes refused bank holidays. *V*

> We asked hotels to estimate their 2001 tariffs, but many preferred not to think so far ahead and gave their 2000 tariffs. Prices should always be checked on booking.

REYNOLDSTON Swansea   Map 3

Fairyhill   *Tel* (01792) 390139
Reynoldston, nr Swansea SA3 1BS   *Fax* (01792) 391358
                                                 E-mail postbox@fairyhill.net
                                                 Website www.fairyhill.net

"A most enjoyable three nights, and a lovely big room facing the
spacious grounds." "A relaxing stay; the owners and staff were unfailingly correct, charming and cheerful." "Reception was wonderfully
welcoming." "The best of the family-type hotels we have stayed in.
Perfect, down to the last detail." Most guests continue to praise this
creeper-covered 18th-century house, owned by Andrew Hetherington
("an excellent front-of-house"), Jane and Peter Camm, and Paul
Davies, who is co-chef with Adrian Coulthard. All agree, however:
"It's not a place for cost counting." Set amid lovely scenery, its large
grounds ("restful and not over-prettified") include woodland, a trout
stream and a lake with wild ducks, and it makes a peaceful base from
which to explore the beauties of the Gower coast. But "huge trees
round the edge of the house make it sunless, which some find depressing". The bedrooms, recently redecorated (some are "cramped"), have
a good bathroom and a CD-player; there's a huge library of discs
downstairs. In the green-and-yellow restaurant, the enterprising
"modern Welsh" food in-
cludes dishes such as laverbread tart; seared local
seabass; loin of Brecon venison; grilled fillet of Welsh
black beef. The kitchen team
makes its own jam, biscuits
and bread: The wine list is
"excellent but expensive".
(*Patricia Darby, Simon
Willbourn, and others*)

Open All year, except Christmas.
Rooms 8 double.
Facilities Lounge, bar, 2 dining rooms; piped classical/jazz/rock music. 24-
acre grounds: croquet, woodland, stream, lake. Beaches, water sports nearby.
Unsuitable for &.
Location 11 miles W of Swansea. M4 exit 47 to Gowerton; then B4295 for
9 miles.
Restrictions No smoking in restaurant. No children under 8. No dogs.
Credit cards Amex, MasterCard, Visa.
Terms [2000] B&B double £110–£190. Set lunch £14.50–£17.50, dinner
£25–£32. 2-day breaks. 1-night bookings sometimes refused.

****

Hotel in Bedfordshire. The hostess's telephone manner was
abrupt and rude. Her dogs and cats seem to live in the kitchen.
Cleanliness was not a strong point – the cobwebs in the bedroom were off-putting, and we were served tea in a cup with a
large and dirty crack.

****

RHYDGALED Ceredigion   Map 3

Conrah Country House   *Tel* (01970) 617941
Rhydgaled, Chancery   *Fax* (01970) 624546
nr Aberystwyth SY23 4DF   *E-mail* hotel@conrah.freeserve.co.uk

"Excellent." "A lovely old hotel." "Dinner was delicious." New praise
in 1999/2000 for this handsome country house, antique-furnished and
full of flowers, where owners John and Pat Heading, with their son and
daughter-in-law, Paul and Sarah, are "excellent hosts". It stands in
landscaped grounds, "with the largest ha-ha wall in Wales", just south
of Aberystwyth. Staff, "caring and cheerful", are mainly Welsh,
helped sometimes by young French trainees in the dining room. In this
"beautiful room with wonderful views over the countryside", chef
Stephen West provides "international cooking", making imaginative
use of local ingredients – Welsh lamb and beef, Carmarthen ham, and
Pencarreg cheese. Try the "tastiest ever leek and potato soup"; fried
fritters of laverbread, cockles and capsicum; roast lamb with oranges,
pine nuts, black beans and Grand Marnier sauce. But one reader felt
that the menu changed too rarely, and another would have liked to be
able to order small portions. Breakfasts are mostly admired, save for
the coffee, thin toast and packet orange juice. Best bedrooms are in the
main house: one has "comfy armchairs, a bathroom tiled in blue and
yellow". Rooms in the "courtyard motel" are less appealing: but three
luxury rooms in *Magnolia Court* have just opened. There is a heated
swimming pool in a separate building, but it lacks changing facilities.
Paths through the estate's fields and woods lead to footpaths to the
coast. (*AD and J Lloyd, Dr M Tannahill, Dr and Mrs James Stewart,
Mrs E Benford*)

Open All year, except Christmas week.
Rooms 1 family, 14 double, 2 single. 3 in bungalow, 3 in *Magnolia Court*.
3 on ground floor.
Facilities 3 lounges, bar, restaurant. No background music. 20-acre grounds:
indoor swimming pool, sauna; croquet, table-tennis; vegetable garden, wood-
land walks. River ½ mile, sea 3 miles; golf, fishing, riding nearby. Unsuitable
for &. Civil wedding licence.
Location 3½ miles S of Aberystwyth on A487 coast road. Train:
Aberystwyth.
Restrictions No smoking: restaurant, bedrooms. No children under 5. No
dogs.
Credit cards All major cards accepted.
Terms [2000] B&B: single £68–£80, double £90–£130. Set lunch £19,
dinner £27.

ST DAVID'S Pembrokeshire *See SHORTLIST*   Map 3

SWANSEA *See SHORTLIST*   Map 3

Before making a long detour to a small hotel, do check that it
is open. Some are known to close on impulse.

TALSARNAU Gwynedd   Map 3

Maes-y-Neuadd   *Tel* (01766) 780200
Talsarnau LL47 6YA   *Fax* (01766) 780211
                                                     E-mail maes@neuadd.com
                                                     Website www.neuadd.com

A grey granite-and-slate mansion (Pride of Britain) set amid lawns,
orchards and paddocks, on a wooded hillside with views across to the
Snowdonia National Park. The approach is by a narrow lane up a steep
hill. Inside are oak beams, good antique and modern furniture, displays of photographs and watercolours, and a bar with an inglenook
fireplace. The bedrooms vary greatly in style and size; some are in the
main house, others in a converted coach house. Some have pine furniture, others antiques; three have a spa bath. They have flowers, fresh
fruit, water and good lighting and a smart bathroom. In the panelled
dining room, with service by young, mostly French or Polish staff,
guests may choose three, four or five courses. The menus might
include potted game with home-made chutney; seafood hotpot with
leek and herb sauce. There is always a vegetarian main course. The
meal ends with "Diweddglo Mawreddog" (the grand finale): Welsh
cheeses followed by three desserts (you can have the lot). Inspectors
have found the food "imaginative and delicious" and the staff friendly.
The hotel has a new look this year: the former co-owners, the
Horsfalls, have retired, and Mr and Mrs Slatter are now joined by Peter
Jackson (he is also "chef/patron") and his wife. "It is as good as ever,"
says a visitor in January 2000. The Royal St David's golf course,
Harlech and Caernarfon castles and Portmeirion are nearby. June
Slatter runs "Steam and Cuisine", a weekly dining service on the
narrow-gauge Rheilffordd Ffestiniog steam railway. (*Gordon Hands*)

Open All year.
Rooms 2 suites, 13 double, 1 single. 4 in coach house, 10 yds. 3 on ground
floor.
Facilities Lift, ramps. Lounge, bar, conservatory, restaurant, business facili-
ties; terrace. No background music. 8-acre grounds: croquet, orchard, pad-
dock. Sea, golf, riding, sailing, fishing, climbing, clay-pigeon shooting nearby.
Civil wedding licence.
Location 3 miles NE of Harlech, signposted off B4573. ½ mile up steep lane.
Train: Harlech/Blaenau Ffestiniog; hotel will meet.
Restrictions No smoking in restaurant. No children under 7 in dining room at
night. Dogs by arrangement; supervised in bedrooms, not in public rooms.
Credit cards All major cards accepted.
Terms [2000] B&B: single £69, double £127–£177, suite £155–£177;
D,B&B: single £90–£94, double £153–£230, suite £183–£230. Set lunch (1 to
3 courses) £9.50–£13.75, dinner (3 to 5 courses) £27–£34. 2-night breaks all
year; 3-day breaks Nov–Mar. Christmas, New Year packages. *V*

THREE COCKS Powys   **Map 3**

Three Cocks Hotel   *Tel* (01497) 847215
Three Cocks, nr Brecon LD3 0SL   *Fax* (01497) 847339
                                    Website www.hay-on-wye.co.uk/3cocks

The famous second-hand book centre of Hay-on-Wye and the high
Brecon Beacons (fine walking country) are both quite close to this
15th-century ivy-clad inn, a restaurant-with-rooms in a village by the
River Wye. After some earlier criticisms, the *Three Cocks* was
enjoyed again this year and last. It has a cobbled forecourt, a small
flowery garden, great oak beams – and a Belgian accent, for its
owners, Michael Winstone (chef) and his Belgian wife Marie-Jeanne
(front-of-house), formerly ran a restaurant in Belgium. Its food also
has a Belgian flavour (eg, mussel soup; smoked Ardennes ham; frogs'
legs; roast guinea fowl Sambre et Meuse) – "outstanding", "marvellous", "delicious and well served", readers have called it, with special
praise for the fish, the duck, the grouse, and the puddings. The menu
changes daily; the dining room is spacious, with a massive French
armoire, and tapestries on the stone walls. The "excellent breakfasts"
are cooked to order, the bread is freshly baked, and there's a good
choice of Belgian beers. Bedrooms and bathrooms are small but
comfortable, but some floors "slope all ways", and plumbing can be
noisy. "Avoid Room 6 if you want to read in bed," is one word of
caution this year. The sitting room, with oak panelling and an open
fire, has new sofas this year. (*CC Schofield, Sara Price, and others*)

Open Mid-Feb–end Nov.
Rooms 7 double. No telephone/TV (available on request).
Facilities Lounge, TV lounge, breakfast room, restaurant (piped classical
music at night). ½-acre grounds. Golf, canoeing, riding, fishing nearby.
Unsuitable for &.
Location 5 miles SW of Hay-on-Wye on A438 Hereford–Brecon. Rear rooms
quietest. Large carpark. Local buses.
Restriction No dogs.
Credit cards MasterCard, Visa.
Terms B&B: single £40, double £67; D,B&B: single £67, double £121. Set
lunch/dinner £28; full alc £35. ***V***

****

Hotel in Cornwall. We struggled with our luggage into the
entrance hall, where the receptionists sat fiddling with a new
computer. Neither of them looked up nor gave us a welcoming
smile or help with our luggage. They were too busy trying to
make the computer work. Our bedroom was shabby, with a
grubby carpet and wallpaper. The two small single beds had
cheap cane headboards, and when we moved the beds together,
we found that the headboards were not fixed to the bed, but
merely propped up against them. We had to clean the bath
before we could use it. The bathroom had peeling paint on the
ceiling and the edging around the bath was black. The basin tap
yielded only a trickle of water.

****

Scotland

Three Chimneys Restaurant and House Over-by, Colbost

ABERDEEN *See SHORTLIST*   **Map 5**

ACHILTIBUIE Highland   **Map 5**

Summer Isles Hotel   *Tel* (01854) 622282
Achiltibuie   *Fax* (01854) 622251
by Ullapool IV26 2YG   *E-mail* smilehotel@aol.com
                         Website www.summerisleshotel.co.uk

♥ *César award in 1993*

"Superb. At the upper price range, but worth every penny." "Is there a more perfect place to be, when the weather is fine? The hotel complements the setting so well." "Comfortable, efficient and friendly." Praise this year for this "uniquely remote place", much frequented by "rugged gourmet intellectuals". Another devotee wrote: "This is no luxury hotel, but something infinitely more valuable – a supremely civilised place, with bedrooms that range from basic but comfortable to a lavish new cottage suite. We love our blissfully quiet room in the turf-roofed annexe. The atmosphere in the lounge is unique, with regulars and newcomers involved in friendly conversation. In the dining room, guests chat between courses. Mark and Geraldine Irvine's genuine concern for their guests creates a happy atmosphere." Set up a single-track road off the road north from Ullapool, the hotel is in a "wildly beautiful" area of the Western Highlands, amid jagged peaks. It has "magical views" of the islands and hills from the small, glassed-in public rooms in front, where fires burn even in summer. The chef, Chris Firth-Bernard, has a *Michelin* star for his modern British cooking, based on local produce: fish and shellfish caught each day, fruit and vegetables grown in a local hydroponicum. Dinner, at 8, proceeds at a leisurely pace. "The first course might be scallops, or langoustines in filo pastry; the second, crab ravioli; main courses are fish and meat on alternate days: wonderfully tender roe deer venison; turbot or halibut straight from the sea. All are quite simply cooked, and served with plain vegetables that do not detract from the quality of the ingredients, and well-reduced sauces." There is a "serious cheese trolley" ("the explanations take some time"), and a pudding trolley laden with gâteaux, hot nursery puddings and tarts. The wine list is "wide-ranging and they do not necessarily steer you to the most expensive bottles". "Only demur: we wish they could have offered an option of fewer courses for the appetite-impaired older generation." Four bedrooms are in the main building; some overlook the carpark. One visitor wished there were more sea-facing rooms, and sound insulation is not always perfect. "Superb breakfasts" have home-made bread and rolls, muesli, fruit, and cooked dishes. Bar lunches are served. "The weather can range from Arctic to Aegean within a week," say the Irvines. "Bring your wellingtons, comfortable old clothes, your dog, binoculars, paint-boxes and midge cream." Underwater scenery can be explored with the local diving school. (*Colin Pearson, A Gradon, HR, Mrs M Box, Conrad and Marilyn Dehn; also Patricia M Simpson*)

Open Mid-Apr–early Oct.
Rooms 3 suites, 11 double. 10 in annexes. Some on ground floor. TV in suites only.
Facilities Sitting room, study/TV room, cocktail bar, public bar, restaurant. No background music. Small garden. Sea 100 yds; bathing 3 miles. Lochs, fly-fishing (end June–end Sept) nearby. Unsuitable for &.
Location NW of Ullapool; after 10 miles turn off A835 on to single-track road skirting lochs Lurgain, Badagyle and Oscaig. Hotel just past village post office, 15 miles. Bus from Ullapool twice daily.
Restrictions Smoking banned in dining room, discouraged in bedrooms. No children under 6. No dogs in public rooms.
Credit cards MasterCard, Visa.
Terms B&B: single £55, double £120, suite £200. Bar lunches. Set dinner £39. 10% discount for 6 or more nights.

ANNAN Dumfries and Galloway *See SHORTLIST*   **Map 5**

ARDVOURLIE Western Isles   Map 5

Ardvourlie Castle   *Tel* (01859) 502307
Aird a Mhulaidh   *Fax* (01859) 502348
Isle of Harris HS3 3AB

"Our fourth annual visit; it is one of our favourite places. We feel we are guests in a private house where our hosts anticipate our every need." Praise continues for this "wonderful pile" which brother and sister Derek and Pamela Martin have resurrected from near ruin. It is on the broad foreshore of Loch Seaforth (*Aird a Mhulaidh* is Gaelic for "the headland below the high peak"). Its position, in the centre of the island, makes it a good base for exploring Lewis and also the mountains and lochs of north Harris. Antiques and Victorian furnishings "give a feeling of what the place would have been like in the 19th century": oil and gas lights in the dining room, open fires in the lounge and library; oak panelling and Victorian or Edwardian beds in the bedrooms. But there are modern comforts aplenty, including lots of hot water. Meals are served "in great style, matching the grandeur of the house". Derek Martin's cooking is traditional, and benefits from superb local produce, particularly lamb and fish, "which are prepared with subtle feeling for herbs and spices". The no-choice menu features such dishes as honey-roast duck with orange liqueur sauce and crunchy-topped creamed potatoes; grilled local lamb with rosemary, served with sauté potatoes, peas and courgette gratin. There are old-fashioned puddings, eg, orange trifle and Chantilly meringues with hot fudge sauce, and unusual Scottish cheeses. The Martins "have no concept of portion control" and cater for appetites whetted by walking, birdwatching and flower-spotting. Breakfasts include locally smoked fish, locally produced bacon, home-baked bread, home-made marmalade and preserves, and there are home-baked scones and cakes at teatime. The Martins, not young, are sometimes assisted by Mr Martin's son and daughter-in-law. (*Conrad and Marilyn Dehn*)

Open Apr–end Oct. Dining room closed to non-residents.
Rooms 4 double. 1 on ground floor. No telephone/TV.
Facilities Lounge with honesty bar, library with piano, dining room. No background music. 13-acre grounds. 50 yds to rocky foreshore. Loch/river fishing nearby. Unsuitable for &.
Location Off A859 12 miles NE of Tarbert, 25 miles S of Stornoway. Occasional buses from both.
Restrictions Smoking banned in restaurant; by agreement with other guests in lounges. Children must be old enough to dine with parents. No dogs.
Credit cards None accepted.
Terms [2000] B&B £65–£85; D,B&B £70–£90. Set dinner (residents only) £25. Single supplement £20. Child accommodated in parents' room: under 12, 50% of adult rate. Reductions for 5 nights or more. 1-night bookings not accepted if made before Mar.

Inevitably some hotels change hands or close after we have gone to press. It is prudent to check the ownership when booking, particularly in the case of small establishments.

ARISAIG Highland   Map 5

Arisaig Hotel   `NEW/BUDGET`   *Tel* (01687) 450210
Arisaig PH39 4NH   *Fax* (01687) 450310
                              E-mail arisaighotel@dial.pipex.com
                              Website www.arisaighotel.co.uk

*Mr and Mrs Ross's modest hotel, dating from 1720. Near pier, on
Road to the Isles, but traffic not a problem, says nominator. 13
spacious bedrooms; front ones with lovely views. Smart residents'
lounge, public bar with live music at weekends. Good plain cooking
(much use of local fish, langoustines, etc), in no-smoking restaurant
("easy listening" background music). Closed Christmas. Unsuitable
for &. MasterCard, Visa accepted. B&B £25–£36. Full alc £21.50.*

Arisaig House   *Tel* (01687) 450622
Beasdale   *Fax* (01687) 450626
by Arisaig PH39 4NR   *E-mail* ArisaigHse@aol.com
                                               Website www.ArisaigHouse.co.uk

"Very pleasant staff; not at all stuffy. The food is good, if a shade pretentious. The grounds are beautiful, and the terraced gardens and
kitchen garden are quite exceptional." "Continues to delight in all
aspects. Ambience of a country house; every need is met apparently
with no effort – it takes great attention to detail to achieve that." "Real
luxury, at luxury prices. They employ two gardeners and an army of
waiters. Breakfast and dinner were fantastic." Praise this year and last
for the Smither family's handsome Victorian mansion (Relais &
Châteaux). It is set up a drive on a large estate west of Fort William,
at the end of one of the most spectacular roads to the isles. The public
rooms are large and light. There is an entrance hall with high windows,
Oriental rugs and a carved oak staircase; a drawing room with vaulted
ceiling and log fire; and a billiard room with an antique billiard table,
and decorated with college oars. But lighting may be too dim for reading. The bedrooms, priced according to size and view (most are
spacious), are "charming and traditional"; the best ones overlook the
sea. In summer, light lunches and teas are served on a terrace with
beds of roses and begonias. In the grounds you can walk through
rhododendrons, azaleas and conifers to a crescent of beach and rocky
promontories with "breathtaking views" across the water. The walled
kitchen garden provides some unusual ingredients for the kitchen, and
fresh local produce is used by the chef, Duncan Gibson, in his
"Scottish dishes with a French influence", eg, risotto of garden
asparagus and parsley with parmesan; loin of Highland venison with
creamed celeriac and a juniper game jus; dark chocolate and pecan nut
mousse with a raspberry and white chocolate cream. If you want a dish
more simply prepared, you can ask. Breakfast is personally served,
rather than self-help, and it has a wide choice of fruit, yogurt, etc, as
well as a high-cholesterol Scottish affair. The manager, Vincent
Gullon, is new this year. A good base for exploring the jagged
Highland coast, Skye and the Hebrides. (*Nicholas Penny, and others*)

Open Mar–Nov inclusive.
Rooms 2 suites, 10 double.
Facilities Reception lounge, 2 lounges, lounge bar, billiard room, restaurant; meeting room. No background music. 20-acre grounds: croquet, helipad. Sea loch 15 mins' walk. Unsuitable for &.
Location On A830 Fort William–Mallaig, 3 miles E of Arisaig village. Train: Beasdale, 1 mile; hotel will meet.
Restrictions No smoking in restaurant. No children under 10. Guide dogs only.
Credit cards MasterCard, Visa.
Terms [2000] B&B: single from £95, double £100–£290, suite £160–£220. Set dinner £39.50. Reductions for 5 or more nights May, June, July, Sept.

The Old Library Lodge   *Tel* (01687) 450651
Arisaig PH39 4NH   *Fax* (01687) 450219
                              E-mail oldlibrary.arisaig@btinternet.com
                              Website www.road-to-the-isles.org

"We found it excellent. With the changing menu, each meal was a memorable experience," says a visitor this year to this popular bistro-style restaurant-with-rooms. It has been converted by owner/chef Alan Broadhurst and his wife, Angela, from 200-year-old stables (later a library). It stands on the waterfront of the old village, looking across Loch Nan Ceall, where *Local Hero* was filmed, to the Inner Hebrides (reached by a ferry). All around is beautiful Highland scenery. The cooking is "modern Scottish with French touches". Plenty of choice on the dinner menu, which might include beetroot and apple soup with home-made bread; fillets of venison with a port and orange sauce; grilled peach with honey and lemon, and home-made crème fraîche ice-cream. Lunches of soups, salads, venisonburgers and omelettes are served, on the front patio in fine weather. There is a residents' lounge upstairs. Two bedrooms are in the main house; the others are in an extension at the rear. These have a little balcony with a table and chairs, overlooking the small terraced garden. On the walls are watercolours by a local artist (some are for sale). Some rooms have poor sound insulation. Guests arriving by train are met at the station. (*Roger Hughes*)

Open Apr–Oct. Restaurant closed midday Tues.
Rooms 6 double, 4, with access to garden, in extension.
Facilities Lounge, restaurant (low-level jazz during dinner). Small garden. Loch foreshore across road (shingle beach; no bathing). Unsuitable for &.
Location Village centre, on waterfront (little traffic at night). Public parking.
Restrictions No smoking: restaurant, bedrooms. No dogs.
Credit cards Amex, MasterCard, Visa.
Terms B&B £34–£48. Full alc lunch £12.50. Set dinner £24. 10% reduction for 3 nights or more.

****

Hotel in Wales. The faxed confirmation of our booking consisted of six pages, including menus going back to 1998. When we telephoned to straighten out some problems the owner left the telephone no fewer than three times during our conversation; we could hear him taking payment for accommodation.

****

AUCHTERHOUSE Angus   Map 5

Old Mansion House NEW   *Tel* (01382) 320366
By Dundee   *Fax* (01382) 320400
DD3 0QN   *E-mail* oldmansionhouse@netscapeonline.co.uk
                               Website www.angusanddundee.co.uk/members/285

Set on a knoll in large wooded grounds near Dundee, this handsome
white mansion has a proud history. Built on the site of a medieval
castle, whose vaults survive, it was rebuilt as a mansion in the
17th/18th centuries, and was home to the Earls of Strathmore, the
Buchans, Ogilvies and others. It is now a stylish and sumptuous small
hotel, owned and run by Maxine and Jannick Bertschy (they are
Scottish, he is of Swiss extraction), with Theresa Donnelly as manager. "She greeted us affably," say visitors in 2000, "and gave us the
Ogilvie suite, the only room left. It was smallish and a bit over-furnished, but had more than the standard comforts, and nice touches
such as sherry, books, a good bathroom with plenty of toiletries. We
had drinks in the library/bar, which was charming save for its gas 'log'
fire: but there was a real log fire in the main hall, providing a lovely
welcome. The dining room is wonderfully surreal, with an ornate
[Jacobean] plasterwork ceiling like stalactite deposits in a fairyland
castle, and an impressive mantel with heraldic emblems. It was all like
a Fellini film set. The meal was one of the finest we have had: the lobster bisque with seafood, plus ceremonious ladling of flaming brandy,
was superb. So were the local crayfish and Angus beef with excellent
vegetables. The manageress and her staff were courteous and efficient." Chef Tim Cribben provides Scottish and European cooking,
with some choice on the *prix-fixe* menu, and plenty on the "Taste of
Scotland" *carte* (eg, gâteau of haggis, neeps and tatties). There is a
cheaper courtyard bistro. Some bedrooms are large, with four-posters.
In the Vaulted Room (*c.* 1245) you can play chess or listen to music.
The Bertschys have won the Booker Prize for Excellence 2000, for the
best hotel and caterer in the UK. Children are welcomed. (*AJM
Ribeiro dos Santos*)

Open All year.
Rooms 2 suites (one, for 4, on ground floor, in Lodge House), 5 double.
Facilities Lounge, library/bar (classical/Scottish background music), court-
yard bar/bistro, dining room, private dining room. 14 acre grounds: tennis, cro-
quet, squash, swimming pool, river. Clay-pigeon shooting, horse riding,
off-road driving, golf nearby.
Location 5 miles NW of Dundee. Take A923 (Coupar–Angus) off Kingsway;
through Birkhill village, join B954. House 2 miles on left, outside
Auchterhouse.
Restrictions No smoking: restaurant, some other public areas, bedrooms.
Dogs by arrangement (Lodge House only).
Credit cards All major cards accepted.
Terms B&B: single £85, double £110, suite £145; D,B&B double £75 per
person. Set lunch £18.50, dinner £29; full alc £32.75. Christmas/Easter
packages. *V*

For details of the Voucher scheme see page xxx.

AVIEMORE Highland   Map 5

Corrour House   NEW/BUDGET   *Tel* (01479) 810220
Inverdruie, by Aviemore   *Fax* (01479) 811500
PH22 1QH   *Website* www.corrourhouse.co.uk

Standing in wooded grounds well away from busy Aviemore, David
and Sheana Catto's small guest house makes a good base for exploring the Cairngorms, says its nominator. It has views of the mountains,
and there is "not another house in sight". "The welcome we received
was the best of our trip to Scotland. Our front bedroom, while not
modern, was large and spotless, with everything we could want.
During an excellent dinner, we watched deer stroll across the lawn.
Breakfast was equally good, with unusual jams. Excellent value for
money." The Victorian house was originally a dower house for the
Rothiemurchus estate, which now has many tourist activities – Land
Rover safaris, etc. The short dinner menu is based on locally produced
ingredients and home-grown herbs and vegetables. Two choices of
each course, eg, asparagus and Mull cheddar tart; venison with juniper
stuffing and port wine sauce; peaches baked in marsala. (*Don Parker*)

Open 27 Dec–31 Oct.
Rooms 8 double.
Facilities Lounge, bar, dining room; classical background music at night.
4-acre grounds. River, fishing, skiing, golf nearby. Unsuitable for &.
Location ½ mile S of Aviemore on B970, signposted Glenmore and
Coylumbridge. Train/bus from Aviemore.
Restrictions No smoking: dining room, bedrooms. No dogs in public rooms.
Credit cards MasterCard, Visa.
Terms B&B £30–£40; D,B&B £50–£65. Set dinner £25. *V*

BALLANTRAE South Ayrshire   Map 5

Cosses Country House   *Tel* (01465) 831363
Ballantrae, nr Girvan   *Fax* (01465) 831598
KA26 0LR   *E-mail* cosses@compuserve.com

A pretty, low, white building set amid flower-filled gardens and woodland in a secluded valley, just outside an old fishing village in an
unspoilt corner of south-west Scotland. Originally a 17th-century
shooting lodge, it is now a Wolsey Lodge member, run by Robin and
Susan Crosthwaite (she is a finalist in the AA's Landlady of the Year
award 2000). The decor (antiques, souvenirs, etc) reflects the many
years that the Crosthwaites spent in the Middle and Far East. The communal dinners, "which last all evening", make a feature of local produce, eg, garlic-and-ginger roasted Ayrshire lamb fillet with Madeira
and redcurrant sauce; fillet of local salmon with lime and green pep-
percorns and gooseberry and dill cream; Dunsyre blue cheese pancakes with fresh tomato sauce. Vegetables, fruit and herbs are home
grown. A Scottish breakfast is served informally in the kitchen, and in
fine weather tea can be taken in the garden. Two large suites, big
enough for a family, are in converted byres and stables across a courtyard; a smaller one is in the main house; all have a kingsize bed, TV,

fruit, local information, etc. A utility room with drying facilities is available to guests. There are good walks from the grounds, with views across the sea to the Kintyre peninsula, Ailsa Craig and the Isle of Arran, and by the seashore. Local attractions include Burns's birthplace, Culzean Castle, Logan Botanical Gardens. The Irish ferry terminals are nearby. More reports, please.

Open 1 Mar–31 Oct.
Rooms 3 suites. 2 across courtyard.
Facilities Lounge, games room, utility room, dining room. No background music. 12-acre grounds: garden, woods. Golf, fishing, walking, cycling, sea, safe bathing nearby. Unsuitable for &.
Location 2 miles E of Ballantrae. Take A77 towards Stranraer; 1st left, at caravan sign, towards Laggan. *Cosses* is 2 miles up road, on right.
Restrictions No smoking: dining room, bedrooms. No children under 12. No dogs in public rooms.
Credit cards MasterCard, Visa.
Terms B&B £32–£48; D,B&B £57–£73. Set dinner from £25. Reduced rates for children by arrangement. Reductions for 3 or more nights.

BALLATER Aberdeenshire   **Map 5**

Balgonie Country House   *Tel/Fax* (013397) 55482
Braemar Place
Ballater AB35 5NQ

Ballater, eight miles from Balmoral on Royal Deeside, has had a long association with the royal family, who still attend the Highland Games here each year. John and Priscilla Finnie's Edwardian country house is on the outskirts of the thriving village, popular with tourists. Its peaceful grounds with mature trees and lawns look over the Ballater golf course to the hills of Glen Muick beyond; for entertainment, the owners offer croquet and "weeding opportunities". The bedrooms are called after fishing pools on the River Dee. Five of them, and the dining room, have recently been redecorated. The cooking is "Scottish with a French classical approach", with much use of excellent local produce. Main courses include, eg, pan-fried fillet of seabass with marinated vegetables and a sweet-and-sour sauce; braised haunch of venison wrapped in Savoy cabbage, with fondant potato and a game jus. Desserts include blueberry and almond tart with crème fraîche; hot beignet of bramble compote with vanilla ice-cream. There are special meals for children. "A first-class hotel in terms of comfort, service and food," one visitor wrote; others praised the "considerate owners" and the value for money. Salmon fishing can be arranged (the Finnies have rights on half a mile of the Dee). Good walking nearby, and plenty of local attractions: Balmoral and other inhabited castles, castle ruins, gardens, art galleries and artists' studios, and the Lochnagar whisky distillery. (*WR*)

Open Feb–Dec (incl. New Year), lunch by reservation only.
Rooms 9 double.
Facilities Sitting room, bar, dining room. No background music. 4-acre grounds: croquet. Salmon fishing on River Dee; golf, hill-walking, skiing nearby. Only dining room suitable for &.

Location Outskirts of Ballater, off A93 Aberdeen–Perth. Bus 201 from Aberdeen, 40 miles.
Restrictions No smoking in dining room. No dogs in public rooms, or unattended in bedrooms.
Credit cards All major cards accepted.
Terms B&B £40–£70; D,B&B £70–£100. 10% reduction for 6 nights or more. Set lunch £18.50, dinner £30–£31.50. 1-night bookings sometimes refused. *V*

Darroch Learg	*Tel* (013397) 55443
Braemar Road	*Fax* (013397) 55252
Ballater AB35 5UX	*E-mail* nigel@darroch-learg.demon.co.uk.
	Website www.darroch-learg.demon.co.uk

The Gaelic name of this hotel means an oak wood on a sunny hillside. It looks over the Dee valley and Ballater's golf course to Lochnagar mountain. It is made up of two Victorian listed buildings: the main house is baronial and turreted, the other, *Oakhall*, a pink and granite former hunting lodge, has cheaper bedrooms and is suitable for a group booking. Owned by the Franks family for over 40 years, the place is now run by Nigel and Fiona Franks, and is liked by *Guide* readers for its setting, food and country house ambience. "It is almost our favourite in Scotland," runs a 2000 report. "The views are superb, the cream, blue and yellow colour scheme of our room was very pleasant. Breakfasts are great (delicious porridge); my husband had a superb dinner, and my dietary needs were well catered for. But one night we had to wait ages for dinner to be served." Others wrote of "friendly owners" and "charming staff". Drinks are served in an attractive drawing room with a log fire. The restaurant, candlelit at night, has well-spaced tables, some in a conservatory extension. David Mutter cooks modern Scottish dishes on menus with plenty of choice, eg, fish and shellfish stew in curry; pot-roast squab with confit of pork belly, in red wine sauce; sticky toffee pudding. The "excellent wine list" includes plenty of half bottles; and a fixed mark-up per bottle means that the higher quality wines are good value. The bedrooms vary; most have lovely views. Many have just been upgraded, and given bathrobes, flowers and fruit. Some upper rooms in *Oakhall* can be cramped. This year, one reader found the garden a bit run-down, with a lack of places to sit. Children are welcomed, though there are no special facilities for them. A good base for exploring Crathes and Drum, Corgarff Castle and the Speyside distilleries, and for a golfing or fishing holiday. (*Fiona Dick, Colin Pearson, Jane Grant*)

Open Feb–Dec.
Rooms 17 double, 1 single. 5 in *Oakhall*. 1 on ground floor.
Facilities Ramp. 2 lounges, smoking room, restaurant/conservatory. No background music. 4-acre grounds. River Dee, fishing ¼ mile (prior notice needed); birdwatching, shooting, golf, riding, hang-gliding nearby.
Location On A93, ½ mile W of Ballater. Bus from Aberdeen.
Restrictions No smoking: restaurant, 2 lounges, 4 bedrooms. No dogs in public rooms.
Credit cards All major cards accepted.
Terms B&B £40–£77; D,B&B £60–£105. Set Sun lunch £19.50, dinner £34. Child accommodated in parents' room: under 12, free. Autumn, spring

breaks. New Year package. 1-night bookings occasionally refused. *V*
(Oct–Mar)

BALQUHIDDER Stirling   **Map 5**

Monachyle Mhor   *Tel* (01877) 384622
Lochearnhead FK19 8PQ   *Fax* (01877) 384305
                                          Website www.monachylemhor.com

In a "breathtaking setting" overlooking lochs Voil and Doine, this
"magical place" was once the home of the family of Rob Roy
MacGregor. He is buried in the village church four miles away. Now
owned by Jean and Rob Lewis and their son Tom, the pink-washed old
farmhouse stands at the end of the narrow road, mentioned in
Stevenson's *Kidnapped*, that winds along Loch Voil through the Braes
o' Balquhidder. The 2,000-acre estate encompasses a working farm
and two lakes with fishing; deer-stalking and grouse-shooting are
offered in season. The house is decorated with sporting and scenic pictures. The restaurant and sitting room have just been refurbished in a
"classic modern style". The best bedrooms look over a loch – a "stunning room with a four-poster and a long, deep bath" is fondly remembered by one visitor. But some rooms and shower rooms are small, and
lighting can be dim. The Lewises are in the process of redecorating a
four-bedroom Victorian house in Strathyre (eight miles away) "to take
the overflow". It should be ready for summer 2000. The much-
admired, eclectic cooking of Tom Lewis is served in a conservatory-
style restaurant. A sample menu includes artichoke and rosemary
soup; pan-fried grouse with chanterelles and sage and shallot stuffing;
bread-and-butter pudding with whisky and raisin custard. Meat and
fish are locally produced, and the organic walled garden provides
vegetables and herbs. The wines are fairly priced. There are scrambled
eggs and smoked salmon for breakfast, and home-baked bread and
scones. Good bar meals too, and "extraordinarily delicious sandwiches". "Visiting here is like staying in the wonderful home of old
friends," says one devotee. (*CC Schofield, FG*)

Open All year.
Rooms 4 suites, 10 double. 5 in courtyard. Self-catering cottages.
Facilities Ramps. Lounge, bar, restaurant. No background music. 2,000-acre
estate: garden, loch, river, grouse moor; walking, salmon/trout-fishing, deer-
stalking. Wedding facilities.
Location 11 miles NW of Callander. Turn right off A84 at Kingshouse; hotel
6 miles along glen.
Restrictions No smoking: restaurant, bedrooms. No children under 12. No
dogs.
Credit cards MasterCard, Visa.
Terms B&B: single £50–£70, double £70–£95. Set lunch £17.50–£19.50,
dinner £29. Christmas package.

By sending us reports you automatically qualify for the Report
of the Year competition. Each of 12 winners is awarded a
bottle of champagne and a free copy of the *Guide*.

BIGGAR Dumfries and Galloway   Map 5

Toftcombs   *Tel* (01899) 220142
Peebles Road   *Fax* (01899) 221771
Biggar ML12 6QX   *E-mail* toftcombs@aol.com
                                           Website www.travelcheck.co.uk/hotel/732

Just N of centre, on A702 to Edinburgh, restaurant with 4 bedrooms, recently opened by Charlie and Vivian Little after "awesome refurbishment". 10-acre grounds: walled garden and picnic tables; views of border hills; good walking nearby. Manageress/chef Jane Barrell provides modern/traditional cooking in green-walled restaurant. Bar lunches and suppers; afternoon teas and high teas. Classical background music in public areas. Only restaurant suitable for ♿. No smoking: restaurant, bedrooms. Guide dogs only. All major credit cards accepted. 4 bedrooms. B&B: single £45, double £65, family £85. Full alc £20. More reports, please.

BLAIRGOWRIE Perth and Kinross   Map 5

Kinloch House   NEW   *Tel* (01250) 884237
by Blairgowrie PH10 6SG   *Fax* (01250) 884333
                                           E-mail info@kinlochhouse.com
                                           Website www.kinlochhouse.com

"Still extremely good," say visitors this year, restoring this grand 19th-century Scottish mansion to the *Guide*. It stands in large, peaceful wooded grounds with Highland cattle and a Victorian walled garden. The "very professional" Shentall family (they have run the hotel since 1981) are also "very welcoming", and "the standard of cooking is high". David Shentall "resplendent in his kilt and very witty", presides in the bar before dinner. "Service by the friendly young staff cannot be faulted." The "country house atmosphere" is admired: oak panelling, family portraits, *objets d'art* and books in the public rooms; some bedrooms have a four-poster and a large Victorian bath. At breakfast there is a huge selection of cooked dishes, including kedgeree. Bill McNicoll's "modern Scottish" menus are based on local produce, eg, Highland salmon marinated in whisky, honey and herbs; Kyle of Lochalsh scallops with leeks, bacon and mushrooms; pan-fried Aberdeen Angus steak. You can end with a savoury such as creamed smoked haddock or devilled kidneys if you prefer that to dessert. To match all this, men are expected to wear a jacket and tie at dinner. There is also a vegetarian menu. Popular with shooting parties (the house has a game larder, drying facilities and kennels for gun dogs), fishermen (plenty of lochs and rivers nearby), and golfers (30 courses within an hour's drive). (*Ian Dewey, Janice Carrera*)

Open All year, except 18–29 Dec.
Rooms 2 suites, 14 double, 4 single. Some on ground floor.
Facilities Ramp. Drawing room, conservatory, bar, 2 dining rooms. No background music. 30-acre grounds: Health and fitness centre (sauna, steam room, spa, exercise pool, gym). Fishing, sailing, golf nearby.

Location 3 miles W of Blairgowrie, on A923 to Dunkeld. Train: Perth (16 miles), then taxi.
Restrictions No smoking: restaurant, some bedrooms. No children under 7 in restaurant. No dogs in public rooms.
Credit cards All major cards accepted.
Terms B&B from £90; D,B&B £98–£135. Set lunch £17.95, dinner £34.50. Winter breaks, New Year package.

BRODICK North Ayrshire　　　　　　　　　　　　Map 5

Kilmichael Country House
Glen Cloy, by Brodick
Isle of Arran KA27 8BY

Tel (01770) 302219
Fax (01770) 302068

In a secluded setting just outside the large resort village of Brodick, this late 17th-century listed building, said to be the oldest in Arran, is reached up an unmade road. It is much admired: "A beautiful setting." "A most delightful house" (it contains a collection of Levantine and Oriental antiques). "A more comfortable place to stay I cannot imagine." The owners, Geoffrey Botterill and Antony Butterworth, and their staff are "very friendly". The extensive grounds, patrolled by ducks and peacocks, have spectacular views of Arran's mountains. The food, served with fine silver and crystal, is "a blend of traditional and modern, with a strong Mediterranean influence". Two choices of each course on the four-course menu; eg, chestnut and garlic soup; Campari and grapefruit sorbet; seabass with tiger prawns, with a lemongrass and ginger butter; "a bachelor's pudding with proper custard". A vegetarian dish can be requested, and a light room-service meal can be served. The wine list "could be more exciting, but the generous range of single malt whiskies is good compensation". Reservations are for B&B; you must book a table for dinner. The bedrooms, supplied with fresh flowers and fruit, are distinctively decorated. Each is described in detail in the brochure: the Blue Room is done in blue and rose; Grizel's Room, named for the wife of a former owner, has a declaration of love, dated 1681, carved in its wall. Some rooms are in converted stables, leading off the landscaped garden. "Wonderful peaty brown water" in the pretty bathrooms. Log fires sometimes burn in the public rooms.

There is good walking from the door. Arran, the most southerly and the most accessible of the Scottish islands, has seven golf courses and many interesting geological sites. Brodick Castle, home of the Dukes of Hamilton, is open to the public. More reports, please.

Open Mar–Oct; other times by arrangement. Lunch not served.
Rooms 3 suites, 4 double, 1 single. 3 in converted stables. 7 on ground floor.
Facilities 2 drawing rooms, dining room ("classical/nostalgic" background music during meals). 30-acre grounds. Beach 1 mile; sailing, golf, walking nearby.

Location Ferry from Ardrossan; from ferry terminal, go N on A841; turn inland opposite golf club; follow signs to long drive leading to house. Taxi from ferry.
Restrictions Smoking in 1 drawing room only. No children under 12. No dogs in public rooms.
Credit cards MasterCard, Visa.
Terms [2000] B&B £40–£75. Set dinner £25.50. Discounts for 3 nights; ferry-inclusive packages available. 1-night bookings sometimes refused Sat.

BUNCHREW Highland   Map 5

Bunchrew House   *Tel* (01463) 234917
Bunchrew   *Fax* (01463) 710620
Inverness IV3 8TA   *E-mail* welcome@bunchrew-inverness.co.uk
         Website www.bunchrew-inverness.co.uk

Silver-spired, castellated 17th-century mansion in fine position over-looking Black Isle, on shores of Beauly Firth, 2½ miles NW of Inverness. "Wonderful value; pure Scottish hospitality," runs recent accolade for owners Janet and Graham Cross (he tells good stories of the house ghost). 11 bedrooms. Ambitious French-influenced Scottish food in spacious dining room overlooking Beauly Firth; "gorgeous bar"; Celtic/classical background music in public rooms. Conference/function facilities; wedding facilities. 20-acre grounds with landscaped gardens, fishing. Golf, skiing, sailing nearby. Unsuitable for &. No smoking in restaurant. No dogs in public rooms. Open all year. Amex, MasterCard, Visa accepted. B&B: single £85–£120, double £110–£180; D,B&B £70–£140 per person. Set lunch £23, dinner £28. More reports, please.

CALLANDER Stirling   Map 5

The Roman Camp   *Tel* (01877) 330003
off Main Street   *Fax* (01877) 331533
Callander FK17 8BG   *E-mail* mail@roman-camp-hotel.co.uk
         Website www.roman-camp-hotel.co.uk

Reached off the main street of this old town to the east of the Trossachs, this pink, turreted building stands on the banks of the River Teith (with private fishing). The name comes from earthworks to the east of the walled garden, believed to be the site of a Roman fort. In its large, romantic grounds is a field said to be the site of the oldest football pitch in Scotland, if not the world. The former hunting lodge (built in 1625 for the Dukes of Perth) has been much extended over the centuries. It is now run as a luxury hotel by Eric and Marion Brown, and admired for its country house atmosphere, with log fires, piles of antique leather suitcases, log baskets, old walking sticks. Teas, light lunches and drinks are served in the drawing room; there is an oak-beamed bar, a panelled library and a tiny chapel. Accommodation varies: some bedrooms are high-ceilinged, with an ornate fireplace; others are "small and cosy, with furniture dating back 200 years"; a family suite at the top of the house is said to be "cramped". Spacious modern rooms in a new wing have "a rather bland decor", but some have a door leading directly on to the gardens (patrolled by peacocks). The elaborate dinners cooked by Ian McNaught include, eg, ravioli of lobster; oyster and lettuce soup with caviar Chantilly; breast of guinea fowl with foie gras and truffle fumet; bitter chocolate marquise with a mint and orange cream sauce. Copious breakfasts have clootie dumplings, haggis and black pudding, as well as more conventional items. Guests have access to the golf course nearby. More reports, please.

Open All year.
Rooms 4 suites, 10 double. 7 on ground floor (1 adapted for &.).
Facilities Drawing room, library, bar, conservatory, restaurant; chapel; conference/function facilities. No background music. 20-acre grounds: river, ¾-mile fishing. Golf nearby. Wedding facilities.
Location E end of Main St (small driveway between 2 pink cottages). Bus from Stirling.
Restrictions No smoking in restaurant. No dogs in public rooms.
Credit cards All major cards accepted.
Terms B&B: single £85–£125, double £95–£165, suite £185; D,B&B: single £122–£162, double £169–£243, suite £263. Set lunch £19.50, dinner £37; full alc £48.50. 2-day off-season breaks. Christmas package. *V*

CANONBIE Dumfries and Galloway   Map 5

Riverside Inn   *Tel* (013873) 71512 and 71295
Canonbie DG14 0UX

"The welcome is unfailingly pleasant," says a regular visitor to this civilised little black-and-white inn, which Robert and Susan Phillips have run for over a quarter of a century. It is particularly admired for the quality of the cooking, served in the beamed dining room with its wooden tables and candles in brass candlesticks, and in the friendly split-level bar, which is decorated with stuffed wildlife, and frequented by locals. The food is "both wholesome and innovative", eg, spinach and anchovy tart; roast organic duck with mushroom and peppercorn sauce; steamed date pudding with toffee sauce. Local ingredients are used when possible; fresh fish is delivered regularly. The wine list is "sensibly priced", and there is a wide choice of wines by the glass, a huge variety of malts, and some "good local beers". On Sundays a traditional lunch is served. Also admired: the "excellent kippers" at breakfast (it also includes home-made bread, marmalade and jams). The bedrooms, which vary in size, are "homely" and "interestingly dated, but well maintained". They have electric blankets, flowers, a basket of fruit and an old-fashioned bathroom. Two rooms are in a secluded cottage across the road, overlooking the river. Some others get traffic noise. Canonbie is at the eastern end of the Scots Dyke, a ditch three and a half miles wide that marks the border between England and Scotland. It makes a useful staging post on the way north or south (the northern end of the M6 is only 12 miles away). For those who choose to linger, it is a good base for exploring Hadrian's Wall and the Solway coast, and it is popular with fisher folk.
(*John Townsend, Good Pub Guide*)

Open All year, except 25/26 Dec, 1/2 Jan, 2 weeks Feb, 2 weeks Nov.
Rooms 7 double. 2 in garden cottage. 1 on ground floor. No telephone.
Facilities 2 lounges, lounge bar, dining room. No background music. ½-acre garden. River Esk opposite, fishing. Unsuitable for &.
Location M6 exit 44. 10 miles N on A7; turn into Canonbie. Bottom of hill by Esk bridge. Private carpark. Bus from Carlisle, Edinburgh, Galashiels.
Restrictions No smoking in dining room. No children under 5. No dogs in public rooms.
Credit cards MasterCard, Visa.
Terms B&B: single from £55, double from £70. Bar meals £5–£15. Set dinner £19.50; full alc £27. 2-day winter breaks; weekly rate.

CARDROSS Argyll and Bute   Map 5

Kirkton House   **NEW**   *Tel* (01389) 841951
Darleith Road   *Fax* (01389) 841868
Cardross G82 5EZ
                                      E-mail ghg@kirktonhouse.co.uk
                                      Website www.kirktonhouse.co.uk

With wide views across the Clyde, this 160-year-old farmhouse, built around a courtyard, is informally run by Stewart and Gillian Macdonald. "We may be small," they write, "but this permits us to give personal attention to our guests' needs." And a visitor from America found the place "lovely", and the hospitality "more than generous". A reasonably priced evening meal, by arrangement, is communally served by oil lamplight, and the traditional menus include, eg, haggis 'n' neeps; beef and venison steaks; banana split. For breakfast there are Loch Fyne kippers; smoked haddock; large grills. The bedrooms are "comfortable, with charming, simple furniture", but not all have the view. Children are welcomed (baby-sitting can be arranged), and so are pets. A good base for touring: Glasgow is only 18 miles away. "One of the things we most enjoyed was going for a long stroll down country roads after the delicious dinner." (*Charlotte Stradtman, Bob and Alison Darling*)

Open Feb–Nov.
Rooms 6 double. 2 on ground floor. 1 suitable for &.
Facilities Lounge, dining rooms. No background music. 2-acre grounds: children's playground, paddock, stabling.
Location Turn N at W end of village, up Darleith Rd. Hotel ½ mile on right after 3 cottages.
Restrictions Smoking banned in dining rooms, allowed in other public rooms "if other guests agree". Dogs in public rooms by arrangement.
Credit cards All major cards accepted.
Terms B&B £33.50–£45; D,B&B £53.25–£64.75. Set dinner £16–£19.75. Child accommodated in parents' room: baby free; under 12, from £11.

****

Hotel in Kent. Dinner was marred by the piped music; given that the building is Tudor, modern rock music was hardly appropriate. The chef suffers from timbalitis: if in doubt, stick the food in a timbale – easy presentation and small portions. And he was so carried away by flavours that you could not actually taste what you were eating.

****

COLBOST Highland   Map 5

 Three Chimneys Restaurant   NEW   *Tel* (01470) 511258
and House Over-by   *Fax* (01470) 511358
Colbost, Dunvegan   *E-mail* eatandstay@threechimneys.co.uk
Isle of Skye IV55 8ZT   *Website* www.threechimneys.co.uk

César award: Newcomer of the year

"It's terrific!" An inspector in 2000 sent a euphoric account of this amazing operation: in the far north-west of the Isle of Skye, a super-gastronomic restaurant with a brilliant modern design, plus six luxury suites just added in a house across the courtyard ("over-by" is the Scottish way of saying "next door"). "Despite its remoteness, the venture has been an outstanding success, with 'gastro pilgrims' beating a path to the door of Eddie and Shirley Spear's tiny place. Her cooking has won constant praise and awards [eg, the Taste of Scotland prize for 1999] while Eddie has compiled a stunning wine list. Tall and bespectacled, with a huge smile, he greeted us warmly. Shirley was very helpful, up early after a packed dining room the night before. All staff were most pleasant. Both buildings have been made to resemble typical crofters' cottages from outside, but the interiors are pure designer chic. They are the work of Diana Mackie, who has used natural but luxurious fabrics, with soft colours and uncluttered lines. Our large split-level room had tall windows opening on to wild scenery, and carried the sweet musky smell of new wood. The large bed was sublimely comfortable, with reading lamps the best ever. The marble bathroom had luxurious taps, bath and loo, lots of toiletries. Breakfast, a perfect buffet, offered porridge with thick cream; smoked duck, venison and salmon, home-made oatcakes and jams. The two cosy little dining rooms have candles, dark beams, white walls, a fire in the adjoining bar. We enjoyed the *amuse-bouches* served with drinks, then voted the lobster bisque the soup of the millennium (one of us had a bowl of it for lunch the next day, sitting in the garden). Also excellent were loin of lamb; seafood brochette with fiery chilli couscous; Skye lobster with avocado and salad of organic leaves; roast wild mallard; marmalade pudding with Drambuie custard. The charming eldest son of the house is enthusiastic about wines. The whole atmosphere is one of folk taking pride and enjoyment in what they are doing, without pomp or ceremony. There's a wide choice of videos and books. The position on the edge of a sea loch ensures a huge variety of wildlife – seals galore, golden eagles, gulls, cormorants, etc. There are neat flowerbeds with pansies, and lush grass – no mean feat, as marauding sheep will gain entrance however many gates and walls you build." To reach the house you need to tackle a sheep grid and a gate; there is some traffic noise.

Open Feb–Dec.
Rooms 6 suites, all in separate building. Some on ground floor.
Facilities Ramps. Lounge, bar, breakfast room, restaurant. No background music. Garden on loch. Wedding facilities.
Location 5 miles W of Dunvegan, by B884 (single track road), on shore of Loch Dunvegan.
Restrictions Smoking in bar only. No dogs.

Credit cards Amex, MasterCard, Visa.
Terms B&B double £130–£155. Set lunch £18; full alc dinner £45. Child accommodated in parents' room: under 6, free. Autumn, winter breaks. Christmas, New Year packages.

CRINAN Argyll and Bute Map 5

Crinan Hotel NEW · *Tel* (0154) 683 0261
Crinan PA31 8SR · *Fax* (0154) 683 0292
E-mail nryan@crinanhotel.com
Website www.crinanhotel.com

In "one of the finest locations in Britain", this large white building by the sea has "stunning views" of Crinan village, its fishing boats, yachts and lighthouse, and across to Mull and Jura. It has been owned and run for 30 years by Nick and Frances Ryan (the artist Frances Macdonald) who are "delightful, eccentric hosts". What's more, Nick Ryan was in 1999 named hotelier of the year by *Caterer and Hotelkeeper*. "It is very comfortable, with superb food," wrote one *Guide* reader in 2000, while another added: "The position is marvellous. A genial Mr Ryan pottered about in his crumpled suit, and he seemed to set the atmosphere of the place." Bedrooms are simple; some are small (as are some bathrooms). They have good fabrics, pine furniture; nine have a private balcony. One, suitable for a family, has bunk beds. In the public rooms are lots of antiques and "exciting decor, with lovely paintings". The hotel was dropped from the *Guide* last year, when there were some reports of worn bedroom carpets, sub-standard bathrooms, erratic service and housekeeping. But Mr Ryan, who recently was ill, has been redecorating, and all visitors agree that the food is better than ever, under a new chef, Craig Wood: "He is young, enthusiastic and inventive." "The cooking has a real touch of class." Two restaurants: *Westward*, on the ground floor, serving fish, local beef and venison; and the pricier top-floor *Lock 16*, for seafood, where diners watch the sunset through picture windows as they eat very fresh fish (try the local mussels poulette; wild Scottish salmon; whole Jura lobster). The rooftop bar has a colonial-style decor. There is a public bar serving light lunches, and a coffee shop for snacks and teas with home-made cakes. Breakfasts have been found less perfect. The garden is featured in *The Good Gardens Guide*. There is good walking from the doorstep, along the canal and in woods noted for wildlife. (*Paul Jackson, Patricia Darby, MWB MacEacharn*)

Open All year, except Christmas.
Rooms 1 suite, 19 double.
Facilities Lift, ramp. 2 lounges, 3 bars, 2 restaurants. No background music. Garden. Safe, sandy beaches nearby; fishing. Boat trips. Wedding facilities.
Location In Lochgilphead, take A816 to Oban; left after 2 miles on to B841 to Crinan. Bus from Lochgilphead.
Restrictions No smoking: restaurants, bar at lunchtime. No dogs in restaurants.
Credit cards Amex, MasterCard, Visa.
Terms B&B £50–£85; D,B&B £65–£120. Breakfast £12.50. Bar lunches from £10. Set dinner: *Westward* £37.50, *Lock 16* £42.50. Winter rates.

DAIRSIE Fife   Map 5

Todhall House   BUDGET   *Tel* (01334) 656344
Dairsie   *Fax* (01334) 650791
by Cupar KY15 4RQ   *E-mail* todhallhouse@ukgateway.net
                                     Website www.scotland2000.com/todhall

Much liked again this year, John and Gill Donald's "exemplary guest
house", a handsome stone building, stands by a lily pond in its quiet
garden outside a village near St Andrews. "We are just a simple
B&B," they say modestly; but the house has fine furniture and some
good paintings, and gives "the feeling of a much-loved home".
Breakfast is "excellent" and elegantly served, with silver, crystal and
Spode china: "Delicious fruit compote, fresh strawberries, splendid
porridge, locally smoked haddock." A "good, straightforward"
evening meal, by arrangement, is prepared with a slant on local produce, eg, lemon sole with cream; casserole of venison; Scottish trifle.
"It was served with enthusiasm, in generous portions." No licence;
bring your own drink (no corkage charge). "All is immaculate,
delightful and welcoming. Our bedroom even had binoculars for looking at the lovely views." The dogs, Hanna and Bracken, "are as
friendly as their owners". There is a large selection of guidebooks,
maps, etc, in the lounge. Numerous golf courses are nearby; so are
National Trust of Scotland properties, such as Hill of Tarvit and Kellie
Castle and the East Neuk fishing villages, and there is good walking
on the coast and in the hills. (*AJM Ribeiro dos Santos, EC*)

Open Mar–end Oct.
Rooms 3 double. No telephone (pay-phone available).
Facilities Lounge, dining room. No background music. 2-acre garden. Beach
7 miles: safe bathing. Unsuitable for &.
Location Off A91, 2 miles NE of Cupar, ½ mile before Dairsie village. House
½ mile from main road; look for sign at road end. Train: Cupar/Leuchars; they
will meet.
Restrictions No smoking. No children under 12. No dogs.
Credit cards MasterCard, Visa.
Terms B&B £26–£43; D,B&B £44–£64. Set dinner (by arrangement)
£18–£25. (Bring your own wine/drinks.) 10% discount for 7-day stay. 1-night
bookings refused July/Aug.

DARVEL East Ayrshire   Map 5

Scoretulloch House   *Tel* (01560) 323331
Darvel KA17 0LR   *Fax* (01560) 323441
                                     E-mail mail@scoretulloch.com
                                     Website www.scoretulloch.com

"We've got rid of all our pompous, idiotic, arrogant chefs: Annie is
back, hurrah!" writes owner Donald Smith with bold marital loyalty:
after two recent changes, his wife is now again in charge of the cooking, "modern Scots and international". And our reports this year also
give applause, but qualified: good rack of lamb, but guinea fowl too
dry; vegetable plate "so tiny it was a joke", but "divine" orange
sponge, "delicious" pre-dinner canapés in the bar, and "best-ever"

scrambled eggs and smoked salmon at breakfast (the Smiths have their own smokery). In an area rich in wildlife and good local produce, they have built this long, single-storey building on the site of a 15th-century house, using some of its old stones. The land, on a hill with wide views over a grouse moor and the wooded valley of the River Irvine, was once owned by the Knights Templar. More than 100 different species of birds, from curlews to peregrine hawks, have been spotted nearby. The house is furnished with old furniture and family heirlooms, and the walls are hung with bird photographs taken by Mr Smith, who is a naturalist and wildlife photographer. Ornithological books abound, binoculars lie ready for sightings of rare birds, and the Smiths enjoy showing their guests the best places for watching. The half-panelled restaurant, with its huge picture window looking towards Loudoun Hill, has been admired: "Tables are well spaced and smartly set, with a candle and flowers; service is by nice local women." Soft light classical music is played during lunch and dinner. "Mr Smith is proud of his wine list, but he can make mistakes." There is also a new brasserie. Bedrooms have been complimented for their comfort, but some are small. The Smiths are pet-lovers and their three dogs are much in evidence. A "lazy cat" presides over the bar. "A find. We loved the cats, dogs and ambience; we felt at ease; we will return," said a visitor in 2000. (*Simon Willbourn, and others*)

Open All year, except Boxing Day, New Year's Day.
Rooms 1 suite, 7 double. 4 in stable block. All on ground floor.
Facilities Ramp. Lounge, lounge bar, brasserie, restaurant. Soft light classical/Scottish background music in evening. 5-acre garden. Fishing, golf, shooting nearby. Wedding facilities.
Location 2 miles E of Darvel. Turn off A71; follow signs.
Restrictions Smoking in smoking lounge only. "Well-behaved children and dogs are welcomed", but no dogs in public rooms.
Credit cards All major cards accepted.
Terms B&B: single £75, double £110, suite £125. Set lunch £18.50, dinner £29.95; full alc (brasserie) £25. Weekend breaks. *V*

DERVAIG Argyll and Bute   **Map 5**

Druimard Country House   *Tel* (01688) 400291 and 400345
Dervaig, nr Tobermory   *Fax* (01688) 400345
Isle of Mull PA75 6QW   *Website* www.smoothhound.co.uk/hotels/druimard

A "magical drive" through a long, quiet glen leads to this mellow Victorian house, set on a hill just outside a pretty stone-built village in the north of the island. It has views over open countryside and the marshy estuary at the mouth of the Bellart River to the hills beyond, and it makes a good base for enjoying the Mull's castles, walking and wildlife. Most reports this year have found the owners, Haydn and Wendy Hubbard, "friendly and eager to please, without being intrusive"; "they create an atmosphere of peace". But one dissenter thought the service "offhand". The bedrooms are warm and comfortable, with knick-knacks, fruit, mineral water, ample closet space. Some are large, others rather small; most have a shower rather than a bath. "The lounge has comfy seating; books, personal photos and memorabilia give the feel of being in a private home." There's a small conservatory/bar presided over by Mr Hubbard. The five-course set dinner, cooked by Mrs Hubbard (no choice until dessert), is "outstanding, each course a visual and tasty delight", though portions are over-large for some. "An excellent dill and salmon quiche starter; mouth-watering home-made soups and bread; we also enjoyed fish medley with courgettes and mashed potato, crab mousse, moist guinea fowl, great puds – sticky toffee pudding, apple bramble crumble. Breakfasts were equally good, including home-made muesli; we particularly commend the Drambuie porridge." "Responsibly behaved" children are welcomed, and they can have high tea at 5.30. A converted cow byre in the grounds houses the world's smallest professional theatre, the 43-seat Mull Little Theatre, which plays from April to October. Pre-theatre meals are served on performance nights. Good for walking; *Druimard* has ample drying facilities. Calgary beach, a wide expanse of white sand, is close by; boat trips can be arranged to see minke whales, puffins on Lunga, and Fingal's Cave on Staffa. Tobermory, the capital of Mull, is eight miles away. (*Mrs Shirley Tennent, Mr and Mrs GA Lilley, A Gradon, and others*)

Open April–end Oct. Restaurant closed midday (snack meals available for residents), to non-residents Sun evening.
Rooms 7 double. Some on ground floor.
Facilities Ramp. Lounge, conservatory/bar, restaurant (classical background music at night). 1-acre grounds: theatre. Golf, beaches, fishing (ghillie available) nearby.
Location From Craignure ferry, A849 W through Salen. Left to Dervaig after 1½ miles. Hotel on right before village.
Restrictions Smoking banned in restaurant, discouraged in bedrooms. No dogs in public rooms.
Credit cards MasterCard, Visa.
Terms D,B&B £60–£85. Set dinner £29.50. Child accommodated in parents' room: under 14, £20.

DOUNE Perth and Kinross   **Map 5**

Mackeanston House   NEW   *Tel* (01786) 850213
                                                 Fax (01786) 850414
                                    E-mail mackean.house@cwcom.net
                         Website www.aboutscotland.com/stirling/mackeanston

Amid the lochs and mountains of the Trossachs ("Braveheart and Rob Roy country"), this Wolsey Lodge is the family home of Colin and Fiona Graham. He belongs to a port-importing family, and will play the bagpipes before dinner. "She is an excellent chef," says the nominator, "and she thinks of everything a guest might want." Both are "very knowledgeable about wine". Their two small boys, Rory and Neil, and two energetic spaniels, Winnie and Jennie Wren, "are always pleased to see visiting children". Two bedrooms are in the main house; they have antique furniture, and watercolours painted by members of the family. Two more rooms are in a modern bungalow about 400 yards away, which can be let on a self-catering basis. No separate lounge for guests; but there is a large conservatory/dining

room. Home-cooked meals use free-range eggs, local smoked fish,
fresh vegetables from the garden, home-made bread and preserves.
"The location is a bit unusual, near to a farmyard turned transport
yard, but this does not de-
tract in any way. The house
is up a separate drive, and is
very nice, and well main-
tained." Doune, a small,
winding village, has one
of Scotland's best-preserved
medieval castle ruins, and a
motor museum that houses the
second-oldest Rolls-Royce in
the world.

Open All year, except Christmas.
Rooms 4 double. 2 on ground floor. 2 in cottage (can be self-catering).
Facilities Conservatory dining/sitting room. 1-acre garden: tennis. Fishing in
River Teith nearby.
Location From M9 Stirling–Perth, take exit 10 to A84. After 5 miles, B826 to
Thornhill; after 2 miles, take driveway on left. Right at end of farm road.
Restrictions No smoking. No dogs in public rooms.
Credit cards MasterCard, Visa.
Terms B&B £35; D,B&B £57.

DULNAIN BRIDGE Highland   Map 5

Auchendean Lodge   *Tel/Fax* (01479) 851347
Dulnain Bridge   *E-mail* hotel@auchendean.com
Grantown-on-Spey PH26 3LU   *Website* www.auchendean.com

"This wonderful place" (praise again this year) is a white Edwardian
hunting lodge on a hillside in the Cairngorms, with splendid views
over the Spey valley. It is run as an informal guest house by Ian Kirk
and his partner Eric Hart, who is chef and will take guests on forays
for wild mushrooms (they feature often on his menus, and he has a
growing reputation as a mycologist). The place may not suit all comers: some bedrooms are small, with "overpoweringly large" pictures
and heavy furniture (but beds are "properly made" with good linen,
and all the rooms have facilities *en suite*); some of the knick-knacks
which cram the public rooms are "of a most unusual kind". But admirers think that the decor "falls just the right side of kitsch", and they
enjoy the "peace, the comfort and the gastronomic delights", which
make much use of local produce: vegetables are home grown (there
are 26 varieties of potatoes). As well as mushroom-based fare (eg,
wild chanterelle and walnut soup), you might find dishes such as mallard in port sauce; wild hare with juniper cream; Cranachan. The set-
price menus vary daily. There is an "impressive" wine list. Ian Kirk,
kilted in the evening, serves drinks and takes dinner orders in the bar
– "he has a very nice, professional manner." Guests are introduced and
chit-chat is encouraged; "sociable evenings with spontaneous piano-
playing" can develop. Behind the house is a wooded hill with excellent walking, wild flowers, plenty of wildlife. A border collie, Jock,

will go for walks with guests; three cats and a goose patrol the garden. Breakfast is a "tour de force", with home-made marmalade and jams, honey from the garden and free-range eggs. Dogs are welcomed. (*Dr K Langford, and others*)

Open All year. Restaurant closed midday.
Rooms 5 double, 2 single. No telephone.
Facilities 2 lounges, restaurant. No background music. 2-acre garden: putting. 200-acre woodland adjacent; river 300 yds, fishing. Golf, skiing, water sports, shooting nearby. Only restaurant suitable for &.
Location 1 mile S of Dulnain Bridge, on A95 to Aviemore (some rooms might get slight traffic noise). Train/bus: Aviemore, 10 miles; then taxi.
Restrictions No smoking: restaurant, 1 lounge. Dogs in bedrooms and 1 lounge only.
Credit cards All major cards accepted.
Terms B&B £35.50–£51; D,B&B £61.50–£71. Picnic lunches by arrangement. Set dinner £27. Discounts for 3 days or more. Christmas package.

Muckrach Lodge	*Tel* (01479) 851257
Dulnain Bridge	*Fax* (01479) 851325
Grantown-on-Spey PH26 3LY	*E-mail* muckrach.lodge@sol.co.uk
	Website www.muckrach.co.uk

This former Victorian sporting lodge (its name means "haunt of the wild boar" in Gaelic) stands amid the woods and farms of the Muckrach estate with its 16th-century castle. It looks across the Spey valley to the Cairngorms, and it stands in its own large grounds with landscaped gardens, a duck pond and Highland cattle. The owners, James and Dawn Macfarlane, bought the hotel in 1996 and have busily renovated. They cater for sporting holidays of all sorts: salmon-fishing on the Spey, deer-stalking, grouse- and pheasant-shooting, etc. They also court business guests. But other visitors, too, have praised the welcome (with tea and biscuits), the smiling hosts, pleasant staff and peaceful atmosphere. Wood fires burn in the public rooms, and the bedrooms and bathrooms are attractive. In the conservatory-style restaurant, the food, "modern Scottish with continental influences", has been admired too: there's a new chef this year, Alistair McGrath, so we'd welcome further reports. Main dishes might include tournedos of local beef, or roast breast and confit leg of guinea fowl. A good base for touring the Highlands. Inverness airport is 30 miles away. (*S and JS, and others*)

Open All year, except Christmas.
Rooms 2 suites (1 equipped for &), 9 double, 2 single. 4 in coach house.
Facilities Ramps. Drawing room, bar/brasserie (taped jazz/classical background music), dining room, conservatory restaurant; conference/function facilities. 10-acre grounds: garden, duck pond. River, fishing, shooting, skiing, walking, etc, nearby. Wedding facilities.
Location 3 miles SW of Grantown-on-Spey. On A938 Dulnain Bridge–Carrbridge. Train: Aviemore or Carrbridge; then bus.
Restrictions Smoking banned in restaurants, discouraged in bedrooms. No dogs in public rooms.
Credit cards All major cards accepted.
Terms B&B £25–£65. Set dinner £27.50. Child accommodated in parents' room: under 12, free. New Year package. Off-peak breaks. *V*

DUNDEE *See SHORTLIST*   **Map 5**

DUNKELD Perth and Kinross   **Map 5**

Kinnaird   *Tel* (01796) 482440
Kinnaird Estate   *Fax* (01796) 482289
by Dunkeld PH8 0LB   *E-mail* enquiry@kinnairdestate.demon.co.uk
                               Website www.kinnairdestate.com

"An exceptional hotel" (Relais & Châteaux) runs this year's praise for
this handsome creeper-covered 18th-century Grade B listed house. It
stands in its 9,000-acre estate in the heart of Perthshire; the River Tay,
one of Scotland's best fishing rivers, flows through the grounds. The
owner, Constance Ward, and many of her guests, are American: "A
beguiling blend of luxurious small hotel and welcoming home," wrote
one. The public rooms are much as they would have been 80 years
ago, when the then dower house to Blair Castle was filled with house
parties. They have family portraits, a grand piano with sheet music,
antiques and flowers, billiards, backgammon and bridge, and "perpet-
ually burning fires". The bedrooms, each with a gas log fire, are luxurious; most are large, with a view of the valley. "A superb staff,
enormous for the size of the place; they do everything exactly right,
without the slightest whiff of pretension or visible effort, somehow
striking the balance between polished assurance and natural, unstud-
ied warmth." The manager, Douglas Jack, "is a treasure". A jacket and
tie are expected of male diners in the chandeliered and frescoed restaurant, and the meals cooked by Trevor Brooks might include pressed
layers of foie gras and guinea fowl confit with caramelised pear; roast
rabbit with salsify, gnocchi and a parsley and mustard jus; hot apple
tart with vanilla ice-cream. The wine list is comprehensive, with many
half bottles. Guests may fish for salmon in the Tay and for trout in
Kinnaird's lochs, and many other activities are available on the estate
(see below). (*Margaret Watson, and others*)

Open All year. Thurs–Sun only, 1 Jan–1 Mar.
Rooms 1 suite, 8 double, 1 on ground floor. Also 7 holiday cottages.
Facilities Lift, ramps. Drawing room, morning room, study, billiard room,
2 dining rooms; function facilities. No background music. 9,000-acre estate:
gardens, bowling lawn, tennis, croquet, shooting, walking, birdwatching,
salmon-fishing on River Tay. 3 trout lochs. Riding, golf, clay-pigeon shooting
nearby. Wedding facilities.
Location NW of Dunkeld. From A9 Perth–Pitlochry, left on to B898
Dalguise–Balnaguard 2 miles after Dunkeld. *Kinnaird* 4½ miles on right.
Restrictions No smoking in dining rooms. No children under 12. Dogs by
arrangement; not in house (kennels available).
Credit cards Amex, MasterCard, Visa.
Terms D,B&B double £195–£275. Packed lunch available. Set lunch £30,
dinner £45.

When you nominate a hotel, please, if possible, send us its
brochure.

DUNOON Argyll and Bute   Map 5

The Enmore   NEW/BUDGET   *Tel* (01369) 702230
Marine Parade, Kirn   *Fax* (01369) 702148
Dunoon PA23 8HH   *E-mail* enmorehotel@btinternet.com
                                   Website www.enmorehotel.co.uk

"Pleasant and well maintained," says an inspector, restoring this small
hotel/guest house to the *Guide*. It stands across a road from the
seafront of a town once much frequented by American service per-
sonnel from Holy Loch, now rather run-down. Recently upgraded and
redecorated, this is very much a family affair, run by an exuberant
hostess, Angela Wilson, with her "very nice, quietly spoken" husband
David (he is the cook) and their two teenage children. A convivial
atmosphere is encouraged, with guests being introduced, chatting in
the lounge and dining room, etc. The set menu has limited choice, "but
they will vary it according to your appetite". "The house is pretty, with
a cared-for front garden. There is a lovely, large drawing room with
nice pictures and a big log fire. Our bedroom was charming, light and
bright, with much yellow, fresh flowers and a nice, bright bathroom."
But one room is said to be noisy because of the kitchen below. Some
visitors have thought the food "very tasty", but both dinner and breakfast came in for some criticism this year, and dinners were thought
overpriced. This idiosyncratic place owns the only squash courts in
this part of Argyll (with video-replay facilities). Children and dogs are
welcomed.

Open Mid-Feb–mid-Dec.
Rooms 1 suite, 8 double, 1 single.
Facilities Lounge, bar, dining room (background CDs as required); meeting
rooms. Squash court. 1½-acre garden. Shingle beach opposite. Unsuitable
for &.
Location Seafront. 1 mile from centre.
Restriction No smoking in dining room.
Credit cards Amex, MasterCard, Visa.
Terms B&B: single £35–£59, double £50–£75, suite £100–£150; D,B&B:
single £60–£84, double £100–£125, suite £150–£200. Set lunch £10–£15, din-
ner £25; full alc £28. *V*

EDINBURGH   Map 5

The Bonham   *Tel* (0131) 226 6050
25 Drumsheugh Gardens   *Fax* (0131) 226 6080
Edinburgh EH3 7RN   *E-mail* reserve@thebonham.com
                                      Website www.thebonham.com

"Highly recommended, posh and chic, with fancy prices", this was
voted "one of the world's coolest hotels" by Condé Nast's *Traveller*
in late 1999. Owned by Peter Taylor (he also owns *The Howard* [*qv*]
in Edinburgh New Town), and managed by Fiona Vernon, it is made
up of two Victorian buildings on a quiet square. Earlier it was a
maternity hospital, then a university residence. It is geared to the business trade, with "pioneering communications technology" in all the

bedrooms. Our reporter was enthusiastic: "A gorgeous building in a great West End location, quite near Princes Street." Some of the spacious bedrooms have a huge bay window looking across town to the Firth of Forth. All are different, with a "plush and designerish" decor. One room has black bedspreads, gold cushions, lots of polished dark wood; in another there is a burgundy carpet and blue chairs. One suite has a huge sitting room with 12-foot-high ceiling, a neo-Adam chimney piece and an Arts and Crafts-style cabinet concealing the TV and mini-bar. Paintings by young Scottish artists hang throughout the building. The restaurant, which is open to the public, serves "Californian-inspired" food by Pelham Hill, eg, sauté of wild mushrooms in tarragon and basil; baked guinea fowl with sweetcorn fritters; celeriac and leek crumble; Black Forest cheesecake. (*GR, BL*)

Open All year, except Christmas (when restaurant is open for lunch).
Rooms 2 suites, 36 double, 10 single.
Facilities Lift, ramps. Reception/lounge, restaurant (modern jazz during meals).
Location West End, 5 mins' walk from Princes Street, ½ mile from station. Street parking. Bus from centre.
Restriction No smoking: lounge, bedrooms. Guide dogs only.
Credit cards All major cards accepted.
Terms B&B: single £135–£165, double £155–£225, suite £295. Full alc £34. Various breaks. ***V***

The Howard   *Tel* (0131) 557 3500
34 Great King Street   *Fax* (0131) 557 6515
Edinburgh EH3 6QH   *E-mail* reserve@thehoward.com
                                          Website www.thehoward.com

Three well-restored Georgian houses now form this stylish and rather formal little hotel, owned by Peter Taylor (his Town House Company also includes *The Bonham*, see above, and *Channings*, see Shortlist). It stands on a cobbled New Town street, with some traffic by day but quiet at night. The chintzy public rooms have brocade curtains, antiques and oil paintings; period bakelite telephones are in the bedrooms; baths are roll-top. Drinks and tea are served by an open fire in the drawing room, under a huge chandelier. In the basement, the fashionable *36* restaurant, by contrast, has contemporary design (but one critic thought its background music "gruesome"). Here chef Malcolm Warham's cooking is generally found "excellent", though there is a report of a disappointing meal this year. His cooking is modern and complex, eg, terrine of confit rabbit with cucumber and red onion piccalilli; roast guinea fowl filled with black pudding and smoked bacon; salmon with goat's cheese and pesto ravioli; pecan and Florentine fudge tart. The bedrooms are called by old Edinburgh street names (Abercrombie, Charlotte, etc). Many are spacious, and the single rooms are unusually attractive. "An exceptionally friendly staff, and a most comfortable ambience," wrote a recent visitor. "Breakfast, in a pretty room with painted panels, was relaxed and enjoyable." (*MT*)

Open All year, except Christmas (restaurant open for lunch).
Rooms 2 suites, 11 double, 2 single. 1 on ground floor.

Facilities Lift. Drawing room (classical background music), bar, restaurant; meeting room. 24-hour room service.
Location New Town, 10 mins' walk from Princes Street. Private carpark. Bus from centre.
Restriction No smoking: restaurant, bedrooms. Guide dogs only.
Credit cards All major cards accepted.
Terms B&B: single £135–£165, double £245–£275, suite £325. Set lunch £17; full alc £37. Various breaks. *V*

Saxe Coburg House NEW	*Tel* (0131) 332 2717
24 Saxe Coburg Place	*Fax* (0131) 315 3375
Edinburgh EH3 5BP	*E-mail* birrell@zetnet.co.uk
	Website www.saxe-coburg-house.co.uk

In a quiet setting near the cafés and restaurants of the "bohemian village setting" of Stockbridge, this Georgian house is the home of the Scottish writers George Birrell and Gillian Glover (he a historian of Scotland, she a restaurant critic). They run it as a select B&B, much liked this year: "A larger room, a larger bathroom, a bigger breakfast than I had in a much more expensive city-centre hotel on a previous visit. It didn't feel like a B&B (one didn't mind having the owners' cat invade the bedroom)." Children are welcomed. The centre is reached by "one of the finest architectural walks in Europe". In the bedrooms are TV, bathrobes, quality Egyptian linen. There is a drawing room in period style. Courses on Scottish history, literature and cooking are held, and golf and leisure tours of Scotland can be arranged. (*Nicholas Penny; also Michael Crick*)

Open All year, except Christmas, several weeks Jan.
Rooms 1 family suite, 3 double, 1 single.
Facilities Drawing room, breakfast room. Unsuitable for ♿.
Location Stockbridge: 15 mins' walk, or bus/taxi to centre.
Restrictions No smoking. No pets.
Credit cards Amex, MasterCard, Visa.
Terms B&B: single £40–£50, double £75–£98, suite £95–£120. *V*

---

7 Danube Street	*Tel* (0131) 332 2755
7 Danube Street	*Fax* (0131) 343 3648
Edinburgh EH4 1NN	*E-mail* seven.danubestreet@virgin.net
	Website www.aboutedinburgh.com/danube

"A splendid place to stay. Fiona Mitchell-Rose is a delight – relaxed, amusing and thoughtful. And George her pug is cute. My room had so many touches lacking in chain hotels, with classy toiletries in the bathroom. And breakfast was refreshingly original, with compotes and sourdough bread." "Friendly and informal. Our room had a kingsize four-poster bed, garden view, every knick-knack." More praise this year for this "excellent B&B" in a typical New Town Georgian house in the Stockbridge area. It is owned by Mrs Mitchell-Rose and her "charming husband" Colin. It has a beautiful cupolated staircase, and plenty of evidence that it is a family home – skis and dogs' cushions in the hallway; inherited pictures and furniture, "all in excellent taste". The guest bedrooms are on the lower floor. All are well supplied with extras; beds have an electric blanket. Spick-and-span bathrooms have a power shower, "lush Egyptian cotton bathtowels", and various toiletries – even dental floss. Breakfast, served at one large table, includes home-made bread and jam, freshly squeezed juice, fresh fruit salad, and cooked dishes if required. Danube Street is a curved cobbled street, "a quiet backwater away from the city noise", yet within walking distance of Princes Street. (*John and Helen Disley, Stephen Duckworth, and others*)

Open All year, except Christmas.
Rooms 2 double, 1 single. Also 1 self-catering flat for 4–6 people, 50 yds.
Facilities Breakfast room. No background music. Small garden. Unsuitable for &.
Location About 1 mile from Waverley Station/city centre. Meter parking in street.
Restriction No smoking.
Credit cards MasterCard, Visa.
Terms B&B: single £50–£60, double £90–£110. Reductions for long stays. *V*

Sibbet House
26 Northumberland Street
Edinburgh EH3 6LS

Tel (0131) 556 1078
Fax (0131) 557 9445
E-mail sibbet.house@zetnet.co.uk
Website www.sibbet-house.co.uk

This was the first of the upmarket B&Bs in classic Georgian New Town houses. It has been lavishly and meticulously furnished by the owners, Jim and Aurore Sibbet – they have resumed day-to-day management. They recently increased the number of bedrooms with the acquisition of the house next door. The bedrooms are large; some are up two flights of stairs. The suite downstairs has its own kitchen, a conservatory dining room draped with a luxuriant vine, a large dressing area, good lighting, and the use of a garage and a washing machine. A "quiet and spacious" sitting room with a bar is available for guests. "Brilliant breakfasts" include an unusual selection of cooked dishes, eg, frittatas, apple and sultana quiche, French toast and omelettes. Jim Sibbet will play his bagpipes when asked. More reports, please.

Open All year except Christmas period.
Rooms 1 suite, 6 double, 1 single.
Facilities Lounge with bar, breakfast room.
Location Within walking distance of Princes St and Waverley Station. Private parking.
Restrictions No smoking. No babies. No dogs.
Credit cards MasterCard, Visa.
Terms B&B: single £50–£55, double £90–£110, suite £110-£130. Discounts negotiable for long stays. 1-night bookings sometimes refused July, Aug.

The second volume of the *Guide*, containing nearly 1,000 continental hotels, will be published early in 2001. Deadline for reports on continental hotels: 30 September 2000; for new nominations: 14 September 2000.

24 Northumberland Street   *Tel* (0131) 556 8140
24 Northumberland Street   *Fax* (0131) 556 4423
Edinburgh EH3 6LS   *E-mail* ingram@ednet.co.uk
                                        Website www.ingrams.co.uk

"A treat. The house is spacious, beautifully cared for, and within easy
reach of the tourist sights, but peacefully located. The owners were
charming and helpful, yet unobtrusive." "We spent two fantastic
evenings with David and Theresa Ingram. He is idiosyncratically
delightful; she is full of energy. Breakfast is superb" (with scrambled
eggs and fresh fruit salad), and "attentively served", in a large room
with fine antiques. This classic New Town house, with its four storeys
leading off a stone staircase lit by an oval cupola, is "a gem of ver-
nacular architecture". The goatee-bearded owner, who is also an
antique dealer, is "extraordinarily generous in sharing his erudition on
innumerable topics" and the house "is in perfect order, and furnished
in keeping with its age". The bedrooms have TV and an eclectic selection of books; bathrooms have lashings of fast-running hot water. Two
cats: Ginny, a handsome marmalade, is friendly; Ben (aged 16) is
more standoffish. Restaurants of all kinds are nearby. (*Julie Kellie,
Robert Musante; also Robin and Anne Sharp*)

Open All year, except Christmas.
Rooms 3 double.
Facilities Sitting room, breakfast room (Baroque background music).
Unsuitable for &.
Location In New Town, 5 mins' walk from centre. Private parking.
Restrictions No smoking. Preferably no children under 15. No dogs.
Credit cards Diners, MasterCard, Visa.
Terms [2000] B&B: single £50, double £80.

Windmill House   NEW   *Tel/Fax* (0131) 346 0024
Coltbridge Gardens   *E-mail* info@hoppo.com
Edinburgh EH12 6AQ   *Website* www.windmillhouse.co.uk

A "large, beautifully appointed house", furnished with antiques and set
in a quiet, wooded river valley, but within sight of Edinburgh Castle, a
mile away. "We treat our guests as friends," say the owners, Vivien and
Mike Scott. And the American nominator wrote: "It feels like coming
home. The Scotts attend to every request with a smile. The grounds are
beautiful, with views of the Pentland Hills." The spacious bedrooms
have a sitting area, TV and video, complimentary sherry, nuts, tea and
coffee. The suite is in an old windmill, and there is also a self-catering
cottage. Fires burn in the lounge, and in the room where breakfast is
served (in fine weather it can be taken on a terrace). (*Grace Pollak*)

Open All year, except Christmas/New Year.
Rooms 1 suite in old windmill, 3 double. Also self-catering cottage. No tele-
phone.
Facilities Drawing room, breakfast room. terrace. No background music. 2-
acre garden, riverside walks. Unsuitable for &.
Location 1 mile from centre. From Murrayfield Ave, turn into Coltbridge
Ave, leading to Coltbridge Gdns. Go to end of road; fork left up drive, left
through stone gate pillars. Bus from centre.

Restrictions No smoking: breakfast room, bedrooms. No dogs.
Credit card Visa.
Terms [2000] B&B: double £85–£100, suite £120–£140. Child accommodated in parents' room: £25. *V*

See also SHORTLIST

ERISKA Argyll and Bute   **Map 5**

Isle of Eriska   *Tel* (01631) 720371
Ledaig   *Fax* (01631) 720531
by Oban PA37 1SD   *E-mail* office@eriska-hotel
                                    Website www.eriska-hotel.co.uk

"This hideaway hotel is about as good as it gets: efficient, friendly staff, quality fabrics and furniture, super cuisine, good facilities, superb setting." More admiration for this baronial mansion amid trees, set on a tiny private island linked to the mainland by a wrought iron bridge. Built in 1884, it was turned into a hotel by Robin and Sheena Buchanan-Smith 26 years ago. It is now run by their "energetic" son Beppo, attended by two golden labradors. The panelled public rooms are "comfortable, rather than smart", furnished with old-fashioned chintzes, leather chairs and standard lamps. "The aura of wood smoke from the log fire in the hall instils a homely feeling." There is a collection of malt whiskies in the library, and a piano, which visitors may play, in the bay-windowed drawing room. Each bedroom is named for a Hebridean island: some are large and light, with a huge bathroom, but others are small. Breakfasts are "substantial" and dinners are a "wonderful seven-course affair" – the menu is shown to guests during afternoon tea (which is free). Robert MacPherson's elaborate cooking is "traditional Scottish", elegantly served with good crystal and silver. The menus include, eg, wild rabbit and courgette timbale with Bresse pigeon; poached home-smoked cod on a wild herb salad; guinea fowl with a gâteau of artichokes and mushrooms. Male guests are requested to wear jacket and tie at dinner. There is family accommodation, and high tea for children under ten. Wildlife abounds, including otters, seals, herons and deer; tame badgers come to the library door for their supper of bread and milk. The sporting facilities include a leisure centre with an "excellent" 17-foot swimming pool; also an all-weather tennis court, and a "challenging" nine-hole golf course. On booking, prospective guests are asked to pay a non-returnable deposit of £50 per person. Oban, Mull, Iona and Inverary can be visited easily from here. (*M and MH, and others*)

Open All year, except Jan.
Rooms 16 double, 1 single. 2 on ground floor.
Facilities 2 drawing rooms, bar/library, dining room; leisure centre: indoor, heated swimming pool, gym, sauna, games room. No background music. 300-acre island: tennis, croquet, golf, water sports, riding, clay-pigeon shooting. Wedding facilities.
Location 12 miles N of Oban. 4 miles W of A828. Train: Connel Ferry, 6 miles.

Restrictions No smoking in dining room. No children under 5 in swimming pool, under 15 in gym. No children under 10 at dinner. No dogs in public rooms.
Credit cards Amex, MasterCard, Visa.
Terms [2000] (Min. 2 nights) B&B: single £175, double £210–£260. Set dinner £37.50. Weekly rates. Off-season breaks; Christmas package.

FORSS Highland   Map 5

Forss House   *Tel* (01847) 861201
Forss, by Thurso KW14 7XY   *Fax* (01847) 861301
                                            E-mail Jamie@freeserve.co.uk

"A delightful hotel. Jamie MacGregor is the perfect host – always solicitous of guests' interests and wants. His stock of over 200 malt whiskies should not be overlooked, and he dispenses these eagerly and with great knowledge." A tribute this year to James and Jacqueline MacGregor's Grade II listed house by the River Forss. There is a waterfall and a mill, and plenty of wildlife (sea birds, buzzards, foxes and otters) in the large wooded grounds (though the previously recommended walk along the river to a ruined kirk on a rocky beach was too overgrown this year). The building, dating from 1810, is austere, with tall chimneys and crenellations, but inside it is full of "homely comfort", and the "relaxed environment" is admired. The owners add "a lot of little things that count: a sandwich and soup lunch when we didn't feel up to a long day out – which didn't appear on the bill – a late-night dram, etc". There are open fires in the panelled lounge and bar. The dining room is smart and light, with a green decor and a carved Adam-style fireplace, but reports on the food are mixed. Some visitors have written of heavy sauces, overcooked vegetables and tasteless fish, but a specially ordered lobster starter was "delicious", and grilled venison steaks were enjoyed. The simpler dishes on the long menu are generally thought to be the best. Snacks are available to residents, as an alternative to "the full blow-out". An "average" breakfast ("packet orange juice and plastic toast") is served in a conservatory overlooking the garden. The bedrooms and bathrooms are commended for comfort and spaciousness. Some rooms are in "sportsmen's lodges" in the grounds (sound-proofing may not be perfect). Many of *Forss House*'s guests are there for the fishing (salmon and trout) – "this is a paradise for anglers". Ghillies and tuition are available, and there are a drying room, freezing facilities, etc. Children are welcomed; cots, high chairs, baby-listening and an early supper are provided. Dounreay nuclear plant is two miles away. (*Mr JK Lunn, Dr K Langford, Colin Pearson, Moira and John Cole, R Gower*)

Open 6 Jan–23 Dec.
Rooms 1 suite, 9 double. 1 equipped for &. 5 in lodges in the grounds.
Facilities Reception, lounge, cocktail bar, restaurant, conservatory. No background music. 25-acre grounds: river, rookery, woodlands. Beaches, fishing, walking, birdwatching, seals nearby. Wedding facilities.
Location 5 miles W of Thurso on A836. Train: Thurso. Air: Wick.
Restrictions No smoking: restaurant, conservatory. Dogs by arrangement; not in public rooms.

Credit cards Amex, MasterCard, Visa.
Terms B&B: single £54.50, double £90, suite £110; D,B&B £66.50–£76.50 per person. Set dinner £21.50. Fishing packages.

FORT WILLIAM Highland   Map 5

Ashburn House   BUDGET   *Tel* (01397) 706000
Achintore Road   *Fax* (01397) 702024
Fort William PH33 6RQ   *E-mail* ashburn.house@tinyworld.co.uk
                               Website www.scotland2000.com/ashburn

Close to the shore of Loch Linnhe, looking across to the Ardgour Hills, this Victorian house was once the home of the town's sheriff – the castellated tower, now used as a fire escape, may have been added for his benefit. The owners, local couple Allan and Sandra Henderson, "are warmly welcoming", say all visitors. "We felt pampered." The complimentary tea on arrival, and the servicing of bedrooms at night, are appreciated. The large conservatory lounge with loch views is "a pleasant place for relaxing". Two bedrooms are on the ground floor; the others are reached by a barley-twist pine staircase. The four double rooms all now have a "super-kingsize" bed ("to suit American tastes"). Breakfast, served in a room that also looks over the loch, includes fruit, yogurt, a Highland grill, and "heavenly" Aga-baked scones. The house has a musical theme: it is filled with musical instruments; menus are decorated with quavers; soft traditional Highland music is played in the breakfast room much of the day (one visitor was not too keen on this), and the three children who still live at home can sometimes be heard practising on their instruments. The other four children, also musicians, are away at college. A good selection of eating places is nearby, also Ben Nevis and the West Highland Museum (with Jacobite artefacts). The Hendersons can arrange private tours of the Highlands, Inverness and Skye. (*VN, Simon Willbourn*)

Open Mar–14 Dec.
Rooms 4 double, 3 single. 2 on ground floor.
Facilities Conservatory/lounge, breakfast room (soft traditional Highland music all day). ¾-acre garden: stream. Yachting, fishing, cruising nearby.
Location 10 mins' walk from centre. 450 yds after entering 30 mph zone (A82 south). Train, bus stations nearby. Private parking.
Restrictions No smoking. Guide dogs only.
Credit cards Amex, MasterCard, Visa.
Terms B&B £30–£45. Reductions for weekly stays.

Crolinnhe   *Tel* (01397) 702709
Grange Road   *Fax* (01397) 700506
Fort William PH33 6JF   *E-mail* crolinnhe@yahoo.com

Half a mile from the town centre, this white Victorian villa, now a B&B, stands on a hillside in a quiet district, with a pleasant garden in front. The name is Gaelic for "above the Linnhe", and the terrace and most bedrooms have a "gorgeous view" over the loch to the north-western Highlands. The guests' lounge has potted plants and an open fire. "Flora Mackenzie is the most accommodating of hostesses," runs a recent report. "Our room and bathroom were lovely, spotless and well equipped." Breakfast "is very good, especially the haggis". Or you can choose Mallaig kippers, or a fresh fruit platter with yogurt. Fort William, at the foot of Ben Nevis, is a major tourist centre for the Highlands; there are many outdoor activities in the countryside around. More reports, please.

Open Easter–31 Oct.
Rooms 3 double, 1 with spa bath. No telephone.
Facilities Lounge, breakfast room (background radio). 1-acre grounds. Loch 200 yds. Unsuitable for &.
Location 10 mins' walk from centre. From roundabout at W end of dual carriageway, turn up Lundavra Rd; fork right into Grange Rd. Private parking. Station ½ mile.
Restrictions No smoking. No children under 12. No dogs.
Credit cards Accepted for reservation purposes only.
Terms B&B £38–£60.

The Grange   *Tel* (01397) 705516
Grange Road   *Fax* (01397) 701595
Fort William PH33 6JF

"Our hosts were most courteous; they took great trouble over little details, eg, the times of the Skye ferry. The elegance of this B&B manifested itself in many ways." A report this year on Joan and John Campbell's white-painted and bay-windowed late-Victorian house. It stands above sloping grounds with statuary, looking down to Loch Linnhe. The town centre is a short walk away. Breakfast, ordered the night before from an extensive menu, is served on "beautiful glass-topped tables" and it includes fruit compote, Mallaig kippers and haggis. There are fresh flowers and sherry in the "tastefully furnished" bedrooms; they look over the garden and the loch. The Garden Room is the most peaceful; Rob Roy, which has a colonial-style bed and a spacious bathroom, is named in honour of Jessica Lange, who stayed here during the filming of *Rob Roy*. The Terrace Room (the best) has its own terrace leading on to the gardens. There is "a cheerful log fire in the cosy lounge", and hand-crafted walking sticks are for sale – "a bargain at £3". No dinners, but *Crannog*, "fantastic fish in a casual, friendly ambience", is recommended. Or you could try *Inverlochy Castle* (see below) five miles away. (*John and Helen Disley*)

Open Mar–Nov.
Rooms 4 double. 1 on ground floor. No telephone.
Facilities Lounge, breakfast room (classical background music). ¾-acre garden. Sea loch 100 yds. Unsuitable for &.
Location 10 mins' walk from centre. From High St take A82 towards Glasgow. Left into Ashburn Lane; *Grange* at top on left. Private parking. Station ½ mile.
Restrictions No smoking. No children under 12. No dogs.
Credit cards MasterCard, Visa (to guarantee booking, not for payment).
Terms B&B £38–£96. Reductions in late Oct.

All our inspections are carried out anonymously.

Inverlochy Castle   *Tel* (01397) 702177
Torlundy   *Fax* (01397) 702953
Fort William PH33 6SN   *E-mail* info@inverlochy.co.uk
                                            Website www.inverlochy.co.uk

ℚ *César award in 1984*

"For us, the best hotel in the UK; a splendid place, with natural,
friendly staff." "The warmth of the welcome was exceptional." "A
very happy hotel." Praise continues for this baronial pile, set amid the
magnificent scenery of the foothills of Ben Nevis. It was built by Lord
Abinger in 1863, near the site of the original 13th-century castle, and
later visited by Queen Victoria. Now owned by an overseas business-
man, it is a luxurious hotel (Relais & Châteaux); Michael Leonard, the
exemplary managing director, has presided for many years. The
exterior may look rather austere, but inside all is traditional opulence.
There is a Great Hall with Venetian chandeliers and a frescoed ceiling
with cherubs among clouds, and a billiard room with a high ceiling
and a marble fireplace. The drawing room has open fires, comfortable
sofas and well-polished antiques. Some of the restaurant's furniture
was a gift from a king of Norway. The spacious bedrooms in the main
building look over the gardens; they are bright and beautifully furnished. You can stay "for a fraction of the price" in the annexe, the
Factor's House, "a lovely walk away", and use the hotel's facilities
(but these rooms are not serviced at night). The chef, Simon Haigh,
trained with Raymond Blanc. He has a *Michelin* star for his modern
cooking with a strong emphasis on local produce, eg, grilled turbot
with lobster ravioli; seabass with red pepper spice jus and roasted
Loch Linnhe prawns; pan-fried loin of hill lamb with aubergine caviar
and tapenade jus. The wine list is impressive. One visitor, however,
thought that the food, though "competent", did not reach the "super-
high standards set by the hotel". But he praised the "high-quality"
room-service breakfast, and the Scottish breakfast in the restaurant
(included in the room price) is also admired. What many find impressive in a hotel of this grandeur is the kindness of the service. Two
bedraggled, mud-caked hill-walkers, exhausted by Rannoch Moor,
were "treated like princes, our tatty rucksacks handled like Louis
Vuitton suitcases, our wet and dirty clothes transformed into respect-
ability by room service". Another couple, arriving unannounced
because of a car breakdown, were so thoughtfully looked after that the
memory of their earlier "dismal experience" was eradicated by the
stay at *Inverlochy*. Children are welcomed. The grounds are beautiful,
and "the views and sense of isolation are perfect". Many sporting
activities – fly-fishing, stalking, shooting, golf, etc – are available, and
given notice, a falconry display can be arranged. (*Paul Hingston,
Margaret Watson, Conrad and Marilyn Dehn, Robin McKie*)

Open All year, except 4 Jan–11 Feb.
Rooms 1 suite, 15 double, 1 single. 5 in *Factor's House*.
Facilities Great Hall (pianist at weekends), drawing room, billiard room,
restaurant; function facilities. In 500-acre estate: gardens, tennis, loch, fishing,
birdwatching. Golf, skiing nearby. Chauffeur-driven limousines for hire.
Unsuitable for &. Wedding facilities.

Location On A82 3 miles NE of Fort William, just past golf club. Follow signs to hotel; ignore signs to Inverlochy village/Inverlochy Castle ruins.
Restrictions Smoking banned in restaurant, discouraged in bedrooms. Dogs in car only, at management's discretion.
Credit cards Amex, MasterCard, Visa.
Terms [2000] B&B: single £180–£255, double £250–£480, suite £390–£480. Set lunch £28.50, dinner £45. Christmas, New Year packages.

GLASGOW   Map 5

Malmaison   *Tel* (0141) 572 1000
278 West George Street   *Fax* (0141) 572 1002
G2 4LL   *E-mail* glasgow@malmaison.com
                                       Website www.malmaison.com

With the aim of "catering for individuals" in a relaxed style, Ken McCulloch started his small group with a *Malmaison* in Edinburgh (see Shortlist) and this one in the centre of Glasgow. It is perhaps the most attractive of them all – there are now also branches in Manchester, Newcastle and Leeds. This was once a Greek Orthodox church, built at the turn of the 20th century. An extension was added in 1997. It has a magnificent Art Nouveau central staircase, and individually designed bedrooms, with bold colours and stripes, a CD-player, a minibar, a huge bed, a decent shower. Some suites are on two levels. For keep-fit enthusiasts there is the Gymtonic. Two eating places: the Italian-style *Café Mal* serves pasta, pizzas, grills and salads all day. The "light and cheerful" bar/brasserie opens to the glass roof of the first floor, and serves informal meals, including braised lamb shanks with polenta; salmon fish-cakes; duck confit with celeriac; chowder, etc. Breakfast has fresh fruit, cereals, croissants, as well as good cooked dishes. Reports are mixed this year: one visitor complained of "grubbiness", poor room maintenance, disorganised service at breakfast and therefore poor value for money, while others commended it as "really well done, modern, friendly, great breakfast . . . a good way to be a part of the UK's most exciting city". "An extremely pleasing decor, masculine in feeling." As we went to press, the *Malmaison* group was up for sale. We'd like more reports, please.

Open All year.
Rooms 8 suites, 64 double. Some on ground floor. 4 adapted for ♿.
Facilities Lift. Café, bar/brasserie; fitness room; meeting room. Background music in public areas all day.
Location Central (rooms double-glazed). Corner of West George and Pitt streets, opposite police station. NCP parking nearby.
Restrictions No smoking in 18 bedrooms. Guide dogs only.
Credit cards All major cards accepted.
Terms Room: single/double £105, suite £145–£165. Breakfast: continental £8.50, Scottish £10.50. Full alc £25–£30. Discounts and packages subject to availability.

> Report forms (Freepost in UK) will be found at the end of the *Guide*. If you need more, please ask. But it is not essential that you use them for your reports.

Nairns   *Tel* (0141) 353 0707
13 Woodside Crescent   *Fax* (0141) 331 1684
Glasgow G3 7UL
                                            E-mail info@nairns.co.uk
                                            Website www.nairns.co.uk

A stylishly designed and popular restaurant-with-rooms in an elegant
crescent near the western end of Sauchiehall Street. Owned by the
Scottish celebrity chef Nick Nairn and his brother Christopher, it is run
by the "excellent" manager, Jim Kerr. There has been change in the
kitchens again; former second chef, Derek Blair, has taken over, so
we'd like reports on his "modern and classic" Scottish cooking, eg,
chicken liver and foie gras parfait with Cumberland sauce; peppered
monkfish with braised leeks and mussel, spring onion and marjoram
broth; rice pudding with strawberry jam ice-cream. The striking decor
mixes original features of the 18th-century house with contemporary
furnishings, plain walls and carpeting and polished wooden floors.
There are four bedrooms: the larger two on the first floor, smaller ones
above. Each has been decorated by a different designer. Amber is
large, done in red and yellow, with an enormous four-poster with a
fake fur bedcover, a huge wardrobe, halogen spotlights and a large
bathroom. Silver, slightly smaller, is chrome, silver and grey, with a
view of the nearby motorway, a steel four-poster bed, and a pile of
cushions on the floor in place of a sofa. Nantucket, on the top, has
green walls, and a slipper bath by an open fire. Vermeer has a *trompe
l'oeil* mural, thought "ghastly" this year. The simple continental
breakfast is served in the bedroom. More reports, please.

Open All year, except 25/26 Dec, New Year. Restaurant closed Sun.
Rooms 4 double.
Facilities Bar, 2 dining rooms; light background music during meals. Access
to private gardens opposite. Unsuitable for &.
Location 10 mins' walk from centre (2 rooms might get traffic noise).
Restrictions No smoking in restaurant before coffee. No dogs.
Credit cards All major cards accepted.
Terms Room: single £110–£120, double £140–£150. Breakfast £7.50. Set
lunch (2 to 3 courses) £13.50–£17, dinner £27.50. *V*

One Devonshire Gardens   *Tel* (0141) 339 2001
1–3 Devonshire Gardens   *Fax* (0141) 337 1663
Glasgow G12 0UX
                                       E-mail onedevonshire@btconnect.com
                                       Website www.one-devonshire-gardens.co.uk

This lavish hotel, in a tree-lined Victorian terrace, has changed hands
this year: Ken McCulloch has sold it to Residence International, a
Scottish time-share company, which has put in a new managing director, Brian Martin. But manager Mark Calpin, and most of the other
staff, remain the same. Last year, a honeymoon couple had "the most
sumptuous room, huge and panelled, with a beautiful wooden four-
poster, heavy drapes, lovely pictures, flowers and ornaments. The
bathroom had an indulgently deep bath." Individually styled bedrooms have dark colours, heavy fabrics, lights with dimmer switches,
fruit, magazines, a CD-player. The hotel's weak point is its position,
at a busy traffic crossing two miles from the centre, but windows are

double-glazed. It is made up of three listed buildings that are not inter-connected; reception is in Number 3, the restaurant in Number 1 (umbrellas are provided for rainy days). "The enjoyable if expensive room-service breakfast included porridge, pastries, a massive cooked plate." In the smart restaurant, recently redecorated, Andrew Fairlie's *Michelin*-starred modern cooking includes, eg, foie gras and almond terrine; cassoulet de Toulouse; spiced soufflé with rum raisins and mulled wine. The staff are "polite and discreet throughout". Maids wear white pinafores, and the hotel is said to aim at a Victorian private-house atmosphere. But no less a pundit than Jilly Cooper has said: "It is perfect for illicit weekends – you can get in and out without having to use the front door." And one of our readers has called it "really good fun". More reports on all this please, and on the new regime.

Open All year.
Rooms 2 suites, 25 double. 1 on ground floor.
Facilities 2 drawing rooms, 2 residents' bars, restaurant; jazz/"easy listening" background music; boardroom, private dining room; patio garden. Unsuitable for &. Wedding facilities.
Location 2 miles from centre at intersection of Great Western and Hyndland roads. Back rooms quietest. Off-street parking in front.
Restrictions No smoking in restaurant. No dogs in public rooms.
Credit cards All major cards accepted.
Terms [2000] Room: single £145–£210, double £170–£215, suite £220–£230. Breakfast: continental £10.50, Scottish £14.50. Set lunch (2 to 3 courses) £21–£27.50. Full alc dinner £60. Weekend breaks.

The Town House	*Tel* (0141) 357 0862
4 Hughenden Terrace, Hyndland	*Fax* (0141) 339 9605
Glasgow G12 9XR	*E-mail* hospitality@thetownhouseglasgow.com
	Website www.thetownhouseglasgow.com

Michael Ferguson's B&B hotel is housed in a handsome double-fronted late-Victorian sandstone building in a quiet street in a conservation area in Glasgow's West End. Inside are deep cornices, high ceilings and elaborately carved architraves, and simple furnishings. One visitor and his young son both enjoyed their stay: "The atmosphere, welcome and comfort outclass many posher, more expensive hotels." The setting is quiet, the parking is easy and the staff are "helpful and concerned for guests' comfort, without being fussy". "The cooked breakfasts are excellent" (they include seafood). Fruit, sweets and shortbread in the bedroom are replenished daily. Only drawbacks: shower rooms are on the small side, and sometimes awkwardly placed; bedrooms at the top are tiny. There is a large book collection in the drawing room. Snack meals and packed lunches are available. Guests have access to the sports and social facilities of the adjacent Western Lawn Tennis and Hillhead sports clubs. The restaurants and shops in Byres Road, the Botanic Gardens and the University are all within ten to 15 minutes' walk. There is another hotel called *Town House* in Glasgow, in Royal Crescent; make sure the taxi driver knows which one you are heading for. (*Robin and Tom McKie*)

Open All year.
Rooms 2 family, 8 double. All with shower. 1 on ground floor.
Facilities Lounge, breakfast room. No background music. Small garden. Access to adjacent sports clubs (visitors' fee £2–£4). Unsuitable for ⓴.
Location 1½ miles W of centre. Leave A82 at Hyndland Rd, 1st right into Hughenden Rd, then right at mini-roundabout. Street parking. Bus 59 from centre.
Restrictions No smoking in dining room. No dogs.
Credit cards MasterCard, Visa.
Terms B&B £34–£58. Child accommodated in parents' room: under 5, £5; 6–12, £8.

See also SHORTLIST

GLEN CANNICH Highland   **Map 5**

Mullardoch House   *Tel/Fax* (01456) 415460
Glen Cannich   *E-mail* andy@mullhouse1.demon.co.uk
by Beauly IV4 7LX   *Website* www.mullhouse1.demon.co.uk

A handsome white hunting lodge, which was built in 1912 by Chisholm of Chisholm. Its present owner, Andy Johnston, has been careful to preserve its character. Set in the heart of the Highlands, with views across Loch Sealbhanach to the Affric mountains, it is "ideal for those who want to get away from it all", says its nominator. The hunting lodge is reached by an eight-mile drive up a single-track road through beautiful Glen Cannich. Wildlife abounds and you might well see a stag appear out of the mist on any nearby hill. "The peace is wonderful; the air is sweet. Only the water in the burn tumbling down the hillside and the munching of occasional sheep can be heard at night. The staff are young and friendly. Dinners (no choice) are superb, with generous servings." They might include mushroom and oregano ravioli; leek and potato soup; grilled salmon fillet on sun-dried tomato pasta; raspberry soufflé with chocolate cream. There are log fires, flowered fabrics and old furniture in the public rooms; spacious bedrooms have stunning views, bathrooms "with, for once, baths of a good length". Plenty of sporting activities are available: walking of all degrees of difficulty, from strolls along the river to several Munros; fishing in the hotel's beats or on local estates; boating on ten-mile-long Loch Mullardoch. (*J de W*)

Open All year.
Rooms 1 suite, 6 double.
Facilities Large hall, lounge, bar, dining room. No background music. 2-acre grounds: lawns, wooded walks. Shooting, stalking, fishing arranged; golf nearby. Unsuitable for ⓴. Wedding facilities.
Location A831 from Beauly, then unclassified road for 8 miles through Glen Cannich. Transport to and from Inverness airport/station can be arranged.
Restrictions No smoking: restaurant, bedrooms. No dogs in public rooms.
Credit cards Amex, MasterCard, Visa.
Terms B&B double £96; D,B&B double £150. Set dinner £27. 3-night breaks Nov–May.

GLENELG Highland   Map 5

Glenelg Inn   *Tel* (01599) 522273
Glenelg Bay   *Fax* (01599) 522283
by Kyle of Lochalsh   *E-mail* christopher.main@glenelg-inn.com
IV40 8JR   *Website* www.glenelg-inn.com

"A room raw and dirty; bare walls, a variety of bad smells, a coarse
black table . . ." Much has changed since Dr Johnson, accompanied by
Boswell, visited this inn in 1773. It is now clean, warm and lively, "the
centre of village life". But getting there is still "an adventure: a drive
up a single-track road, climbing dramatically past heather-strewn
fields and mountains, with spectacular views to the lochs below". Now
owned and run by Christopher Main, "very dashing in his kilt in the
evenings", it has a superb setting on Glenelg Bay, the haunt of the
legendary local hero, Fionn Mac Cumhail. All six bedrooms look
across the Sound of Sleat to the mountains of Skye. This year, a reader
liked the "wonderful views over the loch with superb sunsets", and
added: "All staff are local, which is nice, as so many hotels in Scotland
nowadays are full of Australians who know nothing about the area.
The residents' sitting room is rather cold and unwelcoming, maybe
because everyone congregates in the bar, which can be noisy and
smoky – traditional Scottish and Welsh music is played there constantly. Bedrooms are above the pub area in the old stables: ours was
newly decorated, very spacious, with radiators piping hot." Evening
meals have plenty of choice, with fresh fish and seafood daily. They
were mostly enjoyed, with "very good desserts", but one visitor in
2000 found the cooking uneven. "Good choice at breakfast, but staff
were sometimes rather forgetful. Super bar lunches, and there are nice
gardens with tables – if you can stand the midges." The bar, large and
panelled, is full of local fishermen and farmers; occasional *ceilidhs* are
held here. Residents' meals are served in a quiet dining room with
flowers and candlelight. Local ingredients feature in dishes such as
mussels steamed with garlic, parsley and cream; monkfish roasted
with cinnamon and red wine; kidneys with marsala and fresh thyme.
Wild salmon is served in season. Winter house parties are good value.
Dogs are "most welcome, except in the restaurant". Mr Main's wife,
Rebecca, has created a "large and wonderful garden", and her large oil
paintings (landscapes and seascapes) hang in the dining room. Mr
Main will take guests on an exhilarating power-boat trip. Glenelg is
the nearest place on the mainland to Skye; a little ferry takes cars
across in summer. There's plenty of wildlife; several castles are
nearby and other local attractions include Gavin Maxwell's Sandaig.
(*Janice Carrera, Good Pub Guide, and others*)

Open All year ("more or less").
Rooms 6 double. 1 on ground floor. No telephone, TV.
Facilities Morning room, bar (traditional background music all day; *ceilidhs* 2
or 3 times a month), dining room. 2-acre grounds: garden down to sea, sailing,
fishing, power-boat trips. Birdwatching, hill-walking, golf nearby. Small wed-
ding facilities.
Location Seafront of village on Sound of Sleat.
Restriction No smoking in dining room.

Credit cards Diners, MasterCard, Visa.
Terms D,B&B £50–£90. Bar meals. Set dinner £24. Christmas package.

GULLANE East Lothian   Map 5

Greywalls   *Tel* (01620) 842144
Muirfield, Gullane EH31 2EG   *Fax* (01620) 842241
                                          E-mail hotel@greywalls.co.uk
                                          Website www.greywalls.co.uk

"Lots of character. Comfortable and with excellent service. An important bit of architecture in a really beautiful garden." Built in 1901, this
crescent-shaped country house, built of honey-coloured stone, is the
only remaining example in Scotland of Lutyens' domestic architecture; its gardens are attributed to Gertrude Jekyll. It has been run as a
luxury hotel since 1977 – Giles and Ros Weaver, son and daughter-in-
law of the founder, Colonel John Weaver, are now in command. It is
much patronised by American golfers; one of its main drawing points
is the situation, "within a mashie niblick shot of the 18th green of
Muirfield golf club". An earlier enthusiast wrote: "I don't believe I
have stayed in a better country house hotel." It has a beautiful panelled
library, an "equally inviting" sun porch, and a lounge with an open
fire. The best bedrooms are furnished with antiques, and have views of
the links, the Firth of Forth, or the Lammermuir Hills. One bedroom
in the garden is called the King's Loo, recalling its purpose in the days
when Edward VII was a visitor. The clientele is "quite sophisticated –
ladies and gentlemen in the old-fashioned sense". In the formal restaurant, decorated in green, men are asked to wear a jacket and tie at dinner (you must reserve your table). The chef, Simon Burns, serves
"interesting variations of traditional dishes", eg, warm salad of
smoked venison with grilled artichokes; hickory-smoked North
Berwick lobster with a wild garlic and herb butter; steamed blueberry
pudding with pistachio ice-cream. Service is "most attentive".
(*Nicholas Penny, MH*)

Open Apr–Oct inclusive.
Rooms 19 double, 4 single. 5 in lodges in grounds. 2 on ground floor.
Facilities 2 sitting rooms, library, sunroom, bar, restaurant. No background
music. 4-acre grounds: walled garden, croquet, tennis, putting. Golf course
adjacent; sea, safe bathing, 5 mins' drive.
Location In village off A198.
Restrictions No smoking in restaurant. No dogs in public rooms.
Credit cards All major cards accepted.
Terms B&B: single £105, double £180–£220. Set lunch £20, dinner £40.
Spring and autumn breaks. *V*

****

Hotel in Suffolk. At £125 for two for B&B, breakfast in this
posh country house hotel should have been good. It was not. We
were served poached eggs with the consistency of rubber, and
toast-like biscuits. Both had to be sent back. Smoked haddock
was watery and tasteless. We came to the conclusion that the
breakfast chef needed to wake up earlier.

****

INVERNESS Highland   Map 5

Culloden House	*Tel* (01463) 790461
Culloden	*Fax* (01463) 792181
Inverness IV2 7BZ	*E-mail* info@cullodenhouse.co.uk
	Website www.cullodenhouse.co.uk

A luxurious hotel in a handsome Palladian mansion, "beautifully set" in a huge park with ancient trees, cattle, and occasional sightings of roe deer. It was built in the 18th century, on the site of an earlier house used as headquarters by Bonnie Prince Charlie before the fatal battle that took place nearby in 1746; his vanquisher, "Butcher" Cumberland, later celebrated victory here. It is owned by an American company, and one of the partners – the former manager, Major Richard Gillis from Connecticut – is operations director but is based at *Hunstrete House*, Hunstrete (*qv*), the luxurious hotel near Bath under the same ownership. Stephen Davies is now the manager here. Many guests are from the United States. The bedrooms are large and comfortable, though there is no lift to the second floor. Four suites are in a pavilion in the grounds, recently built but perfectly compatible with the style of the original mansion. The elegant public rooms have ornate plasterwork and plaster reliefs, high ceilings, chandeliers and antique furniture. The admired cooking of chef Michael Simpson is "Scottish with classical influences". His menus are commendably brief, concentrating on good Scottish ingredients, eg, terrine of highland game with wild mushrooms and rowan port sauce; pan-fried loin of venison; sea-trout and smoked salmon tartare; athol brose. Breakfast, cooked to order, includes venison or Cumberland sausages, and a platter of Scottish cheeses. A piper sometimes plays on the lawn, and there is Scottish musical entertainment in season. Functions and small conferences are catered for. Many sporting activities are available (see below). The battlefield of Culloden is close at hand, and the hotel will arrange chauffeured visits to Cawdor Castle, the Clava Cairns, Loch Ness, local whisky distilleries, etc. Inverness airport is nearby. More reports, please.

Open All year.
Rooms 10 suites, 15 double, 3 single. 5 in pavilion in garden.
Facilities Lounge (Scottish background music sometimes), morning room, library/bar, dining room; conference room; sauna. 40-acre grounds: walled garden, tennis, croquet, bowling, badminton, walking, clay-pigeon shooting. Fishing, golf, horse riding nearby. Unsuitable for &.
Location NE of Inverness. From city take A96; right after 1 mile, at sign to Culloden. Culloden House 1 mile further on left.
Restrictions No smoking: dining room, some bedrooms. No children under 10. Dogs by arrangement, not in public rooms.
Credit cards All major cards accepted.
Terms [2000] B&B: single £145, double £190–£260, suite £270. Set dinner £35. Christmas package. *V*

Don't let old favourites down. Hotels are dropped when there is no endorsement.

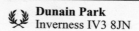

Dunain Park
Inverness IV3 8JN

Tel (01463) 230512
Fax (01463) 224532
E-mail dunainparkhotel@btinternet.com
Website www.dunainpark.co.uk

César award: Scottish country house hotel of the year

"What a wonderful hotel, especially for a family! The meals were delicious, especially breakfast." "The best room, the best view, the most comfortable bed I have had in any hotel." "The guests were international and all delightful; the owners were delightful too." "Luxury at a price, worth every penny." Four quotes from the chorus of praise that has come again this year for this Italianate 19th-century mansion, now an "opulent country hotel", "lovely and idiosyncratic", owned and run by Edward and Ann Nicoll. Set in large, well-tended gardens and woodland, it overlooks the River Ness and the Caledonian Canal. It has a homely feel: leather settees, comfortable armchairs, log fires in cold weather, huge windows facing the garden, family photographs in the lounges. But also: "The furniture and pictures are a curious mix of period pieces and modern kitsch." The bedrooms in the main house, recently renovated, all now have a bathroom *en suite*. The suites in the new wing are attractive and spacious. There is a "quirky" small indoor swimming pool (very warm), a sauna in a cabin in the grounds, and a drying room. Edward Nicoll is "discreet, attentive". Ann Nicoll is the extrovert chef, whose "wonderful cooking" is "modern Scottish with French influence"; choice is varied and portions are large. There is a separate steak menu (all the meat comes from Aberdeen Angus accredited herds), and an *à la carte* menu of elaborate dishes, such as ragout of salmon and turbot in a caviar sauce; lamb stuffed with chicken livers and figs wrapped in bacon on a tawny port sauce; fried duck with red cabbage and haggis. "The delicious desserts, full of cream, should carry a health warning." Many ingredients are home grown. Children have a separate menu. Over 200 malt whiskies are stocked, leading to conviviality after dinner. Breakfasts are copious, with all the usual cooked dishes. Excellent walking and climbing nearby, 20 golf courses, and plenty to see, including Loch Ness, Cawdor Castle and Culloden battlefield. (*Katherine Galligan, Colin Hendrie, Sheelagh Innes, John and Helen Disley, Tom Craigmyle*)

Open All year.
Rooms 8 suites (1 with access for &) 5 double; also two 2-bedroomed cottages in grounds.
Facilities 2 lounges, restaurant. No background music. 6-acre grounds: croquet, covered swimming pool, sauna. Fishing, shooting, golf, tennis, winter sports nearby.
Location 1 mile S of Inverness. Turn left off A82 after Craig Dunain hospital. Station 2½ miles; then taxi.
Restrictions No smoking: restaurant, some bedrooms. "Well-behaved children welcomed." Dogs by arrangement, not in public rooms.
Credit cards All major cards accepted.
Terms [2000] B&B £49–£99, D,B&B £69–£124. Full alc £36.85. Low-season rates; 3-day breaks; Christmas/New Year packages. 1-night bookings refused Easter.

See also SHORTLIST

ISLE ORNSAY Highland   Map 5

The Duisdale   *Tel* (01471) 833202
Isle Ornsay, Sleat   *Fax* (01471) 833404
Isle of Skye IV43 8QW   *E-mail* marie@duisdalehotel.demon.co.uk

Set above the Sound of Sleat, in 25-acre grounds with woods and wildlife, this 19th-century hunting lodge is now owned and run as a hotel by Mrs Marie Campbell. The decor is traditional, "and everything is done with taste", says our latest report. There are antiques, good fabrics throughout; log fires in the lounges; lovely views from many bedrooms, four of which have been given carved oak four-poster beds this year. Some rooms can be small. The young staff are "informal and friendly"; Mrs Campbell is "omnipresent", and her cooking is "exceptional". The menus include, eg, prawn chowder; roast organic chicken; grilled bass with a coriander and lime dressing; honeycomb parfait with glazed peaches. Many of the herbs and vegetables are home grown. Mrs Campbell writes that she has now

improved the breakfast choice, with "eggs Benedict, smoked salmon, wild mushrooms, haddock kedgeree". Children are made welcome, and will enjoy the dovecote, the lambs and chickens on the farm, and the seals and otters on the beach nearby. Very popular for weddings. (*JH; also Good Pub Guide*)

Open Apr–Oct.
Rooms 4 suites, 13 double, 3 single. No TV.
Facilities Lounge, library/bar, TV room, dining room/conservatory (Scottish piper occasionally). 25-acre grounds: gardens, croquet, putting, forest walks. Sea 500 yds. Unsuitable for &. Wedding facilities.
Location Near Armadale ferry and Skye Bridge.
Restrictions No smoking: restaurant, lounge, 3 bedrooms. No dogs.
Credit cards Amex, MasterCard, Visa.
Terms B&B: single £70–£80, double £90–£140, suite £140–£150; D,B&B: single £100–£110, double £150–£200, suite £200–£210. Set dinner £32. *V*

KELSO Scottish Borders   Map 5

Ednam House   `NEW`   *Tel* (01573) 224168
Bridge Street   *Fax* (01573) 226319
Kelso TD5 7HT   *E-mail* ednamhouse@excite.co.uk
                          Website www.ednamhouse.com

"What a wonderful find!" says this year's nominator. It is a handsome Georgian mansion (1761), set in three-acre gardens and facing the

River Tweed, Kelso bridge and open country, yet close to the centre of this small Borders town. It has been owned and run as a hotel by the Brooks family since 1928. "Excellent in every respect. Wonderful location. Very friendly and helpful; old-fashioned service at its best. Large comfortable bedrooms, priced according to location. Spacious public rooms with lovely views. Five-course dinners superb. Excellent breakfasts too: fresh haddock with poached egg, etc. Lovely table settings." Cooking, by the family, includes "creative Scottish" dishes based on local produce, eg, Tweed valley sweetbreads in Madeira gravy; Highland venison with Drambuie sauce; plus sweets such as tarte Tatin. "Dogs are welcome in all areas; pooper scoopers provided in the garden." Golf breaks are available, and excursions are arranged – to such places as Bamburgh Castle and Holy Island. (*Janice Carrera*)

Open 8 Jan–24 Dec.
Rooms 21 double, 11 single.
Facilities 3 lounges, 2 bars, restaurant. No background music. 3-acre garden. Unsuitable for &. Wedding facilities.
Location Central. Parking.
Restrictions No smoking: bedrooms, some public areas. No dogs in restaurant.
Credit cards MasterCard, Visa.
Terms B&B: single £55–£60, double £80–£112; D,B&B: single £72.50–£77.50, double £113.50–£147. Alc lunch from £5; set dinner £22. Golf breaks.

KENTALLEN Argyll and Bute   Map 5

Ardsheal House   *Tel* (01631) 740227
Kentallen of Appin   *Fax* (01631) 740342
PA38 4BX
                                    E-mail info@ardsheal.co.uk
                                    Website www.ardsheal.co.uk

Two miles from the main road, "with nothing to disturb the peace except wind and birdsong", the historic home of the Stewarts of Appin is set on a hill in a huge wooded estate. It has "breathtaking views" over Loch Linnhe to the mountains of Morvern. Nearby is the scene of the Appin murder, the central inspiration for Robert Louis Stevenson's *Kidnapped*. *Ardsheal* is run by Neil and Philippa Sutherland, whose family was forced to sell it in 1968 to pay death duties, but regained it in 1994, and it is furnished with family antiques and portraits. "The house and its hosts are warm and welcoming," said the nominator. Neil Sutherland wears a kilt most of the time, and guests are piped into dinner with bagpipes and martial music. Philippa Sutherland is the cook, aided by a couple from the Philippines. The four-course menus, which always include soup, have no choice, but vegetarians and special diets are catered for with advance warning. The cooking is "traditional Scottish with international influence", eg, twice-baked goat's cheese soufflé; seared salmon and scallops with risotto; raspberry and peach Pavlova. Dishes are presented in Asian style, with sculpted vegetables. Breakfasts include freshly squeezed orange juice and good porridge. The bedrooms vary in size; the best ones look over the loch. (*MG*)

Open Feb–Nov; occasional closures during this period. Lunch not served.
Rooms 1 family, 5 double, 1 single. No TV.
Facilities Lobby with seating, 2 sitting rooms, dining room (occasional Scottish background music during dinner), billiard room. 11-acre garden in 800-acre estate: riding, fishing, boating. Sea loch with pebble beach ½ mile. Unsuitable for &.
Location 17 miles SW of Fort William, on A828, 5 miles S of Ballachulish Bridge. Train to Fort William or bus to Ballachulish.
Restrictions No smoking: dining room, some bedrooms. Dogs by arrangement; not in dining room.
Credit cards Amex, MasterCard, Visa.
Terms B&B £45. Set dinner £25.

KILCHRENAN Argyll and Bute	**Map 5**

Ardanaiseig	*Tel* (01866) 833333
Kilchrenan	*Fax* (01866) 833222
by Taynuilt PA35 1HE	*E-mail* ardanaiseig@clara.net
	Website www.ardanaiseig.com

This delightfully unusual place has this year acquired "a wonderful old steam launch, to take guests on Loch Awe", by whose banks it stands. A grand mansion in a romantic location, it is set in glorious, rambling gardens at the end of a three-mile road. It was built in the Scottish baronial manner for Colonel Archibald Campbell in 1834 and later became a sedate luxury hotel. But this changed when the bearded present owner, antiquarian and naturalist Bennie Gray, bought it recently on a whim, adding it to his empire of art workshops, including the Custard Factory in Birmingham. He has created a small classical Greek-style amphitheatre by the water, where some rather way-out performances of song and dance are held, many of them based on the Celtic myths that fascinate Mr Gray. The large bedrooms have a "slightly eccentric" decor, with antiquities and some strange colour schemes. But manager Robert Francis provides a reassuring presence. And in the "good, aspiring to great" restaurant, overlooking the lake, chef Gary Goldie serves French and other dishes, eg, cream of haricot blanc soup with truffle oil; salmon and scallops with sauce vierge; roast venison with Savoy cabbage and pancetta; passion fruit soufflé. Coffee, with home-made petits fours, is served in the drawing room, "with the intoxicating smell of a wood fire". "The whole place struck us as very slightly 'off the wall' but in a rather delightful way." And its visitors' book this year is again packed with raves: "Wonderful", "amazing". Plans have been mooted for a honeymoon lodge on an island, and the magnificent grounds are being brought back to life. Dougal, Hector and William Wallace, the friendly highland cattle, graze in a pasture near the boat house. "They love being fed and having their hair combed," says Mr Francis. (*DW, M and MH, and others*)

Open All year, except Jan.
Rooms 16 double. Some on ground floor. Also cottage ¼ mile.
Facilities Library/ bar, drawing room, snooker/games room, restaurant (occasional quiet Scottish instrumental music). 250-acre grounds on loch: gardens, open-air theatre, tennis, croquet, safe bathing, fishing. Wedding facilities.
Location From A85, 1 mile E of Taynuilt, follow B845 to Kilchrenan. Left at

single track by *Kilchrenan Inn*. Continue for 3 miles. Easijet package from Luton can be arranged.
Restrictions No smoking: restaurant, some other public rooms. No children under 10 in restaurant at night. No dogs in public rooms.
Credit cards Amex, MasterCard, Visa.
Terms B&B: £73–£120. Set dinner £35. Christmas package. Reductions in spring/autumn.

Taychreggan   *Tel* (01866) 833211 and 833366
Kilchrenan   *Fax* (01866) 833244
by Taynuilt PA35 1HQ   *E-mail* taychreggan@btinternet.com

In a "truly tranquil setting" in large wooded grounds on the banks of Loch Awe, this 300-year-old stone drovers' inn is now a smart hotel owned by Annie Paul. She runs it with a "friendly young staff": "we liked their professionalism", one visitor wrote. Many guests have come for the fishing. "The view down the loch is always magical," says a report this year, and there is "fantastic scenery" all around. The buildings are arranged around a flowery cobbled courtyard, and furnished in country house style. There are flagstone floors, good fabrics and rugs, and modern art. The bedrooms are lavishly draped and well equipped; some have a four-poster bed. The best rooms in the old house have loch views, though others looking on to a grassy bank, with bluebells and azaleas in season, have also pleased. Good, if less characterful, bedrooms are in a new wing which also houses a billiard room. There is a new chef, Jerome Prodanu, this year, and the five-course dinner, served at candlelit antique tables overlooking the loch, might include baked asparagus with gruyère; sweet potato and orange soup; pheasant with sautéed vegetables and garlic jus; choux crown of caramelised pears with vanilla ice-cream, followed by Scottish cheeses. Bar lunches are served, alfresco in fine weather, and there is an impressive array of malt whiskies. The restaurant and most bedrooms are no-smoking, but some guests would like a no-smoking sitting area as well. The drive up the north side of the loch is recommended. Lots to do locally: fishing and boating on the loch; walking and picnicking in the magnificent forests; historic houses and castles to visit; Inverawe Smokehouse for gourmets; 13 Munros within an hour's drive. No-children Christmas and New Year house parties are a regular feature. (*Fiona Dick*)

Open All year.
Rooms 1 suite, 18 double. No TV.
Facilities 2 lounges, TV lounge, bar, restaurant; jazz/classical background music; snooker room; function rooms. 40-acre grounds on loch: boats, water sports, fishing (ghillie available). Riding, deer-stalking, walking, climbing, golf nearby. Unsuitable for &. Wedding facilities.
Location 22 miles SE of Oban. 1 mile E of Taynuilt, turn off A85 on to B845; follow signs to lochside. Hotel at end of 7-mile single track. Train/bus: Taynuilt; hotel will meet.
Restrictions No smoking: restaurant, most bedrooms. No children under 14. Dogs by arrangement; not in public rooms.
Credit cards Amex, MasterCard, Visa.
Terms B&B £52–£97; D,B&B £80–£125. Set lunch £19.50, dinner £30. Autumn, winter, spring, Christmas, New Year breaks. *V*

KILDRUMMY Aberdeenshire   Map 5

Kildrummy Castle Hotel   *Tel* (019755) 71288
Kildrummy   *Fax* (019755) 71345
by Alford AB33 8RA   *E-mail* bookings@kildrummycastlehotel.co.uk
                          Website www.kildrummycastlehotel.co.uk

An impressive gabled and castellated house, now a stylish and comfortable country hotel. It stands in manicured lawns by the romantic ruins of a 13th-century castle, and has been run for 20 years by Thomas and Mary Hanna with a long-serving staff. The "warm welcome, excellent housekeeping and above-average food" are all admired. The spacious public rooms, which include a small library, have ornate panelled walls and ceilings, open fires, a magnificent carved oak staircase and original tapestries commissioned in 1900 by Colonel "Soapy" Ogston, who built the house after selling his detergent business in Aberdeen to a then unknown entrepreneur named Lever. The bedrooms vary greatly in shape, size and outlook; some have antique furniture and a four-poster; others are modern in style. The chef, Kenneth Whyte, uses local produce, served in the traditional way. The four-course menu offers choices such as trio of smoked salmon, gravadlax and hot-kiln-smoked salmon; Cullen skink; grilled medallions of venison with a black cherry and herb sauce; selections from an "irresistible" dessert trolley, and a good choice of local cheeses. The beautifully kept gardens have a large collection of rare alpine plants, shrubs and specimen trees. The Hannas own a private stretch of fishing on the River Don two miles away. Local attractions include the Great Garden at Pitmedden; Fyvie, Balmoral and Crathes castles; and distilleries on the Malt Whisky Trail; the Transport Museum at Alford is a popular excursion; and there is skiing on the Lecht slopes, 20 minutes' drive away. More reports, please.

Open 3 Feb–2 Jan.
Rooms 15 double, 1 single.
Facilities Drawing room, library, lounge bar, restaurant; snooker room. No background music. 15-acre grounds: ruined castle, gardens. Private trout/salmon-fishing on River Don, 2 miles. Unsuitable for &. Wedding facilities.
Location 35 miles W of Aberdeen. NE of Ballater off A97 Ballater–Huntly.
Restrictions No smoking: restaurant, drawing room. No dogs in public rooms.
Credit cards Amex, MasterCard, Visa.
Terms B&B £65–£90; D,B&B £65–£121. Set lunch £17, dinner £32; full alc £35. Short breaks. Christmas, New Year package. Child accommodated in parents' room: £5–£15 (meals charged as taken).

KINGUSSIE Highland   Map 5

The Cross   *Tel* (01540) 661166
Tweed Mill Brae   *Fax* (01540) 661080
Kingussie PH21 1TC   *E-mail* relax@thecross.co.uk
                             Website www.thecross.co.uk

"Service and cuisine are of a very high standard", runs praise bestowed again this year on Tony and Ruth Hadley's restaurant-with-

rooms in an "immaculately converted" 19th-century stone-built tweed
mill by the River Gynack. "Very comfortable though by no means luxurious", it stands on the edge of the village, in wooded grounds with
native trees and wild flowers, and plenty of wildlife. The modest
building provides plain but pleasant bedrooms, some of them spacious
("ours had a Scandinavian feel"). Bathrooms are well equipped. There
is a chess set in the upstairs sitting room. The "Scottish eclectic" cooking of Ruth Hadley, now joined by Becca Henderson, is served in a
room with rough stone walls and heavy beams. "Our five-course menu
embraced squat lobster, red pepper soup, steak or guinea fowl, and
dessert; the suggestion of a chilled Tarrango was delicious and appropriate. The cooking, presentation, the setting with imaginative artwork, could not be faulted." Others have praised the "excellent raw
materials", the smoked haddie tart; pears poached in wine with a butterscotch sauce. "Much of the atmosphere derives from Tony
Hadley's bubbly personality; he is always on hand to give advice or to
chat." Even egg-and-bacon addicts enjoy the continental breakfasts:
"bowls of fresh raspberries, beautiful cherries, peaches and cereals,
fresh croissants and home-made jams". A nice touch comes with the
bill – guests are presented with all the menus they had, and the names
of the wines. The restaurant is closed on Tuesdays, and "Kingussie has
little else to offer". Local activities embrace skiing at Aviemore, water
sports at Loch Insh, pony-trekking and gliding. The wildlife in the
grounds includes red squirrels, a few roe deer. The Gynack "varies
from a gentle stream in summer to a raging torrent in spring when the
snow melts". (*John and Helen Disley, WS*)

Open 1 Mar–1 Dec. Restaurant closed Tues evening.
Rooms 9 double. TV, etc, on request.
Facilities Ramp. 2 lounges (1 with TV), restaurant. No background music.
4-acre grounds, river (no fishing). Golf, walking, climbing nearby. Only
restaurant suitable for &.
Location 350 yds up Ardbroilach Rd from traffic lights at town centre. Left at
sign down private road. Train/coach to Kingussie; then taxi, "or we collect".
Restrictions No smoking: restaurant, bedrooms. No children under 12. No
dogs.
Credit cards MasterCard, Visa.
Terms Double room: B&B £150, D,B&B £230. Set dinner £37.50. Guests
staying 1 night only are expected to dine in. Wine weekends Nov.

KINROSS Perth and Kinross   **Map 5**

Green Hotel   NEW   *Tel* (01577) 863467
2 The Muirs   *Fax* (01577) 863180
Kinross KY13 8AS   *E-mail* reservations@green-hotel.com
                              Website www.green-hotel.com

A conventional resort-type hotel at the edge of the old town on the
shores of Loch Leven (where Mary, Queen of Scots was imprisoned
in a castle on an island). "I have used it for many years as a staging
post on the way to and from the north of Scotland," says its nominator.
"It has grown over the years, but the quality of service and the friendly
welcome have remained unchanged. Enlargement and modernisation

have in no way detracted from its charms: splendid gardens, ample car parking, good-sized bedrooms with all reasonable mod cons; all the help one can want with luggage, etc; good food at both breakfast and dinner. My 91-year-old mother-in-law was treated with care and respect." The Montgomery family has owned the hotel since 1927. "Every conceivable sport" is catered for (see below). Two bedrooms are suitable for disabled guests. Food is "traditional Scottish/French". "Only half a mile from the M90 between Edinburgh and Perth, but quiet, especially the courtyard rooms." (*Sir John B Hall*)

Open All year, except Christmas.
Rooms 4 family, 42 double. 2 on ground floor.
Facilities Lounge area, cocktail bar, lounge bar (no backgound music); games rooms. 3-acre grounds: leisure complex: covered swimming pool, sauna, solarium; tennis, croquet, putting, *pétanque*; 48 boats on loch; access to 2 18-hole golf courses, 4-sheet curling rink.
Location ½ mile from centre (most rooms away from road). 5 mins' drive from M90, exit 6. Parking.
Restrictions No smoking in bedrooms. No dogs where food is served.
Credit cards All major cards accepted.
Terms B&B: single £75–£95, double £135–£155, family £145–£155; D,B&B £75–£120 per person. Bar meals. Set dinner £27.50. ***V***

KIRKCUDBRIGHT Dumfries and Galloway   Map 5

Gladstone House   BUDGET   *Tel/Fax* (01557) 331734
48 High Street
Kirkcudbright DG6 4JX

Once the home of a well-to-do 17th-century merchant, this imposing Georgian house, in a central but quiet street, is owned and run by Susan and James Westbrook. "It is one of our favourite B&Bs," runs a recent report, "always welcoming, with high standards of service, and the bonus of no smoking and no piped music." Of the three guest bedrooms, the best is a double whose window seats overlook "the wonderful architecture of the high street and a maze of gardens running to the river". The bathrooms have a power shower and plenty of towels. One bedroom is small; some walls are thin. The residents' lounge is snug. Breakfast offers plenty of choice, including scrambled eggs and smoked salmon, and "very good haggis". The Westbrooks also run a coffee business, so many types of coffee are on offer. Tea is served in the garden in summer. Susan Westbrook, "cheerful and chatty", is a mine of local information. There are restaurants nearby. Once a thriving port, this "most attractive" town (its name is pronounced "Kurcoobrie") is now much favoured by artists: the hotel is in a conservation district. It makes a good base for visiting the Burns trail; Broughton House, a National Trust for Scotland property, is just down the road. Good walking and golf are nearby. More reports, please.

Open All year, except Christmas/New Year.
Rooms 3 double. No telephone.
Facilities Lounge, breakfast room. No background music. ⅓-acre garden. Harbour 5 mins' walk. Unsuitable for &.

Location Centre of town, behind MacLellan's Castle, two doors away from Tolbooth. Street parking. Train: Dumfries; then bus/taxi.
Restrictions No smoking. No children under 12. No dogs.
Credit cards MasterCard, Visa.
Terms B&B £30–£39.

LOCHINVER Highland   Map 5

The Albannach NEW   *Tel* (01571) 844407
Baddidarroch   *Fax* (01571) 844285
Lochinver IV27 4LP

High above Lochinver's busy fishing harbour, looking across the bay to the Assynt mountains, this 19th-century house stands in a walled garden. The public rooms and all but one bedroom enjoy the view. The "young, enthusiastic" owners, Colin Craig and Lesley Crosfield, write: "Our aim is quality without formality, and an emphasis on the best of Scottish foodstuffs." "They are genuinely welcoming," says the nominator. "The five-course set dinner menu is based on local produce, and with great skill Lesley Crosfield blends tastes and textures. Her partner keeps a good cellar; we always take his advice and have never been disappointed." The dinners, served by a fire in the panelled restaurant, include fresh-caught fish, and free-range beef and lamb, cooked in a contemporary way, eg, seared scallops and duck livers with mixed leaves and walnut vinaigrette; monkfish tails with saffron and seaweed risotto, roast pepper sauce and asparagus spears; roast Highland lamb with root vegetable tartlet, Puy lentils and port wine sauce. But special dietary needs are also catered for. No bar: drinks and coffee are taken in the panelled "snug" with its central fireplace, or in a conservatory. Bread and oatcakes are home made, and *The Albannach* was a runner-up in a Best Breakfast award. Plenty of local information. (*Mrs W Montague, Barbara M Wooldridge*)

Open 16 Mar–30 Nov. Occasionally closed Mon.
Rooms 5 double. 1 in byre, with private patio, 5 yds. No TV.
Facilities Ramp. Snug, conservatory, dining room. No background music. ½-acre garden, 12 acres wild croft land. Sea loch at foot of drive; sandy beaches 2 miles.
Location At foot of hill at entrance to village. Right over old stone bridge, signposted Baddidarroch; after ½ mile, cross cattle grid; turn left.
Restrictions No smoking. No children under 12. No dogs.
Credit cards MasterCard, Visa.
Terms [2000] D,B&B £70–£102. Set dinner £32.

We need feedback on all hotels: big and small, far and near, famous and first-timers.

Inver Lodge   *Tel* (01571) 844496
Iolaire Road   *Fax* (01571) 844395
Lochinver IV27 4LU   *E-mail* stay@inverlodge.com
                                   Website www.inverlodge.com

Anne and Edmund Vestey's modern clifftop hotel stands amid superb Highland scenery, looking across to the Western Isles, above the harbour of a quiet fishing village. To the rear are views of mountains. From below it may look "a bit like an army barracks", but not so inside, where the public rooms are spacious, with traditional decor: patterned carpets, stags' heads, an open fire in the lounge. Returning visitors this year admired the "very pleasant" service, "impeccable" housekeeping: "We had a sophisticated bathroom, newly tiled in dark green." The manager, Nicholas Gorton, "runs the place with great efficiency". The chef, William Hay, is new this year, and we'd be glad to hear if he is keeping up the "good quality" of his predecessor. Roast venison and saddle of Highland lamb can appear on daily menus in the restaurant, where "tables are impeccably set, and the staff are pleasant, and chatty if we are". Its picture windows look over the loch, and seals can often be seen. But a reader this year was sorry to find no sign of the "dinner cabaret" of deer grazing outside the patio windows. Breakfasts include porridge, fruit, yogurt, smoked haddock, salmon kedgeree. The spacious bedrooms are named after local lochs and peaks: Canisp, Suilven, Assynt, etc. They are "subdued and restful", and all have good views, a large bed, fruit renewed daily, fresh flowers. Fishing and stalking can be arranged. (*Jean and George Dundas*)

Open Mar–Dec. Closed Christmas/New Year.
Rooms 20 double.
Facilities 2 lounges, bar, restaurant; sauna, solarium; gift shop. No background music. 1-acre garden. Sea ½ mile; loch/river trout-fishing, birdwatching, walking, stalking nearby. Unsuitable for &. Wedding facilities.
Location A837 from Ullapool. Hotel ½ mile from village, above Lochinver Bay. Bus from Inverness, Ullapool, Lairg.
Restrictions No smoking in restaurant. No children under 7 in restaurant at night. No dogs in public rooms.
Credit cards All major cards accepted.
Terms [2000] B&B £65–£80; D,B&B £75–£100. Set dinner £30. Discounts for stays of 2 nights or more. *V*

LOCHRANZA North Ayrshire   **Map 5**

Apple Lodge   `BUDGET`   *Tel/Fax* (01770) 830229
Lochranza   *E-mail* applelodge@easicom.com
Isle of Arran KA27 8HJ

Q *César award in 1999*

"Our favourite stay in Scotland. Difficult to find fault. The silence was deafening. Excellent value for money." More praise for John and Jeannie Boyd's little guest house, close to the sea and a mile from the Kintyre ferry. Once the village manse, it has three rooms in the main house, all named for a type of apple, and an adjacent cottage suite, which costs only £5 extra per person. The "welcoming hosts" are much admired (he manages, she cooks). The bedrooms are warm and comfortable and prettily decorated and "the meals are delicious and attractively served". Guests are consulted in advance about the set dinner – no one dish is repeated during a stay – which is served at separate tables with candles, crystal and freshly cut flowers. A typical menu includes oak-smoked breast of chicken; salmon in a filo parcel with a lemon and chive cream sauce; chocolate and orange mousse. Vegetarian dishes have included roulade of wild mushrooms, brie and spinach, with tomato and basil sauce. No licence; bring your own wine. The lounge has a fire and board games. There is excellent hill-walking from the doorstep in this "lovely area of Arran", and a golf course close by. Brodick Castle and gardens are worth a visit. Eagles fly over the house; the resident red deer are often only feet away; otters and basking sharks are sometimes seen. And the sun sets romantically over the ruins of Lochranza Castle. (*J Wilkinson, J and MT*)

Open All year, except Christmas, New Year.
Rooms 1 self-contained cottage suite, 3 double. No telephone (pay-phone available).
Facilities Lounge, 2 dining rooms (light classical background music during dinner). ¼-acre garden. Sea loch 200 yds: rocky beach, fishing, sailing. Golf nearby. Unsuitable for &.
Location N side of island, on A841, ½ mile past village sign, opposite golf course. Bus from ferry.
Restrictions No smoking: dining room, bedrooms. No children under 12. No dogs.
Credit cards None accepted.
Terms B&B £30–£37. Set dinner £18. Weekend, midweek off-season breaks. 1-night bookings refused if made in advance; min. 3-night stay usually required in high season.

LYBSTER Highland   Map 5

Portland Arms   NEW   *Tel* (01593) 721721
Lybster KW3 6BS   *Fax* (01593) 721722
                                    E-mail portland.arms@btconnect.com

"What a pleasure," says the nominator in 2000 of this handsome old coaching inn on the A99, a mile from the sea south of Wick, and one of our northernmost entries. It has just been taken over by Jim and Jo Sutherland, with Mark Stevens as manager, and a "friendly staff". "It is beautifully furnished, by someone with a real eye for fabrics. A lovely lounge with a blazing fire. Our room had a tester bed, a bit high but very firm, and lots of space, plus a clean, bright bathroom. Very good breakfast; and they were prepared to serve us supper at 9.15 pm, on our return from an outing." The chef, Meg Sibbald, provides dishes such as marinated duck breast with red berry and thyme compote, or guinea fowl on a tartlet of apples, as well as a wide range of snacks, home-made puddings (eg, oaty fruit crumble) and jokily named delights for the young ("dinosaurs for dinner"; "jiggly jelly"). Toys, books, videos, etc, are supplied for children. "Executive singles" have a CD-player, with free loan of discs. The hotel is set back from the main road, and "there is some noise from lorries". Nearby is the dramatic Caithness coast with its wildlife and heritage centres; the Orkney Islands are within reach for a day-trip. (*Fiona Dick*)

Open All year.
Rooms 4 family, 13 double, 5 single. Some on ground floor.
Facilities Lounge, 2 bars, restaurant; function/wedding facilities. No background music. Small garden. Sea, fishing, rock beach 1 mile; golf, deer-stalking, grouse-shooting, pony-trekking nearby.
Location On A99, 13 miles SW of Wick, 3 miles N of Latheron. Carpark.
Restrictions No smoking: restaurant, some bedrooms. No dogs.
Credit cards All major cards accepted.
Terms B&B: single £45–£50, double £68–£75, suite £75–£85. Full alc £20. Christmas package. Child accommodated in parents' room: under 2, free; reductions for 2–12.

MARYCULTER Aberdeenshire *See SHORTLIST*   · **Map 5**

MAYBOLE South Ayrshire   **Map 5**

Ladyburn   *Tel* (01655) 740585
by Maybole KA19 7SG   *Fax* (01655) 740580
                           E-mail jhdh@ladyburn.freeserve.co.uk
                                   Website www.ladyburn.co.uk

Set amid woods and fields with horses, in a lovely Ayrshire valley, this large white house is the home of David and Jane Hepburn and their family, "who invite their guests to share it with them". It is run in a very personal way by the hostess – "she is very good company". The public rooms are furnished with family antiques. The bedrooms are "comfortable, but not grand". No choice on the dinner menu but preferences are discussed with guests in advance of their stay. Mrs Hepburn serves "good traditional Scottish home cooking", eg, tomato and courgette soup; oven-baked mushrooms in a herb and garlic butter; beef Wellington; Grand Marnier syllabub with fresh raspberries. Afternoon tea is available. In spring rhododendrons, azaleas and bluebells grow in the large grounds. *Ladyburn*'s guests may walk in the grounds of the magnificent adjacent Kilkerran estate, owned by Sir Charles Fergusson. Shooting parties are catered for. The golf courses at Turnberry and Troon are a short drive away, and many other sporting activities are available locally (see below). A good base for touring Burns country. When there is racing at nearby Ayr, *Ladyburn* is usually full. More reports, please.

Open All year, except 2 weeks Nov. Meals not served 4 weeks Jan–Mar. Advance booking essential Oct–Mar.
Rooms 4 double, 4 single. Also 2-bedroom ground-floor flat (can be self-catering).
Facilities Drawing room, library, dining room. No background music. 25-acre grounds: 5-acre garden, river. Fishing, sand/rock beach, golf, shooting, horse-racing nearby. Unsuitable for &. Civil wedding facilities.
Location From Maybole, on A77 Glasgow–Stranraer, take B7023 to Crosshill. Right at war memorial in Crosshill on to B741, signposted Girvan.

Left after 2 miles, signposted Kilkerran/Ladyburn; house ¾ mile on right.
Train: Maybole; bus from Prestwick, 15 miles.
Restrictions No smoking except in library. No children under 16. Guide dogs
only.
Credit cards MasterCard, Amex, Visa.
Terms [2000] (*Excluding 5% service charge*) B&B: single £100–£115,
double £145–£155. Lunch from £15, dinner from £30.

MELROSE Scottish Borders *See SHORTLIST*   **Map 5**

MOFFAT Dumfries and Galloway   **Map 5**

Beechwood Country House   *Tel* (01683) 220210
Harthope Place   *Fax* (01683) 220889
Moffat DG10 9RS
                                    E-mail info@beechwoodhousehotel.co.uk
                                    Website www.beechwoodhousehotel.co.uk

"A superb hotel." "Delightful owners; charming staff." There is
mostly praise again for this old stone house, set amid beech trees in
large grounds, overlooking the Annan valley. "The delights include
the peaceful position high above Moffat, and the warm welcome and
attentive service offered by Jeff and Lynda Rogers – all within about
a mile of the M74." (*Beechwood* is well placed for a stop on the way
north or south.) The "professionalism" and "hard work" of the proprietors are commended. Bedrooms and bathrooms "are equipped
with every possible extra", beds are comfortable, and the lounges and
dining room are spacious and elegant, though one visitor thought the
decor "fussy". The chef, Alan Mitchell, is new, and the food is
generally enjoyed – perhaps not for a long stay, however: "The menu
changes only once a week." The five-course meal might include
seafood risotto cake with white wine and dill sauce, or gâteau of
haggis, neeps and tatties; soup or sorbet; roasted rack of Annan lamb
with a minted jus, or roast breast of pheasant on a red wine jus; millefeuille of summer berries, or strawberry parfait. But one visitor wrote
of "seriously over-large" portions, and others found the vegetables
overcooked and the background music "so loud we had difficulty in
communicating". At breakfast, "grapefruit comes in an artistic
arrangement of pink and white and orange segments", and oatcakes
and preserves are home made. Moffat is a frequent winner of the
"Scotland in Bloom" award. At least 12 stately homes are less than an
hour's drive away. Edinburgh and Glasgow are within easy reach
(53 and 54 miles respectively). (*Dr Michael Allen, Margaret Box, Mr
and Mrs GA Lilley, Philip Connelly, WK Wood, Patricia Darby,
and others*)

Open 16 Feb–2 Jan.
Rooms 7 double.
Facilities Lounge, lounge bar, conservatory, restaurant (background opera in
kitchen during meals). 1½-acre garden. Fishing in River Annan ½ mile; golf,
tennis, riding, pony-trekking, rough shooting nearby. Unsuitable for &. Civil
wedding facilities.
Location ½ mile from town centre. Turn right off High St at church. Parking.
Train: Lockerbie, then bus.

Restriction No smoking: restaurant, lounge.
Credit cards Amex, MasterCard, Visa.
Terms B&B: single £56, double £80; D,B&B: single £72.50, double £121. Set lunch £16, dinner £25.50. Reduced rates for children. Winter discounts. Christmas package. *V*

Moffat House　　NEW 　　　　　　　　　　*Tel* (01683) 220039
High Street　　　　　　　　　　　　　　　*Fax* (01683) 221288
Moffat DG10 9HL

In centre of "delightful town" in Annan valley (53 miles S of Edinburgh), handsome John Adam house with fine staircase; hotel since 1950, well modernised but retaining period charm. Lounge/bar with log fire, sun lounge, garden. Good food (French chef). Amex, MasterCard, Visa accepted. 20 bedrooms, 1 with four-poster. B&B single £60, double £90. Bar lunches. Set dinner £22 [2000]. Golf packages in conjunction with local club. Fuller reports welcome.

See also SHORTLIST

MUIR OF ORD Highland　　　　　　　　　　　　　　**Map 5**

The Dower House　　　　　　　　　*Tel/Fax* (01463) 870090
Highfield　　　　　　　　　　*E-mail* TGHG@thedowerhouse.co.uk
Muir of Ord IV6 7XN　　　　　*Website* www.thedowerhouse.co.uk

"A unique home." "A charming house; our room had an abundance of antique pieces, flowery wallpaper, an old carved bed. The gardens are well kept; herbaceous borders abound, lawns are well trimmed. Other guests very friendly, with chatting between tables at dinner." "An idyllic place, with high standards. Our small son was made very welcome." This dower house in *cottage orné* style stands in large grounds between the rivers Beauly and Conon. The owners, Robyn and Mena Aitchison, cater for individual guests and house parties. Most reports continue to be enthusiastic, though one visitor thought the place expensive for what is offered, and another described the food as "bland". The small lounge has a bar concealed in a cupboard, potted plants and many books. Some bedrooms and bathrooms are small, but the best rooms are "luxurious, with an enormous, comfortable bed and a huge bathroom with a freestanding Victorian bath, fluffy towels and every conceivable extra". "Our son enjoyed playing the pump organ at the foot of his little bed in the suite's (fortunately sound-proof) sitting room." Guests are expected to dine in. The three-course, no-choice home-cooked dinner (£30) is "modern with Mediterranean and Eastern influences", eg, roasted red pepper on bruschetta; fillet of local beef with herb sauce; warm raspberry soufflé or cheese. Home-made chocolates accompany after-dinner coffee. Generous breakfasts include local heather honey. Good birdwatching in the grounds. Close by is some of Scotland's most spectacular scenery with excellent walking; also castles, gardens, beaches, distilleries, etc. (*Jean Dundas, A Gradon, and others*)

Open All year, except Christmas.
Rooms 1 suite, 4 double. All on ground floor. 3 in lodge (also let as self-catering unit).
Facilities Sitting room, dining room. No background music. 5-acre grounds: small formal garden, swings, treehouse. Walking, fishing, golf, beaches nearby.
Location 15 miles NW of Inverness. 1 mile N of Muir of Ord, on A862 to Dingwall: left at double bend sign; through maroon gates.
Restrictions No smoking: dining room, bedrooms. No dogs in public rooms.
Credit cards MasterCard, Visa.
Terms B&B £45–£85. Set lunch £19.50, dinner £30.

NAIRN Highland   **Map 5**

Clifton House   *Tel* (01667) 453119
Viewfield Street   *Fax* (01667) 452836
Nairn IV12 4HW   *E-mail* macintyre@clifton-hotel.co.uk
                                  Website www.clifton-hotel.co.uk

♥ *César award in 1987*

"The most eccentric hotel I have ever stayed in. At the same time it is truly warm, friendly and comfortable," a beguiled visitor writes this year. The Victorian stone villa, with a rose-covered façade, has been the family home of J Gordon Macintyre for 69 years. Kilted every evening, he presides with two cats, Zauberflöte and Oberon, and an "enthusiastic and helpful" staff: "One even ran a couple of hundred yards through the park to bring us a map, since his English and our French were not up to giving and receiving oral road directions." The place is crammed with antiques, pictures and theatrical memorabilia and filled with (mostly home-grown) flowers. In winter, concerts and recitals are staged. The drawing room has an open fire and hand-blocked Pugin wallpaper identical to that used in the robing room of the Palace of Westminster in 1849. There are two dining rooms, each with a sense of theatrical occasion; indeed the larger serves as a theatre in winter. Mr Macintyre cooks too, though his son Charles is the principal chef. The ingredients are mostly local or home grown; almost every source is personally known, eg: "Prime fish comes through Duncan Fraser, who has supplied the house since the early 1930s." There is plenty of choice on the daily-changing menu. The first two courses, written in French, are well-executed Gallic dishes such as foie d'agneau au vin rouge, or tartelette de chèvre frais au tapenade; filet de boeuf au stilton, or coquilles St Jacques au vermouth. Then come such British puddings as caramel custard, or meringues and cream; then Scottish cheeses. The food is thought good "and there is a tome of a wine list". Breakfasts, served "without time limit", eschew packaged cereals: there are fresh juices, proper coffee, a large selection of teas, porridge, home-made bread, muesli and oatcakes, free-range eggs, fresh kippers. Snack lunches and picnics are available. Stylish bedrooms, some quite small, some a bit awkwardly shaped, have antique furniture; some have silk-covered walls, and mirrors to create an illusion of space. One is a "delightful top-floor eyrie", looking over the Moray Firth (steps up to the second floor are quite steep).

Duvets can be changed to conventional bedding on request. "Guests might like to check whether the bathroom is a separate room, as open-plan bathing might not suit everyone," one correspondent advises this year. Nairn, a pretty grey stone town spread along a park by the shore, is a good centre for sightseeing: Brodie and Cawdor castles, Culloden, Loch Ness, etc. Mr Macintyre is a fount of knowledge about the area. (*Colin Pearson, and others*)

Open Mid-Jan–mid-Dec.
Rooms 8 double, 4 single. All with bath (no shower). No telephone/TV.
Facilities Sitting room, drawing room, TV room/library, 2 dining rooms (classical background music during dinner); concerts, recitals Sept–Apr. 1-acre garden. Beach, golf, tennis, public swimming pool, fishing, shooting, riding nearby. Unsuitable for &. Wedding facilities.
Location Turn E at roundabout on A96 in town centre. Private parking. Train/bus stations nearby.
Restrictions No smoking in 1 dining room. No dogs in dining rooms.
Credit cards All major cards accepted.
Terms [2000] B&B: single £60, double £95–£107; D,B&B £85 per person. Full alc £31. Reduced rates for children. Special rates for guests attending concerts, etc. *V*

NEWTON STEWART Dumfries and Galloway   **Map 5**

Creebridge House   *Tel* (01671) 402121
Minnigaff, Creebridge   *Fax* (01671) 403258
Newton Stewart DG8 6NP

E-mail info@creebridge.co.uk
Website www.creebridge.co.uk

Chris and Sue Walker's 18th-century house 2 mins' walk from centre of market town. Originally home of Earl of Galloway, now 19-bedroom hotel, recently refurbished. "Excellent for an overnight stop, with lovely food, wonderful breakfasts," says a 2000 visitor. Local fish and meat, with ambitious range of dishes, served in Garden Restaurant *(closed Nov–Mar) and informal brasserie (classical/pop background music); bar well stocked with malts. Comfortable bedrooms "with many amenities". 3-acre garden: croquet, putting. Dogs welcomed. Closed Christmas. Unsuitable for &. No smoking in restaurants. Amex, MasterCard, Visa accepted. B&B: single £59, double £70–£118; D,B&B £69–£79 per person. Set dinner £22.50. Fishing, golfing breaks.* *V*

****

Hotel in Dorset. Our bedroom was small and over-furnished; an obstacle course which was a challenge to our young legs and would have confounded every other resident we saw.

****

Kirroughtree House   `NEW`   *Tel* (01671) 402141
Newton Stewart DG8 6AN   *Fax* (01671) 402425
                           E-mail kirroughtree@n-stewart.demon.co.uk
                                  Website www.mcmillanhotels.com

"A lovely house, professionally managed," says the nominator of this
impressive white building near a holiday resort/market town on the
River Cree. Built as a private house in 1719, and later much visited by
Robert Burns, it has been run as a hotel by the McMillan family since
1952. Its oak-panelled lounge, hung with oil paintings, has French
windows leading out to landscaped grounds. A wooden "modesty
staircase" (with small panels to prevent a glimpse of the ankles of any
descending lady) leads to spacious bedrooms. Many have good views.
"Mine, in a tower, was warm and comfortable, with an adjoining sitting room." The "superb chef", Ian Bennett, offers plenty of choice on
the *table d'hôte* menus, eg, Solway scallops on roquette with orange,
cardamom and vanilla oil; fresh salmon with braised fennel, asparagus
tips, deep-fried carrot and Hollandaise sauce; lemon tart with vanilla
ice-cream and cassis sauce, or local cheeses. Tables are set with white
linen, crystal and bone china. "Some hiccoughs at breakfast one morning." Nearby are many wonderful gardens, and the delightful town of
Kircudbright. Golf packages can be arranged on the nearby Cally
course. (*Dr M Tannahill*)

Open Mid-Feb–3 Jan.
Rooms 3 suites, 12 double, 2 single.
Facilities 2 lounges, restaurant. No background music. 8-acre grounds: gar-
dens, croquet, pitch 'n' putt. Golf, fishing, shooting, stalking, hill-walking,
nearby. Unsuitable for &.
Location 2 miles NE of Newton Stewart. From A75, take A712 to New
Galloway. Hotel driveway 300 yds on left. Train: Stranraer, bus to Newton
Stewart.
Restrictions No smoking in restaurant. No children under 10. No dogs in
public rooms.
Credit cards Amex, MasterCard, Visa.
Terms B&B: single £75–£80, double £120–£150, suite £160–£170; D,B&B:
single £100–£105, double £170–£190, suite £210–£220. Set lunch £13.50,
dinner £30. Golfing, gardens breaks, etc. Christmas, New Year packages.

OBAN Argyll and Bute   **Map 5**

The Manor House   *Tel* (01631) 562087
Gallanach Road   *Fax* (01631) 563053
Oban PA34 4LS   *E-mail* me@managed-estates.co.uk
                                  Website www.highlandholidays.net

"Very comfortable and beautifully situated", this stone Georgian house
was built in 1780 as the main residence of the Duke of Argyll's estate.
"Delightful and unspoilt", it is on a quiet road up a rocky headland
some half a mile from the town centre, and has superb views across
Oban Bay. The public rooms are not especially large, nor are the bedrooms, but they are well maintained and lit, with repro furniture, heavily lined and expensive curtains and covers, and coat hangers "which
assume guests are not thieves". Fresh local produce, and game, lamb

and beef from the Killiechronan estate on Mull (where the *Manor House* has a sister hotel) are used in the kitchen. In the green-walled, tartan-carpeted dining room, the elaborate dishes of chef Patrick Freytag are "French-influenced Scottish", eg, goat's cheese tartlet with red onion marmalade; fillet steak with Meaux mustard cream; turbot with squat lobster ragout. "Amazing breakfasts" include freshly squeezed orange juice, non-packaged jams and butter, the usual cooked dishes plus such exotica as kippers marinated in white wine, with dill, shallots and quails' eggs, and "a delicious crêpe with woodland mushrooms, avocado and cheese". "The waitresses at dinner and breakfast were smiling and efficient," said an inspector, but she found reception "not so welcoming (no help with luggage)". Day-trips are organised by ferry to surrounding islands. More reports, please.

Open All year, except Christmas, and Sun pm–Tues pm Nov–Mar. Restaurant open midday by arrangement only.
Rooms 11 double.
Facilities 2 lounges, bar, restaurant; classical background music, noon–11 pm. ½-acre grounds. Unsuitable for &. Wedding facilities.
Location ½ mile from centre. Follow ferry terminal signs; house is 200 yds up road.
Restrictions No smoking: restaurant, bedrooms. No children under 12. Dogs by arrangement; not in public rooms.
Credit cards Amex, MasterCard, Visa.
Terms B&B: single £45–£85, double £64–£112; D,B&B: single £70–£110, double £100–£160. Set lunch (by arrangement) £12, dinner £24.95; full alc £26.

Maridon House   NEW/BUDGET   *Tel* (01631) 562760
Dunuaran Road   *E-mail* maridonhse@aol.com
Oban PA34 4NE   *Website* www.west-scotland-tourism.com/maridon-house

At S end of Oban bay, conveniently set 200 yards behind pier where island ferries leave: trim old house newly refurbished and painted blue, owned and run as B&B, "quiet and friendly, simple but comfortable", by Mrs Fiona Hall. 8 bedrooms. Dogs welcomed. Bedrooms, new bathrooms, cooked breakfasts, all praised this year. TV lounge. No smoking. Unsuitable for &. Fine view of islands from hill behind; town centre 10 minutes' walk. Occasional closures for owners' holidays. Credit cards not accepted. B&B £16–£20.

See also SHORTLIST

OLDMELDRUM Aberdeenshire *See SHORTLIST*   **Map 5**

****
Hotel in Sussex. At breakfast the choice of cereals was limited, and ours were brought to us with the milk already added, so they were disagreeably soggy. The toast arrived not well done, but burnt.
****

ONICH Highland   Map 5

Cuilcheanna House   NEW/BUDGET   *Tel* (01855) 821226
Onich, by Fort William PH33 6SD

E-mail relax@cuilcheanna.freeserve.co.uk

Quietly secluded beside Loch Linnhe, this neat white country house
stands in its own grounds with views across the lake to the Mull mountains – "a wonderful setting", says its nominator. "It is comfortable,
and Russell and Linda Scott are warm, hospitable hosts. Linda uses
quality ingredients for her creative dinners, served by candlelight. The
six bedrooms are well furnished, and some have loch views. The
lounge, comfortable but a little small, has log fires, books and television." Smoked venison with avocado; breast of duck in a mulled
wine sauce; pear and bramble oatmeal crumble, might feature on the
simple no-choice menus (the Scotts describe the food as "traditional
home cooking, with peasant and foreign influences"). The house has
just been refurbished. Local wildlife includes roe deer, red squirrels,
seals and otters. Fort William and Glencoe are within easy reach. So
is Corran ferry, making day-trips possible to Morvern, the Isle of Mull
or the lovely Ardnanmurchan peninsula. Autumn breaks are offered
(when the colours are particularly beautiful); wine and food weekends
are held. (*Sheila Matthews*)

Open Easter–end Oct.
Rooms 7 double. No telephone/TV.
Facilities Lounge with TV, dining room. No background music. Garden. 110
metres from Loch Linnhe. Shingle beach. Unsuitable for &.
Location 10 miles SW of Fort William (infrequent buses); off A82 (sign-
posted).
Restrictions No smoking. No children under 12. No dogs in public rooms.
Credit cards MasterCard, Visa.
Terms B&B £29–£44; D,B&B £48–£63. Set dinner £19. Autumn breaks.
Stays of more than 1 night encouraged over bank holidays, etc.

PEEBLES Scottish Borders   Map 5

Castle Venlaw   *Tel* (01721) 720384
Edinburgh Road   *Fax* (01721) 724066
Peebles EH45 8QG

E-mail enquiries@venlaw.co.uk
Website www.venlaw.co.uk

"A good find, and a good spot for breaking the north/south journey,"
a regular *Guide* correspondent wrote this year. An earlier visitor "was
delighted with every aspect of his stay". But there is one report this
year of a disappointing breakfast. The romantic, turreted 18th-century
mansion is set in large wooded grounds on the slopes of the Moorfoot
Hills ("stunning views"). The "relaxing feel" and "efficient staff" are
admired, and "recent tasteful refurbishment has created a homely
feel". The owners, John and Shirley Sloggie, formerly ran Dryburgh
Abbey, St Boswells. "The food was a wonderful surprise." Good
traditional Scottish ingredients, with some dashing sauces, are served
in generous portions by Alex Burns, eg, roast saddle of lamb, with

apricots and herbs and a redcurrant and mint essence; fillet of venison
with aubergines and a red wine glaze; roast breast of duck with a
banana and nutmeg cream. Light meals are available. Many bedrooms
are large. The young are welcomed: the family suite in the tower has
a children's "den" with bunk beds, games and books. Fishing on the
Tweed can be arranged. You can leave your car and take a regular bus
for a day's outing to Edinburgh, 24 miles away. (*John Campbell,
Peter Fowler*)

Open All year.
Rooms One 2-roomed family suite, 12 double.
Facilities Library bar (background music), restaurant. 4-acre grounds.
Fishing, walking, golf, cycling nearby. Unsuitable for &.
Location 2 miles NE of Peebles. Take A702 to Edinburgh. Hotel drive on
right ¾ mile.
Restrictions No smoking: restaurant, some bedrooms. No children under 5 in
restaurant after 7.30 pm. No dogs in public rooms.
Credit cards MasterCard, Visa.
Terms B&B £50–£80; D,B&B £59.50–£90. Set dinner £23.50; full alc £35.
Child accommodated in parents' room: under 2, free; 2–12, B&B £12.50.
Christmas, New Year packages. *V*

See also SHORTLIST

PENNYGHAEL Argyll and Bute   **Map 5**

Pennyghael Hotel   BUDGET   *Tel* (01681) 704288
Isle of Mull PA70 6HB   *Fax* (01681) 704205

"A delightful place," says a visitor this year of this small, informally
run hotel. "Owners Tony and Sandra Read manage the right blend of
friendliness and professionalism." Others wrote of "excellent hosts"
and "value for money". The decor may be "somewhat old-
fashioned", and one visitor thought the place "lacked ambience . . .
outside is stark, with a huge, grey carpark". But a visitor on her own
appreciated not being charged a single supplement off-season. She
admired the breakfasts ("nothing packaged"), and the dinners:
"Limited choice (ordered at breakfast); everything beautifully cooked
and presented; wonderful puddings." The small white 17th-century
farmhouse stands on the shores of Loch Scridain, a deep inlet on the
west coast of the island. The lounge/bar, recently redecorated, has a
good supply of malt whiskies; the dining room has an open fire and
views from Ben More (Mull's highest peak) to Iona ("We have one
of the best views in the UK," say the Reads). "The sunsets are wonderful." Local fish, seafood and lamb, traditionally cooked (eg, cullen
skink; roast rack of lamb), are served by candlelight. Breakfast
includes fruit salad as well as a traditional Scottish breakfast. The
bedrooms and bathrooms are simple and spotless; all but one have a
loch view. There are some spacious self-catering cottages, suitable
for families – children under 12 are not allowed in the hotel itself. The
rocky shoreline is home to a huge variety of wildlife: otters, golden
eagles, buzzards, red deer, and perhaps a pine marten. The island also

has a great variety of wild flowers. Buses are infrequent; a car is essential if you want to tour. (*Julia MacKenzie, Mrs J Wilkinson, and others*)

Open Mar–Oct.
Rooms 6 double. 2 on ground floor, with ramp. Also 3 self-catering cottages.
Facilities Lounge/bar (occasional "semi-classical" background music), dining room. 1-acre grounds on sea loch (shingle beach).
Location On A849 to Iona, beside Loch Scridain. Ferry from Oban.
Restrictions No smoking in dining room. Children under 12 in self-catering cottages only. Small dogs only; not in public rooms.
Credit cards MasterCard, Visa.
Terms B&B £30–£46; D,B&B £50–£66. Set dinner £19.95. Reductions for 3 nights or more.

PLOCKTON Highland   Map 5

The Haven   NEW   *Tel* (01599) 544223 and 544334
Plockton IV52 8TW   *Fax* (01599) 544467
                        Website www.smoothhound.co.uk/hotels/thehaven

A converted merchants' house, built around 1900, which stands near the harbour in a picturesque National Trust village – "a crescent of white cottages, with views of small boats, even palm trees, and steep blue hills ringing the opposite shore". The owners, Annan and Jill Dryburgh, "maintain high standards", says a visitor in 2000, reintroducing it to our pages. "They have refurbished the bedrooms to a pleasing ambience." One guest had a spacious single bedroom; others wrote of rooms that were "bright and pretty", with good views. Two suites have been added this year. The owners offer "remarkable value", all agree. The large dining room, graced by a pipe organ, is popular with non-residents. Here Ian Fraser's modern Scottish cooking was found "still superb", with a choice of five or six dishes for each course, "all originally conceived" (eg, cocotte of lobster tails; roast chicken stuffed with black pudding; Aberdeen Angus fillet on a hazelnut galette with red wine gravy and quenelles of celeriac). "Excellent range and quality of half-bottle wines. Good breakfast too, but little use of fresh fruit. I had to complain about the piped music – either a Gaelic dirge or mindless rock." Service is "Irish and intelligent". There are log fires in the lounges for winter, a conservatory for summer. Nearby are Glenelg, and Sandaig where Gavin Maxwell lived (you may see otters on the banks of the loch). (*CC Schofield, EM Arnold*)

Open 1 Feb–20 Dec. Restaurant closed midday.
Rooms 2 suites, 12 double, 1 single.
Facilities 2 lounges, conservatory, cocktail bar, dining room; Scottish background music evenings. 1¼-acre grounds. Loch 30 yds; boating, fishing, sea trips, etc. Unsuitable for &.
Location In village, 5 miles N of Kyle of Lochalsh. Private parking.
Restrictions No smoking in dining room and in 1 lounge. No children under 7. No dogs in public rooms.
Credit cards MasterCard, Visa.
Terms B&B £36–£39; D,B&B £53–£75. Set dinner £27. Mini-breaks.

PORT APPIN Argyll and Bute   **Map 5**

The Airds Hotel   *Tel* (01631) 730236
Port Appin PA38 4DF   *Fax* (01631) 730535
                                            E-mail airds@airds-hotel.com
                                            Website www.airds-hotel.com

♀ *César award in 1994*

"A cosseting atmosphere, and a warm welcome from our old friends
Betty and Eric Allen" – another delighted plaudit this year from devotees of this small hotel overlooking Loch Linnhe. Other visitors
thought it "lovely in almost every regard". Once a ferry inn, it is now
a sybaritic Relais & Châteaux member, owned by the Allens for many
years. Their son Graeme is manager, and co-chef with Steve
McCallum. Other recent praise: "Everything is delightful, the food is
superb." "Modern British" in style, its *Michelin* star was again found
well merited this year: "We loved the glorious venison, seared salmon
with a champagne sauce, monkfish with asparagus and red cabbage,
red pepper soup." "The chicken, fish and lamb are all local, each with
an unusual sauce; lovely puddings, eg, prune and almond tart with
prune and Armagnac ice-cream. Impeccable table settings; impeccable young staff. Delicious snack lunches, served on pretty china." "An
excellent picnic lunch, well worth the modest cost." "Breakfasts
lovely." There is a colourful little garden in front of the hotel. The bedrooms and bathrooms are chic and pretty (some, at the top, are small).
"Ours was charming and spacious. It looked over the garden, a field of
yellow buttercups, the loch, with a wee lighthouse, to the mountains
beyond." The drawing rooms are "friendly", with chintzes, patterned
carpets, pictures of Scottish scenes, open fires and flowers. The little
conservatory, in front, is "a delightful place for pre-dinner drinks,
always accompanied by delicious nibbles". A short walk leads to
Port Appin and a boat trip to Lismore; seals can sometimes be seen
playing in the loch. (*George and Jean Dundas, John and Sandy
Chute, and others*)

Open All year, except Christmas, Restaurant closed 6–26 Jan.
Rooms 1 suite, 11 double. 2 on ground floor. Also 4 double (budget) in *Linnhe
House* 60 yds.
Facilities 2 lounges, conservatory restaurant. No background music. 1-acre
garden. Near loch: shingle beach, bathing, fishing, boating; pony-trekking, for-
est walks nearby. Unsuitable for &.
Location 2 miles off A828, 25 miles from Fort William (N) and Oban (S).
Parking.
Restrictions No smoking in restaurant. No children under 8 in restaurant at
night. Dogs by arrangement; not in public rooms.
Credit cards MasterCard, Visa.
Terms [2000] D,B&B £98 (winter)–£149 (*Linnhe House* £85). Set dinner £45.

There are many expensive hotels in the *Guide*. We are keen to
increase our coverage at the other end of the scale. If you know
of a simple place giving simple satisfaction, do please write
and tell us about it.

PORTPATRICK Dumfries and Galloway   **Map 5**

Knockinaam Lodge   NEW   *Tel* (01776) 810471
                                               Fax (01776) 810435

"Splendid." "A triumph of understated luxury." "Enjoyable cosseting, and all meals were superb." Several readers write to reinstate this grey house by the sea (Pride of Britain), which fell from last year's *Guide* after criticisms. Its Canadian owners, Michael Bricker and Pauline Ashworth, offer "warm hospitality", and it is "splendidly secluded", up a three-mile track through wooded hills: "The only sounds in the subtropical gardens are the gentle lapping of the sea and the birdsong." The setting is spectacular, with cliffs on three sides, and it is so remote that Eisenhower and Churchill met here secretly during the war (you can sleep in the latter's bedroom). On a clear day the Irish coast is visible. Bedrooms vary in size (some are a bit cramped) and some have bath only, no shower. All have videos, books, etc. "Our room had a huge bed, and the bathtub was a vast antique. A vase of lilies greeted us." "Everywhere was spotless and well looked after." The cooking, by Salford-born Tony Pierce, is "modern British", and wins a *Michelin* star plus *Guide* readers' praise: "Excellent hot vichyssoise soup, salmon fillet with Parmesan, guinea fowl with Bayonne ham and garlic sauce; superb raspberry soufflé and bittersweet chocolate tart. Delicious warm pre-dinner nibbles (eg, mini pots of caviar). Wines were well served, from a very long list" (they are expensive). Food is "beautifully presented, and served with panache by an enthusiastic Scottish and French staff". "We enjoyed the staff, who seemed to enjoy us too." They will baby-sit by intercom, and "our labrador was made as welcome as us, for £10 a night". Breakfasts are liked. The garden seems to have been tidied up, but the beach can become litter-strewn. Logan, Castle Kennedy and Ardwell House gardens are nearby, and the dangerous tidal race at the Mull of Galloway is worth watching. (*TW Child, Shirley Tennent, Ran Ogston, Peter and Elizabeth Shattuck*)

Open All year.
Rooms 9 double, 1 single.
Facilities 2 lounges, bar, restaurant (light classical music during meals). 30-acre grounds: garden, children's play area, croquet; beach 50 yds. Bathing, sea fishing, golf nearby. Only restaurant suitable for &.
Location 8 miles SW of Stranraer. From A77/A75 follow signs for Portpatrick. Left at *Knockinaam* sign (2 miles W of Lochans); follow signs to hotel (3 miles).
Restrictions No smoking in restaurant. No children under 12 in dining room after 7 pm (high tea 6 pm). No dogs in public rooms.
Credit cards All major cards accepted.
Terms [2000] D,B&B £80.50–£175. Set lunch £29, dinner £38. Special rates for 3 days or more. Christmas package. *V*

The "New" label indicates hotels which are appearing in the *Guide* for the first time, or which have been readmitted after an absence.

PORTREE Highland   Map 5

Viewfield House   *Tel* (01478) 612217
Portree, Isle of Skye IV51 9EU   *Fax* (01478) 613517
                                        Website www.skye.co.uk/viewfield

Q *César award in 1993*

Telephones have been installed in the bedrooms this year – a rare concession to the modern world that may worry some of its admirers – at this baronial pile where little else (save the plumbing) has changed since before 1914. "Splendidly eccentric" and with "charming owners", it stands in large wooded grounds outside Skye's main town, and is run as a guest house by Hugh Macdonald, whose family home it has been since the 18th century. Stags' horns, stuffed eagles and fading family portraits are among its adornments. The hall is a repository of imperial mementos: Persian carpets, Burmese gongs, Benares brass, and bric-à-brac of the Raj. Visitors enjoy its good food and warm friendliness – notably Americans, one of whom thought it "the best deal of any place I've stayed in Scotland". He enjoyed the after-dinner conversation with fellow guests. Another view: "The atmosphere is quirky, but it grew on us over five days. The downstairs gentlemen's cloakroom is a museum piece. The dining room is amazing – the wallpaper must be 100 years old." An open fire burns in the "gorgeous sitting room". Do not expect hotel-style reception and facilities or a formal bar, but drinks are served at any time on request. A gong sounds for dinner, served with heavy old family silver and crystal; the meal is generally communal, but there are some separate tables. The laird's Californian wife, Linda, cooks five-course traditional Scottish dinners; no choice, but vegetarian dishes, and a fish option for the main course are always available. Pheasant breasts with whisky sauce might follow goat's cheese and red onion marmalade parcels. Helpings are huge, with up to five different vegetables. Puddings include elderflower syrup cake with strawberries. Breakfast is "excellent, with high-quality local produce". The bedrooms are "spotless and well furnished"; most are large, with a large bathroom (no shampoos, etc), and a view of the loch, but one on the nursery floor is small, with a minute bathroom, and one was found cold in April. (*Conrad and Marilyn Dehn*)

Open Mid-Apr–mid-Oct.
Rooms 10 double, 2 single, 10 with private facilities. 1 on ground floor. No TV.
Facilities Drawing room, morning/TV room, dining room. No background music. 20-acre grounds: croquet, swings, woodland walks, garden centre. Sea fishing 200 yds, river fishing 2 miles.
Location S side of Portree, 10 mins' walk from centre. Take A87 towards Broadford; turn right just after BP station on left. Bus from Portree passes entrance.
Restrictions Smoking banned in dining room, discouraged in bedrooms. No dogs in public rooms.
Credit cards MasterCard, Visa
Terms B&B £35–£47.50. Set dinner £20. Packed lunches available. 3/5-day rates. 1-night group bookings sometimes refused.

ST ANDREWS Fife *See SHORTLIST*   **Map 5**

ST MARGARET'S HOPE Orkney   **Map 5**

The Creel Inn   *Tel* (01856) 831311
Front Road
St Margaret's Hope KW17 2SL

Restaurant with 3 bedrooms in main village of South Ronaldsay, 20 mins' drive S of Orkney's capital, Kirkwall. On village seafront, with lovely views across bay. Much admired for cooking "with Orcadian influence" of chef/proprietor Alan Craigie, especially seafood and local beef, eg, lobster and wolf-fish broth; roasted sea scallop and monkfish tails. His wife, Joyce, "is an excellent host". "Bedrooms fine but not luxurious; excellent breakfasts (porridge, local kippers); good value for money." Open daily May–Sept, weekends in winter, except Oct, Jan, Feb. Small lounge, 2 dining rooms. Unsuitable for &. No smoking: restaurant, bedrooms. No dogs. MasterCard, Visa accepted. B&B: single £40–£45, double £60–£65. Full alc £34. More reports, please.

SHIELDAIG Highland   **Map 5**

Tigh an Eilean   *Tel* (01520) 755251
Shieldaig   *Fax* (01520) 755321
by Strathcarron IV54 8XN   *E-mail* tighaneileanhotel@shieldaig.fsnet.co.uk

New owners Christopher and Cathryn Field took over from Callum and Elizabeth Stewart in 1999, and visitors since then have found that this old inn remains "a lovely place to stay". "It is still our favourite hotel." "Mrs Field is omnipresent, the ambience is relaxed and the general impression is excellent." It is a group of old slated buildings beside a sea loch, in a village (touristy in season) amid the Torridon Hills of Wester Ross. No garden, but you can eat or drink on benches outside the bar, looking across the shore to Shieldaig island, a sanctuary for ancient pines (National Trust). Bedrooms are "very clean and tastefully furnished". There is a "neat and prettily decorated" two-room lounge; its library has been extended to include more books on the area. The dining room has a "light, open feeling". Christopher Field and Fiona Peacock (who has stayed on from the previous regime) produce cooking that is "as superb as ever". There is an emphasis on local shellfish and fish (delivered from the village jetty that day) and game, plus such assorted dishes as carrot, ginger and honey soup; osso bucco; medallions of beef Café de Paris; apple crumble. The menus change each night, and the wine list "contains some real bargains". Good bar snacks are served. The copious breakfasts include "excellent porridge"; but one reader found the coffee poor. Children are flexibly catered for, and "well-behaved dogs" are welcomed. Fishing (salmon, sea- and brown trout) can be arranged on the River Balgy and Loch Damh. Guests may look at the stars through the owners' ten-inch astronomical telescope. There is excellent walking and climbing, and a nine-hole golf course at Lochcarron. (*John and Anne Heaton, David and Hannah Rampton, and others; also Good Pub Guide*)

Open Early Apr–end Oct.
Rooms 8 double, 3 single. No telephone/TV.
Facilities Lounge, TV lounge, bar/library, public bar (separate entrance), dining room; drying room. No background music. Fishing, swimming, hillwalking, golf nearby. Unsuitable for &.
Location Centre of quiet village off A896. Parking opposite. Train: Strathcarran; bus connects with lunchtime train, or hotel will meet.
Restrictions No smoking in dining room. No dogs in public rooms.
Credit cards MasterCard, Visa.
Terms [2000] B&B £48.55–£53.80; D,B&B £74.80–£80.05. Bar meals. Set dinner £26.25. Child accommodated in parents' room: under 8, free; 8–13, 50% of adult rate. Reductions for 5 nights or more.

SKIRLING Scottish Borders						**Map 5**

Skirling House						*Tel* (01899) 860274
Skirling, Biggar ML12 6HD						*Fax* (01899) 860255
						E-mail enquiry@skirlinghouse.com
						Website www.skirlinghouse.com

Again this year, there are rave reviews for perhaps the best-loved of all our Scottish entries. "Kind and gracious hosts." "Lovely country house atmosphere, delicious food." "Maybe the best of the small hotels we've ever visited." On the green of a tiny village amid lovely Borders scenery, it is run as a Wolsey Lodge by Bob and Isobel Hunter. Built in 1908 as the summer home of a Scottish art connoisseur, Lord Carmichael, it is a fine example of the Arts and Crafts movement, with decorative carvings, remarkable wrought iron sculptures of animals, and in the drawing room a 16th-century carved wood Florentine ceiling. "It is a fascinating house, beautifully looked after"; "We were entranced"; "It all looked freshly painted", visitors have written. Others have admired the sophisticated style, the elegant furnishings, the exquisite china, the large beds in large bedrooms, the "big white fluffy towels and bathrobes". Bob Hunter is in charge of the guests and the cooking (his wife has a full-time job in Edinburgh, but is present in the evenings). The food is "modern Scottish, with influences from the southern and south-western US", and the four-course no-choice dinners, served at 8 pm (usually at separate tables) are always much enjoyed, eg, tomato and spinach risotto; Southern barbecue pork; Barbary duck with teriyaki sauce; "superb" goat's cheese soufflé; lemon and lime posset. There is an "excellent wine list". You can take drinks in the garden; afternoon tea with fruitcake, and after-dinner coffee are served by a fire in the lounge. "Great breakfasts" include "wonderful spiced fruit", "delicious home-made potato scones served with bacon and eggs", "fish-cakes with perfectly poached eggs". A study has been added this year and the conservatory rebuilt. The owners' two black labradors and "two beautiful cats" are much in evidence. A good base for exploring the Borders, also Neidpath

Castle, Trequair House, and Peebles. (*Robert Friedus, Margaret Kershaw, Mrs E Brice, Charlotte Stadtman, and others*)

Open Mar–Dec (including New Year). Closed Christmas, 1 week in Nov.
Rooms 4 double. 1 on ground floor. Also 2 cottages (normally self-catering units).
Facilities Drawing room, study, dining room, conservatory. No background music. 5½-acre garden: tennis, croquet. Fishing on River Tweed.
Location Facing green in lower part of village on A72, 2 miles E of Biggar. Local buses.
Restrictions No smoking. Dogs by arrangement, not in public rooms.
Credit cards MasterCard, Visa.
Terms B&B £35–£45. Set dinner £22. *V*

SPEAN BRIDGE Highland   Map 5

Corriegour Lodge   *Tel* (01397) 712685
Loch Lochy   *Fax* (01397) 712696
by Spean Bridge PH34 4EB   *E-mail* info@corriegour-lodge-hotel.com
                                  Website www.corriegour-lodge-hotel.com

A Victorian hunting lodge owned by Christian Drew, who runs it with her son Ian (the chef). It stands above Loch Lochy in wooded grounds, and it looks across the water, a mature garden, and an attractive private beach with a jetty (a boat and fishing reels are available). One visitor writes of the "very friendly welcome, especially from the cat" (there are also three dogs), and of the "very comfortable residents' lounge". "Cosy rather than smart", it has patterned wallpaper, stripped pine, a log fire. There are flowery fabrics and bits of old furniture in the bedrooms (most overlook the view), and board games in the family room. In the conservatory restaurant (with a "wonderful view over the loch"), the cooking is "pretty good, freshly cooked and attractively presented", with service by local women. "Traditional dishes with a modern influence" use Scottish produce, eg, sweet Orkney herrings with a caper and lemon vinaigrette; chargrilled Aberdeen Angus sirloin steak with grilled red onions; fondant of chocolate with a Drambuie and hazelnut sauce. Vegetarians and special diets are catered for, given notice. The grounds up the hillside behind the house are good for walking and there are two Munros directly opposite. Spean Bridge is famous for Scott Sutherland's dramatic Commando Memorial, erected in 1952 (the commandos trained in the surrounding countryside during World War II). A good base for touring: the Great Glen, Loch Ness, Castle Urquhart, Ben Nevis, the Ardnamurchan peninsula, a drive to Skye or Inverness. (*Fiona Dick*)

Open Apr–Nov, 27 Dec–4 Jan; weekends only Feb, Mar.
Rooms 7 double, 2 single.
Facilities Lounge, cocktail bar, dining room (Celtic background music at dinner). 9-acre grounds on loch: beach, fishing, jetty, mooring for guests' boats, woods, waterfall. Skiing, climbing, sailing nearby. Unsuitable for &.
Location 17 miles NE of Fort William, on A82, on S side of Loch Lochy, between Spean Bridge and Invergarry. Train: Spean Bridge (9 miles), Fort William (17 miles).
Restrictions No smoking: restaurant, 3 bedrooms. No children under 8. No dogs.

Credit cards Diners, MasterCard, Visa.
Terms B&B £46–£59.50; D,B&B £66–£69.50. Set lunch £10.50, dinner £29.50. Spring, autumn, New Year packages; fishing package with tuition. *V*

Old Pines
Spean Bridge
by Fort William
PH34 4EG

Tel (01397) 712324
Fax (01397) 712433
E-mail billandsukie@oldpines.co.uk
Website www.oldpines.co.uk

"A real find." "Excellent food, very friendly staff." More enthusiasm this year for Bill and Sukie Barber's informally run restaurant-with-rooms (it is a *Good Food Guide* restaurant of the year in 2000, and Mrs Barber is a Master Chef of Great Britain). It was converted in 1990 from their family home, which was built some 20 years ago in Scandinavian style. It stands among Scots pines in large grounds above this Highland village, with fine views across to Aonach Mor and Ben Nevis. "Highly original, a marvellous place," wrote inspectors, while others have enjoyed "the relaxed atmosphere, the excellent food, and the helpful young Australian staff". Dining is communal, at tables of four or six. "It can lend to the atmosphere, and we had interesting companions. Mrs Barber's cooking is of a high dinner-party standard: warm chicken liver salad; red pepper soup; salmon then cheese and ice-cream. For breakfast, home-smoked salmon, scrambled eggs from the Barbers' hens." No choice on the dinner menu, served at 8; it is displayed at teatime so that alternatives can be requested. Bread, preserves, pasta and ice-creams are home made; locally grown organic fruit and vegetables are used, and the Barbers have their own smoke-house. The friendly atmosphere is largely thanks to the host: "He has great charm, chatting with guests, creating a house-party ambience. First names are often used." The bedrooms have a smart modern rustic decor (but some bathrooms are small). As it is all on one level, the house is suitable for visitors in a wheelchair. Children are welcomed (the Barbers have six of their own) and are charged just £7.50 per visit, plus food. They take high tea in the kitchen with the hosts' children – "it was a delight to see them play together among the ducks, geese and assorted resident animals". The half-board rate includes early morning tea, and afternoon tea with scones and cakes. (*Mr and Mrs JT Mills, and others*)

Open Almost all year (please check). Restaurant closed Sun to non-residents Apr–Sept, occasionally in winter.
Rooms 1 family suite, 1 family room, 5 double, 1 single. All on ground floor; 1 adapted for ♿. No telephone.
Facilities Ramp. 3 sitting rooms, restaurant; children's playroom. No background music. 30-acre grounds: children's play areas. Free loch fishing 2 miles, sea 10 miles. Wedding facilities.
Location 1 mile N of Spean Bridge. Turn off A82 on to B8004 by Commando Memorial; 300 yds on right. Train: Fort William; then bus, or they will meet.
Restrictions No smoking. No small children in restaurant at night. No dogs in house.
Credit cards MasterCard, Visa.
Terms D,B&B £60–£75, family room for 4, £135–£225. Set dinner £24.50–£30. Child accommodated in parents' room: £7.50 plus food. 3- to 7-night rates. New Year package. *V*

STRATHYRE Stirling **Map 5**

Creagan House   *Tel* (01877) 384638
Strathyre FK18 8ND   *Fax* (01877) 384319
                               E-mail mail@creaganhouse.fsnet.co.uk
                               Website www.milford.co.uk/go/creaganhouse.html

"It was first-class," runs this year's comment on Gordon and Cherry
Gunn's restaurant-with-rooms in a 17th-century farmhouse. It stands
in a sheltered valley at the head of Loch Lubnaig, on a road that is busy
by day but quiet by night. It has been called "a quaint place": the old
parlour and the small, cosy drawing room are filled with ornately
carved antique pieces of Scottish furniture, and a miscellany of objects
and souvenirs. The dining room is an "amazing 1970s baronial-style
addition". It has a steep vaulted ceiling, a highly polished oak floor and
trestle tables. A vast fireplace, flanked by stone lions and adorned with
swords and flags, occupies one end of the room, which is warmed by
a vigorous gas log fire. Mrs Gunn "makes every guest feel special";
her husband is "a talented chef" who describes his cooking as classical French with strong Scottish overtones, eg, smokie in a pokie (a
smoked fish starter); braised lamb on clapshot flavoured with garlic
and rosemary; John Dory on Provençal vegetables. The plentiful
vegetables, many organically grown, are "cooked to perfection", and
the home-made desserts are "mouth-watering", says this year's visitor. The bedrooms are cottagey, with dark oak beams and furniture;
one has a four-poster bed. "Heavenly" breakfasts include good porridge, eggs "from across the road", cooked any way, honey from local
bees. "Good value for money" is the general verdict. There is a new
"head receptionist" (Bruce, a Gordon setter), the Gunns tell us, and
visitors' dogs are welcomed (their owners are asked to make a donation to Guide Dogs for the Blind). Plenty of activities are available
(see below); local sights include Scone Palace, Stirling Castle,
Drummond Castle's gardens, the Scottish antique and arts centre at
Doune. (*Mrs W Montague*)

Open All year, except 28 Jan–2 Mar, 1 week Oct. Restaurant opened midday
for groups only.
Rooms 5 double. 1 on ground floor. TV on request. No telephone.
Facilities Lounge, restaurant; writing room/private dining room. No back-
ground music. 1-acre grounds: stream; access to Queen Elizabeth Forest Park.
Golf, fishing, shooting, climbing, cycling, water sports nearby.
Location ¼ mile N of village, set back from A84 (some traffic noise).
Restrictions No smoking: restaurant, bedrooms. No dogs in public rooms.
Credit cards Amex, MasterCard, Visa.
Terms B&B: single £52.50, double £85. Set dinner £25.50. 10% reduction for
3 or more days; Christmas package. ***V***

****

Hotel in Worcestershire. The bedroom was dingy. The lights
flickered off and on, and then failed; the staff admitted to us that
the wiring was faulty. The windows had frosted glass, so we had
no view.

****

STRONTIAN Highland   Map 5

Kilcamb Lodge	*Tel* (01967) 402257
Strontian, Acharacle	*Fax* (01967) 402041
PH36 4HY	*E-mail* kilcamblodge@aol.com
	Website www.lochaber.com

۞ *César award in 1997*

"Most romantic", yet with "highly professional service", Peter and Anne Blakeway's stone house, Georgian with Victorian additions, has "an incomparable setting" on the edge of a small village on Loch Sunart. It was enjoyed again this year: "Our room was beautifully furnished in yellow and blue, and the view from it was breathtaking. Dinner and breakfast, welcome and comfort, and the turn-down service at night, were all excellent." The hotel has many faithful guests who have been coming for years; the Blakeways have had to cope with the death last year of Mrs Blakeway senior, but her husband, Gordon, is still here; he grows vegetables and goes fishing for the kitchen. On the way to the Ardnamurchan peninsula, the house is reached by a steep drive off a scenic road through Glen Tarbert, after a short ride on the Corran ferry. In spring its large grounds are colourful with rhododendrons, azaleas and rare wild flowers. There's plenty of wildlife too: red deer, squirrels, otters and seals, pine martens, hawks and golden eagles. Inside, the lounges, "comfortable in a chintzy way", have open fires, fresh flowers, decorative plates. The bedrooms are priced according to size and aspect; the best ones are spacious, with handsome fabrics, a window seat and a loch view. Neil Mellis cooks modern dishes on menus with plenty of choice, eg, warm salad of hare with black pudding; roast saddle of venison with red cabbage and chocolate sauce; Crannachan. The Gordon girls – free-range chickens – provide fresh eggs every day, and breakfast has freshly squeezed fruit juices, freshly baked croissants, and a good selection of cereals, etc. "The cooking has gained in maturity," wrote one visitor, who also appreciated the new pricing structure: you pay for the room, and breakfast and dinner are added, priced according to what you consume. But another commented: "Though wider, paradoxically, the menu is now less varied; only the soup changed during our four-day stay." A day-trip to Mull or Skye is possible, or an outing in the hotel's fishing boat. (*Mrs E Brice, Padi Howard, Patricia Simpson, John CP Cole*)

Open Mar–Nov, New Year.
Rooms 10 double, 1 single. No telephone. 2 self-catering cottages.
Facilities Drawing room, lounge/bar, restaurant. No background music. 28-acre grounds on loch: private beach, fishing, boating; mountain bikes available. Pony-trekking, golf, stalking nearby.
Location From A82 S of Fort William take Corran ferry, then A861 to Strontian.
Restrictions No smoking: restaurant, bedrooms. Dogs by arrangement; not in public rooms.
Credit cards MasterCard, Visa.
Terms [2000] Room: single £48–£90, double £64–£130. Breakfast £8.50–£12.50. Set dinner (2 to 4 courses) £20.50–£29.50. 10% discount for 3–5 nights. New Year package.

SWINTON Scottish Borders   **Map 5**

The Wheatsheaf	*Tel* (01890) 860257
Main Street	*Fax* (01890) 860688
Swinton, nr Duns TD11 3JJ	

Alan and Julie Reid's "extremely well-run and rather civilised" old stone-built inn is on the green of a peaceful village, close to the Berwickshire coast and the River Tweed. And in 2000 Mr Reid, who is also chef, again won the Scottish Borders Tourist Board's top award for the best eating place in the region. Our readers also found his modern cooking "very enjoyable". It is served informally in the bar, which has a daily-changing blackboard menu, and in the smarter restaurant, which specialises in Scottish game and seafood. Its menu, changing according to season, includes, eg, black pudding and clap-shot cake with breast of wood pigeon; Barbary duck with poached apple on a cider and Calvados sauce; braised oxtails in real ale sauce; iced Drambuie parfait with raspberry coulis. No residents' lounge, but there is a small conservatory with a pine vaulted ceiling and walls of local stone. The bedrooms are simple, and those on the road side can get traffic noise. All have a bathroom or shower *en suite*. Service is "friendly and welcoming", and breakfast, "served with style and verve", includes freshly squeezed orange juice, smoked salmon with scrambled egg, grilled kippers, or a grilled vegetarian dish. "Very good packed lunches for fishermen and walkers." All around is the agricultural land of Merse. Local attractions include Paxton House, Abbotsford (home of Sir Walter Scott), and Mellerstain, a fine Adam house. (*Good Pub Guide, AJM Ribeiro dos Santos, JL*)

Open All year, except 1st week Jan, Christmas. Restaurant closed Mon midday.
Rooms 2 suites, 4 double, 1 single. 3 with telephone.
Facilities Lounge bar, public bar, restaurant, conservatory; boot room, drying room. No background music. 1-acre garden: patio, children's play area. River Tweed 4 miles; fishing; golf nearby. Unsuitable for &.
Location Centre of village 12 miles SW of Berwick-upon-Tweed, on road to Kelso (also 12 miles). The 2 front rooms get traffic noise. Parking. Train: Berwick; then taxi.
Restrictions No smoking: restaurant, bedrooms. No dogs in public rooms.
Credit cards MasterCard, Visa.
Terms B&B: single £49–£65, double £82–£85, suite £98–£105. Full alc: lunch £15–£18, dinner £25–£30. Stay 7 nights, pay for 6.

TALISKER Highland   **Map 5**

Talisker House	*Tel* (01478) 640245
Talisker	*Fax* (01478) 640214
Isle of Skye IV47 85F	*E-mail* jon_and_ros.wathen@virgin.net
	Website www.talisker.co.uk

"Helpful hosts, very good food, large cosy bedroom," runs new praise in 2000 for this "lovely Georgian house in a beautiful setting" on the dramatic west coast of Skye, beneath Preshal Mhor. Built in the 1720s as the dower house of the MacLeod family, it was visited by Johnson and Boswell on their tour of the Hebrides in 1773. "It is still a family home," say the owners, Jon and Ros Wathen. And one reader thought it the nicest Scottish guest house he had ever visited – "an interesting building, with superb plasterwork, in the magically beautiful setting of a large garden and mature trees. Delicious home-cooked food." The Wathens describe this as "modern Australian eclectic". A no-choice menu: eg, cheese and leek soup; poached salmon with garlic, kale and salsa verde; date pudding with caramel sauce. Some ingredients are home-grown. Ice-creams are home-made; bread is home-baked. Picnic lunches are good, and the "excellent cooked breakfast" comes with home-made preserves, on "tables set with silver jugs". Fine views from the large bedrooms, with lavender bags on the pillows "for sweet dreams". All this is enjoyed in a smoke-free, piped music-free environment. It is a Wolsey Lodge, "so there is socialising, but two tables at dinner are just for two". Talisker Bay has safe swimming, and a sandy beach at low tide. The nearby distillery produces a classic single malt. (*BW, and others*)

Open Mid-Mar–end Oct.
Rooms 4 double. No telephone/TV. 1 suitable for &.
Facilities Drawing room, dining room. No background music. 5-acre grounds: formal garden, croquet lawn. 10-min walk to Talisker Bay: sandy beach at low tide; swimming.
Location W coast of Skye. Turn left off A863 from Sligachan on to B8009 to Carbost. Veer left at top of village. Follow signs to Talisker (4 miles).
Restrictions No smoking. No dogs in house.
Credit cards MasterCard, Visa.
Terms [2000] B&B £43. Single supplement £14. Packed lunch £5. Set dinner £25.

TANGASDALE Western Isles   **Map 5**

The Isle of Barra Hotel   BUDGET   *Tel* (01871) 810383
Tangasdale Beach   *Fax* (01871) 810385
Isle of Barra HS9 5XW   *E-mail* barrahotel@aol.com
                                   Website www.isleofbarra.com/iob

You can reach Diane Worthington's purpose-built hotel either romantically, and somewhat scarily, by a small plane which lands on the cockleshell beach, or by ferry from Oban. The setting is spectacular, overlooking Halaman Bay and the Atlantic, and with panoramic views of Ben Tangaval. The cocktail bar has sea-shell pictures; the restaurant has views over the sea. The meals are "good, not too fancy", with plenty of choice, eg, fresh Barra crab with Marie Rose sauce, or smoked salmon; soup or sorbet; Barra scallops sautéed with Pernod and crème fraîche, or a vegetarian dish, such as onion and mushroom risotto in a filo basket; fruit syllabub and brandy snaps, or cheese. The 1970s-style bedrooms are functional and not especially large, but the beds are comfortable and there is plenty of hot water. The half-board rate is thought good value. Coach parties are often accommodated. Although the island is just four miles by eight there is plenty to do: walking, bicycling, wild-flower spotting, seal watching, golf, fishing, and scuba diving, and ancient Kisimul Castle, on a rocky outcrop in the bay, is worth a visit. (*M and JC*)

Open End March–early Oct, Christmas, New Year.
Rooms 30 double. No telephone.
Facilities Residents' lounge, cocktail bar, public bar (light background music; Gaelic singer once a week), restaurant. Walking, fishing, sea angling, scuba diving; golf nearby. Unsuitable for &.
Location W side of island. Ferry, 4 times a week, from Oban to Castlebay, or British Airways Express daily flight from Glasgow. Bus from ferry and airport.
Restrictions No smoking: restaurant, lounge. No dogs in public rooms.
Credit cards MasterCard, Visa.
Terms B&B £33–£47; D,B&B £47–£60. Set dinner £20.95. 7 nights for the price of 6. Child accommodated in parents' room: under 2, free; 2–5, £5; 6–12, £10. Christmas package. *V*

TARBERT Western Isles   Map 5

Leachin House   *Tel/Fax* (01859) 502157
Tarbert   *E-mail* leachin.house@virgin.net
Isle of Harris HS3 3AH   *Website* www.leachin-house.com

Linda and Diarmuid Evelyn Wood's small stone inn stands alone in a pretty garden on the shores of West Loch, facing the mountains across the loch, Taransay and the Atlantic ocean beyond, with Gilleval Glas rising to 1,500 feet immediately behind. The name of this Wolsey Lodge, pronounced lee-ak-in, means "house among the rocks", and it was built 100 years ago by Norman MacLeod, reputedly the founder of the Harris tweed industry. Diarmuid Wood's early career at sea shows in the decor: ship models, mounted seamen's knots, photographs of breaking waves, and "shipshape maintenance" everywhere. The "helpful hosts" are praised, and the house is thought "delightful". The dining room, where meals are communally served, has the original 100-year-old hand-painted French wallpaper. No liquor licence, but a carafe of wine comes with the no-choice set dinner, cooked by Linda Wood, eg, smoked wild venison; breast of duck in a mango sauce; strawberry Pavlova roulade. Coffee and chocolates afterwards, by the fire in the cosy drawing room. Morning coffee and afternoon tea are included in the price, and breakfasts are huge. Bedrooms are spacious, with "interesting old furniture"; some have a loch view. Tarbert village (population 400) is a mile away. Local attractions include beaches, seals and otters, mountain walks, and wonderful wild scenery. Fishing and sea trips can be arranged, and bicycles hired. Rugged, treeless Harris is a paradise for walkers and naturalists: orchids in April and May, and in June and July the hills are dotted with wild flowers. More reports, please.

Open All year, except Christmas/New Year.
Rooms 3 double. 1 with facilities *en suite*. No telephone.
Facilities Drawing room, dining room. No background music. ½-acre garden. Sea 60 yds: safe bathing; fishing, walking nearby. Unsuitable for &.
Location 1 mile W of Tarbert on A859. Signposted on loch side. Bus from Tarbert/Stornoway.
Restrictions No smoking. No children under 10. Dogs by arrangement; not in house.

Credit cards MasterCard, Visa.
Terms B&B £45; D,B&B £75. Set dinner £30. 1-night bookings occasionally refused. 5-day breaks. ***V*** (Nov–Feb, as alternative to house discounts)

THURSO Highland *See SHORTLIST*   **Map 5**

TIGHNABRUAICH Argyll and Bute   **Map 5**

Royal Hotel NEW   *Tel* (01700) 811239
Shore Road   *Fax* (01700) 811300
Tighnabruaich PA21 2BE   *E-mail* royalhotel@btinternet.com
                                           Website www.royalhotel.org.uk

Amid lovely scenery on shores of Kyles of Bute, traditional hotel which new owners, Roger (the chef) and Bea McKie, are refurbishing. Bold colours, local paintings and sculptures in public rooms; lots of books, family memorabilia. 11 bedrooms: best ones are "classy", with Edwardian furniture, good views, thoughtful touches. Lounge, restaurant (no smoking), brasserie/bar; jazz, classical background music. "Very good cooking, using local ingredients (venison, scallops, lobster, etc)," say inspectors. Unsuitable for &. Closed Christmas. Double room: B&B £74–£104; D,B&B £90–£160. Set dinner £25.50 [2000]. More reports, please. ***V***

TIMSGARRY Western Isles   **Map 5**

Baile-na-Cille BUDGET   *Tel* (01851) 672242
Timsgarry, Uig   *Fax* (01851) 672241
Isle of Lewis HS2 9JD   *E-mail* randjgollin@compuserve.com
                                     Website www.witb.co.uk/links/bailenacille.com

Q *César award in 1990*

Ideal for children, but less ideal for fastidious adults – one possible verdict on the Gollins' very personal seaside guest house, "way further than the back of beyond", set gloriously on a sunny bank amid sheep and rabbits, facing a lovely long white beach. "We had a splendid stay. The meals were great, the hospitality superb, and our comfortable family suite had a fine view. Richard Gollin is very good with children: he took ours under his wing, taking them on boat trips, etc. The perfect vacation!" So ran one new plaudit this year: but another visitor thought that the cheerful informality of the place "had tipped over too far towards sloppiness". Richard and Joanna Gollin have held sway for 21 years in this old manse plus converted cowshed. There are simple but well-appointed bedrooms in the main house; some can be combined to make a family unit. The three in the cowshed are cheaper but fairly basic, and this year the housekeeping and upkeep throughout the hotel were found rather poor. Mrs Gollin is often away these days – in Florida, where she runs a helicopter business, but she is there in June, July and August. The food, if not quite as good in her absence, is still enjoyed: "It was tasty, like a comforting supper: quiche, venison stew, sliced lamb. But service we found rushed." Dinners are communal: no choice, preferences discussed in advance; vegetarians are well catered for. No wine list: bottles come at two prices – "We support and drink Breaky Bottom, much to the amusement of our Scottish guests, who would die rather than try it," writes Mr Gollin. One reader thought breakfast disappointing, but another found the black pudding and local pork sausages "superb". In summer, there are sometimes games of cricket on the beach until late. And alike for old and young there are "loads of books, games and movies". Richard Gollin, "informal and funny", "offers a cheery welcome to children, dogs and grannies". One verdict: "It is a great place for families: our children loved the beach, being allowed to feed Ernie the pet lamb. But both the owners and *Baile-na-Cille* itself seemed tired." The Gollins may soon be selling, but for the moment they are planning to be in their "Shangri-La of the Outer Hebrides" for the 2001 season. (*Marshall Clarke, and others*)

Open 1 Mar–7 Oct.
Rooms 2 family suites, 8 double, 2 single. 8 with bath. 3 in cottage annexe. Some on ground floor. No telephone/TV.
Facilities 3 lounges (1 with TV, 1 with music), dining room, conservatory; games room, drying room. No background music. 3-acre grounds: walled garden, tennis, children's play area, beach (dinghy, windsurfer, fishing rods available). Beaches, safe bathing, fishing, sailing nearby. Unsuitable for ⑂.
Location 34 miles W of Stornoway. By air: Glasgow/Inverness to Stornoway; ferry from Ullapool. A858 to Garynahine, B8011 towards Uig; at Timsgarry shop (brown sign) turn right to shore. Post bus from Stornoway twice daily.
Restriction No smoking: dining room, bedrooms.
Credit cards MasterCard, Visa.
Terms B&B £24–£39; D,B&B £48–£63. Snack lunch £2–£10. Set dinner £24. Child in bunk room: B&B £14. Weekly rates.

TIRORAN Argyll and Bute   **Map 5**

Tiroran House   *Tel* (01681) 705232
Tiroran, Isle of Mull   *Fax* (01681) 705240
PA69 6ES   *E-mail* info@tiroran.com
                                                   Website www.tiroran.com

"We took French friends to this beautiful hotel, and like us they could not speak highly enough of it. The welcoming owners spoiled us with a gastronomic dinner including local lobster. The bedrooms, each with its own character, were most comfortable." So ran a report this year on Colin and Jane Tindal's old white-fronted house, set in secluded grounds with a burn and waterfalls running down to Loch Scridain. It is a Wolsey Lodge member, but not a typical one, since meals are not communally served, and the Tindals seldom eat with their guests. But it is run in similar personal style. "We try to provide guests with a relaxing stay, with chat and laughter," they write. "We do not cater for casual callers, but we welcome outside guests for dinner, by arrangement. No reductions for children." The Tindals are helped by "two charming young assistants". The six bedrooms are well decorated; the bathrooms are simple. The host looks after the lovely grounds. Using local ingredients, his wife cooks in a "down-to-earth way". Two choices each of starter and main course, eg, smoked venison with artichoke salad; roast guinea fowl with white wine, tarragon and apples; crème brûlée with summer fruit. Meals are served in a small dining room or the adjoining sunroom. Log fires in the lounges. No bar, but a restricted liquor licence. In the grounds are two self-catering cottages. The hotel is a good base for visiting Iona and Staffa, or climbing Ben More, the island's highest mountain. (*PM Lang, TG*)

Open Late Mar–end Oct. Lunch not served.
Rooms 6 double. 2 on ground floor. 2 self-catering cottages. No telephone.
Facilities 2 lounges (1 with classical radio station playing quietly before dinner), dining room with sunroom. 16-acre grounds: river, path to seashore.
Location From car ferry at Craignure or Fishnish take A849 towards Iona ferry. Right on B8035 towards Gruline. After 4 miles along sea loch, turn left at converted church. Tiroran is 1 mile further on minor road.
Restrictions No smoking. Not really suitable for children under 12. Dogs by arrangement; not in house.
Credit cards MasterCard, Visa.
Terms B&B £35–£50; D,B&B £58–£75. Set dinner £25. 1-night bookings refused high season.

TOBERMORY Argyll and Bute   **Map 5**

Western Isles Hotel   *Tel* (01688) 302012
Tobermory, Isle of Mull   *Fax* (01688) 302297
PA75 6PR   *E-mail* wihotel@aol.com
                                          Website www.mullhotel.com

"We love it," say recent guests at Michael and Sue Fink's Victorian hotel, which faces the attractive harbour of Mull's main town. "The view from the dining room and terrace, down the Sound of Mull and across to Morvern, must be one of the finest in Britain." The Finks have done much refurbishment: the decor is traditional, with patterned carpets, flowery fabrics, stags' heads on walls. "It is a 'proper' hotel in a rather old-fashioned sense, without phoney charm or masquerading as someone's country home. It provides an efficient, comfortable and enjoyable hotel experience. Best are the suites and garden rooms, and those with a sea view. The public rooms are large and relaxing. The Finks have a loyal, professional staff: many have been there for years. The food is consistently good." The restaurant, formal and traditional, serves, eg, local haggis with an orange and Glayva sauce; roast duckling with plum and spring onion sauce; warm apple crumble on a vanilla egg custard. Meals are also served in the conservatory bar. Breakfasts are "suitably copious, in Scottish style". Two rooms, Mendelssohn and Staffa, can get noise from the bar, which is open until midnight. Three other rooms have been added this year. Iona, Staffa and Fingal's Cave are easily reached. More reports, please.

Open All year, except 14–28 Dec.
Rooms 2 suites, 23 double, 3 single.
Facilities Lounge, bar, dining room; classical background music all day. 1-acre grounds. Sea 250 yds. Golf, pony-trekking nearby. Unsuitable for &. Wedding facilities.

Location Above Tobermory harbour. Hotel will help with ferry arrangements.
Restrictions No smoking in restaurant. No dogs in public rooms.
Credit cards Amex, MasterCard, Visa.
Terms B&B £45–£98; D,B&B: £54.50–£122. Bar lunch £6. Set dinner £25.
Autumn/winter breaks. *V*

ULLAPOOL Highland   **Map 5**

Altnaharrie   *Tel* (01854) 633230
Ullapool IV26 2SS

 Q *César award in 1987*

A famous and controversial restaurant-with-rooms, found mildly
eccentric by some readers, but adored by others. "It has great aesthetic
and culinary luxury," wrote one this year, who loved the
"Scandinavian beauty" of the decor, and the background of "fabulous
mountain scenery". In a remote setting on the southern shores of Loch
Broom, *Altnaharrie* cannot be reached by road, so guests make the
ten-minute crossing from Ullapool in a launch. It is the only place in
Scotland with two *Michelin* stars, awarded for the inventive and
"superb" cooking of Norwegian-born Gunn Eriksen. She is almost
never seen; her husband, Fred Brown, is front-of-house, and their staff
are "an absolute delight". Meals are served at polished antique
wooden tables "with superb cutlery", and there is no menu; Mr Brown
recites each dish and, at the end, the names of up to 20 makes of
cheese. Specialities include langoustine and scallops in champagne
gelée; two soups of artichoke with quail and foie gras; marinated fillet
of Scottish calf with roasted vegetables. "It is very, very expensive,
and very, very good. Starter, soups, sweets all exceptional. Delicious
game, superb fish," says a recent visitor. No choice until dessert; preferences are discussed at the time of booking. The wine list is "extensive and sensibly priced". "Very good porridge" at breakfast. The
bedrooms, notably those in the main building, an old drover's house,
are small; the ones in cottages in the grounds are fairly simple. They
have a kingsize bed, "masses of towels in the bathroom". No radio or
TV; lots of books. No mains electricity supply: the generator is turned
off late at night, hence the torch by the bed. "The rooms are done sensitively, with a minimum of useless frippery, yes, but with exquisite
colour and beauty, splendid warmth," says one reporter. He also
enjoyed the "comfort and taste" of the two lounges, "with flagstone
floor, rugs, candles and lamps, log fire, comfortable couches and
chairs". And all agree about the food. There is limited walking from
the house, up a steep track; further afield are heather-clad hills. Stout
footwear is recommended. Plenty of wildlife, including golden eagles,
seals and otters. Further verdicts welcome. (*Prof. NC Craig Sharp*)

Open Most of the year (please telephone).
Rooms 8 double. 3 in 2 separate buildings. No telephone/TV, etc.
Facilities 2 lounges, dining room. No background music. 2-acre garden on
loch: stream, pond, pebble beach, safe (cold) bathing; trout/salmon-fishing by
arrangement. Unsuitable for &.
Location On S shore of Loch Broom, reached by private launch (telephone
from Ullapool). Free safe parking in Ullapool. Bus from Inverness to Ullapool.

Restrictions No smoking. No children under 8. No dogs: public rooms, main house bedrooms.
Credit cards Amex, MasterCard, Visa.
Terms [2000] D,B&B £165–£245. Set 5-course dinner £70. 1-night bookings occasionally refused Sat.

The Ceilidh Place   *Tel* (01854) 612103
14 West Argyle Street   *Fax* (01854) 612886
Ullapool IV26 2TY   *E-mail* reservations@ceilidh.demon.co.uk
Q *César award in 1986*

As its name suggests, *ceilidhs*, or else jazz/blues evenings, are held three or four times weekly in summer at this "joyous place, full of character and originality". It comprises a bar, bistro, hotel, bakery, wholefood shop and arts centre with plays, poetry readings and shows by Scottish artists. It started as a coffee shop in an old boat-shed, founded by Jean and Robert Urquhart in 1970. Mrs Urquhart, now widowed, still presides. Not everyone likes the non-stop background music (classical and trad), and one visitor saw the place as "an up-market youth hostel". But most enjoy its relaxed atmosphere, myriad entertainments and genuine friendliness. The food has been praised. It is "Scottish eclectic", eg, local smoked salmon and seafood; venison pie; vegetarian dishes. In summer there is a self-service café, open all day. The lounge has games, books, a small pantry with free tea and coffee, and an honesty bar, and the furniture is crafted from local materials. "The place is stylishly furnished, comfortable, warm. In our bathroom the lovely large bars of soap were good to smell and to handle." Cheap accommodation (bunk beds, some shared rooms) is in the bunkhouse across the street. "It offers luxurious rough sleeping," says Mrs Urquhart. Ullapool, a pleasant fishing port and holiday resort near the mouth of Loch Broom, was laid out in a grid pattern in the 18th century. (*Good Pub Guide, and others*)

Open All year. Restaurant closed occasionally; coffee shop open in summer.
Rooms 10 double, 3 single. 11 more in bunkhouse across street. No TV.
Facilities Residents' lounge, café bar, parlour bar, restaurant, coffee shop; classical/trad background music all day; conference/function/wedding facilities; games room, book shop. ½-acre garden. Rocky beach, sea angling, water skiing, loch fishing, pony-trekking nearby. Only public areas suitable for &.
Location 1st right after pier at W end of Main St, then 2nd right. Large carpark. Bus twice daily, Mon–Sat, from Inverness, 64 miles.
Restrictions No smoking: restaurant, some bedrooms. No dogs in public rooms.
Credit cards All major cards accepted.
Terms [2000] Hotel: B&B £43–£60; bunkhouse: bed from £15. Full alc dinner £30. D,B&B rates for 3 nights or more. Christmas, New Year packages.

The Sheiling   BUDGET   *Tel/Fax* (01854) 612947
Garve Road, Ullapool IV26 2SX

"A great spot for lovers of the wild." With "spectacular views" across Loch Broom to the mountains beyond, this guest house, thought "wonderful" by its nominator, was designed and built by Duncan and Mhairi MacKenzie in 1989. They have rights on what they claim is the best wild brown trout-fishing to be had in the north of Scotland; most is free to *Sheiling* residents only; the Mackenzies don't let to outside parties. Fishermen of all degrees of experience and physical fitness are catered for, and a boat is kept on one of the lochs for the use of *Sheiling* guests. A lodge in the grounds houses a self-service laundry, drying room, rod room and sauna. The bedrooms have light pine furniture, good beds, a good bathroom, loch views. The MacKenzies are "welcoming, and helpful with suggestions for local tours, restaurants, etc, but you have to ask; they don't offer or intrude on your plans." The much-admired breakfast is served in a pleasant two-level room with a view of the loch. It includes a wide variety of teas, yogurts, etc, smoked haddock, home-made venison sausages with leeks and peaches. No dinners but Ullapool, though small, is particularly well served for eating places. (*CB*)

Open All year, except Christmas, New Year. No dinners.
Rooms 6 double. 2 on ground floor. No telephone. Some have TV.
Facilities Lounge with TV, breakfast room. No background music. Lodge with laundry, drying room, sauna, shower, rod room, motor-cycle store. 1½-acre grounds: lochside patio. Extensive trout-fishing areas free to guests. 2 rooms suitable for &.
Location On A832, south side of village.
Restrictions No smoking. No dogs.
Credit cards None accepted.
Terms [2000] B&B £23–£35.

WALLS Shetland Islands   **Map 5**

Burrastow House   *Tel* (01595) 809307
Walls, Mainland   *Fax* (01595) 809213
ZE2 9PD   *E-mail* burr.hs.hotel@zetnet.co.uk
                 Website www.users.zetnet.co.uk/burrastow-house-hotel

"Wonderfully comfortable and friendly", "peaceful and beautiful" – more admiration this year for this white Georgian house on the western coast of the largest of the Shetland islands, 40 minutes' drive from Lerwick. The setting is magnificent: it looks across a small bay to the island of Vaila; sightings of black-headed gulls, red-throated divers, seals and otters are quite frequent. All around are rolling hills, wild seas and clear skies. *Burrastow* is the family home of Bo Simmons and Henry Anderton, "charming people and excellent hosts", and their two children. While the atmosphere may be a bit too informal for some, and housekeeping not always perfect, this "marvellous retreat" has delighted many readers. The small public rooms are "crammed with a mixture of antiques and hand-me-downs". Dinner is served in a conservatory, amid scented plants and flowers, or in a small panelled room with a peat fire. The menu changes daily and "Bo's excellent cooking" provides "memorable meals"; special diets are accommodated. Crab, lobster, salmon are all fresh, "and never abused by overcooking or extravagant saucing", and vegetables are grown in the hotel's organic garden. Ingredients for starters and for the breakfast kedgeree come from the local smoke-house; bread and croissants are freshly baked. The two large bedrooms in the main house have a

draped and canopied four-poster; one has a twin-bedded room adjoining, equipped with children's books and games. The rooms in a newer
extension have less character. The owners' boat is available for guests
to explore Vaila Sound. They have put the house on the market, so
there may soon be new owners. (*David and Patricia Hawkins,
Romney Bathurst*)

Open Mar–Dec; closed Oct school half-term.
Rooms 1 2-bedroom family suite, 4 double. 1, on ground floor, suitable for ⅃.
No telephone (pay-phone in hall); TV on request.
Facilities Sitting room, library, dining room, 2 conservatories; small confer-
ence room. No background music. 1-acre grounds in large estate. On sea: safe
(cold) bathing, hotel boat; indoor swimming pool in village 2 miles.
Location 27 miles NW of Lerwick. Take A970 N, then A971 W. Through
Walls; left on brow of hill; 2 miles to dead end. Bus: Lerwick to Walls (daily,
except Sun); they will meet.
Restrictions No smoking: dining room, bedrooms. Dogs by arrangement; not
in public rooms.
Credit cards Amex, MasterCard, Visa.
Terms [2000] D,B&B £65–£85. Full alc £30. Off-season rates by arrangement. Child accommodated in parents' room: under 9, charged only for food;
9–14, 50% of adult rate.

WESTRAY Orkney   **Map 5**

Cleaton House   `BUDGET`   *Tel* (01857) 677508
Pierowall   *Fax* (01857) 677442
Westray KW17 2DB   *E-mail* cleaton@orkney.com

Malcolm Stout's white former manse on his native island, a northerly
Orkney, was liked again this year: "A beautifully furnished, friendly
and efficient hotel, exceptional value for money, with a superb host."
This endorses earlier praise: "A most relaxing place, with interesting
food." "The island of Westray is a green buffer to the Atlantic rollers.
On the lee side is this haven of comfort. Mr Stout will meet you at the
ferry or the airstrip. He is full of local knowledge, and has a library of
Orkney books to go with the Westray chairs in the lounge." The decor
is simple. The bedrooms are "large and welcoming", with views
across the island and the sea; two have an antique four-poster. Lorna
Reid's "sensitive cooking" – notably of fish, seafood and North
Ronaldsay lamb – is "attractively presented", with dishes like Cullen
Skink; local seafood platter; sautéed scallops on home-made pasta,
with mint and coriander; roast ewe on a parsnip crumble and red wine
sauce. With coffee you get "peedie fours", and the host's "endless
store of local lore". The hotel also acts as an inn for locals, and serves
"excellent bar snacks". Mr Stout will deliver guests to distant parts of
the island in his Range Rover, so that they can make their way back on
foot – "the walking is wonderful". The island offers tranquillity, miles
of sandy beaches, the second largest breeding sea bird colony in the
UK (puffins between May and August), daylight until midnight in
summer, free golf at the local course; also trout-fishing, and day-trips
to Papa Westray (via "the world's shortest scheduled flight – 90
seconds"). (*John S Holman, AS, JJ*)

Open All year, except Christmas.
Rooms 5 double, 1 single.
Facilities Lounge, lounge bar, public bar (Scottish dancing most weekends), restaurant (Orcadian music during meals). 1½-acre garden: *pétanque*; sea ¼ mile. Access ramp; ground floor suitable for &.
Location 2 miles SE of Pierowall village. Ferry or small plane from Kirkwall; hotel will meet.
Restrictions No smoking: restaurant, bedrooms. No dogs in public rooms.
Credit cards MasterCard, Visa.
Terms B&B: single £25–£50, double £40–£80; D,B&B: single £40-£72.50, double £70–£125. Bar meals. Set dinner £22.50. *V*

WHITEBRIDGE Highland   **Map 5**

Knockie Lodge   *Tel* (01456) 486276
Whitebridge IV2 6UP   *Fax* (01456) 486389
                                          E-mail info@knockielodge.co.uk
                                          Website www.knockielodge.co.uk

In a magnificent, isolated setting overlooking Loch Nan Lann, this handsome Georgian hunting lodge was built for the chief of Clan Fraser. It is now an elegant and comfortable hotel (Pride of Britain), run by the owners, Nicholas Bean and Louise Dawson. Their "personal style" and their "admirable young staff from around the world" are admired by *Guide* readers. "A wonderful and tranquil spot for lovers of natural history and sports, with magical walks, stalking, shooting, tremendous lochs for fishing." No TV, no background music – after-dinner entertainment consists of chatting with hosts and fellow guests over coffee by the log and peat fire in the lounge, or a session at the full-size snooker table. The house is furnished with antiques and comfortable furniture; the dining room has excellent silverware and napery. Dinner is a five-course affair, with no choice of the first three courses; everyone, including the owners, eats at the same time, but at separate tables. The chef, Mark Dexter, serves French-influenced Scottish cooking, eg, tempura-fried langoustine; tomato and basil tart with a sweet pepper dressing; fresh lobster cooked in port; local strawberry tarte Tatin. Some bedrooms are large, some have wonderful views. (*PJL, RR*)

Open May–Oct.
Rooms 8 double, 2 single. No TV.
Facilities 2 lounges, snooker room, dining room. No background music. 11-acre grounds: clay-pigeon shooting; archery. Two lochs 5 mins' walk with free fishing, sailing for guests. Deer-stalking, pony-trekking, golf nearby. Unsuitable for &.
Location 24 miles SW of Inverness. From A9 at Daviot take B851 (B862) towards Fort Augustus. After 23 miles turn right at sign; continue 2 miles.
Restrictions No smoking: restaurant, bedrooms. No children under 10. Dogs by arrangement in bedrooms; not in public rooms.

Credit cards All major cards accepted.
Terms B&B: single £75–£135, double £120–£185. D,B&B: single £115–£175, double £190–£250. Bar meals/packed lunches available to residents. Set lunch £25, dinner £40. 1-night bookings sometimes refused.

****

Hotel in Wales. A boarding-house atmosphere prevailed at dinner. Course followed course in rapid succession, and dinner was over on both evenings by 8.35 pm, despite our lingering over the cheese. Breakfast had to be ordered before we retired, and because we had ordered coffee one day, it was assumed that we would want it the next day as well.

****

Hotel in London. We had been looking forward for years to trying out this *Michelin*-starred restaurant. In the event, it was a great disappointment. The decor was tired and dowdy. At the next table to ours, a man read a newspaper throughout dinner while his lady companion stared at the ceiling. Throughout the meal we had to wait to have our wine glasses refilled. There was a most unhelpful attitude when a vegetarian dish was requested. Our host wrote to the hotel to complain, and received a reply that was correct but expressed no repentance.

****

Hotel in Northumberland. We came down for dinner at the suggested time of 7.30. During a sojourn by the front desk, we got the occasional passing attention of a vague but friendly, casually dressed young man, and a distant view of a rumpled version of a waiter mooching around the dining area. Our first course was a bland pâté and a white Bordeaux that, despite its price of £13 and the assurance of the receptionist that it would probably taste better once it had cooled, was as uninspired as the list it came from. Closer inspection of the rumpled figure we had seen earlier suggested that his career, like his forays into learning English, had begun only recently.

****

Hotel in Ireland. Pre-dinner drinks were ordered three times. Brandy and ginger ale caused a major problem. The first time, a ginger beer arrived in a half-pint tumbler; the second attempt was ginger beer and brandy. At dinner, the waiting staff had no clue about service or presentation. We attempted to see the owners. To our horror we were informed that some of the staff, all of whom are Australian, had arrived only the day before, and there was no management on site. We watched in amazement as gentlemen were served before ladies; we continually asked for the wine to be poured, and on each occasion only the person who had asked was served, while the others looked blank. When we switched to red wine for our second course, it was poured into the residue of the white wine in our glasses. A request to the waiter for clean glasses produced a look that made us melt under the table.

****

Channel Islands

White House, Herm

HERM   **Map 1**

White House   *Tel* (01481) 722159
Herm, via Guernsey GY1 3HR   *Fax* (01481) 710066
                                                       Website www.herm-island.com

✿ *César award in 1987*

Herm, a tiny island one and a half miles long, is "heaven on earth, with peace, perfect peace, no cars or TV", also pristine beaches, high cliffs, a little harbour, pastel-painted cottages, three shops, an inn, a campsite, a 10th-century chapel – and just 97 inhabitants. Some of them work at this "wonderful, friendly family hotel", created from an old house in 1949. The lease to the island is owned by Pennie Heyworth, who runs the hotel with her husband, Adrian, and manager Sue Hester. Accolades this year: "A delightful staff, delicious food." "A charming rustic experience. Great views of the rolling hills, the sea and Guernsey." "An enchanting island, ideal for children to explore. The hotel cleverly creates an atmosphere of harmony, and is well geared for a family holiday: staff are helpful, younger children can have separate meals. Catering is excellent, prices are incredibly reasonable: house wines only £6–£7 a bottle." The comfortable lounges have plenty of board games; the "delightful garden" has a swimming pool by the sea. No telephones in the bedrooms, but there is baby-listening. The hotel has its own oyster bed, and the island is perfect for bird-watching, shell gathering, bathing, snorkelling and fishing. Guernsey and Sark are a short boat trip away, and visits to Jersey and France can be arranged. In summer Herm is much visited by day-trippers, but they are gone by the late afternoon. The hotel will help guests with travel arrangements. (*Jon Dorey, Eraj Shirvani, JR*)

Open Approximately 31 Mar–9 Oct.
Rooms 12 family suites, 24 double, 2 single. 22 in 3 cottage annexes (some on ground level). No telephone/TV. Also 18 self-catering cottages.
Facilities Lounges, 2 bars, carvery, restaurant. 1-acre garden: tennis, croquet, swimming pool; beach 100 yds. Boating, fishing, snorkelling. Unsuitable for &.
Location By harbour. Air or sea to Guernsey; ferry to Herm. Travel arrangements ABC Travel, *tel* (01481) 235551.
Restrictions No smoking: restaurant, 1 lounge, bedrooms. Guide dogs only.
Credit cards Amex, MasterCard, Visa.
Terms D,B&B: £58.50–£79. Set lunch from £13.50, dinner £22.

ROZEL BAY Jersey   **Map 1**

Château La Chaire   *Tel* (01534) 863354
Rozel Bay   *Fax* (01534) 865137
St Martin JE3 6AJ   *E-mail* res@chateau-la-chaire.co.uk
                                         Website www.chateau-la-chaire.co.uk

Owned by the Hiscox family and managed by Seán Copp, this small, stylish hotel, "lovely and restful", stands above the Rozel valley in north-east Jersey, "tucked away in an unpopulated area, with beautiful cliff walks". "We really like it," says a visitor this year. Its steep terraced gardens, home to red squirrels and barn owls, overlook a pretty fishing harbour. The interior is smart: panelled public rooms, chandeliers, mouldings with cherubs – "the drawing room is a triumph of plasterwork". Some bedrooms are large and luxurious, with a spa bath, a chandelier and a balcony. The attic rooms are smaller, "but sweet", and some bathrooms may have a low ceiling, which may make shaving difficult for some. A returning visitor thought the food "even better" this year. Earlier she had written: "We love this hotel with passion, even though the cutlery is appalling. Our room, beautifully furnished, had lovely curtains, and was very peaceful. The bar is old-fashioned, well mannered. The chef is inspired." He, Simon Walker, serves modern British cooking, with an emphasis on seafood, eg, tian of crab with a lemon dressing; roast John Dory with lime leaf and coriander. "The vegetarian alternatives are delicious; wild mushroom risotto the best I have tasted." Another visitor was less enthusiastic about the food, but thought the wines excellent and good value. The staff is generally thought courteous and friendly. Tea is served on a terrace with a fountain. No entertainments for children, so there tend to be few of them. Cliff walks and safe beaches are nearby, and all manner of activities can be arranged, including yachting and flying lessons. Jersey's capital, St Helier, with its duty-free shopping is nearby. (*CC Schofield, Linda Brook, and others*)

Open All year.
Rooms 1 suite, 13 double.
Facilities Drawing room, bar, restaurant with conservatory; classical background music in public areas all day. 6-acre garden. Sandy beach, safe bathing nearby. Golf, fishing, yachting, flying available. Only restaurant suitable for &.
Location 5 miles NE of St Helier. Follow signs for St Martin's church, then Rozel. 1st left in village; hotel carpark 200 yds on left.
Restrictions No smoking in conservatory. No children under 7. No dogs.
Credit cards All major cards accepted.
Terms [2000] B&B: single £80–£115, double £105–£145, suite £185–£215; D,B&B £65–£130 per person. Set lunch £14.95, dinner £27.50. Winter breaks. Christmas package. 1-night bookings sometimes refused in season.

ST BRELADE Jersey   **Map 1**

Atlantic Hotel   *Tel* (01534) 744101
Le Mont de la Pulente   *Fax* (01534) 744102
St Brelade JE3 8HE   *E-mail* atlantic@itl.net
                                               Website www.slh.com/atlantic

Radically refurbished this year, with most bedrooms enlarged and upgraded, and the exterior given a "more horizontal feel", this already luxurious hotel has been called "the best value we have found in the Channel Islands". It adjoins the La Moye championship golf course, and overlooks the superb five-mile beach of St Ouen's Bay. A large, modern white building, it was opened in 1970 by the father of the present owner, Patrick Burke. "His manager, Simon Dufty, is first rate, all staff are excellent, and room balconies have great views," says a visitor this year. The interior contains antique terracotta flagstones, a wrought-iron staircase, rich carpeting, urns, fountains, antiques and specially designed modern furniture. There is a leisure centre, the Palm Club, with an indoor swimming pool, mini-gym, etc, to which guests have free access. In summer the hotel is popular with families. Many rooms face the golf course, or look over the swimming pool to pine trees and the sea beyond. The suites in a ground-floor annexe are spacious, but have no view. Some bedrooms are on the small side, "and the ones by the lift are to be avoided". The food was admired again this year, notably the seafood. Ken Healy's menus include, eg, sauté of local scallops and lobster; artichoke with warm chorizo salad; salmon with red onion marmalade; caramelised rice pudding with grated chocolate and cinnamon custard. Light lunches are served, by the pool in fine weather. "Excellent breakfasts." "The breaks are superb value." The airport is ten minutes' drive away. (*IU, RC*)

Open Mar–Dec.
Rooms 2 suites, 48 double.
Facilities Lounges, cocktail bar, restaurant; background music in public areas;

fitness centre: swimming pool, sauna. 3-acre grounds: tennis, swimming pool. Golf club, beach ½ mile. Unsuitable for &.
Location 5 miles W of St Helier; taxi/bus.
Restriction No dogs.
Credit cards All major cards accepted.
Terms [2000] B&B: double £160–£240, suite £235–£385. Set lunch £16.50, dinner £25; full alc £40. Special breaks. Christmas package.

| **St Brelade's Bay Hotel** NEW | *Tel* (01534) 746141 |
| St Brelade JE3 8EF | *Fax* (01534) 747278 |

An "all-round-excellent family hotel, luxurious throughout", run by the Colley family. The long white modern building faces the sandy beach on Jersey's loveliest bay. After a time with no reports, it is now restored enthusiastically to the *Guide*: "Wonderful. It caters for children of all ages, without being like a holiday camp. We travelled with a three-year-old and twin babies, and were given cots, high chairs, a good range of baby food, etc (children have tea at 5 pm, and must not be in the dining room after 7 pm – heaven for parents!). There's a children's playroom, pool, playground, etc. Wonderful gardens with tennis courts, *boules*, etc. Bedrooms are large and airy: front ones have a balcony and panoramic views over the bay. The staff are all friendly, and the food is a delight, with a superb English breakfast, choice of formal lunch or barbecue, fantastic six-course dinner" (dishes might include fillet of red bream with sautéed grapes; roast breast of turkey with banana fritter and mango sauce). Moulded ceilings, chandeliers, lots of fresh flowers and large grounds complete the picture. The cocktail bar, gym, sauna and sun terrace have just been renovated. (*Emma K Else*)

Open Mid-Apr–mid-Oct.
Rooms 1 suite, 77 double, 4 single.
Facilities Lift. Lounge, reception, TV room, cocktail bar (entertainment 4 nights a week), restaurant; 2 children's playrooms, sun veranda. 7-acre grounds: outdoor restaurant, swimming pool with bar, barbecue, sauna, solarium, exercise room; *boules*, children's play area. Beach across road. Golf nearby.
Location 5 miles W of St Helier. Bus from St Helier.
Restrictions No smoking in restaurant, some public rooms. No dogs.
Credit cards All major cards accepted.
Terms B&B: single £56–£98, double £104–£202, suite £106–£244. D,B&B £67–£137 per person. Set lunch £15, dinner £25; full alc £35.

ST PETER PORT Guernsey   **Map 1**

La Frégate NEW	*Tel* (01481) 724624
Les Côtils	*Fax* (01481) 720443
St Peter Port GY1 1UT	*E-mail* lafregate@guernsey.net

"An outstanding hotel in many respects," runs one of three reports bringing *La Frégate* back into the *Guide* this year. It had foundered recently on criticisms, and there are still some caveats (eg, slow meal service). But everyone likes the position, and the "excellent" French cuisine, which may be the best on Guernsey (eg, suprême de volaille au crabe farcie). This old converted manor house stands in terraced gardens on a hill above the harbour of the island's main town: there are fine views from many rooms, notably those with a balcony. Rooms are "fairly basic" but comfortable, with large bathrooms. Breakfasts are good, generally served in one's room. The bar and restaurant have been smartened up this year, with "designer decor". The dining room staff, some of them Portuguese, are "enthusiastic". But one reader commented wryly: "The *maître d'*, from Madeira, confuses his function with that of a stand-up comedian, and the German barmaid sought to teach me how to order a dry martini, even though she couldn't make one." The hotel has many stairs, but no lift. There may be some noise from ferries and lorries. (*Gordon R Walker, Paul and Christine Butler, Mr and Mrs Dennys Watson*)

Open All year, but may close briefly Jan/Feb 2001.
Rooms 9 double, 4 single.
Facilities Lounge/bar, restaurant, private dining room. Patio (alfresco dining), terraced garden. Unsuitable for &.
Location 5 mins' walk from centre. Hard to find; hotel will send directions. Carpark.
Restrictions No children under 14 in hotel, under 8 in restaurant. No dogs.
Credit cards All major cards accepted.
Terms [2000] B&B: single £63, double £78–£105; D,B&B: single £83, double £118–£145. Set lunch £15, dinner £20, full alc £30–£35. ***V***

ST SAVIOUR Jersey   **Map 1**

Longueville Manor   *Tel* (01534) 725501
Longueville Road   *Fax* (01534) 731613
St Saviour JE2 7WF
                            E-mail longman@itl.net
                    Website www.longuevillemanor.com

 César award in 1986

Jersey's most luxurious hotel, with probably its best restaurant (*Michelin* starred), this Relais & Châteaux member stands in large grounds at the foot of a lovely wooded valley just inland from St Helier. "Very good, very well run", it is also "unstuffy", with country house furnishings; "guests share the reception rooms with the house cats and dogs". The owners, Malcolm Lewis and his sister Sue Dufty, are the third generation at *Longueville*, "and are always around, and attentive". The staff are "hard-working, willing to please, and polite". The decor is "smart without being brash or contrived" – swagged curtains, colourful Oriental rugs, original paintings, antiques, good repro furniture. Served either in a large light room facing the garden, or in a darker panelled one, Andrew Baird's cooking is "modern with a classical influence", eg, roast quail with glazed apple, Lancashire black pudding and bacon; casserole of beef with woodland mushrooms; Jersey brill with calamari. Accolades for the food include: "beautifully cooked and presented, with interesting desserts", "wonderful vegetarian dishes", and "a superb cheese trolley". For a splash, try the Gourmet Menu at £70. "Breakfasts are excellent, with lots of choice – a festival of cholesterol." The spacious and chintzy bedrooms have a comfortable sofa, fresh flowers "and four kinds of soap (excluding those on the multi-channel TV)". "No tea-making equipment, as room service is so swift." The gardens have colourful flowers, and there is a herb and vegetable garden for the kitchen. The swimming pool is heated to a constant 80°F, and there are excellent poolside lunches and teas. Guests may also dine at the nearby "little sister" restaurant, *Suma's.* The Royal Jersey Golf Club is not far away. The winter package, which includes car hire, is good value. Day-trips to France can be arranged. More reports, please.

Open All year.
Rooms 2 suites, 30 double. 8 on ground floor.
Facilities Lift. Drawing room, reading room, cocktail bar, restaurant; conference facilities. 16-acre grounds: gardens, woodland, croquet, tennis, swimming pool, jogging track. Golf, bowls, squash, etc, nearby. Sandy beaches ¾ mile.
Location 1 mile E of St Helier by A3; hotel is on left. Double-glazed throughout.
Restriction No dogs in public rooms.
Credit cards All major cards accepted.
Terms [2000] B&B: single £150–£195, double £180–£270, suite £340–£370. Set lunch £21, dinner from £42; full alc £52. Winter weekend breaks; Christmas package.

SARK   Map 1

Hotel Petit Champ BUDGET	*Tel* (01481) 832046
Sark	*Fax* (01481) 832469
via Guernsey GY9 0SF	*E-mail* hpc@island-of-sark.co.uk
	Website www.island-of-sark.co.uk

Secluded on headland of little Sark's west coast (superb views), Chris and Caroline Robins's modernised late 19th-century granite hotel, well run, not luxurious, but full of comforts. Good French-influenced cooking by Tony Atkins, with some ambitious dishes, some local seafood. Light lunches served, in garden on fine days. Sun lounges, bar, library, TV room, solar-heated swimming pool. No telephone/TV in rooms (deliberately). Secluded beaches with safe bathing nearby. No cars on island, but bicycles; Sark is unsuitable for ♿. Open Easter–early Oct. All major credit cards accepted. 16 bedrooms (some family). B&B: £32.50–£42.50; D,B&B: £47–£57. Children accepted "if old enough to sit with parents at dinner"; plenty of games, puzzles, etc, supplied. No recent reports; more welcome. *V*

La Sablonnerie BUDGET	*Tel* (01481) 832061
Little Sark	*Fax* (01481) 832408
Sark, via Guernsey GY9 0SD	

Stylish and idiosyncratic, this converted 16th-century farmhouse on Sark's southern peninsula is owned by Liz Perrée who, says a delighted visitor this year, "manages to run a well-organised, comfortable, friendly hotel with outstanding food, in a rather remote location. Everyone was warm and friendly, and rarely have I seen hotel staff so eager to please. All our requests were met, including several tractor rides, courtesy of brother Philip Perrée, for my three-year-old tractor-mad son. He also loved the toy airplane, which came stuck into his pizza as a surprise. We stayed in a cottage next to the well-tended tea gardens with their sun parasols. The grounds are lovely. Evening fare was elegant and inventive: venison with lavender sauce; lobster various ways." And two "sweaty cyclists" found the hotel "very welcoming, with some of the best food we have had anywhere". Others have written of the romance of arriving at night by launch from Guernsey: "We drove through the dark with pipistrelle bats swooping down from the trees which overarch the lanes. Liz greeted us in her inimitable, proprietorial but charming manner." The "young and enthusiastic" waiters delight in conversation and gossip (surely the sign of a happily managed hotel). Philip Perrée senior, who must be over 80, serves behind the bar. Many guests are returning visitors, which creates something of a "club" atmosphere, "but a club which readily welcomes kindred spirits", says a reader. Beef, fruit and vegetables come from the hotel's farm; the menus often include oysters, scallops, and lobster (you pay extra). No TV or telephone in the "quite small, but elegant" bedrooms, but good soap, fruit and flowers. The hotel sends its own tractor or horse and cart to meet guests at the port. It advises guests to pack an old pair of rubber-soled shoes for bathing from rocks or shingle, a torch for exploring caves, and a dress or a tie for the evenings. The coast nearby has beautiful cliffs, coves and sandy beaches. (*Marcia Layton, DW Houldsworth, and others*)

Open Easter–Oct.
Rooms 1 suite, 15 double, 6 single. Guests sometimes accommodated in nearby cottages.
Facilities 3 lounges, 2 bars (classical/piano background music), restaurant. 1-acre garden: tea garden/bar, croquet. Bays, beaches, rock pools nearby. Sark unsuitable for &.
Location Southern part of island. Boat from Guernsey; hotel will meet.
Restrictions No smoking in some bedrooms. No dogs in public rooms.
Credit cards Amex, MasterCard, Visa.
Terms (*Excluding 10% service charge*) B&B: £38–£75; D,B&B: £49.50–£87.50; full board £59.50–£92.50. Set lunch £20.80, dinner £26.50; full alc £36.50.

****

Hotel in Scotland. The set dinner on our first evening consisted of a cheese mousse (reminiscent of processed cheese triangles); gammon with pears with a very sweet sauce and a timbale of carrots that was utterly tasteless. The pudding was excessively sweet. The presentation did not deserve the rosettes, crowns, etc, awarded by sundry guides. After-dinner coffee arrangements were strange; there was an extra charge for drinking it in the lounge; one mint per person (lined up at the bar) was allowed.

****

There is no VAT in the Channel Islands.

****

B&B in Wales. We drove up a rutted track and were amazed to see the huts/hovels, which turned out to be the bedrooms. The view from the room was wonderful provided you did not stand up. The curtains were unhemmed squares of cheap material, dangling from a wire. The floor was painted concrete with a sad mat. The bed was of the variety found in second-rate boarding schools – you have to burrow around to find a place between the lumps in the mattress. In the bathroom, where it was impossible to stand up straight, we shared the facilities with a cockroach and a woodlouse. A sign over the basin read: "Water is brown, is normal."

****

Hotel in Cornwall. Being named a hotel of the year by another guide had made the staff of — very aware of its elevated status. They were not snooty; it had been drummed into them that the customer was king. However, staff training seemed to have emphasised obsequiousness, and virtually everything we did or asked for had them thanking us profusely. Uriah Heep would have felt at home. The restaurant staff were surprised that we had no wish to consume a seven-course meal. "It's included in the price," they insisted. Fortunately, their repeated "thank you so much", and enquiries about our well-being, comforted us and we didn't feel too eccentric when we ordered only two courses.

****

Hotel in Scotland. We bumped down a dirt track to find a building that was dismal and unkempt. We thought that a little effort and imagination could have worked a great improvement, but the owners seemed not to care. Our room, in an outbuilding, was similarly dismal and unimaginatively furnished, and the furniture was so worn and characterless that it could have been plucked from a skip. The ceiling was so thin we could hear the occupants above snoring. When we left the owner did not ask if we had enjoyed ourselves. She must have known what a rip-off it was.

****

Hotel in Yorkshire. Our bed sloped downwards from foot to head, and the mattress was lumpy. The shower dribbled into the bath. On the first night the radiator went full blast, making the room intolerably hot. We told a member of staff and he promised to deal with the problem, but by that evening nothing had been done. When we complained to the owner, his response was straight out of Fawlty Towers. He made no genuine apology, but delivered a long rigmarole about "this always happens". When my wife asked for a hair-dryer, he asked: "Do you want one?" (yes, we've just asked for one). The final gobsmacker: he told us: "I'm going to —; I'm a quality inspector."

****

McCausland Hotel, Belfast

ANNALONG Co. Down **Map 6**

Glassdrumman Lodge *Tel* (028) 4376 8451
85 Mill Road *Fax* (028) 4376 7041
Annalong BT34 4RH *E-mail* glassdrumman@yahoo.com

The Mountains o' Mourne sweep down not quite to the sea in fact: between them and the coast is a broad pastoral stretch, where this stylishly converted old farmhouse, long, low and white, stands outside a village. "The owner, Joan Hall, is lovely, she treats you like a guest in her own home," runs one plaudit. Others mostly agree, though one wrote of poor room maintenance and thought that, since reception is not always attended, "a bell would be a useful investment". "Inside, all is a delight, sophisticated yet intimate." "The lounge is graceful yet cosy – old beamed ceiling, imposing open fireplace with a real log fire, velvety sofas, nice lamps, lots of books." Guests can watch, and even take part in, the life of the small home farm (on which pigs, poultry, horses and golden retrievers are bred). It supplies many of the ingredients of the dinners cooked by Joan's son, Jonathan (eg, Irish stew of Mourne lamb; sucking pig pie). Butter is home churned, eggs are free-range, fish and shellfish come from local ports. Guests mostly dine together round a long pine table, but separate tables are available if they prefer. The cooking is "some of the best we have come across in a country house hotel", says one recent visitor. It is served by candle-light with good silver. The bedrooms are beautiful and well kept. "Our large room was superb, with panoramic windows, big sofa, luxury bathroom, gas fire in chilly April" (other rooms vary in size). Breakfast "is good, with lovely home-made breads". There's a well-kept garden with loungers. Many visitors are American golfers with Irish roots, come to play on the Royal County Down golf course close by; riding and pony-trekking can be arranged. (*Franz Opitz, and others*)

Open All year. Lunch not served.
Rooms 2 suites (in annexe), 8 double.
Facilities Drawing room/bar, library, 2 dining rooms (classical/Irish background music during dinner); meeting facilities. 7-acre grounds: fishing lake. Golf, sailing, fishing, riding, pony-trekking nearby. Unsuitable for &.
Location 8 miles S of Newcastle, 1 mile inland from Annalong (turn off at *Halfway House* pub).
Restrictions No smoking: restaurant, some bedrooms. No dogs in house (kennels available).
Credit cards All major cards accepted.
Terms B&B: single £50–£80, double £50–£118, suite £110–£135. Set dinner £30. Christmas package. *V*

BELFAST   **Map 6**

Ash-Rowan   *Tel* (028) 9066 1758
12 Windsor Avenue   *Fax* (028) 9066 3227
Belfast BT9 6EE

Thomas Andrews, designer of the *Titanic* (built in Belfast), lived in this spacious Victorian house, and from here with his wife he set sail on its maiden voyage – never to return. But these sad ghosts need not deter visitors from enjoying what is now a congenial and much-liked guest house, set in a tree-lined street not far from Queen's University. It is owned and run by Evelyn and Sam Hazlett, "genuinely kind and welcoming", supported by a black labrador. Colourful pots of flowers and hanging baskets surround the front door. The house is full of Victoriana, old furniture, lace, curios, and plants. The well-equipped bedrooms, all with a shower, are "cosy, with lovely linen", and pine and cane furniture. Breakfast (ordered the previous evening) includes freshly squeezed orange juice, home-baked bread, "gorgeous" home-made jams, fresh fruit salad, various cooked dishes, notably the Ulster Fry ("not for the faint-hearted") and mushrooms flambéed in sherry. An early breakfast, if needed, "is cheerfully supplied". There's a lounge for residents, with daily papers, and a large conservatory is new this year. An evening meal is available by arrangement, with main courses like fillet steak flambéed in whiskey, and poached or fried fish of the day, and there are other restaurants nearby: *Cayanne* in Shaftesbury Square is warmly recommended this year. (*MQ, NR*)

Open 6 Jan–23 Dec.
Rooms 3 double, 2 single.
Facilities Lounge, dining room, conservatory. No background music. ½-acre garden. Unsuitable for &.
Location Just off Lisburn Rd, 1½ miles SW of centre. Carpark. Bus from centre.
Restrictions No smoking: breakfast room, 2 bedrooms. No children under 12. No dogs.
Credit cards Amex, MasterCard, Visa.
Terms B&B: single £48–£59, double £66–£79. Evening meal (by arrangement) £30.

McCausland Hotel NEW   *Tel* (028) 9022 0200
34–38 Victoria Street   *Fax* (028) 9022 0220
Belfast BT1 3GH   *E-mail* info@mccauslandhotel.com
    Website www.slh.com/causland

Near the River Lagan, in the city's commercial heart, two adjacent 1850s red brick industrial warehouses have been stylishly converted into a fairly luxurious hotel with modern design, opened in 1998 – a welcome new venture for Belfast. "It is most attractive, with lots of exposed brick and girders in the rooms," says this year's nominator. "Reception was friendly and professional, my bathroom was luxurious, and I had reasonable food in the café/bar/bistro. The main restaurant is said to be good, too." This, with Eamon O'Cathain as chef, offers French-style cooking, eg, goat's cheese pissaladière and grilled raddichio; confit of duck with Puy lentils; grilled lamb's liver with wild mushroom risotto and truffle oil. "Most guests were American tourists", but there's a business centre too. (*Peter David*)

Open All year, except 24–27 Dec.
Rooms 9 suites, 51 double. 3 adapted for &.
Facilities Lift. 2 bars, café, restaurant; business centre; classical/"easy-listening" background music in public areas; live music in café Thurs/Fri/Sat night.
Location Central, just W of River Lagan, between Anne St and the Albert clock tower. Private parking
Restrictions No smoking in 33 bedrooms. Guide dogs only.
Credit cards All major cards accepted.
Terms [2000] Room: single £120, double £150–£170, suite £200. Breakfast £10. Set lunch £12.50; full alc £34. *V*

See also SHORTLIST

****

Hotel in Scotland. The welcome was poor, the food frightful (too much reliance on the microwave), and does one really need a teddy bear in tartan trews on the bed? In the bathroom, cold water came out of the tap marked "Hot".

****

DERRY Co. Londonderry   Map 6

Beech Hill House   *Tel* (028) 7134 9279
32 Ardmore Road   *Fax* (028) 7134 5366
Derry BT47 3QP   *E-mail* info@beech-hill.com
                                              Website www.beech-hill.com

With "warm, attentive and always friendly service, and good, freshly
cooked and reasonably priced food", this is one of the most reputable
hotels in Northern Ireland. Built in 1729 as the private home of a sea
captain, it is now owned by local people, Mr Donnelly and Mrs
O'Kane, and managed by Crawford McIlwaine. The handsome white
house stands just outside this interesting and attractive town, in a large
park with ponds, waterfalls, birds and wildlife and beech trees.
"Everyone who is anyone seems to turn up here" (Senator Edward
Kennedy was a recent guest) and local people use the big bar as a kind
of pub. "The bedrooms were comfortable, warm and tastefully furnished, partly with antiques," says a visitor this year. They are bright
and spacious, and many have lovely views. The new chef, Adrian
Catterall, presides over the *Ardmore Restaurant*, which looks over the
landscaped gardens, and is open all day. His cooking is based on fresh
local beef, poultry and game, and home-grown vegetables. There is a
short vegetarian menu. Light lunches are served, and for the hearty
appetite there is a traditional Ulster Fry at breakfast. "Superb breads"
are served at all meals. The house's original private chapel, on the first
floor, can be used for christenings, wedding blessings and mass. The
owners are "full of kindness", their staff "friendly and flexible". The
lovely scenery of Donegal is just across the border, and this is a good
base for exploring the Antrim coast. (*SW Harris*)

Open All year, except 24/25 Dec.
Rooms 4 suites, 22 double, 1 single.
Facilities Lift. Lounge, morning room, bar, restaurant; conference facilities;
fitness club; chapel. Classical background music all day in public areas.
32-acre grounds: tennis, ponds, waterfall. Fishing, golf, sailing, flying nearby.
Location 2 miles SE of Derry, off Belfast road (signposted to right). Carpark.
Restriction No dogs.
Credit cards Amex, MasterCard, Visa.
Terms B&B: single £80, double £100, suite £150. Set lunch £18.95, dinner
£28.95; full alc £43.80. 2-day breaks. Christmas package.

HOLYWOOD Co. Down   Map 6

Rayanne Country House   *Tel* (028) 9042 5859
60 Demesne Road   *Fax* (028) 9042 3364
Belfast BT18 9EX

In an eastern coastal residential suburb, firmly in Protestant territory,
Holywood is one of the most affluent parts of greater Belfast. This
small, upmarket hotel is set well back from the road in large gardens.
Outwardly suburban-looking, it has a lavish Victorian decor. "All is
clean and well furnished, giving an atmosphere of welcome and culture," said one recent visitor. "The staff are very friendly. Everything

is done with great attention to detail." Another wrote: "One of the nicest places I have stayed at for a long time. My large bedroom had a fruit bowl, and a spacious bathroom." Breakfast is hugely admired (it has won several awards); unusual choices range from prune soufflé on a purée of green figs via raspberry porridge to smoked salmon with scrambled eggs or grilled black and white pudding on French toast with spiced apple compote. Dinners are served (also to non-residents), with main courses like baked salmon on a red pepper and herb sauce; grilled lamb cutlets with an apricot and mint sauce. Sadly Raymond McClelland died recently, but his widow Anne is carrying on the running, with her son Mark as chef. More reports, please.

Open 3 Jan–23 Dec.
Rooms 1 family, 7 double, 1 single.
Facilities 2 lounges, restaurant (soft background music). Function/wedding facilities. ¾-acre garden. Seafront, small beach, 400 yds.
Location In Holywood, 5 miles E of Belfast. Take A2 past airport towards Bangor. Turn off dual carriageway to right at Holywood town centre exit; almost immediately, turn right up Jackson's Rd, leading to Demesne Rd. House on right past golf course. Bus and train stops close by. Private parking.
Restrictions No smoking: restaurant, bedrooms. No dogs.
Credit cards All major cards accepted.
Terms [2000] (*Excluding 10% service charge added to meals*) B&B £35–£45. Set dinner £30. Weekend breaks.

PORTAFERRY Co. Down   **Map 6**

The Narrows   NEW   *Tel* (028) 4272 8148
8 Shore Road   *Fax* (028) 4272 8105
Portaferry BT22 1JY
                                     E-mail info@narrows.co.uk
                                     Website www.narrows.co.uk

The delightful village of Portaferry is on an inlet of the Ards peninsula. And by the waterside, with fine views across Strangford Lough (a marine nature reserve), stands Will and James Brown's "engaging and stylish" yet unpretentious little hotel. Formerly their father's home, it is built round an 18th-century courtyard. The pleasant bedrooms have a modern decor: simple colours, pale wooden floors, white bedlinen. The light, airy restaurant, looking across the water, serves "excellent contemporary cooking", particularly of seafood (eg, mussels with bacon and garlic; roast hake with cannelini beans, fennel and shellfish broth). "Breakfast is stupendous," says the nominator, "and the staff are both friendly and professional." The house is wheelchair accessible throughout, and some rooms are inter-connecting and good for a family. "We serve sausages, baked beans and chips (£2.95)," say the Browns, "but we also encourage children to experiment with our *à la carte* menu." (*Alice Naylor*)

Open All year.
Rooms 12 double, 1 single. Some on ground floor. Some suitable for &.
Facilities Lift, sitting room, restaurant (classical/"easy listening" background music); events room. Courtyard, large walled garden.
Location On shorefront. Bus from Belfast.
Restrictions No smoking: restaurant, bedrooms. Dogs allowed in 1 bedroom only.

Credit cards All major cards accepted
Terms [2000] B&B: single £57.50, double £85; D,B&B: single £74, double
£118. Light lunches served; full alc dinner £27. Special rates.

Portaferry Hotel *Tel* (028) 4272 8231
10 The Strand *Fax* (028) 4272 8999
Portaferry BT22 1PE *E-mail* info@portaferryhotel.com
Website www.portaferryhotel.com

Owned and run by John and Marie Herlihy, this traditional old quayside pub stands by the ferry landing in a pleasant village at the mouth
of Strangford Lough, a long inland sea studded with tiny islands. It is
a lovely peaceful setting for "a very sympathetic hotel", quite plain
outside but nicely modernised inside, and with "a warm, unpretentious" atmosphere. Mr Herlihy, "charming, urbane and breezy", is
omnipresent, chatting with guests. The staff are "friendly, smartly
dressed and courteous". The public rooms overlook the broad estuary-
like sound. There is a pleasant residents' lounge, with Irish paintings,
fresh garden flowers and *objets d'art*. The lively bar has "an informal
ambience, good food and youthful service". The restaurant offers such
dishes as poached salmon with asparagus and a light prawn cream;
baked cod with a soft herb crust and a mustard cream sauce; roast rack
of lamb with a tarragon jus. The cooking has been enjoyed in the past,
so we'd welcome reports on the work of the new chef, Robert
Ingleston. The bedrooms are well furnished, but some beds are small.
With a busy tourist trade in season, this enterprising hotel offers painting, opera, sailing and riding courses; there are fine walks and cycle
trails all round and eight golf courses within reach. The lough is a
marine nature reserve and bird sanctuary, also a yachting centre.

Open All year, except 23–25 Dec.
Rooms 13 double, 1 single.
Facilities 2 lounges, residents' lounge, bar, restaurant; background music in
public areas. Golf, riding, sailing, cycling, birdwatching, nearby. Unsuitable
for &.
Location In village, on seafront. Parking. Bus from Belfast.
Restrictions No smoking in some bedrooms. Guide dogs only.
Credit cards All major cards accepted.
Terms B&B £45–£57.50. Set lunch £16.50, dinner £30–£32. *V*

****

Hotel in Cumbria. Every wall of this restaurant is covered with
evidence of how good the chef/proprietor wants you to think he
is: There are awards, plaques, diplomas, certificates, magazine
articles, etc, all extolling the excellence of his cooking. But the
ambience is more bistro than upmarket restaurant; tablecloths
look as if they had been stored in a tumble dryer, and serve to
hide tables made of the shoddiest materials. There were no
floral decorations or anything else to cheer up the depressing
atmosphere. Of the famous owner, there was no sign during our
stay – for all I know, he may have been well away, instructing
gullible restaurant critics in the art of writing "puff" pieces.

****

Republic of Ireland

Temple Country House and Health Spa, Moate

Some new Irish hotels have entered the *Guide* this year. Most are along the south coast, and two are within easy reach of the Rosslare ferry and the Wexford opera festival, eg, *Slaney House* at Ferrycarrig, where in the garden you can even sleep in a mud cabin (plus all mod cons!) of the kind that Irish peasants had as their home in olden days.

Most of our Irish entries are in the west or south, or in Dublin, where the tourist boom continues and has led to the opening of some ambitious new hotels. We also have some interesting entries in the often-neglected northern part of the Republic – for example, *Castle Leslie,* Glaslough, which recently won our award for "utterly enjoyable mild eccentricity".

There are one or two small Irish chains, notably Fitzpatrick's and Jurys, but they do not feature in this section, and the big international chains are hardly represented in Ireland. Almost all Irish hotels are privately owned and run; indeed this country is a paradise of the kind of smallish, personal hotel of character that the *Guide* seeks and encourages.

Many of them are stately homes, still lived in by their ancestral owners, the Anglo-Irish gentry, who have turned them into a private hotel or guest house to defray the costs of keeping up a big estate. Or newer owners have acquired them, and run them in the same very personal way. Many belong to the Hidden Ireland association, which is affiliated to the Wolsey Lodge group in the UK. Guests may be surrounded by old family portraits and heirlooms, fine family antiques and furniture. It is all very civilised, though this kind of inspired amateurism in hotel-keeping can have its drawbacks. In many such places, the owners try to create a house party atmosphere, to give their paying clients the illusion that they are personal friends on a visit. Often they dine communally round one big table, at one sitting, and conversation is general, as at a private dinner party. The hosts will sometimes preside: often they are great fun, full of local anecdotes and information, but the whole experience can sometimes be embarrassing, and at worst you may feel that you are paying your host to amuse *him* at dinner.

Most of the best of these stately home hotels are in this guide. In town and country alike, there are also guest houses of all kinds, private homes offering B&B, and – an Irish speciality – farmhouses providing simple bedrooms, big breakfasts, sometimes an evening meal too. You can stay in converted farm buildings or outhouses, get to know the country people, even share briefly in the life of the farm. The Irish Tourist Board, Bord Fáilte, grades all kinds of accommodation; the places it approves generally display at the gate its green shamrock sign.

Food in Irish hotels has been improving greatly. In some places today it is rather sophisticated, and out of national pride (as in Wales and Scotland), the chefs like to call it "modern Irish cooking", though the specifically Irish element is not always evident. A few places win a *Michelin* star or *Bib Gourmand* for quality, and we identify these. But standards remain erratic, and attempts at sophistication do not always succeed. In the stately home hotels, you are more likely to find "country house cooking" done by the hostess – simple, maybe too bland for some tastes, but generally reliable.

As in Britain, VAT is included in bills, but service is not – you should add about 10 per cent. Service, usually by local people, may sometimes lack polish, but it makes up for this by an almost universal Irish cheerfulness and readiness to oblige. And all Irish accommodation provides an ample cooked breakfast.

ADARE Co. Limerick   **Map 6**

Dunraven Arms   NEW   *Tel* (061) 396633
                                                Fax (061) 396541
                                         E-mail dunraven@iol.ie
                                  Website www.dunravenhotel.com

In a pretty village near Limerick, on the banks of the River Maigue, is this old traditional coaching inn, large, handsome and yellow-fronted. "It is wonderfully stylish, a reliable old favourite," runs one of two thumbs-up reports this year, restoring it to the *Guide*. "Bedrooms and public rooms are smart and comfortable, though the decor in the bar is too trendy and bright. The food is first class (superb seafood terrine, Irish rib of beef, full Irish breakfast with delicious bacon). Brian Murphy, the manager, and his son, are much in evidence, and the large, highly professional staff make it all very civilised." "It is a rambling place, but the several newer wings match well with the older parts. Our junior suite was spacious, the welcome was warm and friendly, the service excellent, and the tone in the dining room was of old-fashioned elegance." Sandra Earl's cooking is traditional with a trolley roast each day. Some bedrooms look on to gardens, but front ones face the busy main road. There are several small lounges with fires, "for quiet reading", and a leisure centre with a gym, steam room and large pool. Adorned with many paintings of local hunting scenes, the hotel is geared towards horse riding, and may not appeal to those who hate blood sports; guests can hunt with the famous local packs. Two gripes this year: "The swimming pool is banned to under-16s after 5 pm", and, "One night, the dining room was largely taken over by an American coach party, whose members kept moving between tables." Salmon- and trout-fishing, and an 18-hole championship golf course, are nearby. (*Richard Parish, Lynn Wildgoose*)

Open All year.
Rooms 20 suites, 53 double, 3 single. Some on ground floor.
Facilities Lift. Lounge, writing room. TV room, residents' bar (pianist at weekends), public bar, restaurant, conservatory, conference/function facilities; leisure centre: swimming pool, steam room, gym. 3-acre gardens. River, fishing, golf, riding, fox-hunting nearby.
Location In village 10 miles SW of Limerick. Private parking.
Restrictions No smoking in restaurant. No dogs.
Credit cards All major cards accepted.
Terms [2000] (*Excluding 12½% service charge*) Room: single IR£70–£90, double IR£92–£120, suite IR£130–£160. Breakfast IR£7.50–£10.50. Set Sun lunch IR£17.95, dinner IR£26.95.

AGLISH Co. Tipperary   **Map 6**

Ballycormac House   `BUDGET`   *Tel* (067) 21129
Aglish, nr Borrisokane   *Fax* (067) 21200
                                                 E-mail ballyc@indigo.ie

"It was like staying with friends," say visitors this year to this 350-year-old farmhouse, well converted into a stylish guest house and now owned and run by an English couple, John and Cherylynn Lang. East of Lough Derg, it is not far from Birr with its fine castle. "The Langs made us very welcome and even took us to the pub one night. The rooms were comfortable and the food very good." Others have written of "superb hospitality"; they found the house and small gardens "charming", and enjoyed their "delightfully decorated suite" with a four-poster. Mrs Lang does the much-admired cooking, which is varied and eclectic, using the farm's organically grown fruit and vegetables, plus other local produce. Carrot soup, leg of Irish lamb with wild blackberry sauce, chocolate toffee pudding might be on the menu. The ambience is intimate: there is room for nine guests only. Programmes of outdoor activities (golf, shooting, fishing, riding, etc) can be arranged. "We are keen horse people," say the Langs. They have their own stable of hunters, and in season they offer hunting holidays (several packs are nearby) for guests who are interested in this controversial sport. They also offer "weekend equestrian breaks", and will put up visitors to local hunt balls, arranging transport "so that everyone can have a drink". (*Wendy Rowley, JL*)

Open All year.
Rooms 1 suite, 4 double, 1 single. No telephone.
Facilities Sitting room, dining room; drying room. No background music. 2-acre gardens, 20-acre pastures; horse riding, fox-hunting, shooting arranged. Lough Derg 5 miles, fishing, water sports; golf nearby.
Location From Nenagh, N on N52 to Borrisokane, then N65. Right at signs to hotel. Bus from Nenagh.
Restrictions No smoking. No dogs in house.
Credit cards MasterCard, Visa.
Terms B&B IR£25–£45; D,B&B IR£47–£67. Set lunch IR£12, dinner IR£25. Child accommodated in parents' room: under 15, 50% of adult rate. Off-season, riding, hunting breaks, etc. *V*

BALLINDERRY Co. Tipperary   Map 6

Kylenoe BUDGET   *Tel* (067) 22015
Ballinderry, Nenagh   *Mobile* 087 2756000
                                                          Fax (067) 22275

"A very friendly welcome. Excellent value, great breakfast and a first-class dinner." "After a difficult journey, we collapsed on a sofa by a huge log fire in the lounge. We thought we'd arrived in heaven, and that Virginia Moeran was an angel." "Comfortable and homely surroundings in a lovely area." More tributes, this year and last, to this 200-year-old stone house set on a hilltop with superb views of Lough Derg and the surrounding counties. It has been much redecorated this year. In its huge grounds, where guests may roam, are meadows, woods, apple orchards, masses of wild flowers in spring, birdsong, plenty of wildlife – foxes, deer, red squirrels, etc – and a small horse-breeding farm. The informal atmosphere, the personal attention, and the Irish country house cooking are all enjoyed. "Mrs Moeran's children came and talked with us; we felt we were staying with friends." Guests' children are welcomed too. The spacious bedrooms "have every comfort, including fresh flowers and an electric blanket". At breakfast "everything is home made, including the gorgeous marmalade"; eggs are free-range. An evening meal, based on local produce, is available by arrangement, eg, smoked salmon, roast lamb. It is elegantly served at tables set with flowers and silver. Water is from the estate's own spring. "We are very quiet," says Mrs Moeran, "but buzzing night life and restaurants are ten minutes' drive away." Other local attractions: golf, fishing, sailing, "beautiful walks", Birr and Portumna castles. (*Yvonne Boland, RW, and others*)

Open All year, except 15–30 Dec.
Rooms 3 double. No telephone. TV in one room.

Facilities Stair lift. Drawing room (background music on request), dining room. 150-acre estate with stud, woods, etc. Lake, fishing ½ mile. Golf nearby. Unsuitable for &.
Location Between Ballinderry and Terryglass (signposted). 7 miles NW of Borrisokane.
Credit cards MasterCard, Visa.
Terms B&B IR£30–£35. Set dinner IR£25. ⅓ reduction for children staying more than 1 night. *V* (for a 2-night stay)

BALLINGARRY Co. Limerick   **Map 6**

The Mustard Seed at Echo Lodge   *Tel* (069) 68508
                                                      Fax (069) 68511

Daniel Mullane's handsome white Victorian lodge, once a convent, now a restaurant-with-rooms, stands in large grounds above a very pretty village. It is "not a very sophisticated place", but most readers like it, though this year an inspector warned: "Its melange of weird objects won't be to all tastes": the dramatic decor includes, in the living room, green walls densely hung with prints and photographs; in the handsome dining room, dark blue walls, yellow curtains and bright patterned plates; antiques, open fires. And there is a dark, "claustro-phobic" foyer. But the library "has an excellent collection of books". The staff are friendly, and Mr Mullane is "very cheerful, a real charmer", though one visitor "found his mateyness a bit OTT: at dinner he asked us six times whether we were enjoying ourselves". The chef, Owen Sherry, serves modern Irish cuisine on a wide menu, including, eg, duck, raisin and apple boudin on red cabbage with mustard cream sauce; breast of chicken filled with smoked salmon and chilli. Readers have called the cooking "excellent", though one couple this year thought it erratic. Bedrooms are done in period style, and some have views: their furniture has variously been called "beautiful" and "an ugly clutter". Outdoor activities include golf, fishing, riding, walking in the hills. (*MH, PD, and others*)

Open All year, except Feb, Christmas. Restaurant closed Sun/Mon in low season.
Rooms 1 suite, 9 double, 2 single. 1 on ground floor.
Facilities Ramps to public area. Lounge, library, dining room (mixed background music during dinner). 7-acre grounds: garden, pond. Riding, shooting, angling and golf nearby.
Location 18 miles SW of Limerick. From Limerick take N21; turn left ¼ mile out of Adare, signposted Ballingarry. In village centre, take Newcastle West road for 500 yards; entrance on right.
Restrictions No smoking: restaurant, some bedrooms. No dogs.
Credit cards Amex, MasterCard, Visa.
Terms [2000] B&B: single IR£85–£105, double IR£120–£160, suite IR£150–£160. Set dinner IR£33. Off-season rates.

The Irish punt and the pound sterling do not have the same value. Be sure to check the exchange rate. And remember that Ireland is now using the euro.

BALLYCOTTON Co. Cork   Map 6

Bayview Hotel   NEW   *Tel* (021) 646746
                                                    Fax (021) 646075
                                          E-mail bayhotel@iol.ie

"A really peaceful and comfortable place," says the nominator of this
fairly luxurious holiday hotel, long, low and gleamingly painted
white, set above a fishing village south-east of Cork. "It is a large
house in its own grounds on the edge of the cliffs, with panoramic
views of the bay. It looks Georgian/Victorian but was massively
rebuilt in 1991. All rooms have sea views, and some take in the picturesque harbour, full of boats. Apart from a distant foghorn, the only
sound is of the sea on the rocks and seabirds at dawn. The hotel is well
furnished, with lots of flowers and old paintings. Bedrooms are
spacious: many have full-length windows with a view; housekeeping
is good. One end of the large bar is furnished as a library/lounge, with
an open fire and a cosy atmosphere. The elegant dining room has well-
spaced tables: on the short fixed menu, the food was well cooked and
served with style. Breakfast was mostly waitress service. The garden
is pretty, set in terraces down the cliffs." More reports welcome on the
staff and management, and on the food (Ciaran Scully is chef), which
might include braised pig's cheek with rosti; venison with Savoy cabbage. There are six golf courses in the area. (*Lynn Wildgoose*)

Open Early Apr–end Oct.
Rooms 2 suites, 33 double.
Facilities Cocktail bar, lounge, restaurant; classical background music; 2
meeting rooms. 2-acre grounds. Access to public beach. Wedding facilities.
Location Near village centre and harbour, 27 miles SE of Cork.
Restriction No dogs.
Credit cards Amex, MasterCard, Visa.
Terms [2000] B&B: single IR£75–£87.50, double IR£110–£135, suite
IR£160–£185. Set lunch IR£14.75, dinner IR£29. *V*

BALLYLICKEY Co. Cork   Map 6

Sea View House   *Tel* (027) 50073 and 50462
Ballylickey, Bantry Bay   *Fax* (027) 51555
                                   E-mail seaviewhouse-hotel@eircom.net

This year visitors again appreciated Kathleen O'Sullivan's "warm
personal welcome", and the "outstanding value" at her large, white,
much-windowed Victorian house close to the waterfront, facing
Bantry Bay. She grew up here, and now runs it as an unassuming guest
house, in cheery personal style. It has a well-designed modern extension, and it stands in well-tended, mature gardens. "It is a haven of
peace. The sea view is somewhat distant, but the gardens are magnificent." The decor (patterned carpets, flowery curtains and knick-
knacks) and the food and ambience might not appeal to the
super-sophisticated, but "everything is spotless, gleaming, run by
Miss O'Sullivan with such charm and efficiency". Her staff are
"friendly" and "amusing". The best bedrooms are large, with some

antiques and plenty of cupboard space: some have been found over-furnished, with a too massive wardrobe. Some have "a wonderful view". Bathrooms are well appointed. "In a dining room popular with locals, where Miss Sullivan herself takes the food orders, the food is excellent and varied," says a visitor this year, "with a fair mixture of plain and sauced dishes, and good vegetables in sensible portions." Others have agreed – good local fish and seafood; the plainer dishes probably the most successful. Breakfasts are "outstanding", with Irish potato pancakes, chunky marmalade and good toast. There are large, comfortable public rooms, including a well-stocked library. (*Lynn Wildgoose, and others*)

Open 15 Mar–15 Nov.
Rooms 2 suites, 15 double. 1 on ground floor, suitable for &. More suites planned for Oct 2000.
Facilities Lift. Residents' lounge, library, cocktail, bar, 2 dining rooms. No background music. 5-acre grounds on waterfront, fishing, boating; riding, golf nearby.
Location In village 3 miles N of Bantry towards Glengariff; 70 yds off main road. Bus from Cork, 48 miles.
Restrictions No smoking in dining room. No dogs in public rooms.
Credit cards All major cards accepted.
Terms B&B IR£45–£70; D,B&B IR£65–£95. Set lunch IR£15, dinner IR£25. Special rates negotiable. *V*

BALLYMOTE Co. Sligo   **Map 6**

Temple House   *Tel* (071) 83329
Fax (071) 83808
E-mail guests@templehouse.ie
Website www.templehouse.ie

Sandy Perceval's family has lived since 1665 in this Georgian mansion of "faded grandeur", where he and his wife Deb now take paying guests. It stands in huge grounds with terraced gardens, woods and farmland, beside a lake and a ruined 13th-century Knights Templar castle. Inside is an imposing main hall and stairway, antique furniture, turf and log fires, and canopied beds. The house is well heated in winter, despite the 20-foot-high ceilings. "Anyone with a sense of history should stay here," said one reader. Some of the bedrooms are huge (one is nicknamed "the half-acre"); lighting can be poor, but there has been much redecoration this year. The Percevals are friendly, and helpful with advice about places to visit, and the style is informal. At dinner, guests sit round one table to enjoy Deb Perceval's cooking ("Irish with French connections"). No choice: a menu in 2001 might include: walnut tartlets with an apricot, bacon and red onion filling; peppered home-produced beef; spiced apple wedges; Irish cheeseboard. Vegetarians are catered for if they give advance notice. Much produce comes from the farm, which is stocked with sheep and Kerry cattle; wildlife abounds, and the estate has been designated a European lichen conservation area. You can hire a boat and fish in the lake (pike over 20 lb are not uncommon), and shooting parties are held in winter. Children are welcomed. Because of Mr Perceval's severe allergies,

brought on by sheep dip, guests are asked not to wear scented products. Yeats country is all around, as well as some major archaeological sites, and traditional music and dancing sessions are held regularly in the area. More reports, please.

Open 1 Apr–30 Nov.
Rooms 4 double, 1 single. No telephone/TV.
Facilities Sitting room, snooker room, dining room. No background music. 1,000-acre farm: 1½-acre terraced garden, croquet, woodlands, lake, coarse fishing, boating. Golf, riding nearby. Unsuitable for &.
Location 12 miles S of Sligo by N17, then R293. Signposted beyond Esso garage in Ballymote. Train: Ballymote (4 miles); then taxi.
Restrictions No smoking in dining room. Dogs in car only.
Credit cards Amex, MasterCard, Visa.
Terms B&B IR£45–£55. Set dinner IR£20. Reductions for long stays. 1-night bookings refused public holidays.

BALLYVAUGHAN Co. Clare	**Map 6**

Gregans Castle　　　　　　　　　　　　*Tel* (065) 707 7005
　　　　　　　　　　　　　　　　　　　　Fax (065) 707 7111
　　　　　　　　　　　　　　　　　　E-mail res@gregans.ie
　　　　　　　　　　　　　　　　　Website www.gregans.ie

"An elegant and atmospheric haven, not cheap, but providing real quality," runs new praise this year for Peter and Moira Haden's country house hotel (their son Simon is manager). Set on a hill above Galway Bay, it is on the edge of the Burren, a strange region of rocky scenery, full of rare flowers and plants. "We arrived at 1 am after a six-hour delay at Gatwick, but were warmly welcomed with a room-service supper of organic ham salad. Our room had individuality, plus a cushioned window seat with views of the Burren, its own private garden and a huge double bath. The staff were helpful and warm. Turf fires and paintings of local Galway characters give the hotel an authentically Irish feel." Pictures of local flora add to the decor in the drawing room, whose bay window looks over the lovely garden. The bedrooms (one has a four-poster) are much admired: "Ours was the last word in sophisticated comfort." The dining room, newly extended, offers views of the sun setting over the bay. Locally grown ingredients, organic when possible, are used, and locally caught fish and seafood. The cooking of the French chef, Régis Herviaux, is admired: eg, grilled monkfish with tapenade; Irish beef fillet with roquefort sauce; chocolate and orange mousse. Vegetarians are catered for too. The atmosphere is "quite genteel"; a jacket and tie are expected of male guests at night. There is live classical harp or piano music during dinner, and a pianist plays Irish folk and jazz in the *Corkscrew Bar*, popular for pre-dinner drinks. The lounge is "tranquil, full of books and board games". The library has "an interesting selection of books, including a history of the papacy in umpteen volumes" – and *Hansard* for the House of Lords for the past 40 years. The Burren is also a centre of Irish folk culture (you'll hear good Irish music in its pubs). Nearby are the "awe-inspiring" cliffs of Moher, the golf courses of Lahinch – and Lisdoonvarna with its famous annual matchmaking festival (should you need it). (*Julie Everton, HR*)

Open 5 Apr–late Oct.
Rooms 6 suites, 18 double. Some on ground floor.
Facilities Hall, lounge, library, bar, dining room. No background music. 12-acre grounds: garden, ornamental lake, croquet. Safe sandy beach, swimming 4½ miles; golf, riding, hill-walking nearby.
Location At foot of Corkscrew Hill, 3½ miles SW of Ballyvaughan, on N67 to Lisdoonvarna.
Restrictions No smoking: restaurant, some bedrooms. No dogs.
Credit cards Amex, MasterCard, Visa.
Terms [2000] B&B: single IR£89–£108, double IR£98–£196, suite IR£158–£280. Set dinner IR£38; full alc IR£46. 3-day rates. Child accommodated in parents' room: under 5, IR£10; 5–10, IR£15.

BANTRY Co. Cork   **Map 6**

Bantry House   *Tel* (027) 50047
                                                      Fax (027) 50795
                                E-mail bantry@hidden-ireland.com
                                Website www.hidden-ireland.com/bantry

Set in wide wooded grounds, this grand classical country house has a "stunning location" looking over Bantry Bay and the Caha mountains on the Beara peninsula. It has belonged to the White family since 1739: the present owner, Egerton Shelswell White, is a keen trombone player (as guests can hear). He is a scion of the Earl of Bantry, who received the title for warning the British of the arrival of a French fleet in the bay in 1796. Today the French still come here, with more peaceful intentions: "We liked the atmosphere, the friendly owner and cook, and the snooker table," said one Gallic guest. The house is filled with furniture, paintings and *objets d'art* collected by the second earl on his travels in Europe in the 19th century. He also laid out the formal gardens, with a fountain, parterres and a "stairway to the sky". The bedrooms, in both wings of the house, are much admired: one is "huge, with breathtaking views of the bay, and modern furnishings chosen with taste". A pair of rooms in the west wing is especially suitable for a family. "Very good" breakfasts are served in a "cosy, delightful room". They include freshly squeezed orange juice, fruit, kippers, and eggs in various ways. A "simple and delicious" dinner is available, by arrangement, at 7.30 on weekdays. Limited choice, eg, carrot and orange soup or melon; roast lamb or baked sole. There is a short children's supper menu. The house is open to visitors, and a tour is included in the room price. Guests have the use of a separate sitting room, billiard room and television room, plus free access to the main rooms of the house. (*AK*)

Open Mar–Oct inclusive. Dinner served Mon–Fri by arrangement.
Rooms 1 suite, 7 double. No TV.

Facilities Hall, sitting room, TV room, library (2 or 3 concerts a month), billiard room, bar dining room; craft shop, tea room. No background music. 100-acre estate: formal gardens, woodland. Sea, sandy beach ½ mile; tennis, sailing, fishing, golf, horse riding nearby. Unsuitable for &.
Location ½ mile NE of centre; signposted at Inner Harbour. Bus from Cork (2½ hrs).
Restrictions No smoking: dining room, bedrooms. Dogs in grounds only.
Credit cards Access, MasterCard, Visa.
Terms B&B IR£65–£85. Set lunch IR£10–£12, dinner IR£25.

BEAUFORT Co. Kerry   Map 6

Beaufort House   *Tel/Fax* (064) 44764
E-mail info@beaufortireland.com
Website www.beaufortireland.com

"The jewel in the crown of our Irish visit," say visitors this year to Rachel and Donald Cameron's large white Georgian house near Killarney. "The Camerons, plus their two children and two dogs, were extremely hospitable and helpful, and we were most comfortable." Others have enjoyed the "warmth, food, and efficient, as well as friendly, care". The River Laune, with fishing for trout and salmon, runs through the large wooded grounds. From the upper rooms there is a good view of Macgillicuddy's Reeks, the mountain range with Ireland's highest peak. The bedrooms have been lavishly decorated with coordinated curtains and carpets: "Our superb front room had a bed wide enough for four." Dinner is offered from Monday to Thursday, with 24 hours' notice, and is taken communally at 8 pm. The no-choice four-course menus ("modern country house cooking") includes, eg, ceviche of scallops and brill with home-made focaccia bread; monkfish fillets roasted in bacon; elderflower sorbet. The wine list is admired, and so are the Irish cheeses. The Camerons join their guests over dessert and coffee. Breakfast is generous Irish, with freshly squeezed orange juice, a vast assortment of jams and spreads, and an abundance of toast, as well as eggs cooked any way. The drawing room has "a roaring log fire and plenty of magazines". Nearby is the Ring of Kerry, the lakes of Killarney and Tomies Wood, a huge natural oak forest; three 18-hole golf courses are within five minutes' drive. (*Helen Laing, and others*)

Open Easter–end Sept, groups at other times by arrangement. Dinner served Mon–Thurs, with 24 hours' notice.
Rooms 4 double. 4 self-catering cottages (open all year). No telephone/TV.
Facilities Drawing room, library, dining room. No background music. 42-acre grounds: river, trout/salmon-fishing. Golf nearby. Unsuitable for &.
Location 6 miles W of Killarney on R562. Left over stone bridge opposite petrol station. House immediately on left.
Restrictions Smoking in library only. No dogs in house.
Credit cards MasterCard, Visa.
Terms B&B: single IR£80, double IR£120–£140. Set dinner IR£27.50.

The international dialling code for Ireland is 353.

CARAGH LAKE Co. Kerry   Map 6

Caragh Lodge   *Tel* (066) 9769115
Caragh Lake   *Fax* (066) 9769316
Killorglin   *E-mail* caraghl@iol.ie

"It is very well run and a pleasure to stay in," says a devotee returning
this year to Mary Gaunt's Victorian fishing lodge, set in large gardens
with rare trees and shrubs. It is on the shore of Caragh Lake, and has
views of the lofty Macgillicuddy's Reeks. "A warm welcome, an
excellent room in the new wing, and an outstanding dinner." Mary
Gaunt is much in evidence, and her staff "could not be more attentive
and courteous". The spacious bedrooms in the main building have
splendid views; those in the new wing are "superbly decorated", with
a "top-quality" bathroom. In the restaurant, which overlooks the lake
and is open to the public at weekends, the food is modern Irish, eg,
millefeuille of oyster mushrooms and bacon with garlic sauce; cider-
baked Kerry ham on cabbage with mustard sauce; chocolate nemesis
with crème anglaise. Breads are home baked, and the wine list is large.
Breakfasts include smoked salmon and scrambled eggs. There is
unpolluted swimming in the lake, and free trout-fishing. The Ring of
Kerry and the sandy beaches of Dingle Bay are a short drive away, and
there are ten golf courses nearby. (*David Clarke, EC*)

Open 13 Apr–12 Oct.
Rooms 1 suite, 13 double, 1 single. 3 in garden annexe. Some on ground floor.
Facilities 2 lounges, restaurant (classical/Irish background music during din-
ner). 7-acre grounds: garden, tennis, sauna, lake, swimming, fishing, boating.
Sea 4 miles. Unsuitable for &.
Location 22 miles W of Killarney, off N70. From Killorglin towards
Glenbeigh, take road signposted *Caragh Lodge* 1 mile. Left at lake, lodge on
right.
Restrictions No smoking in restaurant. No children under 12. No dogs.
Credit cards All major cards accepted.
Terms B&B: single IR£75, double IR£115–£145, suite IR£200. Set dinner
IR£33.

CARRIGBYRNE Co. Wexford   Map 6

Cedar Lodge   *Tel* (051) 428386
Carrigbyrne, Newbawn   *Fax* (051) 428222

"A very good overnight stop," says a returning devotee in 2000. "The
owner Tom Martin is still chatting away, his wife, Ailish, is still up at
crack of dawn carrying breakfast trays for people leaving for the
Rosslare ferry." West of Wexford, this modern white building stands
beneath forest slopes, and has recently been improved and extended
by its "talented hotelier": a new wing with spacious bedrooms has
been added, older bedrooms have been refurbished, and the motel-like
façade has had a facelift. Triple glazing has been added this year to
rooms on the main road: "That will remove traffic noise," promises Mr
Martin. "The staff were welcoming, the rooms large and well furnished in executive style," says one report this year. "At dinner, in a

pleasant conservatory, the chairs were really comfortable and the food
was excellent, notably crab, scallops, steak." Others have admired Mrs
Martin's breast of guinea fowl with coriander, or Wexford lamb with
Madeira. Service is not fast but "willing and attentive". Logs burn in
the big brass-canopied fireplace in the middle of the dining room. "The
rather ordinary breakfast is raised to the unusual if you ask for Mrs
Martin's special Irish brown bread." As for the background music,
some have found it irritating, others "not intrusive". There is a garden,
and good walking locally (a guide is provided in the bedrooms).
Nearby is the John F Kennedy Arboretum, which has trees and shrubs
from all over the world, and the lovely Wexford coast. (*Christopher
Brumfit, Ruth West, RSR*)

Open 1 Feb–1 Dec.
Rooms 28 double. Some on ground floor.
Facilities Ramp. Lounge, lounge bar, breakfast room, restaurant. Varied back-
ground music, bar, restaurant. 1½-acre garden. Golf nearby, sandy beaches
12 miles.
Location On N25, 14 miles W of Wexford.
Restrictions No smoking in restaurant. Dogs by arrangement; not in public
rooms.
Credit cards Amex, MasterCard, Visa.
Terms [2000] B&B: single IR£69, double IR£110. Set lunch IR£16, dinner
IR£25. 3-day rates.

CASHEL BAY Co. Galway   Map 6

Zetland House   *Tel* (095) 31111
Fax (095) 31117
E-mail zetland@iol.ie
Website www.connemara.net/zetland

Built for the Earl of Zetland, this handsome white 1850s hunting lodge
stands in large grounds on the edge of Cashel Bay, amid the wild
Connemara landscape. Owners John and Mona Prendergast and their
daughter, Ruaidari, offer "genuine Irish hospitality". Visitors this year
wrote with enthusiasm: "An excellent place, with tasteful decor,
exemplary treatment from the owners, beautifully cooked food served
by a variety of nationalities." The lounges are large, with peat fires,
antiques, soft colour schemes, fresh flowers, books, porcelain, varied
paintings. The dining room is "exquisitely decorated, with dreamy
views over the sea and mountains in the setting sun". The food is generally admired (eg, nettle soup; pan-fried wild duck; baked monkfish
tail). Salmon, lobster and Connemara lamb are cooked in a "progres-
sive Irish" way, and many of the vegetables served are grown in the
garden. Afternoon tea comes with home baking. Most bedrooms are
spacious, with views of the bay. The hotel has its own sea-trout fishery, with 20 lakes and three miles of river. Two championship golf
courses are nearby, also wonderful beaches with safe swimming, and
other sporting activities (see below). Shooting parties can dominate
the place at times. (*Wendy Rowley, and others*)

Open Apr–Oct.
Rooms 10 suites, 7 double, 2 single. 1 on ground floor.

Facilities Drawing room, lounge, cocktail bar, dining room. No background music. 10-acre grounds: tennis, fishing; rocky shore 200 yds. Golf, water sports, sea angling, cycling, shooting, pony-trekking available.
Location 40 miles NW of Galway. Take N59 towards Clifden; turn left after Recess, follow hotel signs. Bus from Galway.
Restrictions No smoking: dining room, bedrooms. No dogs in public rooms.
Credit cards All major cards accepted.
Terms (*Excluding 12½% service charge*) B&B: single IR£77–£88, double IR£107–£130. Set lunch IR£16, dinner IR£32. Child accommodated in parents' room: 50% of adult rate. ***V***

CASTLEBALDWIN Co. Sligo　　　　　　　　　　　　Map 6

Cromleach Lodge　　　　　　　　　　　*Tel* (071) 65155
Castlebaldwin, via Boyle　　　　　　　　*Fax* (071) 65455
　　　　　　　　　　　　　　　E-mail info@cromleach.com
　　　　　　　　　　　　　　　Website www.cromleach.com

♀ *César award in 1999*

"Near perfection," says a reader this year who spent six nights at Christy and Moira Tighe's sophisticated small hotel, enjoying his "delightful, spacious" room and the "excellent food". One of the *Guide*'s most admired rural entries, it is a striking modern building, grey-gabled and glass-fronted, set on a hillside above Lough Arrow; all bedrooms have good views across the lake to the mountains. Mrs Tighe's modern Irish cooking, "with an emphasis on lightness", does not come cheaply but has won many accolades. The menu includes dishes such as crab soufflé and Armagnac bisque; loin of Sligo lamb with rosemary and garlic jus; iced almond and apricot nougat. There is a six-course gourmet menu for residents. Vegetarians are catered for. "The ingredients are of the highest quality, prettily presented." "The desserts are a work of art and the staff are well trained." Guests rotate to different tables each night, so that all get a turn for the best views. "Our bedroom was delightful, with luxurious bathroom and tempting exotica in the fruit bowl." The design in the public rooms has been thought "a bit over-the-top" by some guests, but "absolutely lovely" by others. The large black labrador on the entrance mat can block the way. Families with young children may use a separate dining room. There is good walking in the area; also fishing, golf and archaeological tours. (*John K Chew, JBM, and others*)

Open 2 Feb–6 Nov. Lunch not served.
Rooms 10 double.
Facilities 2 lounges, bar, 3 dining rooms, conservatory. No background music. 30-acre grounds: forest walks, private access to Lough Arrow: fishing, boating, surfing; walking, hill climbing. Golf nearby. Unsuitable for &.
Location 9 miles NW of Boyle, off N4 Dublin–Sligo. Turn E at Castlebaldwin. Train: Boyle; then taxi.
Restrictions No smoking: restaurant, dining rooms, 1 lounge, 5 bedrooms. No dogs in public rooms (kennels provided).
Credit cards All major cards accepted.
Terms B&B IR£75–£145; D,B&B IR£115–£185. Tasting dinner menu IR£40; full alc IR£40. Special rates for 2- to 5-day stays. Cookery courses Feb.

CASTLELYONS Co. Cork   Map 6

Ballyvolane House   *Tel* (025) 36349
                                               Fax (025) 36781
                                          E-mail ballyvol@iol.ie
                              Website www.ballyvolanehouse.ie

Dating from 1728, Merrie and Jeremy Green's sturdy Italianate
country mansion, elegant inside, stands in "magnificent formal gardens", with its own farmland all round, plus a walled kitchen garden
with free-range chickens. "It is a little jewel," runs a recent report:
Roland's Room, for instance, has "a fantastic bath, framed in wood
and big enough to float a liner". And hand-painted murals have been
added to doors off the hallways this year. Guests sit around one table
for dinner, "a slightly formal affair", served with candles, silver and
crystal. The meal, cooked by Mrs Green and Maeve Crofts, offers no
choice until dessert, and may include egg mousse with prawns;
chicken stuffed with herbs and apricots; chocolate mousse or baked
Alaska. Guests can fish for trout in the house's own lakes, and
the Greens have eight beats on about ten miles of the Blackwater,
one of Ireland's premier salmon rivers. Interesting nearby sightseeing includes Blarney Castle, the Rock of Cashel, Killarney and
Kinsale. (*PD*)

Open All year, except Christmas. Dinner served to non-residents by arrange-
ment only.
Rooms 6 double. 1 on ground floor. No telephone.
Facilities 2 sitting rooms, dining room. 8-acre grounds: garden, croquet, 3
trout lakes. 10 miles fishing on River Blackwater. Riding, golf, tennis, horse
racing, seaside, etc, nearby.
Location From Cork, turn off N8 at River Bride, just before Rathcormac.
Follow signs to house.
Restrictions No smoking: dining room, 1 sitting room, bedrooms. No dogs in
house.
Credit cards Amex, MasterCard, Visa.
Terms [2000] B&B: single IR£50–£62, double IR£76–£100; D,B&B
IR£63–£87 per person. Set lunch IR£15, dinner IR£25. Child accommodated
in parents' room: under 12, 80% of adult rate.

CASTLETOWNSHEND Co. Cork   Map 6

The Castle   `BUDGET`   *Tel* (028) 36100
                                               Fax (028) 36166

Somerville and Ross, the cousins who wrote *Some Experiences of an
Irish R.M.*, used to live in this large, attractive village on an inlet of the
sea west of Cork. It is popular with American, European and other
"expats", and is lively in season. The grey crenellated *Castle* stands by
the water's edge, backed by wooded grounds. The seat of the patrician
Townshend family since 1650, it is now run as a guest house combined with self-catering accommodation by Anne Cochrane-
Townshend, the daughter of the family. The atmosphere is "very
baronial: family portraits in the panelled sitting room, lots of creaking
floorboards, etc". Most bedrooms (some are huge) have "stunning"

sea views, as does the "stately room" where breakfast is served. No other meals are offered, but there are good restaurants locally. A good place for sailing, water sports, etc. More reports, please.

Open 15 Jan–15 Dec.
Rooms 6 double, 1 single. 1 on ground floor. No telephone/TV. Also self-catering apartments.
Facilities Sitting room with TV, breakfast room. No background music. 4-acre grounds on shore: sculpture park, safe bathing. Sailing, water sports, fishing, walking, riding, golf nearby.
Location In village 5 miles SE of Skibbereen. Bus from Skibbereen.
Restrictions No smoking in breakfast room. No dogs.
Credit cards MasterCard, Visa.
Terms B&B IR£25–£50. *V*

CLARECASTLE Co. Clare   Map 6

Carnelly House   *Tel* (065) 682 8442
                                              Fax (065) 682 9222
                                              E-mail rgleeson@iol.ie
                                              Website www.carnelly-house.com

Ten miles N of Shannon, between airport and Ennis, on 100-acre estate with woodlands, farm and wildlife: creeper-covered Georgian house found "most impressive" again this year. Friendly owners, Dermot and Rosemarie Gleeson; house-party atmosphere. Elegant period furnishings, beautiful drawing room, tall windows, open fires, wide staircase, spacious bedrooms, "splendid" bathrooms. Good home cooking (no choice), eg, wild Irish salmon; pheasant in port; communally served in red-and-white dining room; generous breakfasts. Classical background music. Fishing, fox-hunting, beaches, surfing, golf nearby. Open 15 Jan–30 Nov. Unsuitable for &. No children under 8. Dogs in grounds only. All major credit cards accepted. 5 bedrooms. B&B IR£65–£85. Set lunch IR£25, dinner IR£35. Endorsed this year, but fuller reports welcome.

CLIFDEN Co. Galway   Map 6

The Quay House   *Tel* (095) 21369
and Destry's Restaurant   *Fax* (095) 21608
Beach Road   *E-mail* thequay@iol.ie

Trim, white and Georgian, this is Clifden's oldest building, and it stands in a garden with tropical plants, beside the harbour with its fishing and pleasure boats. Once the harbourmaster's house, then a convent and Franciscan friary, it is now a small B&B hotel owned and run by Paddy and Julia Foyle, "who couldn't be more hospitable". It has plenty of oddities: "In the hallway is a cabin trunk full of peat, and a couple of battered toppers hanging from antlers on the wall." "The amusingly eccentric decor" is an eclectic mix of serious Irish antiques and paintings, and "the kitschy-cute". The "friendly informality" is enjoyed. The pictures are "fascinating but hardly jolly – Joan of Arc at prayer, the death of General Wolfe". Many bedrooms in the main house have garden or bay views, some have a working fireplace; most are spacious, though some at the top are small. A new section has studios with a kitchenette. The rooms are as full of character as the rest: one is "superb, with marble wall scrolls, a fabulous bed, and French doors leading on to a tiny flower-filled balcony facing the harbour". Another has a huge Baroque mirror as a bedhead. "The bath was vast, and the water ran peaty and soft." Breakfasts are "of high quality, with generous servings of fresh orange juice, good yogurt, and scrambled eggs and smoked salmon". At *Destry's* restaurant, nearby in the main street, the chef serves "international/Irish cooking with intense flavours". We'd be glad of reports on this, and on the hotel.

Open Mar–mid-Nov (other times by arrangement). *Destry's* closed Mon Oct–Mar.
Rooms 14 double. 7 self-catering studios in annexe. 2 on ground floor with access for ♿.
Facilities Ramps. 2 sitting rooms, breakfast room, conservatory, restaurant (in separate building, 10 mins' walk). No background music. ½-acre garden. Fishing, sailing, golf, riding nearby.
Location Harbour; 3 mins' walk from centre. Courtyard parking.
Restrictions No smoking: restaurant, bedrooms. No dogs.
Credit cards MasterCard, Visa.
Terms [2000] B&B: single IR£50–£60, double IR£80–£100. Child under 12 accommodated in parents' room free.

Rock Glen   *Tel* (095) 21035 and 21393
                                  Fax (095) 21737
                          E-mail rockglen@iol.ie
                  Website www.connemara.net/rockglen-hotel

"Great comfort, very good dinner, friendly and efficient service" – more praise this year for a converted 1815 hunting lodge, with "most welcoming" owners, John and Evangeline Roche. Their daughter, Siobhán, is manageress. Set in large grounds by a fjord with the wild Connemara hills behind, and "beautifully quiet", this low white building has a friendly young staff that includes "locals, a Breton head waiter, a Dane and some French hotel management trainees"; Gee Nazri is head chef. The clientele is equally cosmopolitan. There are open turf fires, chandeliers and large sofas, chess and Scrabble in the drawing room; the cocktail bar has a piano, and a resident pianist plays at weekends. Other amenities are a full-size snooker table, and a floodlit tennis court in the large grounds. The candlelit restaurant "is a fine setting for the imaginative, strongly flavoured food". You can take the five-course dinner for IR£34, or pay per course. Local seafood and shellfish are a speciality and cooked in modern style "with a French/Asian influence". Main dishes might include roast Connemara lamb; sauté of fresh local prawns; venison in season. There has been much redecoration this year. The best bedrooms, in front, are "light and attractive; we enjoyed splendid views of hills, water and boats as we lay in bed". Rear ones are soon to get a facelift; some bathrooms are small. The generous breakfast includes scrambled eggs with smoked salmon, and they will cook fish caught by the guests. Children are welcomed. Plenty of outdoor activities are available locally (see below); sandy beaches are nearby. Painting courses are sometimes held by an artist member of the family, Tom Roche. (*Michael Burrows, AJEB, and others*)

Open 15 Mar–20 Nov; possibly also Christmas, New Year.
Rooms 1 suite, 24 double, 1 single. 15 on ground floor.
Facilities Drawing room, cocktail bar/conservatory (pianist weekends), snooker room, restaurant. No background music. 50-acre grounds: tennis, croquet, putting. Riding, pony-trekking, river/deep-sea fishing, mountain climbing available.
Location 1½ miles S of Clifden on Ballyconneely road. Bus from Galway.
Restriction No smoking in restaurant. No dogs in public rooms; in bedrooms by arrangement.
Credit cards All major cards accepted.
Terms [2000] B&B: single IR£90–£101, double IR£110–£135, suite IR£165–£200; D,B&B double IR£169–£259. Set dinner IR£34; full alc IR£45. 1-night bookings refused bank holiday weekends.

CLONES Co. Monaghan — Map 6

Hilton Park
Scothouse, Clones

Tel (047) 56007
Fax (047) 56033
E-mail jm@hiltonpark.ie
Website www.hiltonpark.ie

César award in 1994

Their family's home since 1734, this stately Italianate mansion is now run in house-party style by "genial hosts" Lucy and Johnny Madden. "This is not a hotel," they emphasise. Near the border with Fermanagh, the house has a setting of "exceptional charm and beauty" in its own wooded park, with three lakes, a golf course, and pleasure gardens laid out by John Madden in the 1870s. "It is very good, very comfortable," said one recent visitor. The high-windowed public rooms are elegantly furnished, and full of memorabilia. The bedrooms, some with a four-poster bed, are huge; all rooms have views that are much admired. In the baronial dining room, evening meals are served round one big table (but there are separate tables, too). Lucy Madden, described this year as "one of Ireland's finest cooks", makes her own bread and preserves, and her imaginative cooking draws on the estate's produce, including organically grown vegetables. "The focus is on freshness," she writes. "Nothing is frozen or microwaved. No choice, but we cater for dietary idiosyncrasies." Breakfast is served in a cheerful annexe to the kitchen. Neil Jordan shot his superb film *The Butcher Boy* in nearby Clones, where the lace museum is worth a visit. A good base for exploring the National Trust properties, Castle Coole, the Crom estate and Florence Court, also Armagh and Lough Erne. More reports, please.

Open 1 Apr–end Sept, and to pre-booked groups all year. Dining room closed midday, and to non-residents.
Rooms 1 suite, 5 double. No telephone/TV.
Facilities Drawing room, sitting room, TV room, games room, smoking room, dining room, breakfast room. No background music. 500-acre grounds: 20-acre gardens, park, golf, 3 lakes, swimming, boating, fishing. Unsuitable for ♿.

Location 4 miles S of Clones, on L46 to Ballyhaise. Bus: Clones; then taxi.
Restrictions No smoking: bedrooms, breakfast room, dining room (until end of dinner). No children under 8. Dogs in cars.
Credit cards MasterCard, Visa.
Terms [2000] B&B IR£64–£75. Single supplement £20. Set dinner IR£27.50. Reductions for children 8–16 accommodated in parents' room. Sat night reservations are for B&B only if booked more than 6 weeks ahead.

CLONMEL Co. Tipperary   Map 6

Knocklofty House   *Tel* (052) 38222
                                                      Fax (052) 38300
                                          E-mail knocklofty@eircom.net
                                      Website www.tipp.ie/knocklofty.htm

Historic pile in 105-acre park beside River Suir (trout/salmon-fishing), 4 miles W of Clonmel on Ardfinan road. Managed by Brona Cullen and Stephen Weir ("a terrific host"). Georgian features retained, eg, 2-storey library with wrought iron balustrades, ornamented bookcases. "Superb views, excellent eclectic cooking," said nominator. Dishes with some foreign flourishes, eg, blackened cajun chicken with mozzarella and jalapenos, chilli and garlic sauce. Lounge with TV, bar, all with mixed background music; functions held. Tennis, croquet, leisure centre with 16-metre swimming pool (lessons available), spa bath, gym. Equestrian centre nearby. 17 bedrooms, recently refurbished; also self-catering mews and bungalows. Closed Christmas. Amex, MasterCard, Visa accepted. B&B IR£45–£60; D,B&B IR£70–£85. Set lunch IR£13.95, dinner IR£26. More reports, please. *V*.

CORK Co. Cork   Map 6

Lotamore House   BUDGET   *Tel* (021) 822344
Tivoli   *Fax* (021) 822219
                                              E-mail lotamore@iol.ie

Set apart on a low hillside, off a main road just east of Cork, this fine Georgian manor, now a Grade A guest house, has long been popular with *Guide* readers. The "charming" Len and Mairéad Harty are its efficient hosts. Visitors this year admired the "copious breakfasts, served rapidly", and the "impressive main staircase", but found some areas needing redecoration. Bedrooms however, renovated this year, are comfortable and nicely furnished, with some period pieces. Front ones have views of hills and the River Lee, with some industry in the foreground; rear ones are quietest. Hot and cold snacks are served in the evening, but they are "very light" and do not come speedily. (*François-Pierre and Susan Gingras*)

Open 15 Jan–5 Dec.
Rooms 20 double. Some on ground floor.
Facilities Lounge, breakfast room. No background music. 4-acre grounds.
Location 3 miles E of city centre, off N8.
Restrictions No smoking in some bedrooms. No dogs in public rooms.
Credit cards MasterCard, Amex, Visa.

Terms B&B: single IR£30–£35, double IR£50–£60. Child accommodated in parents' room: 50% of adult rate.

COSTELLO Co. Galway   Map 6

Fermoyle Lodge   *Tel* (091) 786111
                                                            Fax (091) 786154

Found "wonderful" again this year, this small hotel was built in the late 19th century as a sporting lodge. It lies secluded beside Fermoyle Lake on the south side of wild and lovely Connemara. The "engaging young owners", Nicola Stronach and her husband Jean-Pierre Maire, "provide intimate hospitality, yet space and privacy", as a visitor this year relates: "I spent a superb evening with them. The food is home-cooked and good. Bedrooms are well laid out yet simple [they have antiques and original paintings]. I revelled in the luxury of the thick duvets, and the views." There is good lough and sea fishing nearby: "The owners cater for the serious fisherman, though not obsessively, while offering all the creature comforts a non-fisherperson could want. The dining room has huge windows overlooking spectacular scenery. Our bedroom faced the garden, river and lough: the distant Twelve Pins completed the wild and tumbling view." The three-course set dinner (24 hours' notice is required) is served at 7.30. The hosts share the cooking "most successfully". A specimen menu: fresh local scallops with basil, lemon, roasted peppers and courgettes; duck with a port wine and Madeira sauce; summer pudding. There is a small selection of wines. After dinner, coffee and drinks are taken by a wood fire in a sitting room, where guests are joined by their hosts, "who clearly enjoy their work". Five golf courses are within 90 minutes' drive, and trips can be made to the Aran Islands. One snag reported (in August): lots of flies and midges; and be prepared for brown and peaty tap water. (*Ffion Griffith, RB*)

Open Apr–Oct.
Rooms 1 suite, 5 double. 2 on ground floor in adjoining mews.
Facilities 2 sitting rooms, dining room. 11-acre garden. Lakes, sea, sandy beaches, fishing, golf nearby.
Location From Galway take N59 towards Clifden. Turn left before bridge in Oughterard, follow signs for Costello for 11 miles; lodge on right. Bus: Costello or Oughterard; then taxi.
Restrictions No smoking: dining room, bedrooms. Unsuitable for young children. No dogs.
Credit cards MasterCard, Visa.
Terms [2000] B&B IR£45–£60. Set dinner IR£24.

****

Hotel in Scotland. At breakfast, luridly yellow-dyed smoked haddock arrived on a bed of lettuce doused with a sharp vinaigrette sauce; an omelette was well cooked, but fussily decorated with bits and pieces. Toast was commercial; marmalade was over-sweet; tea was exceedingly strong. All this led to gastric mayhem on our homeward drive.

****

CROSSMOLINA Co. Mayo   Map 6

Enniscoe House   *Tel* (096) 31112
Castlehill   *Fax* (096) 31773
                                    E-mail mail@enniscoe.com
                                    Website www.enniscoe.com

This graceful Georgian country house is not far from Ballina, where former president Mary Robinson grew up and her family still lives. It stands in its own large grounds beside Lough Conn, and it has been the home of Susan Kellett's family for centuries; today she owns and runs it as a private hotel. "A party of 28 of us, including 14 children under 10, spent three nights here over the millennium New Year," says a reader, "and we all found Mrs Kellett, her son and staff, to be helpful, efficient and friendly. The food was excellent, particularly the leisurely breakfasts. The setting is peaceful, with nice views over the lake, and the house was wonderful, full of family history and faded grandeur. The most relaxing part of the day was sitting in front of the peat fire after a long walk, with a drink, anticipating a great dinner." Behind the house's plain façade are 18th-century plasterwork, a sweeping staircase, and two large sitting rooms with their original furniture, family portraits and bookcases; family memorabilia are everywhere, and polished wood floors with rugs. Some bedrooms, newly renovated, with a comfortable four-poster, are huge; but only three overlook the lough. Dinner, with limited choice, is Irish country house cooking, eg, kidneys in mustard sauce; casserole of spring lamb; sticky toffee pudding. There's a working farm on the estate, an organic vegetable garden which supplies the kitchen, a walled garden with a tea room, and a resident fishing manager: brown trout can be caught in the lough; other fishing is nearby. Mrs Kellett also runs a heritage centre, helping returning emigrants to trace their Irish roots; it includes a small museum of old farm machinery. Nearby are the great cliffs of north Mayo; also three golf courses. (*Michael Harris*)

Open 1 Apr–14 Oct. Dining room closed midday. Group bookings only for New Year.
Rooms 2 suites, 4 double. Self-catering units in yard behind house.
Facilities 2 sitting rooms, dining room. No background music. 150-acre estate: garden, tea room, farm, heritage centre, lake frontage, fishing (tuition, ghillie). Golf, riding, cycling, shooting nearby. Unsuitable for &.
Location 2 miles S of Crossmolina on R315 to Pontoon and Castlebar. Train/bus: Ballina, 10 miles; then taxi.
Restrictions No smoking: restaurant, 2 bedrooms. Dogs by arrangement.
Credit cards MasterCard, Amex, Visa.
Terms B&B IR£55–£75; D,B&B IR£80–£100. Set dinner (book by 4 pm) IR£26. 10% discount for 3 nights or more. Child accommodated in parents' room: under 2, free; 2–12, 50% of adult rate.

If you agree with our dislike of piped music, do contact Pipedown, the International Campaign for Freedom from Piped Music. PO Box 1722, Salisbury SP4 7US, *e-mail* pipedown@btinternet.com

---

DINGLE Co. Kerry   **Map 6**

Benners `BUDGET`   *Tel* (066) 9151638
Main Street   *Fax* (066) 9151412
                                    E-mail benners@eircom.net

*On main street of old fishing port, "typical small-town hotel" (Best
Western), "the best place to stay in Dingle". Recently renovated behind
250-year-old façade; managed by Pat Galvin. 2 lounges (1 no-
smoking). Sociable bar opening on to main street; traditional restaurant offering local seafood, etc. Irish/classical background music in
public areas. Good breakfast with "superb home-baked brown bread".
Riding, fishing, special rates at championship golf course nearby.
Guide dogs only. Closed Christmas Day. All major credit cards
accepted. 52 comfortable bedrooms, 2 suitable for &. B&B double
IR£75–£130. Set lunch (Sun) IR£13.50, dinner IR£19.50 [2000].*

DONEGAL Co. Donegal   **Map 6**

St Ernan's House   *Tel* (073) 21065
St Ernan's Island   *Fax* (073) 22098
                                   E-mail info@sainternans.com
                                   Website www.sainternans.com

Donegal town is famous for its hand-woven tweed. On a nearby tidal
island, reached by a causeway and named for a 7th-century saint, is
this old house, now run as a hotel by Carmel and Brian O'Dowd. Its
large public rooms are furnished with antiques; large windows look
over the water. One recent visitor had "a magical visit", while an
inspector spells it out: "It is a delightful sight as you approach. A
receptionist welcomed us by name. A lovely staircase, lined with old
prints, leads up to the bedrooms. Our large room overlooked the bay
and the Donegal hills in the distance. It was well kept and comfortable,
with a big bathroom. No garden, but the location makes up for this; the
short walk around the wooded island, full of wild flowers, is very
pleasant. There are log fires in the drawing rooms. The dining room,
looking over the water, has gleaming glassware, spotless linen, good
china. The food is good Irish country house fare [eg, roast guinea fowl
with shallot and bacon sauce; stuffed pork filled with a wholegrain
mustard sauce]. After dinner, Mr O'Dowd came into the drawing
room for a chat. Breakfast was as good as the rest: fresh linen napkins,
freshly squeezed orange juice, farm butter. Quite expensive for one
night, but the three-day tariff is good value." Much of this is endorsed
in 2000, though one visitor wrote of "awful bedroom lighting, bathroom in need of a facelift, and amateurish service". The O'Dowds
have a policy of "no piped music; we are a house of peace and quiet,
and we actively discourage loud noises". Nearby are several craft
centres. More reports, please.

Open 20 Apr–end Oct. Restaurant closed midday.
Rooms 1 suite, 10 double.
Facilities Hall, 2 drawing rooms, restaurant. No background music. 8-acre
grounds. Golf, fishing, horse riding nearby. Unsuitable for &.

Location 2 km S of Donegal, on tidal island. Bus to Donegal; then taxi.
Restrictions No smoking in restaurant; no cigars or pipes in house. No children under 6. No dogs.
Credit cards MasterCard, Visa.
Terms B&B IR£75–£125. Set dinner IR£34.50, full alc £27. Reductions for stays of more than 1 night.

DUBLIN   Map 6

Anglesea Town House   *Tel* (01) 668 3877
63 Anglesea Road   *Fax* (01) 668 3461
Ballsbridge, Dublin 4

Sean and Helen Kirrane's "luxurious B&B" inhabits a handsome Edwardian house on a busy road in residential Ballsbridge, south-east of the city centre. "We strongly recommend it," runs a recent report. "The welcome was warm, with tea and apple tart. Our bedroom was large and attractive; we appreciated the settee after our long walks. The bathroom was modern. And we admired Mrs Kirrane's hospitality and painstaking care. Only drawback: front rooms get traffic noise." Another visitor wrote of a "huge, comfy bed and a beautiful vase of roses". Lavish breakfasts are served in a room with family portraits, an oak table set with fine china and silver: they include fruit compote, baked cereal, porridge, freshly baked breads, kedgeree, sole and salmon. The DART station and buses nearby provide transport to the centre. (*TM, IW*)

Open All year.
Rooms 6 double, 1 single.
Facilities Drawing room, breakfast room. No background music. Small garden. Unsuitable for &.
Location 2 miles SE of city centre, reached by buses and DART railway. Limited parking.
Restrictions No smoking. No dogs.
Credit cards Amex, MasterCard, Visa.
Terms [2000] B&B IR£50–£90.

Belcamp Hutchinson   *Tel* (01) 846 0843
Carrs Lane, Malahide Road   *Fax* (01) 848 5703
Balgriffin, Dublin 17

"A wonderful place and excellent value," runs latest praise for this sturdy creeper-covered Georgian manor, set in a garden with a pond on the north-east fringe of Dublin: it is close to good bathing beaches and to the beautiful old village of Malahide. Former home of Francis Hely-Hutchinson, Earl of Donoughmore, it is now very well run by the "charming" Doreen Gleeson, who co-owns it with Karl Waldburg. With its high ceilings, smart furnishings and moulded fireplaces, it has been called "a great place for a house party", and "very peaceful, with a nice garden, large and comfortable bedrooms". It does not serve main meals, but its Irish breakfast is "superb". Dublin airport is 15 minutes' drive away. (*BT, and others*)

Open All year, except Christmas, 1 week Nov.
Rooms 8 double.
Facilities Drawing room with TV, breakfast room. No background music. 4½-acre garden. Golf, riding, horse racing, nearby. Unsuitable for &.
Location 20 mins' drive NE from centre. Take Malahide road, turn left at Balgriffin. Private parking. Buses from city.
Restrictions Not suitable for children. No dogs in breakfast room.
Credit cards MasterCard, Visa.
Terms B&B IR£50.

The Clarence	*Tel* (01) 407 0800
6–8 Wellington Quay	*Fax* (01) 407 0820
Dublin 2	*E-mail* reservations@theclarence.ie
	Website www.theclarence.ie

The owners, none other than Bono and The Edge of U2, are often present. This year they have installed a new manager, Robert van Eerde, and a new chef, Anthony Ely, at their very modish hotel in an 1850s building by the Liffey, in the super-trendy Temple Bar district. The clientele is fashionable cosmopolitan, but most of the staff are Irish. They have been called "perfectly charming" and "well coiffed". The assertive contemporary decor is in "academic/ecclesiastical" style, with bare floors and walls. "It is really beautiful," writes an American visitor this year; "light oak, mission style, Arts and Crafts-style furniture and fixtures. We were very happy there." The super-equipped bedrooms have specially commissioned Shaker-style furniture, chic lamps, etc, and a bathroom with glittering mosaics. Some beds are "large enough for a pop star and six groupies". The penthouse suite has a baby grand piano, a panoramic rooftop terrace and a dining room seating eight. "It is all so chic that it's almost painful," said one reporter, "but it's nicely done." There's a beautiful reading room, with a roaring fire, newspapers, board games. The high-ceilinged restaurant, oddly named the *Tea Room*, has huge windows and dim lighting; the food there has been found "superb". The new chef's cooking is "European modern, using the best of Irish produce"; we'd welcome reports on his work. Breakfasts are buffet-free and "brilliant, with unusual choices, all cooked to perfection". Works by the hotel's "in-house artist", Guggi (once a member of a pop group called the Virgin Prunes), are displayed in the bedrooms and some public areas. A roof terrace looks over the river. The location, good for night-life, can be noisy with late revellers. (*Robert Freidus, BCS, GP*)

Open All year, except Christmas.
Rooms 5 suites, 45 double. 2 equipped for &. 24-hour room service.
Facilities Residents' lounge, study, bar, restaurant; contemporary background music throughout; conference facilities. Roof terrace.
Location Central, in Temple Bar, by River Liffey. Private parking.
Restriction No dogs.
Credit cards All major cards accepted.
Terms Room: single/double IR£210, suite (1 to 2 bedrooms) IR£450; penthouse suite IR£1,600. Breakfast IR£13–£16. Full alc IR£45. Child accommodated in parents' room: under 12, free.

The Hibernian   *Tel* (01) 668 7666
Eastmoreland Place   *Fax* (01) 660 2655
Ballsbridge, Dublin 4   *E-mail* info@hibernianhotel.com
                                 Website www.slh.com/hibernia

"Very comfortable, with an excellent restaurant." "Welcoming, warm and quiet." "Service was brilliant, friendly, efficient." Three more plaudits, this year and last, for a reliable city hotel in a red brick late-Victorian building down a side street in Ballsbridge, about a mile from the centre. Once a nurses' home, it is furnished with bright colours and floral displays. The "intimate public rooms" are well designed in country house style. Bedrooms are smallish, and generally found comfortable, though one couple thought theirs "gloomy". The Irish members of staff are preferred to the "more perfunctory" French ones. The manager has again changed this year, and is now David Butt. A change of head chef, too, brings Raphael Delage to the cookpots of the hotel's *Patrick Kavanagh* restaurant (named after the poet). We'd be glad of reports on his "contemporary Irish" cooking, whose accent is on fish (eg, terrine of seafood wrapped in spinach; poached salmon with tapenade dressing). A vegetarian menu is available, light meals are served in the lounge, and there is a "constant supply of liquorice allsorts" in reception. Women on their own are treated well, but tour parties "can lead to overcrowding at times". Under the same management is the recently opened 60-room *McCausland*, in Belfast, which has been smartly converted from two warehouses; it makes its *Guide* debut this year. (*Wendy Rowley, EH, SG*)

Open All year, except 24–27 Dec.
Rooms 10 suites, 30 double. 2 adapted for &.
Facilities Lift, ramp. Drawing room, library, sun lounge, conservatory, restaurant. Irish/classical background music round the clock on ground floor. Small garden.
Location Off Baggot St Upper, ⅔ mile SE of St Stephen's Green. Private parking. Buses from centre.
Restrictions No smoking: drawing room, 14 bedrooms. Guide dogs only.
Credit cards All major cards accepted.
Terms [2000] (*Excluding 12½% service charge on meals*) Room: single IR£120, double IR£150–£170, suite IR£185. Breakfast IR£12. Set lunch IR£15.95, full alc dinner IR£37. Child accommodated in parents' room: under 2, free; over 2, 50% of adult rate. *V*

Simmonstown House   *Tel* (01) 660 7260
Sydenham Road   *Fax* (01) 660 7341
Ballsbridge, Dublin 4   *E-mail* info@simmonstownhouse.com
                               Website www.simmonstownhouse.com

Another rave notice came this year for this "superb B&B", set in a quiet cul-de-sac two blocks from the sea, and a mile or so from the centre. "First glance at this terraced house in an unattractive side road made us want to turn round and run, but inside was another story. Finola and James Curry have smothered it outside with flowers, and added a pretty courtyard garden at the rear. Inside, they have contrived an extremely elegant decor, using bold colours throughout. The antique-furnished lounge and dining room are painted dark blue, the bedrooms have some Laura Ashley fabrics; our room had twin beds, lots of freshness, all comforts, plus a bathroom with a luxuriously powerful shower. Breakfast was the best ever, served with exquisite china and silver: a platter of fresh berries with hot croissants and four types of home-made jams, and for my husband the full Irish, with black pudding. Finola was endlessly helpful. It was expensive, but by far the best place we stayed at during our Irish trip." Others wrote, "You feel you are being treated like honoured private guests", and admired the "good, mainly modern paintings". (*Patricia Fenn, AR*)

Open Mid-Jan–mid-Dec.
Rooms 4 double.
Facilities Drawing room, breakfast room. No background music. Patio garden. ½ mile from seafront. Unsuitable for &.
Location 1½ miles from centre, in cul-de-sac off Merrion Rd opposite Royal Dublin Society. Many buses, and DART rail services close by.
Restrictions No smoking. No dogs.
Credit cards Amex, MasterCard, Visa.
Terms B&B IR£45–£65. Child accommodated in parents' room: under 2, free; 2–12, 50% of adult rate. 1-night bookings sometimes refused weekends.

See also SHORTLIST

DUNMANWAY Co. Cork   **Map 6**

Dún Mhuire House   BUDGET   *Tel/Fax* (023) 45162
Kilbarry Road

Liam and Carmel Hayes own and run this "gem of a guest house" in a small inland town west of Cork. They are "warmly friendly", and their lounge with its open fireplace has been called "an excellent place for socialising with other guests". They also operate an award-winning restaurant, where Mrs Hayes' cooking draws many regulars from the nearby towns. "Dinner was a revelation," says a visitor this year, "but the menu is limited." Mrs Hayes makes much use of fresh local fish: her menus might include monkfish wrapped in bacon; poached salmon in cream. There is always a vegetarian dish. Home-made puddings come on a trolley. Most bedrooms are in a building at the back ("it is rather flimsily constructed"). Dunmanway itself is not exciting, but the fine coastal towns of West Cork, such as Kinsale, are not far off (it is a 20-minute drive to the coast) and there is good shopping for antiques nearby. (*FG, Simon Willbourn*)

Open All year, except 23–29 December. Restaurant closed in winter except Fri and Sat nights.
Rooms 6 double. 4 in garden. 4 on ground floor.
Facilities Lounge/bar, restaurant; "easy listening" background music. Small garden. Public swimming pool, leisure centre, tennis nearby; golf, beaches 20 mins' drive.
Location A few mins' walk from centre; signposted.
Restrictions No smoking in restaurant. No dogs.
Credit cards MasterCard, Visa.
Terms B&B: IR£25–£30; D,B&B IR£45–£50. Set dinner IR£20.

ENNISCORTHY Co. Wexford   Map 6

Salville House   `BUDGET`   *Tel/Fax* (054) 35252
Salville   *E-mail* salvillehouse@eircom.net

Owned and run by Jane and Gordon Parker as a small, trim guest
house, this light and bright mid-Victorian building stands on a hilltop
just outside the town, with views over the River Slaney and the
Blackstairs Mountains. It has large windows and a "beautifully
simple" decor. Rosslare ferry is 30 minutes' drive away. "I would love
to return"; "It is wonderfully consistent, and the food is stunning," ran
new plaudits in 1999/2000. Jane Parker is "an all-round friendly person with a nice Dalmatian, Jack"; her husband is "an outstanding culinary enthusiast: we enjoyed his king prawn tempura; marinated squid
with peppers; cod with lemongrass crust; death by pears". The four-
course dinner (no choice), served by an open fire at 8 pm, is by
arrangement. No wine licence, no corkage charge. Others have liked
"the careful way they are preserving the ambience: no television, no
radio". "Our room was home-from-home and most unhotel-like:
creaky floorboards, eccentric shower, but a 'we don't want to get out
of it' bed, and stunning views over the valley. B&B was special, with
fruit compote which had fallen straight off the bush." There are
cooked dishes too (scrambled eggs and salmon; smoked haddock with
poached egg), and newspapers. Rooms are spacious and elegant.
Enniscorthy has a fine cathedral and 13th-century castle; bird sanctuaries, beaches and golf courses are nearby; Wexford is not far. (*Simon
Willbourn, Catherine Fraher*)

Open All year, except Christmas.
Rooms 3 double. Also 2-bedroom self-catering apartment at rear.
Facilities Drawing room, dining room. No background music. 5-acre grounds:
tennis, badminton. Golf nearby; beach, bird sanctuary 10 miles. Unsuitable
for &.
Location 2 miles S of town. Take N11 to Wexford. 1st left after hospital;
uphill, bear left. Entrance sign on left. Train/bus to Enniscorthy; taxi.
Restrictions No smoking in bedrooms. Dogs by arrangement; not in house.
Credit card Visa.
Terms B&B IR£27.50–£35. Set dinner IR£22.50. Child accommodated in par-
ents' room: under 1, free; 1–12, half price. Christmas package by arrangement.

ENNISTYMON Co. Clare   Map 6

Grovemount House   `BUDGET`   *Tel* (065) 7071431
Lahinch Road, Ennistymon   *Fax* (065) 7071823

*On N85 E of Lahinch, 1 km W of old market town of Ennistymon on
River Inagh: inexpensive modern B&B owned and run by Sheila and
Gerald Linnane. Handy for visiting the Burren; golf, sandy beach
nearby. Simple bedrooms. Guest lounge with TV, children's games.
1-acre garden: children's play area. Continental or Irish breakfast
(background music). Open 1 May–31 Oct. 8 bedrooms, some on
ground floor. No dogs. MasterCard, Visa accepted. B&B: single
IR£30–35, double IR£40–£50. More reports, please.*

FERRYCARRIG Co. Wexford   Map 6

Slaney Manor   NEW/BUDGET   *Tel* (053) 20051
                                                  Fax (053) 20510
                                        E-mail slaneymanor@tinet.ie
                                   Website www.new-zealands.com/slaney

A mud-walled cabin with guest bedroom and bathroom, and an assas-
sinated British prime minister in the founding family, make this *Guide*
newcomer thoroughly intriguing. It is a stone manor house deep in the
country near Wexford, built in the 1820s by the Anglo-Irish Perceval
family (Spencer Perceval was killed by a madman in the House of
Commons in 1812). But his ghost is not around, and our nominator
found the place "delightful and peaceful", well restored by its owners,
Esther and James Caulfield. They recently added a conservatory.
Some bedrooms have a four-poster; many have "wonderful views"
over the Slaney estuary; some are in a converted building on a courtyard. "The owners take real pride in their home", which they call "a
pre-Famine time capsule": being tradition-minded, they have installed
in the large grounds an 18th-century mud-walled cabin, "a typical residence of the native Irish" in former days. Here the peasants would
have a pig living with them, which "proved to be very clean". Today,
the cabin has no pig, but a bathroom equally clean. And you might find
pork on the menu of Mrs Caulfield's simple and traditional no-choice
meals using local produce (eg, melon pearls folded in Irish Mist
cream; poached Slaney salmon): we'd be glad of reports. Wine is
available until 11 pm in the large "common room". Nearby are an Irish
National Heritage Park, a museum of the John F Kennedy family, and
good walks amid plenty of wildlife. (*Keith Hatchick*)

Open All year, except Christmas. Dining room open to residents only.
Rooms 2 suites, 36 double. 26 in courtyard, 1 in mud cabin. Some on ground
floor. Telephone in manor bedrooms only.
Facilities Lift. Sitting room, dining room, conservatory, courtyard. No back-
ground music. 150-acre grounds: woodland walks. River; fishing, boating
nearby.
Location 3 miles W of Wexford, on N25, near junction with N11. Bus or train
from Wexford.
Restrictions No smoking. No dogs.
Credit cards All major cards accepted.
Terms B&B: single IR£35–£65, double IR£50–£90, suite IR£110–£130;
D,B&B IR£40–£80 per person. Set dinner (5-courses) IR£25. 10% reduction
for extended stays. Reduced rates for children.

GALWAY   Map 6

Norman Villa   *Tel/Fax* (091) 521131
86 Lower Salthill   *E-mail* normanvilla@oceanfree.net

With its many fringe theatres, musical pubs and folksy bistros, and its
big summer arts festival, Galway is the liveliest Irish town outside
Dublin, a focus for the young and the artistic. This restored Victorian
coach house a mile from the town centre is run as a B&B by Mark and
Dee Keogh. It was admired again this year, by American visitors:

"The finest inn we came across in Ireland. The beautiful breakfast is garnished with edible flowers from their dazzling garden." Others wrote: "We loved this place; it is not luxurious, but is run with the emphasis on quality and personal attention." The house is "like an art gallery", with contemporary paintings (lots of nudes) and sculpture in the public rooms and bedrooms, along with old pine furniture and unusual decorative rustic items. The copious breakfast includes home-made muesli, "superb porridge" and "beautifully presented cooked dishes". "Good crisp linen on antique brass beds" (but some rooms, baths and wardrobes are small). Plenty of eating places in the centre of town, 20 minutes' walk away. The Keoghs will help you plan day-trips to Connemara, the Burren and the spectacular cliffs of Moher. Limited parking space in the courtyard. (*Ken Campbell and Susan Wooddell, DD*)

Open All year.
Rooms 5 double. No telephone/TV.
Facilities Drawing room, breakfast room. Jazz/classical background music. ¼-acre garden. Sandy beach, river, fishing nearby. Unsuitable for &.
Location 1 mile W of centre, at Salthill. Limited courtyard parking.
Restrictions No smoking in bedrooms. No children under 6. No dogs.
Credit cards MasterCard, Visa.
Terms B&B: IR£35–£40.

GLANWORTH Co. Cork   Map 6

Glanworth Mill   *Tel* (025) 38555
                                                Fax (025) 38560
                                        E-mail glanworth@iol.ie
                                        Website www.iol.ie/glanworth

"An exquisite inn, with an enchanting location", by an old bridge over the River Funcheon, below a ruined Norman castle. It is a picturesque wool mill (1790), recently converted into a sophisticated hostelry by the owners, Lynne Glassloe and Emelyn Heaps (Catriona Sheehan is manager). Of the two restaurants, the *Mill Tea Rooms* contains the old mill wheel, still turning, and offers a bistro-style menu: soup, salads, steaks, etc. In the *Fleece'n'Loom* the new chef Ronald Geul serves more elaborate dishes, such as blackened supreme of chicken stuffed with black pudding; monkfish with gnocchi and dill sauce. The well-furnished bedrooms, with colourful fabrics, are named after local writers, including Elizabeth Bowen, and William Trevor, the film of whose book *Felicia's Journey* was partly filmed at Glanworth in 1998. It is an interesting village, with a ruined abbey, medieval buildings and prehistoric sites. Tours of local attractions can be arranged. The inn is about to open a craft shop. More reports, please.

Open All year, except 24 Dec–4 Jan, Good Friday. Restaurant closed Sun evening.
Rooms 10 double. No TV.
Facilities Library, conservatory, 2 restaurants; background jazz/classical music during the day; live music sometimes. 2-acre grounds: courtyard garden, river, mill race, fly-fishing. Riding stables, golf nearby. Only public rooms suitable for &.
Location SE edge of Glanworth village, 4 miles NW of Fermoy. From N8

Mitchelstown–Fermoy, take Glanworth Rd at Kilworth/Glanworth junction. 5 miles to narrow bridge and mill.
Restrictions No smoking in bedrooms. No dogs.
Credit cards Diners, MasterCard, Visa.
Terms [2000] B&B: single IR£52–£55, double IR£84–£90. Full alc: tea rooms IR£22, restaurant IR£35. Child accommodated in parents' room: 1 child 50% of adult rate.

GLASLOUGH Co. Monaghan   Map 6

Castle Leslie
Tel (047) 88109
Fax (047) 88256
E-mail ultan@castle-leslie.ie
Website www.castle-leslie.ie

"So extraordinary it is almost shocking. It will, if you let it, change your life." So runs a new rave report in 2000 for this endearingly eccentric place. Others have called it "outrageous, but amusing". A hefty Victorian castle in a vast estate near the Border, it was built in 1878 by the titled Leslie family, who claim descent from Attila the Hun and have lived on the site since 1661. Crammed to the rafters with Victoriana and hand-me-downs from the Churchill family (relatives by marriage), it has changed little, save for the addition of modern comforts, and is run in high Victorian style, with a great sense of fun. Sir John, the fourth baronet, now 82, presides, but the place is run by his ebullient niece Samantha (Sammy) and her husband Ultan Bannon. Meals are served in the imposing candlelit banqueting hall by waitresses in Victorian dress. Here Paul Clarke's "lovely country house food" was mostly liked again this year: "Mussel and saffron soup, perfect duck breasts, lamb shank with Dublin Coddle (bubble and squeak), monkfish crisp but tasteless, with delicious spicy bits. Puds are the highlight: crème brûlée and rhubarb crumble were extra-ordinary. A bottle of an off-beat Oz wine, a Tarrango, was good value. A pseudo-theatrical troupe, the Plurabelles, entertained us with Joyce and Beckett during and after dinner." "Divine gingerbread" and pre-dinner mulled wine are served in the drawing room. The huge public rooms have fine old tapestries, suits of armour, and other heirlooms – a lovely painted Della Robbia fireplace from a chapel in Florence, a harp given by Wordsworth, an emerald bracelet from the Empress of China. As for bedrooms, one reader's this year was "mind-blowing in its uniqueness, with deep green walls, teddy bears, painted furniture". One room has a big four-poster with heavy velvet drapes, a wooden "thunderbox" loo (authentically Victorian) and taps marked *chaud* for cold and *froid* for hot. Some rooms are intentionally comic, some "truly beautiful"; in one, the former nursery, a vast dolls' house façade conceals the bathroom. Business seminars are held, also events: "Food and erotica gourmet dinner"; "gourmet junk food", classical music, etc, and tourist banquets, at the end of which Sammy, in hooded cloak, regales diners with ghost stories of the house (a child was murdered in one bed). The dogs will take you for a walk in the grounds. (*Ruth West, Simon Willbourn*)

Open All year. Only weekends 4 Jan–10 Feb.
Rooms 14 double. No telephone/TV, etc.
Facilities Drawing room, dining room, gallery; conference/function facilities.
No background music. 1,000-acre grounds: 1-acre pleasure gardens, tennis,
wildlife, lakes, boating, fishing. Unsuitable for &.
Location On N edge of Glaslough village, 6 miles NE of Monaghan town.
Restrictions Smoking in drawing room only. No children under 18. No dogs
in house (kennels available).
Credit cards MasterCard, Visa.
Terms [2000] D,B&B double from IR£135. Single room supplement IR£20.
Full alc IR£35. 1-night bookings refused weekends. Christmas/New Year
packages.

GLENCAIRN Co. Waterford   Map 6

Buggy's Glencairn Inn   *Tel/Fax* (058) 56232
Glencairn, Tallow   *E-mail* buggysglencairninn@eircom.net
                                     Website welcome.to/buggys

In a hamlet below the Knockmealdown Mountains, this small pink
house (1720) is run as a combined B&B, inn and restaurant by its
owners, Ken and Kathleen Buggy, and its many fans find it delightful.
"It's a must for the *Guide*," says one. It has an idiosyncratic decor, a
bar with a slate floor, much wood and copper and an open fire, an old-
fashioned kitchen with a dresser, where meals are served, and five
low-ceilinged little bedrooms whose brass beds have patchwork
quilts. An interesting collection of objects and paintings fills the
house. The food is traditional Irish "and delicious", eg, macaroni,
cheese and basil pie; pot-roasted farm duck in honey; blackberry and
apple crumble. The Blackwater River and the old fortified port of
Youghal are not far off. (*BM*)

Open All year, except first 2 weeks Feb, Christmas.
Rooms 5 double. No telephone.
Facilities Bar (background music at night), restaurant. ½-acre grounds.
Fishing nearby. Unsuitable for &.
Location By crossroads in Glencairn hamlet, off R627, between Lismore and
Tallow (both 3 miles).
Restrictions No smoking: restaurant, bedrooms. No children under 10. No
dogs.
Credit cards MasterCard, Visa.
Terms (*Excluding 10% service charge*) B&B IR£33–£45. D,B&B IR£57–
IR£69. Set dinner IR£24, full alc IR£32. *V*

GLIN Co. Limerick   Map 6

Glin Castle   *Tel* (068) 34173
                                               Fax (068) 34364
                                          E-mail knight@iol.ie
                                    Website www.glincastle.com

A magnificent Georgian Gothic castle, built on the site of an earlier
medieval one on the banks of the Shannon estuary. Set in a large
wooded estate, with gardens and a dairy farm, it is the country home

of Desmond and Olda Fitzgerald. His family has owned the land for 800 years, and he is the Knight of Glin (generally nicknamed "Knightie"). The drawing room has an Adam ceiling and huge windows facing the garden. Dinner is served in the formal dining room with baronial oak furniture and Fitzgerald family portraits. The manager is Bob Duff. The interiors are impressive, with original plasterwork, family antiques, secret doorways, Corinthian pillars, and an unusual flying staircase. The guest bedrooms are lavishly done, with chaises longues, blue-and-white porcelain plates on walls, and views of the river or the garden. Dinner is served in the formal dining room with baronial oak furniture and family portraits. "Despite its grandeur, the castle has a welcoming feel," says a recent visitor. The cooking is "exceptional: imaginative dishes use the best of ingredients". The set menu offers two choices for each course. Many ingredients are grown on the estate; they are simply treated, eg, foie gras in vol au vent with apples; monkfish with green pepper sauce. Breakfasts are excellent too, with "wonderful summer berry compote". "You are looked after on a very personal basis, and made to feel that you are a guest in a home rather than a hotel." Once a week there is live Irish music in the main hall. Some readers think the prices excessive, but others find it worth paying these sums for the experience of staying with an Irish nobleman. Local touring includes the Ring of Kerry, the Burren, the Cliffs of Moher. Glin village, with its very pretty pub, is at the gate. (*WGH*)

Open 1 Feb–30 Nov.
Rooms 2 suites, 13 double. 3 in castle wing.
Facilities Sitting room, garden room, library, 2 dining rooms. No background music. 500-acre estate: 5-acre garden, parkland, dairy farm, tennis, croquet, shooting, tea/craft shop, clay-pigeon shooting; on Shannon estuary: boating, fishing; golf nearby. Unsuitable for &.
Location On edge of village 32 miles W of Limerick. Bus to Foynes (7 miles).
Restrictions No smoking: dining room, 1 sitting room, bedrooms. Children under 8 by arrangement. No dogs in house (kennels available).
Credit cards All major cards accepted.
Terms [2000] B&B: single IR£180, double IR£270, suite IR£380. Set lunch IR£21, dinner IR£35. Weekend midweek rates in low season. Can be taken over by house party (max. 20 people). *V*

****

Hotel in Dorset. The owner entirely lacks charm, and never manages a smile. He seems to have passed on these traits to his young bar staff, all of whom looked surly. He regularly walked straight past us without stopping for a friendly word.

****

GOREY Co. Wexford   Map 6

Marlfield House   *Tel* (055) 21124
Courtown Road   *Fax* (055) 21572
                                E-mail marlf@iol.ie
                          Website www.marlfieldhouse.ie

Q *César award in 1996*

A Regency building, once the principal Irish residence of the Earls of
Courtown. It is now a sophisticated country house hotel (Relais &
Châteaux). It stands in beautiful grounds, with neat lawns, a herb garden, a lake (with ducks, geese and black swans) and a wildfowl
reserve, on the edge of an old-fashioned seaside resort with a long,
sandy beach. Mary and Ray Bowe have owned and run it for 22 years.
The entrance hall is impressive, with goldfish ponds and a resident
peacock, Kane, by the front door; inside are smart antique furniture
and spectacular flower displays. The luxurious best bedrooms have
antiques, dramatic wallpapers and curtains, hand-embroidered sheets,
real lace pillows, a splendid marble bathroom; but some rooms are
small (one was thought "over-furnished" this year), and not all have a
good view. The dining room, with its large domed conservatory extension, frescoes and silver, is "a glorious place to eat". One recent report
speaks of slow meal service, but the food itself has long been admired.
The menus of head chef Henry Stone, described as "classical with
French and Mediterranean influences", are based on wild salmon,
spring salmon, local oysters, mussels and beef; herbs, vegetables and
fruit are grown in the gardens. Lighter lunches are served in the
library, and "excellent breakfasts" include a generous buffet and various combinations of eggs, bacon, etc. Despite *Marlfield*'s grandeur,
children and dogs are welcomed. "Mrs Mary Bowe, entertaining and
welcoming to the manner born, makes every effort to have personal
contact with her guests", and her junior staff are "delightful and
extremely helpful", but some visitors have written of a "perfunctory
greeting". More reports, please.

Open All year, except mid-Dec–late Jan.
Rooms 6 state rooms, 12 double, 2 single. Some on ground floor.
Facilities Reception hall, drawing room, library/bar, restaurant with conserva-
tory. No background music. 36-acre grounds: gardens, tennis, croquet, wild-
fowl reserve, lake. Sea, sandy beaches, safe bathing 2 miles; fishing, golf,
horse riding nearby.
Location 1 mile from Gorey on Courtown road. Train from Dublin/Waterford.
Restrictions No smoking: restaurant, bedrooms. Dogs by arrangement; not in
public rooms.
Credit cards All major cards accepted.
Terms [2000] B&B: IR£95–£168. Set lunch IR£37, dinner IR£42. 1-night
bookings sometimes refused Sat.

The Irish punt and the pound sterling do not have the same
value. Be sure to check the exchange rate. And remember that
Ireland is now using the euro.

INISTIOGE Co. Kilkenny   Map 6

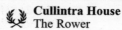 **Cullintra House** **BUDGET**   *Tel/Fax* (051) 423614
The Rower

E-mail cullhse@indigo.ie
Website www.indigo.ie/~cullhse

César award: Utterly enjoyable mild eccentricity

"Lovably eccentric, and probably the best entertainment of any hotel in the UK or Ireland," writes an admiring visitor to this handsome 18th-century creeper-covered farmhouse. In a quiet setting at the foot of Mount Brandon, it lies at the end of a long drive amid 230 acres of farmland, and it has been the home of the Cantlon family for 100 years. The tone is set by the personality of Patricia Cantlon, the hostess, whose paintings fill the house. Some regulars are from the Dublin intellectual world, and one visitor has called the ambience "unaffectedly bohemian", though Ms Cantlon writes that she is not sure about this. Breakfast till midday is one feature (it may not be available before 10 am). Another is the leisurely late candlelit dinners (good French-influenced home cooking, communally served), which are scheduled for 9 pm, but may not take place until much later. Children are given a light early supper "and then to bed". The bedrooms are delightfully pretty and individual, in plush-rustic style, with period furnishings, but the *en suite* showers are simple and the only bathroom is communal. There is a conservatory studio with a piano, where guests can have fun. The exuberant hostess, who does not hide her likes and dislikes, has six adored cats, omnipresent, and will accept guests' dogs only if she is certain that they will behave. No licence; bring your own wine. Inistioge has a tree-lined square beside a fine stone bridge. The grounds of the local estate, Woodstock, are open to the public. Nearby Kilkenny is a picturesque town, with splendid historic castle. (*PD*)

Open All year.
Rooms 6 double. 4 with shower. 2 in barn. No telephone/TV.
Facilities Drawing room, dining room (classical background music during dinner), studio conservatory. 230-acre grounds: 1-acre garden, woodland, private path to Brandon Hill with 4,000-year-old cairn. River bathing, fishing nearby. Unsuitable for &.
Location 6 miles NW of New Ross, off New Ross–Kilkenny road. Take turning E (signposted): hotel 1 mile. Bus to main road (1 mile) once a day.
Restrictions No smoking: dining room, gallery. Dogs by arrangement.
Credit cards None accepted.
Terms B&B IR£20–£35; D,B&B IR£36–£51. Set dinner IR£16–£20. 1-night bookings refused weekends.

****

Hotel in Scotland. We lashed out for an anniversary stay in this beautiful and formal country house hotel. We dressed for dinner and came down to a lovely dining room. Suddenly our worst fear was realised: a lone guest at an adjoining table answered a mobile phone. At breakfast he was at it again, talking loudly into his phone.

****

KANTURK Co. Cork   Map 6

Assolas Country House   *Tel* (029) 50015
                                                        Fax (029) 50795
                                                    E-mail assolas@eircom.com
                                                    Website www.assolas.com

Ʊ *César award in 1995*

This handsome creeper-covered 17th-century manor house, set in lovely grounds, with a lake, swans and a weir, has been the Bourke family's home for over 70 years, and since the 1970s they have run it as a hotel: Joe Bourke and his parents are front-of-house, his wife Hazel is the chef. "Nicer, more welcoming hosts you will not meet," was one recent verdict. Another couple wrote: "The house and grounds are lovely, the wildlife is engaging, the housekeeping impeccable, and our room in the courtyard was pleasant. The food was lovely, beautifully cooked: but meals and drinks took so long to come, and the service seemed a little disorganised." This has been the only caveat about a hotel otherwise much admired, and since that report the Bourkes have decided to serve meals to residents only. The "real country house feel" continues to be admired, and also the "friendly atmosphere among guests". Hazel and Joe Bourke are found "charming". The bedrooms are large and quite plainly furnished, but very comfortable. Some bathrooms are "magnificent, with a whirlpool bath". "Everything is presented so elegantly. One feels utterly pampered." Also enjoyed are the log fires, the afternoon tea, with lemon or chocolate cake, served in the garden or by the fire. There is sparkling glass in the dining room, and damask napkins. Mrs Bourke's country house cooking puts its accent on fish, shellfish and local meat, eg, hake baked with cheddar; roast Kanturk beef; rhubarb and strawberry crumble. The soups, sauces and pastry are much admired; and the wine list is well chosen. Many of the herbs and vegetables come from the hotel's organic garden. There is good hill and forest walking nearby. Also nearby are Millstreet country park and Annesgrove garden at Castletownroche. (*Andrea Dassori*)

Open 16 Mar–1 Nov. Whole house booking only New Year. Dining room closed midday.
Rooms 9 double. 3 in courtyard annexe, 20 yds. No TV.
Facilities Hall, drawing room, dining room; private dining room. No background music. 15-acre grounds: gardens, tennis, croquet, river, boating, trout-fishing. Salmon-fishing, golf nearby. Unsuitable for &.
Location 3½ miles NE of Kanturk; turn off N72 Mallow–Killarney towards Buttevant.
Restrictions No children under 8 in dining room at night. No dogs in house (accommodation in stables).
Credit cards MasterCard, Visa.
Terms B&B IR£55–£80. Set dinner IR£28–£30. 1-night bookings sometimes refused in high season. Child accommodated in parents' room: 25% of adult rate. *V* (low season)

The international dialling code for Ireland is 353.

KENMARE Co. Kerry   Map 6

Hawthorn House BUDGET   *Tel* (064) 41035
Shelbourne Street   *Fax* (064) 41932
                                    E-mail hawthorn@tinet.ie

Our two other entries for this popular little resort at the east end of the
Ring of Kerry are grand and pricey. This sympathetic B&B, by contrast, offers "excellent accommodation at rock-bottom prices". It was
admired again by a regular visitor. The "welcoming owners", Stephen
and Mary O'Brien, are much praised (she is "bubbly, with an infectious sense of humour"). Tea and cake are served in the drawing room
to arriving guests; bedrooms are of different shapes and sizes but all
are "cheerful, welcoming and pretty", tastefully furnished in pine,
with fresh fruit and flowers. Most have a shower rather than a bath.
Breakfast is good, with freshly made porridge and Irish fries. Plenty of
restaurants are nearby (for two posh ones see other Kenmare entries).
And you can take a long scenic walk along the Kerry Way. (*EC*)

Open All year, except Christmas.
Rooms 7 double, 1 single. No telephone.
Facilities TV lounge, breakfast room (mixed background music). Sea ¼ mile;
walking, cycling, golf, water sports, fishing nearby. Unsuitable for &.
Location On S edge of village, close to centre. Private parking.
Restrictions No smoking: restaurant, bedrooms. No dogs.
Credit card Visa.
Terms B&B IR£20–£25. Reductions for children.

Park Hotel Kenmare   *Tel* (064) 41200
                                                Fax (064) 41402
                                      E-mail phkenmare@iol.ie
                                Website www.parkkenmare.com

Set amid fine, unspoiled mountain scenery on the Ring of Kerry, this
attractive but touristy village has two very grand country hotels, both
Relais & Châteaux, and both with four red gables in *Michelin*. The
Park, owned and run by the Brennan family, has a peaceful parkland
setting, with lovely views of the Kenmare estuary and the west Cork
mountains. Outwardly, its long grey hulk is no beauty (it was built in
the 19th century by the Great Southern and Western Railway
Company as an overnight stop for the gentry), but inside are elegant
public rooms with open fires, sculptures, "dazzling paintings" and
flowers. "No conference centre, banqueting rooms or other distrac-
tions, to detract from the well-being of guests," say the Brennans. And
most visitors enjoy it greatly. The restaurant and lounges look over the
sea. This year, a terrace for tea has been added, and verandas for the
garden rooms. The "gorgeous" bedrooms have smart antiques and fine
china; some bathrooms are "splendid", but others can be poorly lit.
The staff are "truly professional with an obvious pride in their job".
The chef, Joe Ryan, provides modern French cooking with Irish influences (such dishes as poached salmon in red wine with lobster potato
purée; grilled roulade of sole on ragout of fennel with mussel herb
butter sauce). One reader found it "excellent" again this year, though

Michelin has withdrawn its star. Breakfast is much admired. The lounge is enlivened at night by the "charming in-house pianist". The bar is "a most pleasing little area, and well staffed". In the large grounds there are tennis, croquet and garden walks; Kenmare golf course is adjacent, and fishing with a ghillie can be arranged. (*EC, and others*)

Open 13 Apr–5 Nov; 23 Dec–2 Jan.
Rooms 9 suites, 36 double, 4 single.
Facilities Lift, ramps. Lounge bar (classical background music all day; pianist at night), restaurant; terrace; fitness suite. 12-acre grounds: tennis, croquet; 18-hole golf course adjacent. Rock beach, safe bathing, water sports 5 mins' walk; fishing, horse riding arranged.
Location 60 miles W of Cork, adjacent to village. Signposted. Train to Killarney or bus to Kenmare; then taxi.
Restrictions No smoking in bedrooms. No children on ground floor after 8 pm. No dogs in building (kennels in grounds).
Credit cards All major cards accepted.
Terms B&B IR£132–£262. Set lunch IR£8–£24, dinner IR£43; full alc IR£48. Christmas, New Year packages.

Sheen Falls Lodge   *Tel* (064) 41600
                                               Fax (064) 41386
                                E-mail info@sheenfallslodge.ie
                                Website www.sheenfallslodge.ie

The location is superb, in huge grounds of woods and fields beside the Sheen Falls, with fine views of Kenmare Bay. This huge Cromwellian manor house, much extended, is now a luxurious resort hotel (Relais & Châteaux), specialising in outdoor pursuits. With a Danish owner, and under Adriaan Bartels' management, it has a cosmopolitan ambience: yet "the welcome and impeccable service are wonderfully Irish, and the atmosphere is family-like". A recent guest found the staff "incredibly kind and helpful" and the food "excellent", notably the breakfast buffet with fresh fruit, porridge, cold meats, etc. The *Cascade* restaurant (with live piano music nightly) has a new chef this year, Chris Farrell, whose ambitious "modern Irish" dishes could include wild salmon on a vegetable ragout; roast pigeon with apple and garlic; hot chocolate fondant with honeycomb ice-cream. If you can't face the full *prix-fixe* meal, you can opt for just a course or two and pay accordingly. A bar/bistro, overlooking the falls, is named for Oscar, the heron resident on the river. It is open from 6 am to 10 pm, and serves children's suppers. The public rooms are "cosy and delightful". The "wonderful library" has up-to-date magazines such as the *New Yorker*, and books in many languages. The bedrooms are huge, with crisp linen sheets and duvets, A CD-player, and a large marble bathroom. The leisure activities include golf, water-skiing and riding: but the horses for guests' use have been found "poorly groomed". There is a health spa with a beauty centre and a thalassotherapy centre; also a discreet conference centre. Guided hill walks are arranged, and guests are sometimes taken sightseeing in the hotel's 1936 Buick convertible. (*HL, and others*)

Open 2 Feb–3 Dec, Christmas, New Year.
Rooms 8 suites, 53 double. 1 adapted for &. Self-catering cottage in grounds.
Facilities Lift, ramps. 2 lounges, billiard room, study, library, bar/bistro,
restaurant; health and fitness centre: swimming pool, spa bath, sauna, gym,
beauty treatments; extensive business facilities. Classical background music in
public areas all day; piano nightly: restaurant, sun lounge. 300-acre grounds:
river, fishing, riding, croquet, tennis, clay-pigeon shooting; hill-walking with
local guide. Golf, lake/river fishing, windsurfing, boating nearby; sea 6 miles.
Location 1½ miles SE of Kenmare, just off N71 to Glengariff. Bus from
Kenmare.
Restrictions Smoking discouraged in restaurants. No dogs in house.
Credit cards All major cards accepted.
Terms Room: single/double IR£168–£258, suite IR£295–£420. Breakfast:
continental IR£12, Irish IR£15. Set dinner IR£40. Half-board rates in low
season. Christmas package.

KILLARNEY Co. Kerry *See SHORTLIST*   **Map 6**

KILLEAGH Co. Cork   **Map 6**

Ballymakeigh House   `BUDGET`   *Tel* (024) 95184
Killeagh, nr Youghal   *Fax* (024) 95370
                                            E-mail ballymakeigh@eircom.net

Margaret Browne's handsome guest house, in an old but well modernised farmhouse, stands amid the green fields of prosperous east
Cork. Recent visitors have called her "a wonderful role model for all
that is good about food and hospitality in Ireland", and indeed she has
won plenty of awards over the years: Landlady of the Year, Housewife
of the Year, Farm Guest House of the Year. Mrs Browne's lavish
home cooking is famous, and she has published a best-selling cook-
book. This year she has opened a new restaurant for dinner, *Browne's,*
beside her new equestrian centre, a mile from the main house, offering such dishes as local seafood chowder; roast duck on a compote of
gooseberries; Cajun chicken with a garlic and cream sauce; and enterprising desserts, eg, banoffi pie with a duo of fruit coulis. Readers have
also praised the "wonderful home-baking", the "swift, friendly and
personal" service, the "excellent breakfasts, served at a time to suit the
guests". There is a spacious flowery conservatory, facing south. "The
bedrooms, done with style and taste, and without TV, have views of
lush farmlands" (but one was thought "dismal" this year). Your wake-
up call is provided by the cows brought in from milking. Being on a
working dairy farm, the house is also a good place for children. The
equestrian centre offers courses in riding, and treks to local sandy
beaches. Mrs Browne is "full of local knowledge". The old port of
Youghal is nearby. More reports, please.

Open 1 April–1 Nov.
Rooms 6 double, 1 single. No telephone/TV.
Facilities TV room, conservatory, restaurant; no background music; 200-acre
farm: 2-acre garden, tennis, children's play area, equestrian centre. Blue Flag
beaches nearby. Unsuitable for &.
Location 6 miles W of Youghal, 1 mile NE of Killeagh. Buses from Cork.

Restrictions No smoking in some bedrooms. No dogs in house.
Credit cards MasterCard, Visa.
Terms B&B IR£35–£40; D,B&B IR£55–£60. Set lunch IR£15, dinner
IR£25; full alc IR£25–£35. Child accommodated in parents' room: 50% of
adult rate.

KILMALLOCK Co. Limerick   Map 6

Flemingstown House   `BUDGET`   *Tel* (063) 98093
                                                     Fax (063) 98546
                                               E-mail keltec@iol.ie
                                          Website www.ils.ie/flemingstown

Kilmallock, south of Limerick, is an interesting medieval town with a
fine Dominican friary. Just outside, amid pleasant open country and
with a river running through it, is this dairy farm with a large 18th-cen-
tury farmhouse, owned and run with friendly informality by Imelda
Sheedy-King, who is much praised again this year in several reports.
"The warmth of her welcome, the superb quality of her cooking, and
the comfort, all made our stay a treat." "She is a treasure. Scrumptious
food, such as home-made soups, on the plentiful menus." They also
include, eg, smoked salmon mousse with dill sauce; wild salmon with
prawns and lemon; tiramisu with whipped cream from the dairy herd.
"She even wrote out recipes for some of her dishes. Our small daughter was made very welcome." "Despite being a busy lady, she always
has time for a chat and advice on places to visit." The bedrooms, previously found smallish, have just been enlarged. Visitors can be
shown round the farm. (*IW, and others*)

Open 1 Feb–1 Nov.
Rooms 1 suite, 4 double. No telephone.
Facilities Lounge with TV, dining room (background music during meals).
2-acre garden. Golf, riding, fishing, cycling nearby. Unsuitable for &.
Location 2 miles SE of Kilmallock on R512 to Fermoy. Bus from Kilmallock.
Restrictions No smoking in dining room. No dogs in public rooms, some
bedrooms.
Credit cards MasterCard, Visa.
Terms B&B: single IR£35, double IR£50. Set dinner IR£20.

KINSALE Co. Cork   Map 6

The Old Presbytery   `BUDGET`   *Tel* (021) 772027
Cork Street   *Fax* (021) 772166
                                               E-mail info@oldpres.com
                                               Website www.oldpres.com

"It is perfect," says a visitor in 2000. "Breakfast is better than excellent." Down a quiet residential street in the town centre, this Georgian
house was once the home of priests at the nearby church of St John the
Baptist. Behind its red door, it is now a stylish B&B, where breakfast
can include home-made yogurt, black pudding, fruit-filled crêpes. The
"chatty and friendly" Noreen and Philip McEvoy are owner/managers,
and recent *Guide* visitors have been impressed. "Our bedroom had a
balcony with superb views, also a brass bed, Irish lace and linen, old

pine furniture and Victorian light fittings – but modern plumbing."
Four bathrooms have a claw-foot Victorian bath. The public rooms
have coal fires; the sitting room is "Victorian in every detail, down to
the music on the upright piano". A self-catering wing has now been
built. In 1996, the EU's top prize for tourism and the environment
went to this old fishing port, which today is rather fashionable, with an
annual gourmet festival and several good fish restaurants: *Man
Friday*, by the harbour, is recommended. (*Simon Willbourn*)

Open All year, except Christmas.
Rooms 6 double. Some on ground floor. Three 2-bedroom self-catering suites.
Facilities Lounge with TV, conservatory, breakfast room (classical background music). Sea/river fishing, water sports, golf nearby. Unsuitable for &.
Location 2 mins' walk from centre, near parish church. Private carpark. Buses from Cork.
Restrictions No smoking. No dogs.
Credit cards MasterCard, Visa.
Terms B&B: single IR£25–£60, double IR£50–£90. *V*

LEENANE Co. Galway   **Map 6**

Delphi Lodge   *Tel* (095) 42222
Leenane, Connemara   *Fax* (095) 42296
                                                    E-mail delfish@iol.ie
                                                    Website www.delphilodge.ie

"Most relaxing and civilised," runs this year's praise for Peter
Mantle's very personal little establishment amid unspoilt mountain
country just north of Connemara. Once the sporting lodge of the
Marquis of Sligo, it is "a charming old house", set by a lake in a large
estate. A notice at the gate says "Private House", and it "does not
consider itself a hotel" (there is no room service – "if your day has to
start with a cuppa, you totter along to the deserted kitchen in your
dressing gown"). But the welcome is "the warmest". Mr Mantle is a
keen fly-fisherman, and his Delphi fishery is famous for its salmon-
and sea-trout-fishing on three lakes and on the pretty Delphi River;
fishing courses are held, and a team of ghillies is available (advance
booking is essential). Other guests besides fishermen enjoy the peaceful atmosphere, the open fires and old pine furniture, the walks amid
wild scenery, and the "excellent food". The cooking, by Mary
Kilcoyne and Cliodhna Prendergast, is essentially "Irish country
house", eg, braised venison with roasted chestnuts and red berries;
roast wild duck with cranberry jus; pear and almond tart with pecan
ice-cream. The "serious wine list" is praised. As in a private home, the
menus offer no choice; and guests eat at a single sitting around one big
oak table. The captor of the day's biggest salmon presides. Mr Mantle
"has the knack of getting on with people", and the evenings are usually
convivial, though one guest this year found the ambience spoilt by a
noisy group. Most of the bedrooms are large, and some have a four-
poster, with "the softest cotton linen"; towels are huge and fluffy.
There is a cosy library, and a billiard room. Several empty sandy
beaches lie within easy reach, and the wildlife is exceptional: otters,
badgers, peregrines, pine martens, etc, and masses of wild flowers.

The house is also available for small conferences and "executive brainstorming sessions". (*James Gibson*)

Open 15 Jan–15 Dec.
Rooms 12 double. 2 on ground floor. No TV. Also 5 self-catering cottages.
Facilities Drawing room, library, billiard room, dining room; function/business facilities. No background music. 600-acre estate: 15-acre gardens, lake, fishing (pre-booking essential), bathing. Golf, riding, beaches nearby.
Location 9 miles N of Leenane on Louisburgh road. 20 miles SW of Westport.
Restrictions Not recommended for children under 12. No dogs.
Credit cards MasterCard, Visa.
Terms (Generally 2 nights min.) B&B: single IR£60–£120, double IR£80–£160. Set lunch IR£10, dinner IR£26. Fly-fishing tuition weekends.

LETTERFRACK Co. Galway   **Map 6**

Rosleague Manor   *Tel* (095) 41101
                                               Fax (095) 41168
                                          E-mail themanor@anu.ie

Above sheltered bay 7 miles NW of Clifden off N59, amid forests and mountains, handsome rambling Regency house in 25-acre grounds (with tennis, path to water's edge). Owned by Foyle family (Mark Foyle is manager). 20 large bedrooms "nicely furnished"; 2 pretty drawing rooms, good for socialising; fine dining room with creaking floorboards and ancestral portraits; Victorian-style conservatory. Good Irish/French cooking by Rosie Curran, specialising in Connemara lamb and fresh seafood, but "minimal breakfast" reported this year. Beautiful beaches and lakes nearby. Open mid-March–end Nov. Unsuitable for &. No smoking: restaurant, 1 lounge. No dogs in public rooms. Amex, MasterCard, Visa accepted. B&B: single IR£50–£80, double IR£90–£150, suite IR£110–£170. Set dinner IR£32. *V*

LISMORE Co. Waterford   **Map 6**

Ballyrafter House   NEW/BUDGET   *Tel* (058) 54002
                                                Fax (058) 53050
                                E-mail info@waterfordhotel.com
                              Website ballyrafter@waterfordhotel.com

One mile W of historic village off N72 on Blackwater River, opposite impressive castle owned by Duke of Devonshire: small, unpretentious hotel well run by Irish owners, Joe and Noreen Willoughby, "friendly and delightful, as are the staff; but the place lacks Irish craic or local colour". Good cooking, using local produce, eg, darne of Blackwater salmon in Thai spices. New room for functions. Pretty 4-acre garden. Game and trout fishing with ghillies arranged (guests have use of rod room, freezer); golf, riding nearby. Open Mar–Nov, New Year. No smoking: dining room, bedrooms. Unsuitable for &. All major credit cards accepted. 14 bedrooms. B&B IR£35–£48; D,B&B IR£45–£68. Set lunch IR£14, dinner IR£22. Renominated this year. More reports, please.

LOUGH ESKE Co. Donegal   Map 6

Ardnamona House
                                        Tel (073) 22650
                                        Fax (073) 22819
                            E-mail ardnamon@tempoweb.com
                            Website www.tempoweb.com/ardnamona

Set amid wild Donegal scenery below the Blue Stack Mountains, this pink 1830s shooting lodge has a "staggeringly beautiful" position on the shores of Lough Eske. It is set in a superb National Heritage garden, created in the 1880s in Himalayan style, with plants from the palace gardens in Kathmandu and the Imperial Gardens in Peking. The ancient rhododendrons (some are 60 and 70 feet high) are especially lovely between mid-March and the end of April. All around is a primeval oak forest of ecological and botanical importance. *Ardnamona* is run by Kieran and Annabel Clarke, in house party style, and more praise came again this year: "The quiet pleasantness of the hosts and their staff greatly enhance the enviable setting." "A pleasant, relaxed and friendly place. An excellent dinner, by a warming fire, and civilised conversation with other guests. Breakfasts were equally good." Mrs Clarke's menus, based on organic vegetables and salads, might include fennel and parmesan gratin; duck legs with cabbage and red onions; chocolate truffle cream with spiced plums. When dinner is not available, you could try *Harvey's Point*, "a rather expensive but good Swiss-run restaurant", two miles away. The bedrooms, south-facing, are brightly decorated; all but one now have a bathroom *en suite*. "The ambience and the dawn and dusk chorus are beyond price. Wonderful views across the lough; walks to the mountains behind." "A combination of wilderness and history almost tangible as one walks around." The house rambles round a courtyard. It has a sunroom and sitting room, and lots of books, especially on music. Mr Clarke is a musician who restores pianos; he will let guests try his Steinway grand, which was once used by Paderewski. Children are welcomed. Plenty of beaches within a half-hour drive. (*Nicolas Robinson, SAW*)

Open All year. Restaurant closed for dinner Sun.
Rooms 6 double. No telephone/TV.
Facilities Sitting room, snug, sunroom, dining room, music room. No background music. 100-acre grounds: garden, lake, fishing, swimming, boating. Unsuitable for &.
Location 7 miles NE of Donegal town. Turn left off N15 3 miles N of Donegal, towards Harvey's Point.
Restrictions No smoking in bedrooms. No dogs in house.
Credit cards Amex, MasterCard, Visa.
Terms [2000] B&B IR£40–£57. Set dinner IR£20. Reduced rates for children. Special breaks negotiable. ***V***

The ***V*** sign at the end of an entry indicates a hotel that has agreed to take part in our Voucher scheme and to give *Guide* readers a 25 per cent discount on their room rates, subject to the conditions explained in *How to read the entries* and listed on the back of the vouchers.

MALLOW Co. Cork   Map 6

Longueville House   *Tel* (022) 47156
                                                     Fax (022) 47459
                                          E-mail info@longuevillehouse.ie
                                          Website www.longuevillehouse.ie

*Splendid white Georgian mansion (Relais & Châteaux), in huge
grounds 3 miles W of Mallow on N72 to Killarney. Owned, and run
with "friendly and expert" staff, by O'Callaghan family, descendants
of former lords of nearby Dromineen Castle, now ruined. Stylishly furnished and "slightly faded"; log fires in lounges. No background
music. In cosy, red-walled, candlelit* Presidents' Restaurant, *excellent
modern French cooking uses produce from home farm, salmon and
trout from Blackwater River, which runs through the 500-acre estate;
white wine from private vineyard. Summer dining in Victorian conservatory. New conference centre. No dogs. Open 2 Mar–16 Dec. All
major credit cards accepted. 22 bedrooms (7 no-smoking; many are
spacious). B&B IR£60–£130; D,B&B IR£93–£163. Set dinner IR£33–
£46. No recent reports: more welcome.*

MAYNOOTH Co. Kildare   Map 6

Moyglare Manor   *Tel* (01) 628 6351
                                                     Fax (01) 628 5405
                                          E-mail moyglare@iol.ie
                                          Website www.iol.ie/moyglaremanor

This little town, just west of Dublin is the site of Ireland's principal
Catholic college and leading venue of the meetings of the Irish bishops.
Its moral influence on the nation has been huge: "This ye may do, but
that ye may nooth," goes an old quip, while Seán O'Casey called the
high spire of its church "a dagger through the heart of Ireland". Two
miles away is this graceful Georgian country manor house, owned by
Nora Devlin. A 2000 report calls it "magical" and "hedonistic", quite
at odds with Maynooth's "dour reputation". It stands imposingly in
large grounds, up a long tree-lined avenue. "Its string of large and small
public rooms are sumptuously furnished, with a clutter of ornaments,
antiques, Oriental rugs and old paintings. Our bedroom with a four-
poster was large and beautiful. Dinner was excellent, pianist serenad-
ing." Others have noted the many decorated lampshades and opulent
flower displays, the meals by candlelight and scent of roses from the
garden, all creating an aura of "fabulous decadence". The careful
menus of the chef, Jim Cullinane, include, eg, smoked chicken salad;
terrine of salmon and prawns; sea-trout with champagne sauce. Fruit
and vegetables are grown on the estate. "The manager, Shay Curran, an
excellent host, had a very Irish mixture of sound advice and good-
humoured chuckling blarney." Log fires indoors; chairs and tables and
statuary on the wide lawn. The Curragh horse country is close, and
Dublin airport is not far away. (*Jonathan Margolis*)

Open All year, except 24–26 Dec.
Rooms 1 suite (for 3 people), 15 double. 2 on ground floor.

Facilities Ramps. 2 lounges, 2 bars (pianist sometimes), TV room, 3 dining rooms; conference facilities. No background music. 17-acre estate: garden. Golf, shooting, hunting, horse riding, tennis nearby.
Location 2 miles N of Maynooth. Bus/train from Dublin; then taxi.
Restrictions No smoking: restaurant, some bedrooms. No children under 12. No dogs.
Credit cards All major cards accepted.
Terms (*Excluding 12½% service charge*) B&B: single IR£105, double IR£170, suite IR£225–£395. Set lunch IR£25, dinner IR£31; full alc IR£38. *V*

MIDLETON Co. Cork   Map 6

Glenview House   *Tel* (021) 631680
Ballinaclasha   *Fax* (021) 634680
                                E-mail glenviewhouse@esatclear.ie
                          Website www.dragnet-systems.ie/dira/glenview

Midleton village is a historic whiskey-producing centre. Nearby, secluded amid wooded country ("utterly quiet"), is this small white Georgian manor house, "the very model of a quality rural guest house". "You feel like a cherished guest," one visitor wrote. The house has been owned for many years by Ken Sherrard, a local gentleman farmer, and his Scottish wife, Beth, who run it on a very personal basis. They say: "We take a warm approach to our guests. No TV or radio; we sit with them round the fire and talk, or we take them to a local pub; in summer we play tennis with them." The house has been restored in excellent taste, with fine antique pieces: "It is elegant, with a fine garden and attractive grounds." Each of the bedrooms is large, lovely and well equipped, with a kingsize bed and a superior bathroom; one on the ground floor has facilities for visitors in a wheelchair. Families are sometimes put up in the two self-catering units. The stylish residents' lounge has a log fire on chilly days. Good silver gleams in the dining room, where "excellent" meals, cooked by Beth Sherrard, are served by candlelight round one big table. No choice of the first two courses, but preferences are discussed: lavish servings of, eg, fresh seafood cocktail; monkfish in a prawn sauce; lemon roulade. Dishes are left on a hotplate, for guests to help themselves to seconds. Unlicensed; bring your own wine. Breakfast is "imaginative and elegantly laid out", with freshly squeezed orange juice, home-made marmalade and soda bread. Fifty hens provide free-range eggs. Rooms have views over the land-scaped flower garden and the fields beyond, where horses graze, and you can take walks. Three German shepherd dogs, and Burmese and Siamese cats, add to the family feel. All types of fishing can be arranged. There are 16 golf courses in the area. The place is often taken over by a house party. (*SR*)

Open All year. Dining room closed midday.
Rooms 7 double. 3 (can be self-catering) in coach house; 1 is equipped for ♿.
No telephone/TV.
Facilities Ramp. Lounge, wine bar, dining room. No background music.
20-acre grounds: patio, garden, tennis, croquet, woodland walks. River/lake
fishing, golf nearby; sea, safe sandy beaches ½ hour's drive.
Location 13 miles E of Cork, 3 miles N of Midleton. From Midleton take L35
towards Fermoy; turn left after 2½ miles (signposted).
Restrictions No smoking: dining room, bedrooms. Guide dogs only.
Credit cards Amex, MasterCard, Visa.
Terms B&B IR£40–£48; D,B&B £60–£68. Set dinner IR£25. Child accommodated in parents' room: under 4, 25% of adult rate; 4–12, 75% of adult rate.

MOATE Co. Meath   **Map 6**

 Temple Country House   *Tel* (0506) 35118
 and Health Spa   *Fax* (0506) 35008
 Horseleap   *E-mail* templespa@spiders.ie
                                   Website www.spiders.ie/templespa

César award: Spa guest house of the year

"A peaceful paradise," says a visitor this year. Bernadette and Declan
Fagan, "young and quiet, with three children", have turned their 250-
year-old farmhouse into a notable venture: a small, superior guest
house with a health spa, sauna, spa bath, in buildings in the grounds.
You can take beauty treatments, hydrotherapy, reflexology, aromatherapy and the like. Around is a large farm with pastures, and a
garden where hens strut on the croquet lawn. In 1999/2000 visitors
were again delighted: "Remote tranquillity, yet easily accessible. We
had a room in the new block, with views to sheep and cows. Declan is
a generous host with a nifty palate, so his wine list is fairly priced and
interesting. His wife is a very proficient cook. Both are completely
unpretentious. I strongly recommend the massage and yoga." "Flights
of birds in the evening, and a spectacular red sunrise. Rooms are
attractive with all expected facilities. Food was first class. All the ther-
apists were professional, pleasant, well dressed." Bedrooms are large,
with a simple decor, matching fabrics, good lights. "No one bothers to
lock the doors." Dinner, served by candlelight, and taken communally
round one large table, "is convivial". Admired this year were the red
peppers stuffed with pine nuts and mushrooms; rack of lamb; roast
pork with caramelised plum; tiramisu; chocolate bavarois. Vegetables
are often home grown and fresh. Vegetarians and vegans are catered
for. "The restful sitting room has a log fire and board games": "We
played Scrabble." Breakfast has local yogurt, good breads, porridge,
home-made jams, cooked items if wanted. Wellies are provided for
farm walks. Nearby are golf courses, and the peat bogs and lakes of
West Meath. The main Dublin to Galway road is only half a mile
away. (*Simon Willbourn, Eithne Scallan*)

Open All year, except 6 Dec–28 Jan. Dining room closed midday, and gener-
ally closed Sun/Mon.
Rooms 7 double, 1 single. 5 in adjacent building.
Facilities 2 lounges, dining room; health spa: sauna, steam room, spa bath,

aromatherapy, etc. No background music. 100-acre farm: 1-acre garden. Walking, cycling, riding, golf, dinghy sailing nearby. Unsuitable for &.
Location Just N of N6, 1 mile W of Horseleap, 4 miles E of Moate.
Restrictions No smoking in restaurant. No children, except in July/Aug school holidays. No dogs in house.
Credit cards Amex, MasterCard, Visa.
Terms [2000] B&B: single IR£40–£60, double IR£80–£100. Set dinner (Tues–Sat) IR£20. Spa packages. 1-night bookings refused weekends.

MOUNTRATH Co. Laois — Map 6

Roundwood House

Tel (0502) 32120
Fax (0502) 32711
E-mail roundwood@eircom.net.ie
Website www.hidden-ireland.com/roundwood

Q *César award in 1990*

"In all respects this beautiful house and its staff take care of you," says a visitor in 2000 to this 18th-century Palladian mansion. The owners, Frank and Rosemarie Kennan, are "cheerful, delightful hosts", who offer "the warmest of Irish welcomes"; even in their absence "the high quality service and hospitality continue unabated". *Roundwood* stands in 20 acres of gardens, pastures and woods (lime, beech and chestnut), at the foot of the Slieve Bloom mountains in the thinly populated Irish "Midlands". It is a beautiful house, full of books and pictures, with creaking floorboards, "a staircase to die for", and a "slightly shabby Irish charm". Bedrooms are "a bit sparse", but large and well appointed. Dinner (no choice) is communal, though you can have a separate table if you prefer. Mrs Kennan's "very adventurous" cooking is "based on what is in the market – nothing frozen except the ice-creams". Much enjoyed by readers, it features such dishes as crêpes filled with ham and mushrooms; local beef en croûte; loin of Welsh lamb; varied Irish cheeses; a choice of desserts (you can try them all). Portions are large, and the wine list is especially good. Later you take coffee and drinks with the hosts round the drawing room fire, with "much talking and laughter". Mr Kennan is "always ready with an amusing anecdote". Breakfast is "highly enjoyable". The house has been partly refurbished, with bathrooms upgraded (some now have showers as well as tubs). Children are welcomed (there is a "wet day" nursery), and are encouraged to feed the animals, which include donkeys, geese and ducks. (*Ruth West, John Crisp*)

Open 27 Jan–31 Dec.
Rooms 10 double. 4 in annexe. No telephone/TV.
Facilities Drawing room, study, dining room; nursery. No background music. 20-acre grounds: croquet, *boules*, swings, stables. Golf, walking, river fishing nearby. Unsuitable for &.
Location N7 Dublin–Limerick. Right at T-junction in Mountrath, then left to Kinnitty. *Roundwood* 3 miles exactly. Train: Portlaoise; they will meet.
Restrictions No smoking: restaurant, some bedrooms. No dogs in house.
Credit cards All major cards accepted.
Terms [2000] B&B IR£43. Single room supplement IR£12. Set dinner IR£25.20. Child accommodated in parents' room: 50% of adult rate. 3-night breaks. *V*

MULRANNY Co. Mayo   Map 6

Rosturk Woods   BUDGET   *Tel/Fax* (098) 36264
                                              E-mail stoney@iol.ie

♀ *César award in 2000*

Louisa and Alan Stoney are "charming and intelligent hosts" at their civilised guest house, a trim white building set amid trees, by the sandy shore of a village on Clew Bay (when the tide is out, you can walk among the small offshore islands). It has long enchanted readers: "One of the nicest places of its kind in the whole of Ireland." "Lovely and peaceful, it has an artistic quality and a family feel." Though quite modern, the house has an old, cottagey atmosphere, with some antique furnishings, interesting books and pictures. The bedrooms have stripped pine doors, soft shades of blue, cotton prints, and views across the bay. Sherry is served in pretty glasses, by a log fire, before the home-cooked dinner, discussed in advance and based on local ingredients: these include wild salmon, turbot, brill and lamb; starters such as home-made organic spinach soup; puddings like apple and rhubarb pie, and chocolate mousse. There are "glorious views from the dining room as the sun sets". Breakfast includes organic muesli, good yogurt and deep-yellow scrambled eggs. With its toys, swings, beach close by, owners' children and small dogs, the place is good for families. There are also self-catering cottages, whose residents may dine in the main house. Very popular, with many European guests, the house is often booked well ahead. It is in real *Playboy of the Western World* country – the remote west coast of Mayo, between the neat, historic town of Westport and the cliffs of Achill Island. (*BT, and many others*)

Open Feb–Dec. Closed Christmas, New Year.
Rooms 1 suite, 2 double. 1 on ground floor, suitable for &. No telephone/TV. Also self-catering accommodation (available all year).
Facilities Sitting room with TV, games room, dining room. No background music. 5-acre wooded grounds: garden, tennis, seashore, bathing, sea angling. Riding, golf, lake/river fishing, sailing nearby.
Location 7½ miles W of Newport, between main road and sea.
Restrictions No smoking: dining room, bedrooms.
Credit cards None accepted.
Terms B&B double IR£50–£65. Set dinner IR£25.

NEWPORT Co. Mayo   Map 6

Newport House   *Tel* (098) 41222
                                               Fax (098) 41613
                                               E-mail kjtl@anu.ie

The former home of a branch of the O'Donels, this creeper-covered Georgian mansion stands near the sea in a much-visited little town on lovely Clew Bay, facing towards Achill Island. There is magnificent scenery all round. Owned and run by Thelma and Kieran Thompson, who offer "great hospitality", it is a Relais & Châteaux member but has an "unstuffy atmosphere" and friendly service. This year, a visitor liked the public rooms (they are impressive, with fine plasterwork, chandeliers, "cheerful fires burning", and there is a grand staircase with a lantern and dome). But he disliked his bedroom in the lodge, and found the dining room "sepulchral" and the cooking disappointing, save for the fish. But other visitors have called the food "a poem of excellence". The chef, John Gavin, cooks ambitious dishes such as poached turbot with garlic spinach; roast duck with rillettes in pastry and orange and blackcurrant sauce. Local oysters are available (for an extra charge). Earlier visitors called this "the best Irish hotel we have ever stayed in"; "marvellous, with wonderful staff"; and wrote of "gloriously old-fashioned bedrooms" (some have a four-poster; some are suitable for a family). You can have eggs Benedict for breakfast, but there is no buffet, and service can be slow. The hotel has its own fishery on the Newport River. The wide grounds were this year thought poorly maintained. More reports, please.

Open 19 Mar–5 Oct.
Rooms 16 double, 2 single. 5 in courtyard. 2 on ground floor. No TV.
Facilities Drawing room, sitting room, bar, restaurant, billiard room, table-tennis room. No background music. 20-acre grounds: walled garden. Private fishing on Newport River, 8 miles; golf, riding, walking, shooting, hang-gliding nearby.
Location In village, 7 miles N of Westport. Bus 25 from Westport 3 times daily.
Restrictions No smoking in restaurant. No dogs.
Credit cards All major cards accepted.
Terms B&B: single IR£69–£73, double IR£138–£180; D,B&B: single IR£103–£107, double IR£206–£248. Set dinner (6 courses) IR£34; full alc IR£28. Child accommodated in parents' room: under 2, free. Child in own room: 2–10, 70% of adult rate. *V*

OUGHTERARD Co. Galway   **Map 6**

Currarevagh House   *Tel* (091) 552312
                                               Fax (091) 552731
                                 E-mail currarevagh@ireland.com

◊ *César award in 1992*

Greatly enjoyed again this year (it has featured in every edition of the *Guide*), this mid-Victorian country house stands in huge grounds beside Lough Corrib, on the edge of Connemara. The Hodgson family have owned it for five generations; Harry and June Hodgson have been resident hosts since 1970, and their "charming daughter" is now front-of-house. "It has high standards and original style, reflecting the warm personalities of the owners. Service is efficient, food is excellent." "The views over the lough were lovely and the meals fantastic." The house is not at all smart, but "rather shambolically comfortable and welcoming, with a hotchpotch of furniture", and one couple disliked their bedroom in the mews. But most visitors enjoy the huge beds (with hot-water bottles), the "comfortable public rooms", and the "exceptional" afternoon teas. On the four-course no-choice, home-cooked dinner menu, prepared by June Hodgson, you may find roast lamb, or venison in season; service is by local women, and guests are expected to be punctual. Second helpings are offered. A visitor this year had "the best roast duck ever" and adored the breakfasts, "served in the country house manner of the last century – true breakfast heaven at last! I want to go back!" It is an old-style buffet, with a range of hot dishes on the sideboard, such as "grilled local trout, kedgeree, blood pudding – and soda bread". There is good fishing, swimming and boating in the lough; rhododendrons and good walking in the grounds. (*Robert Freidus, David Clarke, JCS*)

Open Easter–21 Oct. Only parties of 10 or more in winter (not Christmas, New Year). Lunch by arrangement (residents only).
Rooms 13 double, 2 single. 3 on ground floor, in mews. No telephone/TV.
Facilities Drawing room, sitting room, library, bar, dining room. No background music. 150-acre grounds: lake, fishing (ghillies available), boating, swimming, tennis, croquet. Golf, riding, hill-walking nearby.
Location 4 miles NW of Oughterard. Take N59 (Galway–Clifden) to Oughterard. Right in village square; follow Glann lakeshore road for 4 miles.
Restrictions No smoking in dining room. Children under 12 by arrangement. Dogs by arrangement; not in restaurant.
Credit cards MasterCard, Visa.
Terms (*Excluding 10% service charge*) B&B: single IR£52.50–£64, double IR£103–£125; D,B&B: single £IR£77–£88, double IR£151–£173. Picnic lunch from IR£5.60. Set dinner IR£24,50. 3-day, weekly rates; winter house parties. 1-night bookings sometimes refused if too far ahead.

Ross Lake House	*Tel* (091) 550109
Rosscahill	*Fax* (091) 550184

E-mail rosslake@iol.ie
Website www.iol.ie/-rosslake

In the lovely wilds of Connemara, south of Oughterard and 14 miles NW of Galway city: fine Georgian estate house set in 5-acre wooded grounds with hard tennis court. Once the home of landed gentry, now owned and run by Henry and Elaine Reid as a relaxed and intimate country house – "a gem". Warm period furnishings. Imaginative Irish cooking using local produce; vegetarians well catered for. Large drawing room, bar; light classical background music. Golf and good fishing nearby. Closed 1 Nov–14 Mar. All major credit cards accepted. 13 rooms. B&B IR£45–£70. Set dinner IR£25.50. Service charge of 12½% added. More reports welcome. ***V***

RATHMULLAN Co. Donegal   **Map 6**

Rathmullan House	*Tel* (074) 58188
Rathmullan, Letterkenny	*Fax* (074) 58200

E-mail rathhse@iol.ie

This enterprising country hotel on Lough Swilly (not a lake, but an inlet of the sea) has long been a *Guide* favourite, and it was much liked again in 2000: "Attentive staff, excellent food in the attractive restaurant, spacious well-furnished public rooms; our superior bedroom was also spacious, and comfortable. A bonus is the large indoor swimming pool." There are also tennis courts and a steam room. The handsome white 1800s mansion is outside a sleepy village, near some ugly holiday bungalows, but inside its gateway is a well-tended garden with access to a "glorious beach", and you can go for pleasant walks up the Fanad peninsula, with fine views. The Wheeler family have been resident owners since 1963, and Mark and William Wheeler are now managers. "Though professionally run, it still has the feel of a private house, and always has the same courteous staff, plus well-coached students." The striking conservatory-style dining room, with a tented ceiling, serves an ambitious mix of modern and classical cooking by chef Seamus Douglas, eg, loin of lamb on couscous and tomato garlic sauce; breast of duck and honey with cassis sauce; monkfish tail wrapped in Parma ham with red pepper and basil on saffron risotto cake. Rather than the five-course dinner, you could eat a simpler meal in the refurbished cellar bar/bistro; it serves lunches on a terrace in fine weather. The bedrooms vary: the "superior" ones have a sitting area; some have a balcony; lough-view rooms cost extra. The simpler rooms, good for a family, were recently renovated. "Enjoyable breakfasts" offer an unusually wide choice. Public rooms have high ceilings, chandeliers, antiques, marble fireplaces, log fires, oil paintings. A "holistic week", with yoga and beauty treatments, is offered in early November. Four championship golf courses are nearby. (*AD and J Lloyd*)

Open All year, except early Jan–mid-Feb, Christmas.
Rooms 11 superior, 9 double, 4 single. 2 on ground floor suitable for &.
Facilities Ramp. 4 lounges, TV room, cellar bar/bistro, restaurant; indoor swimming pool, steam room. No background music. 10-acre grounds: tennis; direct access to sandy beach, safe bathing. Golf, boating, riding, hill walking nearby.
Location ½ mile N of village. From Letterkenny, take road to Ramelton (Rathmelton); at bridge in Ramelton turn right to Rathmullen; go through village and head N. Hotel's large gates are just past chapel, on right. Bus: Letterkenny; hotel will meet.
Restrictions No smoking in restaurant. No dogs.
Credit cards All major cards accepted.
Terms (*Excluding 10% service charge*) B&B IR£50–£79; D,B&B IR£80–£109. Set dinner IR£30. Holistic week in Nov. 1-night bookings refused weekends and bank holidays. *V*

RATHNEW Co. Wicklow   Map 6

Hunter's Hotel   *Tel* (0404) 40106
Newrath Bridge   *Fax* (0404) 40338
                                                  E-mail reception@hunters.ie

A "supremely welcoming" old coaching inn. It stands by the River Vartry, north-west of Wicklow. It is run "with old-style charm" by Maureen Gelletlie and her two sons, Richard (the manager) and Tom: the family has owned it since 1825. "It was super, very comfortable, with friendly staff, and very Irish in the nicest way," says a visitor this year. "Our spacious room had a large bed, antique furniture, and a good view of the flowery garden where it is pleasant to sit with a drink. Fires were lit in the public rooms. The hotel was very busy, with residents and locals: it seemed a real part of the local community." The decor is old-fashioned, as if "frozen in a period about 50 years ago", with antiques, polished brass, open fires and fresh flowers. But it is also "gleaming with fresh paint, new carpets and polished wood". The bedrooms are "comfortable in a homely style, with plenty of space to sit and watch TV, and a large and pristine bathroom". Even the singles are generous in size. The extensive dinner menu provides "hearty fare, if not *haute cuisine*": this year, the food was found "patchy" and service slow. Local fish, game, and beef are served, and home-grown vegetables and fruit. Breakfast is "full Irish", with freshly squeezed juice, linen napkins. Whiskey and tea are on offer throughout the day, often simultaneously: tea is served on the lawn in summer. Nobody bothers with keys. There are 15 18-hole golf courses within an hour's drive. Nearby sights include Mount Usher and Powerscourt gardens, Russborough and Avondale houses. (*Lynn Wildgoose, EC*)

Open All year, except 3 days over Christmas.
Rooms 13 double, 3 single. 1 on ground floor.
Facilities Residents' lounge, TV room, bar lounge, dining room; conference room. No background music. 7-acre grounds: 2-acre garden, river, fishing. Golf, tennis, riding, sea, sandy beach, fishing nearby.
Location 28 miles S of Dublin. From Dublin take N11; left at bridge in Ashford; hotel 1½ miles. From S turn right off N11 on leaving Rathnew; hotel ½ mile. Carpark. Bus from Wicklow.
Restrictions No smoking in dining room. No dogs.
Credit cards All major cards accepted.
Terms [2000] B&B IR£55–£130. Set lunch IR£15, dinner IR£27.50. 1-night bookings refused holiday weekends.

Tinakilly House

Tel (0404) 69274
Fax (0404) 67806
E-mail jandrpower@tinakilly.ie
Website www.tinakilly.ie

Off N11 to Dublin, 2 miles N of Wicklow, grey stone 1870s mansion set in large wooded grounds above sea, with wide coastal views from most bedrooms. Now a select and ambitious hotel, owned and run by Power family; younger generation, Josephine and Raymond, has just taken over management. Smart, comfortable public rooms, with gold chandeliers, rococo fireplaces, red carpets, potted plants, glittering bric-à-brac, etc; classical background music "when appropriate". Spacious bedrooms, with modern and antique items, in new block at back. "Modern Irish" cooking, mostly admired; friendly service. Irish entertainment and theatrical evenings sometimes held. 7-acre grounds: tennis, putting. All major credit cards accepted. 30 suites, 22 double rooms. B&B IR£68–£124; D,B&B double IR£104–£112. Set lunch IR£20, dinner IR£36 [2000]. More reports, please.

RIVERSTOWN Co. Sligo   Map 6

Coopershill

Tel (071) 65108
Fax (071) 65466
E-mail ohara@coopershill.com
Website www.coopershill.com

♦ *César award in 1987*

"The best small hotel we have ever stayed in." "It has all the elegance
and polish of an age almost past." "A very lovely house, filled with
real antiques." "You feel privileged to stay here." More paeans came
this year for this firm *Guide* favourite, a grey Palladian mansion set in
a large estate south of Sligo town, near the knobbly hills that Yeats
loved. It has been the home of the O'Hara family since they built it in
1774. Mrs O'Hara senior, who turned it into a hotel many years ago,
is still around, "bright-eyed and jolly", aged 88. Her son Brian and his
wife Lindy, "welcoming and caring", "are so comfortable in their role
as hosts that the guests feel at home too". "Staff are wonderful, and
meticulous thought has gone into every detail." Dinner, cooked by
Lindy O'Hara and served by candlelight, starts at 8.30 and can be
leisurely, since all guests are served each course at the same time, but
diners talk to each other: "We have never been with a more congenial
collection of fellow guests." "The five-course dinner is superlatively
good," runs one report this year, and others agree: barbecued salmon
with avocado might be one dish; or duck with ginger sauce. The wine
list is extensive, "amazingly good value for money". Breakfasts are
admired, too. "There are plenty of serious books and guides on the
history, etc, of the area." And "children are made genuinely welcome". As for bedrooms, "they are large and luxuriously homely, as
indeed is the whole set-up". Some have a *chaise longue*; most have a
four-poster or a canopied bed. Other pleasures: "Walks through the
woods; dogs, peacocks; the gathering of guests in the drawing room
(with an open fire) before and after dinner. Wonderful fudge and
chocolate with coffee; afternoon tea with cakes." The interior is something of a time warp, with spears, hunting trophies, stags' heads and
ancestors decorating the walls. "Much of the estate has been given
over to deer farming, involving a lot of high fencing, but there is no
shortage of Arcadian vistas, with sheep safely grazing." Yeats's grave
is not far away. (*Christopher Brumfit, Robert Freidus, Sheelagh Innes,
HR, and others*)

Open 1 Apr–31 Oct. Out-of-season house parties by arrangement.
Rooms 8 double. No TV.
Facilities 2 halls, drawing room, TV room, dining room; snooker room; table-
tennis. No background music. 500-acre estate: garden, tennis, croquet, woods,
farmland, river with trout-fishing. Lake trout-fishing, sandy beach nearby;
championship golf course 18 miles. Unsuitable for &.
Location 11 miles SE of Sligo: turn off N4 towards Riverstown at Drumfin,
then follow *Coopershill* signs. Train: Ballymote. Air: Sligo/Knock.
Restrictions No smoking: dining room, bedrooms. Dogs with prior notice
only, not in house.
Credit cards All major cards accepted.
Terms B&B IR£52–£90; D,B&B IR£82–£120. Light/picnic lunch IR£6; set

dinner IR£30. 3rd person in triple room £10. Discounts for 3 or more nights. Off-season house parties.

SCHULL Co. Cork   Map 6

Rock Cottage   NEW/BUDGET   *Tel/Fax* (028) 35538
Barnatonicane

Barbara Klötzer (she speaks German) is the owner/chef of this trim black-fronted Georgian hunting lodge, set peacefully amid wooded parkland near Dunmanus Bay, north-west of the lively holiday village of Schull. "It's an oasis of comfort and good taste," says its nominator, "a beautiful old house overlooking a tree-filled paddock. Good housekeeping, excellent breakfasts, quiet good taste with wonderful art on the walls." In the large wooded grounds there is a garden, a walled courtyard, old farm buildings, a large rock which gives the cottage its name. You can walk into the hills for fine views over the bay, or drive to nearby sandy beaches; the lovely south Cork coast is worth exploring. Reports please on the "upmarket home cooking, German, French, Italian": lobsters and seafood can be served in season. (*Catherine Fraher*)

Open All year.
Rooms 3 family, 1 double. 1 in cottage. Also 1 self-catering cottage.
Facilities Lounge (mixed background music "when guests like it", dining room. 17-acre grounds. Sea, sandy beaches nearby.
Location 8 miles NW of Schull. Go W towards Goleen. At Toormore, turn right on to R591 to Durrus. Hotel signpost on left, after 1½ miles. Bus to Schull; then taxi.
Restrictions No smoking: restaurant, bedrooms. Children "preferably over 10". No dogs.
Credit cards MasterCard, Visa.
Terms (Not VAT-rated) B&B single IR£30–£35, double IR£50. Set dinner from IR£22.

SHANAGARRY Co. Cork   Map 6

Ballymaloe House   *Tel* (021) 652531
                                                 Fax (021) 652021
                                         E-mail res@ballymaloe.com
                                         Website www.ballymaloe.com

Q *César award in 1984*

This lovely ivy-covered Georgian house, a "marvellous" hotel, "full of charm", was enjoyed again this year, as much as ever. Headed by the veteran Myrtle Allen, it is very much a family enterprise, run with a special brand of caring hospitality. One daughter-in-law, Hazel, is manageress; head chef is Rory O'Connell, brother of another daughter-in-law, Darina, who runs the Ballymaloe Cookery School. "To stay is a great pleasure, with some of the best cooking in the British Isles. The atmosphere is relaxed and warm, and service is efficient with just the odd hiccough." The house still has its Norman keep (which includes some bedrooms); graceful and rambling, it stands

amid a large home farm, which provides much of what you eat –
"Irish country house cooking" at its best. The restaurant, with five
rooms and a conservatory, draws a civilised clientele from many
lands. Its atmosphere is "friendly, with everyone talking and laugh-
ing". It serves "the freshest ingredients of the day, simply cooked;
each day completely different". "Memorable dishes" include French
peasant soup; roast cod with parsley pesto; steak, kidney and oyster
tart; turkey baked with local cheddar. Plenty of choice for vegetarians. "Breakfasts are outstanding, with a range of mueslis." The
comfortable lounges have log fires in winter; walls are hung with
modern Irish paintings. "After dinner, by the wood fire, we unwound
to Rory's Irish singing, and guests were encouraged to join in." "Our
huge pretty room, with fresh lilies, opened on to lawns, lake and peacocks." Bedrooms vary in size; those in the main house tend to be
larger than annexe ones. Some bathrooms may be cramped. Children
are made very welcome. (*David Clark, HR, and others*)

Open All year, except 24–26 Dec.
Rooms 30 double, 3 single. 10 in adjacent building. 3 on ground floor. TV on
request.
Facilities Drawing room, TV room, conservatory, 5 dining rooms; conference
facilities. No background music. Irish entertainment once weekly. 40-acre
farm: gardens, tennis, swimming pool (heated in summer), 6-hole golf course,
croquet, children's play area; craft shop. Cookery school nearby. Sea 2 miles:
sand and rock beaches; fishing, riding by arrangement.
Location On L35 Ballycotton road, 2 miles E of Cloyne, 20 miles E of Cork.
Train: Cork; then taxi.
Restrictions No smoking in some dining rooms. No dogs in house.
Credit cards All major cards accepted.
Terms [2000] B&B: single IR£80, double IR£130–£170; D,B&B: single
IR£114.50, double IR£209–£249. Set lunch IR£20, dinner IR£36. Child
accommodated in parents' room: 50% of adult rate. Winter, conference rates.

TAGOAT Co. Wexford   **Map 6**

Churchtown House   BUDGET   *Tel/Fax* (053) 32555
Tagoat, Rosslare   *E-mail* churchtown.rosslare@indigo.ir
                                  Website churchtown-rosslare.com

Patricia and Austin Cody are "superb hosts, very professional", at their
handsome white Georgian house, set in large grounds with lawns and
old trees. It has been called "charming", "excellent value", with a
"good ambience". Guests meet in the Garden Room for a sherry before
dinner, which is based on "traditional Irish country cooking", say the
Codys, and may include local seafood, Wexford lamb, and vegetables
from the garden. The wine list is "reasonably priced", but was thought
dull this year. They will also advise on eating places nearby. *Kelly's
Resort Hotel* was liked this year. "Everywhere is warm; a nice fire in
the drawing room." The bedrooms are comfortable and "sparkling
clean", and breakfast is "superb": it can be served early to guests catch-
ing a crack-of-dawn ferry from nearby Rosslare. The medieval walled
town of Wexford is also near, and many guests come for its opera
festival in October (early suppers are served). (*JC, Simon Willbourn*)

Open Mar–Oct.
Rooms 10 double, 2 single. 1 suitable for ♿.
Facilities 2 lounges, dining room. No background music. 4-acre grounds.
Golf, fishing, riding, beaches nearby.
Location ½ mile W of Tagoat village, on R736; 2½ miles W of Rosslare.
Restrictions No smoking except in 1 lounge. Guide dogs only.
Credit cards Amex, MasterCard, Visa.
Terms B&B IR£30–£55. Set dinner IR£25.

THOMASTOWN Co. Kilkenny   Map 6

Mount Juliet   *Tel* (056) 73000
                                                        Fax (056) 73019
                                            E-mail info@mountjuliet.ie
                                            Website www.mountjuliet.ie

One of Ireland's grandest houses, this large creeper-covered mansion
was built in the 1750s by the first Earl of Carrick and named for his
wife Juliana ("Juliet"). It stands in a vast estate of well-kept parkland,
where the River Nore offers fishing for salmon and trout. It has an 18-
hole championship golf course designed by Jack Nicklaus, an equestrian centre, tennis, cycling and archery. Guests can go out with the
famous Kilkenny hunt. Now a superior hotel, the building has Adam
fireplaces, hand-carved marble, and stucco work on the walls and ceilings of the public rooms. The smart dining room serves modern Irish
cooking. The bedrooms are luxurious, with a country house decor:
period furniture, chandeliers and luxurious fabrics. There are suites –
each with two bedrooms, a sitting room and kitchen – in *Rose Garden
Lodges*. Simpler accommodation is in the *Hunter's Yard*, around a
courtyard. This building also houses a spa with a heated swimming
pool, gym, beauty treatments, etc, and it has its own less formal restaurant, *Kendals*. Though it often caters for the conference trade, *Mount
Juliet* has "quite a warm, personal feel" – log fires, family portraits,
and has been thought superb: the "large and luxurious bedrooms", the
"helpful staff", and the "good and plentiful food" are all admired.
Kilkenny town with its superb old castle is ten miles away. More
reports, please.

Open All year.
Rooms 4 suites, 52 double, 3 single. 16 in *Hunter's Yard*, 11 in *Rose Garden
Lodges*. Some on ground floor. 1 equipped for ♿.
Facilities 2 lounges, TV room, 4 bars, 2 restaurants; mixed background music
in public areas; conference facilities. 1,500-acre estate: garden, tennis, 18-hole
golf course, 18-hole putting course, golf academy, equestrian centre, archery,
clay target-shooting, fishing, hunting; leisure centre: indoor swimming pool,
sauna, steam room, gym, beauty treatment; bicycles available; helipad.
Location 1½ miles NW of Thomastown, 10 miles S of Kilkenny. Train/bus
from Kilkenny or Waterford.
Restrictions No smoking: restaurants, 1 bedroom. No pets.
Credit cards All major cards accepted.
Terms [To 31 Oct 2000] Rooms: single IR£120–£160, double IR£160–£250,
suite IR£210–£340. Breakfast IR£12.50. Set lunch IR£22–£35, dinner
IR£30–£45; full alc IR£50. Child accommodated in parents' room: under 12,
free (1 child). Christmas package. 1-night bookings sometimes refused
weekends.

THURLES Co. Tipperary   Map 6

Inch House   BUDGET   *Tel* (0504) 51348 and 51261
Inch, Thurles   *Fax* (0504) 51754
                                     E-mail inchhse@iol.ie
                                Website www.tipp.ie/inch-house

"This abode is truly glorious, and its entrance is awe-inspiring," say American visitors this year to this mansion set up a long drive in the middle of a large working farm. Others enjoyed the architecture and "old-style living". It was owned for nearly 300 years by the Ryan family; their chapel still stands. The "charming owners" since 1985, John and Nora Egan, have sensitively restored the old building. "They and their children work there," runs this year's report. "The food was wonderful and reasonably priced, and we met some lovely local people." Others wrote: "The dining and drawing rooms are magnificent": they are decorated in Adam style, with period furniture. The dining room, elegant in red and green, has a log fire; the drawing room has a huge stained-glass window. The split staircase "is a sight to behold", and the bedrooms are "huge and lovely". "Ours had wonderful views of the crops being harvested as the sun set. The food was delicious, and the wine list interesting (fine wines are available by the glass). Breakfasts, with fruit, yogurt, home-made jams and soda bread, were excellent. A cracking place to stay." The chef, Michael Doyle, cooks such dishes as roast fillet of brill with chive and lemon sauce; grilled veal with apricot stuffing and red wine sauce. Vegetables and herbs are home-grown; meat often comes from the estate. The restored Holy Cross Abbey, four miles away, by a broad stretch of the River Suir, is worth a visit. (*Charlotte Stradtman, JC*)

Open All year, except Christmas. Dining room closed Sun, Mon.
Rooms 5 double.
Facilities Drawing room, lounge, bar, dining room (soft Irish background music during dinner); chapel; conference/function facilities. 3-acre garden in 250-acre farm. Golf, riding, fishing nearby.
Location 4 miles W of Thurles on Nenagh road.
Restrictions No smoking in dining room. No dogs.
Credit cards MasterCard, Visa.
Terms B&B IR£30–£35. Set dinner £25. Child accommodated in parents' room: 20% of adult rate.

TIMOLEAGUE Co. Cork   Map 6

Lettercollum House   NEW/BUDGET   *Tel* (023) 46251
                                              Fax (023) 46270
                                     E-mail info@lettercollum.ie
                                Website www.lettercollum.ie

Set above Courtmacsherry Bay, a mile from the old village (once a thriving port), this solid Victorian guest house/restaurant stands at the end of a tree-lined drive amid gardens and trees. The exterior is "rather stark", says the nominator, but its interior has been softened by a contemporary decor. The informal and "highly original" style of the owner/chefs, Con McCloughlin and Karen Austin, is liked, and the service from a cosmopolitan young staff is "classy but friendly". They serve "very good food" in a former chapel, still with its stained glass windows and hidden confessional box. Main courses might include medallions of monkfish with fresh coriander and lime; aubergine and lentil charlotte with tomato and basil sauce. Breads are home made. Salads and vegetables from the "fabulous vegetable garden, tended by the most 'off-the-wall' gardener I have ever come across". There is also a self-catering kitchen for guests' use. The bedrooms are simple but large, and not expensive. Children are welcomed. Cookery classes, theatre and music nights, and entertainment weekends, ranging from birdwatching to "Murder and Mystery", are held. The whole house can be taken over by a party. (*Nigel Chapman*)

Open Mar–Oct, Christmas, New Year self-catering only.
Rooms 3 family, 6 double. 1 with bath and shower, 8 with shower. 2 behind main building.
Facilities Sitting room, restaurant ("easy listening" background music at mealtimes); small function facilities; kitchen for guests' use. 12-acre grounds: garden, vegetable garden. Sea 3 miles. Unsuitable for &.
Location 26 miles SW of Cork. 1 mile W of village. 1st turning on right, off Clonakilty road.
Restrictions No smoking: restaurant, bedrooms. No dogs.
Credit cards All major cards accepted
Terms [2000] B&B IR£20–£30; D,B&B IR£42–£52. Set lunch IR£13.50, dinner IR£24. Weekly rates. Child accommodated in parents' room: under 3, free; over 3, £12. Cookery classes spring and autumn; entertainment weekends.

WEXFORD Co. Wexford   **Map 6**

McMenamin's Townhouse   `BUDGET`   *Tel/Fax* (053) 46442
3 Auburn Terrace   *E-mail* mcmem@indigo.ie
Redmond Road   *Website* www.wexford-bedandbreakfast.com

"It is as good as ever," say visitors returning this year to Seamus and Kay McMenamin's B&B – a red brick bay-windowed late Victorian house in the town centre. "The usual incredible array of goodies at breakfast, with about ten different home-made breads" (also scrambled eggs with smoked salmon; lambs' kidneys in sherry; porridge cooked slowly all night, then crusted with brown sugar, and with rum added). "Amazing value for money: our hosts, true professionals, exuded charm and honesty." High ceilings, interesting Victorian objects, and a decor of dark red, pink and green, go with framed turn-of-the-century opera posters reflecting Wexford's annual music festival. There is a pleasant lounge and a "cosily pretty" breakfast area. One bedroom has "a spectacular carved canopied bed". Nearby are fine beaches, the Wexford wildfowl reserve and the Irish National Heritage Park. (*Angela and Ray Evans*)

Open All year, except 20–30 Dec.
Rooms 6 double, 1 single. No telephone.
Facilities Lounge, breakfast room. No background music. Small garden. Unsuitable for &.
Location Central, opposite rail/bus station.
Restrictions No smoking: breakfast room, bedrooms. No dogs.

Credit cards MasterCard, Visa.
Terms B&B IR£25–£35.

YOUGHAL Co. Cork — Map 6

Aherne's
163 North Main Street

Tel (024) 92424
Fax (024) 93633
E-mail ahernes@eircom.net
Website www.ahernes.com

César award in 1997

This historic fortified port and market town sits at the mouth of the Blackwater River, east of Cork. The Fitzgibbon family's restaurant-with-rooms, on the main street, looks outwardly modest but is inwardly stylish, and is liked for its good food, "wonderful Irish hospitality", and its well-furnished, "spacious, light and airy" bedrooms (they are at the back, so traffic noise should not be a problem). The lounge is cosy, with a turf fire and books. The local fishing grounds supply the kitchens with sole, monkfish, lobster, clams, etc. The two panelled bars serve light meals (eg, oysters, seafood chowder and pies) as well as teas. The red-walled restaurant also specialises in seafood, quite simply cooked. "The food was stunning, especially the oyster starter, but the vegetables and salads were unadventurous. Local girls played the piano beautifully, creating a warm and relaxed atmosphere. Breakfast included delicious grilled salmon and lovely cold choices including fruit salad and summer fruit compote." Some visitors, however, feel that success has made the place "too touristy", even vulgar; and the bars can get smoky. Nearby are two Blue Flag beaches, golf, and walking. (*FSD*)

Open All year, except 23–28 Dec.
Rooms 5 junior suites, 7 double. 3 on ground floor, 1 with facilities for ♿.
Facilities Drawing room, 2 bars, restaurant; "easy listening" background music; pianist weekends. Beach, bathing, sea/river fishing, riding, golf nearby.
Location On main street, on N25 (bedrooms are at rear). Courtyard parking. Bus from Cork.
Restriction No smoking in some bedrooms. Guide dogs only.
Credit cards All major cards accepted.
Terms B&B: single IR£75–£80, double IR£100–£160. Bar meals. Set lunch IR£18, dinner IR£30; full alc IR£37.

****

Hotel in Scotland. We were greeted by an Australian employee whom we could barely understand, and who did not give the feeling of traditional Scottish hospitality. She kept mumbling about other guests having arrived and been dissatisfied with their room. We were led through a corridor that was smelly due to lack of ventilation. The bedroom was over-heated and only one window worked; the other had to be propped open with a bottle of mineral water. In the bathroom, the loo seat was loose and the carpet had not been vacuum-cleaned.

****

Shortlist

The following hotels, guest houses and B&Bs are listed in order to plug gaps in our maps. Many are in, or within commuting distance of, major cities and towns that do not at present have a *Guide* entry, or that are inadequately represented. We have given the weekday rates for 2000. Many of the city hotels offer remarkably good weekend reductions.

We must emphasise that while some Shortlist hotels are potential full entries – it includes new businesses, recommendations that arrived too late for us to check this year, and places on which we lack recent reports – many, particularly those in cities, are not typical *Guide* entries. The information is taken from various sources, including reports from readers and inspectors. A few of the hotels are large, and some belong to a chain, but we have, as usual, tried to seek out small, owner-managed establishments. Some lack the character of a true *Guide* entry. Some may be altogether too flamboyant. We recognise that this selection is somewhat haphazard, and the standards may be inconsistent. We'd like reports and nominations, please.

Those places which do not also have a full entry in the *Guide* are indicated on the maps with a triangle.

Note It is vital that, when discussing tariffs, you check whether or not VAT is included. Many hotels, particularly in London, quote tariffs without VAT.

ENGLAND

ASHFORD Kent   Map 2
Eastwell Manor, Eastwell Park, Boughton Lees TN25 4HR. *Tel* (01233) 213000, *fax* (01233) 635530. Grand country house hotel in 3,000-acre estate, close to Channel Tunnel. Built in 1928 in Tudor style from materials of a previous house. Much authentic detail: moulded ceilings, huge fireplaces, etc. Lovely gardens. Stable block conversion with 19 family apartments. Restaurant, bars, reception rooms, extensive function facilities, large garden: swimming pool, heated spa, tennis. 61 bedrooms. B&B: single from £150, double from £180, suite from £250.

BIRMINGHAM West Midlands   Map 3
Asquith House, 19 Portland Road, Edgbaston B16 9HN. *Tel* (0121) 454 5282, *fax* (0121) 456 4668. Margaret Gittens' listed ivy-clad red brick Victorian house in large garden, 1¼ miles from city centre off A456. Short drive NEC, ICC. Smart decor: period furniture, Persian rugs, watercolours. Some conference trade. 10 bedrooms. B&B: single £60–£70, double £75.50–£83.
Copperfield House, 60 Upland Road, Selly Park B29 7JS. *Tel*

(0121) 472 8344, *fax* (0121) 415 5655. Red brick, mid-Victorian guest house near university, 2 miles SW of city centre, offering good value for money. Well restored, with sizeable garden, which ground-floor rooms overlook. The owner, John Bodycote, has put it on the market. 17 bedrooms. B&B: single £45–£67.50, double £55–£77.50. Evening meal available.

Jonathans, 16 Wolverhampton Road, Oldbury B68 0LH. *Tel* (0121) 429 3757, *fax* (0121) 434 3107, *e-mail* sales@jonathans. co.uk. Victorian-style hotel: patterned wallpapers, heavy fabrics, bric-à-brac; wind-up gramophone and chess in lounge. Traditional British cooking in restaurant/bistro. Small conference facilities. On busy road, 4 miles W of centre; M5 exit 3 1 mile. 10 suites, 21 bed-rooms. B&B: single from £88, double £110–£170.

The Mill House, 180 Lifford Lane, Kings Norton B30 3NT. *Tel* (0121) 459 5800, *fax* (0121) 459 8553. 7 miles SW of centre (near M42 exit 3), in landscaped garden. Anthony Morgan and Antony Davis's former paper mill. Adjacent *Lombard Room* restaurant (with pianist) serves English/continental cooking; pretty conservatory for drinks, light lunches. Small conference facilities. Indoor plunge pool. 9 smart bedrooms with marble bathroom; 2 with 4-poster; some no-smoking. B&B: single £98, double £150.

BLACKPOOL Lancashire   Map 4
Raffles, 73/75 Hornby Road, Blackpool Central FY1 4QJ. *Tel* (01253) 294713. "A bargain": Graham Poole and Ian Balmforth's small budget hotel in centre. 2 mins from beach, 5 mins' tram ride to Pleasure Beach. "Amazingly cheery" welcome; well-appointed bar and lounge. 18 bedrooms (some themed: Egyptian, Oriental, etc; some are small). B&B £17–£30. Huge breakfast; evening meal by arrangement.

Further afield
Mains Hall, 86 Mains Lane, Little Singleton FY6 7LE. *Tel* (01253) 885130, *fax* (01253) 894132, *e-mail* enquiries@mainshall. co.uk. White-walled Grade II listed house overlooking River Wyre, 6 miles NE of Blackpool. Owned for many years by Roger Yeomans. Library, bar, 2 dining rooms, conservatory (for weddings and con-ferences); 7-acre grounds. 12 bedrooms. B&B: single £40–£60, double £60–£80, suite £120. Set dinner £16.50.

The River House, Skippool Creek, Thornton-le-Fylde FY5 5LF. *Tel* (01253) 883497, *fax* (01253) 892083, *e-mail* theriverhouse@ theriverhouse.org.uk. Bill and Linda Scott's restaurant-with-rooms in 1830s house, 4 miles NE of Blackpool. Log fires, antiques; Victorian conservatory. Mrs Scott looks after bar and dining room (with entry in *Good Food Guide 2000*). Hearty breakfasts. 4 bedrooms. B&B: single £70, double £90. Set lunch £23, dinner £25; full alc £38.

BOURNEMOUTH Dorset   Map 2
Langtry Manor, Derby Road, East Cliff BH1 3QB. *Tel* (01202) 290550, *fax* (01202) 290115. Large mock-Tudor house near sea, 5 mins' walk from station, built in 1877 by Prince of Wales (later

Edward VII) for his young mistress, Lillie Langtry. Ornate restaurant (high ceiling, minstrels' gallery, tapestries, stained glass), sometimes serves an Edwardian feast (food can be OTT). Lounge, conservatory, function room, garden. 28 bedrooms and suites (some family); best ones in main house and lodge, others in annexe; most no-smoking. B&B £54.75–£99.75, D,B&B (min. 2 nights) £64.75–£109.75.

BRADFORD West Yorkshire   Map 4
Quality Victoria, Bridge Street BD1 1JX. *Tel* (01274) 728706, *fax* (01274) 736358, *e-mail* admin@gb646.u-net.com. Opposite coach and rail stations, imposing 19th-century purpose-built hotel, now chain-owned. Oak-panelled restaurant, *Vic and Bert's*, serves charcoal grills, pasta. Pub, leisure centre. Bedroom extras include CD-player. 60 bedrooms: single £73.25–£81.75, double £88.25–£105.50. English breakfast £9.50. Set dinner £13.50.

BRIGHTON East Sussex   Map 2
Adelaide, 51 Regency Square BN1 2FF. *Tel* (01273) 205286, *fax* (01273) 220904, *e-mail* adelaide@pavilion.co.uk. Ruth and Clive Buxton's Grade II listed Regency house on seafront square. NCP carpark opposite. 12 bedrooms. B&B: single £45, double £68–£86.
Ainsley House 28 New Steine BN2 1PD. *Tel* (01273) 605310, *fax* (01273) 688604, *e-mail* ahhotel@fastnet.co.uk. Laurence and Christine King's B&B on E side of garden square just back from seafront. 11 bedrooms, most with facilities *en suite*, some with sea view; some family. Vegetarian, continental, full English breakfast. B&B: single £25–£30, double £44–£78.
Pelirocco, 10 Regency Square BN1 2FG. *Tel* (01273) 327055. B&B £45–£95, *e-mail* info@hotelpelirocco.co.uk. Jane Slater and Mick Robinson's "state-of-the-art" new hotel, "a shrine to youth culture", opposite West Pier. 18 bedrooms designed by various artists, designers, trend-setters. B&B £45–£95.
Prince Regent, 29 Regency Square BN1 2FH. *Tel* (01273) 329962, *fax* (01273) 748162, *e-mail* princeregent@fastnet.co.uk. Alan Ashworth and Stuart Corson's B&B in Regency mansion on seafront square. 20 bedrooms, some with 19th-century 4-poster (one has mirrored canopy). B&B: single from £42, double from £85.
Regency, 28 Regency Square BN1 2FH. *Tel* (01273) 202690, *fax* (01273) 220438. Once owned by Jane, Dowager Duchess of Marlborough: 1820s house on seafront square. Lounge, bar, meeting room. Children welcomed. 14 bedrooms: 7 with sea view; some also with balcony; some no-smoking. B&B: single £45–£55, double £70–£90, suite £120.

BRISTOL   Map 1
Berkeley Square Hotel, 15 Berkeley Square, Clifton BS8 1HB. *Tel* (0117) 925 4000, *fax* (0117) 925 2970. Conversion of 2 houses in sedate Georgian square (guests have access). Flagship (managed by Sharon Love) of group of 4 hotels in Clifton area; ½ mile from centre, close to university, museum, art gallery. Pleasant, if anodyne, decor. Helpful staff, garage. Good value for city centre. Good

breakfast. Modern English cooking in restaurant, *Nightingales*. No residents' lounge. "The bar, which was fun, was in basement." 43 bedrooms (25 singles – some small, some in basement). B&B: single from £86, double from £107.

Henbury Lodge, Station Road, Henbury BS10 7QQ. *Tel* (0117) 950 2615, *fax* (0117) 950 9532. In quiet suburb, 4 miles N of centre (M5 exit 17½ miles), white Palladian-style country house, privately owned. Bright public rooms with games, newspapers, magazines. Dining room serves English/continental cooking on short set menu. Garden with fishpond; patio for summer meals. Small fitness studio, sauna. Accommodating staff. Carpark. 20 bedrooms, some (with beams) in converted stables; 4 family; 6 no-smoking. B&B: single £89.50–£97.50, double £99.50–£107.50.

BURY ST EDMUNDS Suffolk   **Map 2**
The Angel IP33 1LT. *Tel* (01284) 753926, *fax* (01284) 750092, *e-mail* theangel@bestloved.com. On fine central square, opposite abbey, coaching inn dating back to 1452, later visited by Dickens. Run by Gough family (see also *Marlborough*, Ipswich, main entry). Creeper-covered Georgian façade; country house interior. Formal restaurant; brasserie in 12th-century vaults. Business centre. Lounges sometimes busy, especially on market day (Wed). "Superb afternoon teas", sometimes accompanied by harp or piano, served by uniformed waiters. 42 chintzy bedrooms vary greatly; some large, with 4-poster; rear ones quietest. Single from £69, double from £89. Breakfast: continental £7.95, English £11.95.

CAMBRIDGE Cambridgeshire   **Map 2**
Arundel House, 53 Chesterton Road CB4 3AN. *Tel* (01223) 367701, *fax* (01223) 367721. Across road from Cam and Jesus Green, a short walk from centre, well-run, privately owned hotel composed of Victorian town houses. Families welcomed. Some conference trade. 105 unfussy bedrooms, most with facilities *en suite*; 50% no-smoking. Small garden. Private parking. B&B: single £45–£69, double £65–£92.50, family £82.50–£98. Cooked breakfast £3.95 extra. Light meals in conservatory. Set lunch/dinner £15.20–£28.10.

Further afield:
Melbourn Bury, Melbourn, nr Royston SG8 6DE. *Tel* (01763) 261151, *fax* (01763) 262375, *e-mail* mazecare@aol.com. Anthony and Sylvia Hopkinson's manor house, Tudor in origin. Attractive decor: antiques, fine paintings, log fires; garden with lake, wildfowl. 3 no-smoking bedrooms. Bus/train from nearby Royston to Cambridge (10 miles to N). B&B: single £60, double £90. Evening meal by arrangement.

Purlins, 12 High Street, Little Shelford CB2 5ES. *Tel/fax* (01223) 842643. In quiet, picturesque village, 4 miles S of Cambridge, B&B in Olga and David Hindley's family house (relatively new, but in medieval manor style). Conservatory lounge for guests; breakfasts – vegetarian, continental, English – in galleried hall. 2 acres woodland and lawns. Buses to city every 2 hours till 5 pm (weekdays); trains from Great Shelford (25 mins' walk). 3 bedrooms. B&B: single/double £46–£55.

Sheene Mill, Melbourn, nr Royston SG8 6DX. *Tel* (01763) 261393, *fax* (01763) 261376. 17th-century water mill on River Mel, newly refurbished. 3-acre garden. TV chef Steven Saunders operates from adjacent *Pink Geranium* restaurant overlooking river. Also a brasserie; champagne bar. Civil wedding licence. 8 bedrooms. B&B: single from £65, double from £85, suite from £100.

CANTERBURY Kent   Map 2
The Ebury, 65–67 New Dover Road CT1 3DX. *Tel* (01227) 768433/4, *fax* (01227) 459187, *e-mail* info@ ebury-hotel.co.uk. 1 mile SE of centre, set back from main road in 2-acre garden, 2 spacious, adjoining Victorian houses owned for 21 years by Mason family. Period decor (antiques and collection of "bulls eye" clocks in spacious lounge). English cooking/chargrills in no-smoking restaurant. Spa: indoor swimming pool, spa bath. Self-catering flats/bungalows. 15 bedrooms. B&B: single £50–£65, double £65–£79, family £95–£105.

Magnolia House, 36 St Dunstan's Terrace CT2 8AX. *Tel/fax* (01227) 765121. Ann and John Davies' late Georgian house in walled garden, on residential street 10 mins' stroll from centre. Laundry facilities. No smoking. 7 bedrooms. Generous breakfasts. B&B: single £40–£55, double £78–£85, suite £95–£110. Evening meal in winter, by arrangement.

CHELTENHAM Gloucestershire   Map 3
Cleeve Hill Hotel, Cleeve Hill GL52 3PR. *Tel* (01242) 672052, *fax* (01242) 679969, *e-mail* gbtoncleevehill@aol.com. New owners this year (Bob and Georgie Tracey) for B&B 4 miles NE of spa town. In area of outstanding natural beauty (direct access to Cotswold Way). Lounge, lounge bar, breakfast room. ½-acre garden. 9 bedrooms ("tasteful and well appointed"). B&B: single £45–£55, double £65–85, suite £75–£90.

Hotel Kandinsky, Bayshill Road, Montpellier GL50 3AS. *Tel* (01242) 527788, *fax* (01242) 226412, *e-mail* reservations@ hotelkandinsky.com. Recently opened by Nigel Chapman and Nicholas Dickinson of Luxury Family Hotels (see *Woolley Grange*, etc, main entries): a quite different type of hotel, in impressive white building. Stylish decor (a mix of contemporary and traditional). Informal restaurant, *Café Paradiso*, open all day; subterranean nightclub *U-Bahn* (open to residents and members only) is planned. 48 bedrooms with all mod cons. B&B: single £65, double £85–£120.

CHESTER Cheshire   Map 3
Chester Bells, 21 Grosvenor Street CH1 2DD. *Tel* (01244) 324022. Central position with parking. Beamed building run by Ian and Jane Turner. "Friendly, clean, good decor; excellent value." Good restaurants close by. B&B: single £25 (shared bathroom), double £50 (*en suite*).

Chester Grosvenor, Eastgate CH1 1LT. *Tel* (01244) 324024, *fax* (01244) 313246, *e-mail* chesgrov@chestergrosvenor.co.uk. Luxurious hotel in centre of historic city, owned by Duke of Westminster's Grosvenor Estates. Smart drawing room and library; meeting rooms; leisure suite. Access to country club nearby. *Michelin*-starred *Arkle* restaurant (named for famous racehorse owned by Anne, Duchess of Westminster); light meals in informal brasserie. 85 bedrooms: single £152.75–£176.25, double £229.13–£270.25, suite £411.25–£528.75. Breakfast: continental £10.50, English £14.50. 3-course lunch £25, dinner (2–3 courses) £40–£48.

Chester Town House, 23 King Street CH1 2AH. *Tel/fax* (01244) 350021. Dating back to 1680, Mrs Bellis's no-smoking budget B&B in conservation area of cobbled, lamplit streets within city walls. Breakfast room, conservatory lounge, garden. 5 bedrooms (1 across garden). B&B: single £35, double £50. Parking (£1 per day).

Redland Hotel, 64 Hough Green CH4 8JY. *Tel* (01244) 671024, *fax* (01244) 681309. B&B in red brick town house, 1 mile E of centre; ample parking. Victorian ambience: panelling, beams, antiques, period furniture, ornaments. Lounge, bar, solarium, sauna, laundry. 12 bedrooms, some themed (Jacobean, Tudor, etc). B&B: single £45, double £65–£75.

Further afield:

Crabwell Manor, Mollington CH1 6NE. *Tel* (01244) 851666, *fax* (01244) 851400, *e-mail* sales@crabwell.com. Large country house hotel in turreted building, part 16th-century, in own park. 2¼ miles from centre. Extensive leisure facilities; indoor swimming pool; full range of beauty treatments. Spacious public rooms. 42 bedrooms (some have separate sitting area). B&B: single £116, double £140, suite £185.

CHICHESTER West Sussex   Map 2

Crouchers Bottom, Birdham Road PO20 7EH. *Tel* (01243) 784995, *fax* (01243) 539797. Owned by South African Wilson family: hybrid group of old buildings and modern extensions, at bottom of Crouchers Farm, on busy A286 to the Witterings, 2 miles S of centre. Lounge with log fire, deep leather armchairs. Airy dining room (mixed background music). ½-acre garden: pond; ample parking. 17 bedrooms, "bright, clean and functional"; quietest ones on paved courtyard; 2 have &. access. B&B: single £45–£65, double £65–£105.

Suffolk House, 3 East Row PO19 1PD. *Tel* (01243) 778899, *fax* (01243) 787282, *e-mail* reservations@suffolkhshotel.demon.co.uk. Close to cathedral and centre, within walking distance of festival theatre. Town residence of Duke of Richmond in late 18th century. Lounge, restaurant (no smoking); simple decor. Good English breakfast, served in garden in summer. B&B: single from £59, double from £89.

COLCHESTER Essex   Map 2

Rose and Crown, East Street CO1 2TZ. *Tel* (01206) 866677, *fax*

(01206) 866616. Black-and-white timber-framed former posting
house at road junction on edge of town. Exposed brick and beams in
reception rooms and *Tudor Bar* (meals available). Conference/func-
tion facilities; beauty treatment centre. Parking. 30 bedrooms, some
atmospheric with 4-poster, some quite plain; 5 no-smoking.
Single/double £65, suite £99. Breakfast: continental £6.50, English
£8.95. Bar meals available.

COVENTRY West Midlands   **Map 2**
Coombe Abbey, Brinklow Road, Binley CV3 2AB. *Tel*
(024) 7645 0450, *fax* (024) 7663 5101, *e-mail* info@rose-and-
crown.com. 3½ miles E of city centre. Former Cistercian Abbey
(12th-century, with moat, portcullis). Approached by avenue of lime
and chestnut trees through 500-acre park with 80-acre lake, formal
gardens by Capability Brown. "Owner Gordon Bear's love of the old
and atmospheric apparent throughout." Porters in period costume;
medieval evenings with "monks", chanted music, flickering lighting,
banquets in baronial hall. 63 bedrooms; "feature" ones with huge
4-poster, throne loo. Single from £125, double from £135, suite £350.
Breakfast: continental £10, "Full Abbey" £12. Set dinner £25.
Nailcote Hall, Nailcote Lane, Berkswell, West Midlands CV7 7DE.
Tel (024) 7646 6174, *fax* (024) 7647 0720, *e-mail* info@nailcote-
hall.co.uk. 6½ miles SW of centre on B4101 to Knowle; 10 mins
from Birmingham airport. Rick Cressman's Tudor-style manor
house, with subterranean extensions – "a stunning mixture of old and
modern". 15-acre grounds. Extensive leisure facilities (swimming
pool, golf, tennis, beauty treatments, etc). French cooking in *Oak
Room* restaurant; "pasta and pizzazz in shamelessly noisy *Rick's Bar*,
20 feet underground". Live music nights. 38 rooms. B&B: single
£140, double from £150.

DARLINGTON Co. Durham   **Map 4**
Headlam Hall, Headlam, Gainford DL2 3HA. *Tel* (01325) 730238,
fax (01325) 730790, *e-mail* admin@headlamhall.co.uk. In hamlet in
lower Teesdale, amid 200 acres of farmland. Fine half Jacobean, half
18th-century house, converted to a traditional hotel in 1979 by
Robinson family. Hall/lounge, drawing room, cocktail bar, 4 restaurants. Indoor swimming pool, sauna, billiard room. Garden with lake,
tennis, golf, clay-pigeon shooting and croquet. Caters for conferences, weddings, etc. 26 bedrooms, best (large) ones in main house,
simpler ones in coach houses. B&B: single £65–£90, double
£80–£90, suite £90–£105.

DARTMOUTH Devon   **Map 1**
Royal Castle, The Quay TQ6 9PS. *Tel* (01803) 833033, *fax*
(01803) 835445. Famous 17th-century coaching inn, owned since
1983 by Nigel and Anne Way. Regency façade; panelling, beams;
dramatic galleried atrium with winding staircase. *Galleon Bar* (with
open fire) serves light meals; traditional cooking, with emphasis on
seafood, in *Adam Room*, overlooking harbour. "Friendly staff; lively
atmosphere." Garage. 25 smallish bedrooms, with antiques,

ornaments; some with 4-poster, some with spa bath. B&B
£46.95–£71.95.

DOVER Kent   **Map 2**
Loddington House, 14 East Cliff CT16 1LX. *Tel/fax*
(01304) 201947. Kathy and Mike Cupper's Grade II listed guest
house in seafront Regency terrace, close to terminals and Hoverport.
6 bedrooms (4 with facilities *en suite*). B&B: single from £39.50,
double £52–£56. Evening meal by arrangement.
The Old Vicarage, Chilverton Elms, Hougham CT15 7AS. *Tel*
(01304) 210668, *fax* (01304) 225118. Judy and Bryan Evison's large
Victorian home in Elm Vale area, a few mins' drive from port.
Restaurants nearby. 3 double bedrooms (all with private bath/shower
room, 1 *en suite*). B&B single/double £65.

DURHAM Co. Durham   **Map 4**
Lumley Castle, Chester-le-Street, Tyne and Wear DH3 4NX. *Tel*
(0191) 3891111, *fax* (0191) 3871437. 14th-century castle, remodelled by Vanbrugh, creeper clad and battlemented, above River
Wear, 5 miles N of city. Striking setting on hill almost surrounded
"by not so much a moat as its own river". Thick walls, dimly lit
corridors, spiral staircases; whimsical style, "all a bit of a laugh". Bar
in library with huge collection of books; vaulted restaurant serving
international cooking. Elizabethan banquets weekly in *Baron's Hall*,
with staff in medieval dress. Billiard room. Extensive function/
conference facilities. Garden. 66 bedrooms, some, in castle, with
4-poster and concealed bathroom; most (simpler, with beams) in
courtyard; some no-smoking. Single £89.50–£125, double £120–
£175, suite £225. Breakfast: continental £7, English £9.50.

DUXFORD Cambridgeshire   **Map 2**
Duxford Lodge Ickleton Road CB2 4RU. *Tel* (01223) 836444, *fax*
(01223) 832271. Unpretentious square red brick house in village
(famous for Imperial War Museum's magnificent aircraft collection)
off M11. Good British cooking; keenly priced wine list; mixed
classical background music. 1-acre garden. 20 mins' drive from
Newmarket, Cambridge. 15 bedrooms. B&B: single £78–£83;
double £100–£110.

ETON Berkshire   **Map 2**
The Christopher, 110 High Street SL4 6AN. *Tel*
(01753) 852359/811677, *fax* (01753) 830914, *e-mail* sales@
christopher-hotel.co.uk. Best Western member, in building dating
from 1511, with entrance on main street. Rear courtyard with
carpark. Organic food served in restaurant; *Victoria's Bar* is a well-
established Eton haunt. 15 mins from Heathrow. 33 well-furnished,
well-equipped bedrooms: single £100, double £110–£120, suite
£115. Breakfast: continental £7.95, English £9.95.

EXETER Devon   **Map 1**
St Olave's Court, Mary Arches Street EX4 3AZ. *Tel*

(01392) 217736, *fax* (01392) 413054, *e-mail* info@olaves.co.uk. Wyatt family's large 19th-century Georgian town house, opposite carpark, 400 yds from cathedral. ½-acre walled garden with pond, fountain, ancient mulberry tree. Lounge; 2 dining rooms serving good modern cooking. No background music. 15 bedrooms. B&B: single £65–£90, double £75–£105, suite £120. English breakfast £6 extra.

Barton's Cross, Huxham, Stoke Canon EX5 4EJ. *Tel* (01392) 841245, *fax* (01392) 841942. 4 miles NE of Exeter, convenient for Exmoor. "Charming group of old houses", run as hotel/restaurant by Brian Hamilton. Pretty garden for drinks in summer. Chef Paul George Bending produces elaborate but good food. Two lounges, attractive bar; restaurant (background music). 9 bedrooms. B&B: single £65.50, double £85–£90.

FLEETWOOD Lancashire   Map 4
North Euston Hotel, The Esplanade FY7 6BN. *Tel* (01253) 876525, *fax* (01253) 777842, *e-mail* reception@northeustonhotel.co.uk. Imposing low-built brick hotel, constructed by Decimus Burton in 1841 (at end of railway line from London Euston). Overlooking waterfront (good views of Wyre estuary, Cumbrian hills). Personally managed by 2 Fleetwood families for 18 years. Impressive ballroom; restaurant with emphasis on fresh fish; bar with stained-glass frieze, chandelier. Function facilities. 54 bedrooms with pastel colours. B&B: single £54.50, double £80.

FLITWICK Bedfordshire   Map 2
Flitwick Manor, Church Road MK45 1AE. *Tel* (01525) 712242, *fax* (01525) 718753, *e-mail* flitwick@menzies-hotels.co.uk. Georgian manor house with 17th-century origins (now a chain-owned hotel). 2 miles from M1 exit 12. 50-acre grounds, with lake, deerpark, croquet lawn, Gothic grotto, 12th-century church, walled kitchen garden. Traditional decor (antiques, wallpaper, chintz); English cuisine. 17 distinctive bedrooms, some with 4-poster, conservatory, sauna; some with pair of "kissing baths": single £120, double £145–£195.

GATESHEAD Tyne and Wear   Map 4
Eslington Villa, 8 Station Road, Low Fell NE9 6DR. *Tel* (0191) 4876017, *fax* (0191) 4200667. On S bank of Tyne opposite Newcastle, Mr and Mrs Tulip's Edwardian villa in 1½-acre landscaped garden near railway. Lounge with original features. English/French cooking, with friendly service, in popular restaurant. "Easy listening" background music all day in public areas. Ample parking. 12 bedrooms. B&B: single £59.50, double £69.50.

GATWICK West Sussex   Map 2
Alexander House, Turners Hill RH10 4QD. *Tel* (01342) 714914, *fax* (01342) 717328, *e-mail* info@alexanderhouse.co.uk. Part 17th-century house once owned by Shelley's family. In 135-acre grounds: rose garden, tennis, croquet. Elaborate decor throughout (chandeliers, ruched curtains, murals). Drawing room, oak-panelled library,

bar, restaurant ("good food"), beauty salon. 15 bedrooms. B&B: single £129, double £158, suite £225–£295.

Copperwood Guest House, Massetts Road, Horley RH6 7DJ. *Tel* (01293) 783388, *fax* (01293) 420156, *e-mail* copperwood@ cableinet.co.uk. No-smoking B&B owned and run by Paul and Caroline Hooks. Convenient for airport, yet quiet, off busy road. English country decor. B&B double £45–£50.

Vulcan Lodge, 27 Massetts Road, Horley RH6 7DQ. *Tel* (01293) 771522, *fax* (01293) 786206. Colin and Karen Moon's B&B 4 doors away from *Copperwood* (above). B&B: single £35, double £50.

GUILDFORD Surrey   **Map 2**
The Angel, 91 High Street GU1 3DP. *Tel* (01483) 564555, *fax* (01483) 533770. Black-and-white 16th-century inn on cobbled high street (pedestrianised 11 am–4 pm). Drinks, teas in galleried lounge with Jacobean oak fireplace, 17th-century "parliament" clock; panelled dining room; restaurant in 13th-century crypt. Conference facilities. 21 bedrooms: double £135–£140, suite from £150. Breakfast: continental £8.50, English £12.50. Set meals £15–£18.50.

HARROGATE North Yorkshire   **Map 4**
Crescent Lodge, 20 Swan Road HG1 2SA. *Tel* (01423) 503688. Julia Humphris' budget B&B in Grade II listed early Victorian house in quiet terrace near centre. Drawing room with books, guides, ceramics. 4 immaculate, modern bedrooms (2 with facilities *en suite*). Adequate breakfast. Garden. Limited parking. B&B: single £26–£36, double £52–£56.

HARWICH Essex   **Map 2**
Hotel Continental, 28/29 Marine Parade, Dovercourt CO12 3RG. *Tel* (01255) 551298, *fax* (01255) 551698, *e-mail* hotconti@aol.com. White building on seafront with "welcoming owners, Blossom and Gordon, wonderful breakfasts". Within easy reach of Harwich international port; "perfect for travellers to the Continent". Restaurant serving snacks all day; pavement café. 13 bedrooms of varying size; 8 have sea view. Substantial breakfast. B&B: single £30, double £50–£60.

HASTINGS East Sussex   **Map 2**
Beauport Park, Battle Road TN38 8EA. *Tel* (01424) 851222, *fax* (01424) 85246, *e-mail* reservations@beauportprkhotel.demon.co.uk. Kenneth Melsom and Stephen Bayes's Georgian country house (Best Western), formerly home of Gen. Sir George Murray. 3 miles N of town centre. In 37-acre grounds: woodland, formal gardens, swimming pool, tennis, croquet, putting green. Golf courses adjacent. Traditional, "rather charmless" decor; adequate meals in no-smoking restaurant; friendly staff. 25 bedrooms: single £85, double from £110.

HUDDERSFIELD West Yorkshire   **Map 4**
Elm Crest, 2 Queens Road, Edgerton HD2 2AG. *Tel*

(01484) 530990, *fax* (01484) 516227, *e-mail* elmcrest.hotel@ talk21.com. Derek and Hilary Gee's no-smoking Victorian guest house, in residential area 1 mile N of centre. 8 bedrooms, most with facilities *en suite*. Home-cooked breakfast, courteously served. Conservatory; lounge with log fire. Carpark. B&B: single £28–£38, double £48–£60.

The Lodge, 48 Birkby Lodge Road, Birkby HD2 2BG. *Tel* (01484) 431001, *fax* (01484) 421590. Garry and Kevin Birley's substantial stone-built house in pretty garden in prosperous suburb, 1½ miles from city centre. Peaceful and clean; lovely sitting room with Art Nouveau panelled walls and plaster ceiling. Good modern food in popular restaurant. Children welcomed. 11 no-smoking bedrooms, 3 on ground floor. B&B: single £60, double £70–£80. Set lunch £10.95–£14.95, dinner £23.95.

LEAMINGTON SPA Warwickshire   **Map 2**
The Lansdowne, 87 Clarendon Street CV32 4PF. *Tel* (01926) 450505, *fax* (01926) 421313. Owned for many years by David and Gillian Allen, now on the market: small town house hotel at road junction near centre (double glazing). Lounge, bar, restaurant with changing menu. 14 small but pretty bedrooms. B&B: single £49.95–£52.95, double £65–£68. Set dinner £15.95–£18.95.

Leamington Hotel & Bistro, 64 Upper Holly Walk CV32 4JL. *Tel* (01926) 883777, *fax* (01926) 330467. Composed of adjacent town houses recently refurbished by owners Frank Nixey and Hilary Ashover: Best Western member with 30 adequate bedrooms. Functions catered for. Good food in bistro. D,B&B from £60.

LEDBURY Herefordshire   **Map 3**
Feathers, High Street HR8 1DS. *Tel* (01531) 635266, *fax* (01531) 638955, *e-mail* mary@feathers-ledbury.co.uk. 16th-century half-timbered inn. "Breakfasts were good and the ambience fine." Hop-bedecked *Fuggles* brasserie serves modern cooking specialising in fish. Fitness centre; indoor swimming pool: function facilities. 19 bedrooms. B&B: single £69.50–£77.50, double £89.50–£105.

LIVERPOOL Merseyside   **Map 4**
The Bowler Hat, 2 Talbot Road, Prenton, nr Birkenhead, Merseyside CH43 2HH. *Tel* (0151) 652 4931, *fax* (0151) 653 8127. 3 miles SW of Liverpool centre, on Wirral peninsula. Late-Victorian house, recently refurbished, in garden in residential area. Restaurant; club bar, civil wedding licence. 32 bedrooms, some spacious; smaller ones in modern extension. B&B: single £75, double £90.

Thornton Hall, Neston Road, Thornton Hough, Wirral, Merseyside CH63 1JF. *Tel* (0151) 336 3938, *fax* (0151) 336 7864, *e-mail* thorntonhallhotel@btinternet.com. In village in central Wirral, impressive house, built for 18th-century shipping magnate. Some original features: oak carvings, restaurant with leather and mother-of-pearl ceiling. Traditional British cooking. Health club; conference centre. Large garden. 63 bedrooms, most in modern extension. B&B: single £78–£88, double £88–£98, suite £110.

Further afield

The Old Hall, Main Street, Frodsham, Cheshire WA6 7AR. *Tel* (01928) 732052, *fax* (01928) 739046. In village 3 miles S of Runcorn; Liverpool 30 mins by car. Evocative of a country post house hotel, Mr and Mrs Winfield's Tudor building on main street, with inglenooks, roaring log fires, traditional British food. 20 bedrooms. B&B: single £64.50, double £79.50, suite £81.50–£91.50.

LONDON   **Map 2**

Abbey Court, 20 Pembridge Gardens W2 4DU. *Tel* (020) 7221 7518, *fax* (020) 7792 9858, *e-mail* info@ abbeycourthotel.co.uk. 5-storey Victorian stucco town house hotel (no lift), near Notting Hill Gate, Portobello Road. Small red-walled sitting room, antiques, elaborate flower arrangements. conservatory for breakfast. 22 bedrooms (some very small). B&B: single from £99, double from £145. (Underground: Notting Hill Gate.)

Abbey House, 11 Vicarage Gate W8 4AG. *Tel* (020) 7727 2594. Family-run B&B in Victorian house, in quiet road off Kensington Church St. Small lounge; basement breakfast room. 19 simple rooms, none with facilities *en suite*. B&B: single £45, double £74. (Underground: Kensington High St.)

Academy, 17–21 Gower Street WC1E 6HG. *Tel* (020) 7631 4115, *fax* (020) 7636 3442. Well located for British Museum and West End. New owners this year haven't taken it upmarket. Restaurant. 48 bedrooms: single £115, double £185. (Underground: Goodge St.)

Charlotte Street Hotel, 15 Charlotte Street W1P 1HB. *Tel* (020) 7806 2000, *fax* (020) 7806 2002, *e-mail* charlotte@ firmdale.com. Opened June 2000: new Firmdale hotel (see *Pelham*, main entry, *Covent Garden, Dorset Square* below). Modern decor. Large drawing room, library, brasserie, juice bar, gym; "entertainment centre", 2 meeting rooms. 52 bedrooms (with business facilities, CD-player, etc; penthouse suites with wide views): single from £160, double from £180, suite from £255. (Underground: Goodge St, Tottenham Court Rd.)

A number of organisations in London offer B&B in private homes. They include:

At Home in London, 70 Black Lion Lane, London W6 9BE. *Tel* (020) 8748 1943, *fax* (020) 8748 2701, *e-mail* info@ athomeinlondon.co.uk, *website* www.athomeinlondon.co.uk. B&B in over 70 private homes in central and west London, priced according to location. All close to public transport. B&B (2 nights min.): single £28–£56, double £49–£85, triple £68–£85.

Uptown Reservations, 50 Christchurch Street, London SW3 4AR. *Tel* (020) 7351 3445, *fax* (020) 7351 9383, *e-mail* inquiries@uptownres.co.uk, *website* www.uptownres.co.uk. Upmarket accommodation in private homes in central London. B&B: single £65, double £85. Family rooms, studios, 1-bedroom apartments also available.

The Colonnade Town House, 2 Warrington Crescent W9 1ER. *Tel* (020) 7286 1052, *fax* (020) 7286 1057, *e-mail* colonnade@ demon.co.uk. Victorian Grade II listed house in fashionable residential area, Little Venice. Refurbished by new owner (Eton Town House Group) into small, high-quality hotel. 24-hour room service. Restaurant planned. 43 bedrooms. B&B: single £110–£135, double £165–£195. (Underground: Warwick Ave.)

County Hall Travel Inn Capital, Belvedere Road SE1 7PB. *Tel* (020) 7902 1600, *fax* (020) 7902 1619. Huge hotel in old County Hall building, S of Thames between Westminster and Waterloo bridges. Restaurant, bar. 300 adequate bedrooms, all furnished in same style: single/double/family £69.95. Breakfast: continental £4.50, English £6.50. (Underground: Waterloo.)

Covent Garden Hotel, 10 Monmouth Street WC2H 9HB. *Tel* (020) 7806 1000, *fax* (020) 7806 1100, *e-mail* covent@firmdale.com. Former French hospital in Seven Dials (near Covent Garden), cleverly converted into luxurious hotel with theatrical decor. Friendly reception. Classy foyer; wrought iron staircase leads to large, colourful lounge. Lift; gym. Brasserie, room service. Public carpark nearby. 50 spacious bedrooms (some split-level), with cellular phone, CD-player, etc: single from £190, double from £220–£280, suite £325–£595. (Underground: Leicester Sq, Covent Gdn.)

Cranley Gardens Hotel, 8 Cranley Gardens SW7 3DB. *Tel* (020) 7373 3232, *fax* (020) 7373 7944. Conversion of four Georgian terrace houses in South Kensington, looking across quite busy road to garden square. 85 bedrooms, some small. Clean and comfortable; simple decor, friendly staff. Basement breakfast room; bar snacks available. B&B: single £85–£95, double £115–£125. (Underground: Gloucester Rd, South Kensington.)

Dorset Square Hotel, 39–40 Dorset Square NW1 6QN. *Tel* (020) 7723 7874, *fax* (020) 7724 3328, *e-mail* dorset@firmdale.com. Lavishly decorated conversion of Regency town houses, on garden square near Marylebone Rd, Regent's Pk. *Potting Shed* restaurant (live jazz week-nights). Public carpark nearby. 38 bedrooms: single from £98, double from £140, suite from £245. (Underground: Baker St.)

Dukes, 35 St James's Place SW1A 1NY. *Tel* (020) 7491 4840, *fax* (020) 7493 1264, *e-mail* dukeshotel@compuserve.com. Luxurious, civilised hotel in quiet backwater near St James's Palace. Owned by David Naylor-Leyland (see also *Egerton House*, London, main entry, and *Franklin*, below). Traditional decor. Bar, "serving probably the best martinis in London", private dining room, 24-hour room service. 89 bedrooms: single £190, double £210–£250, suite from £280. (Underground: Green Pk.)

Five Sumner Place, 5 Sumner Place SW7 3EE. *Tel* (020) 7584 7586, *fax* (020) 7823 9962, *e-mail* reservations@ sumnerplace.com. B&B in attractive Victorian terrace managed by Tom Tyranowicz. Buffet breakfast in pretty conservatory. Small garden. 13 rooms, most with facilities *en suite*. B&B: single £85, double £120–£130, suite £240–£310. (Underground: South Kensington.)

The Franklin, 28 Egerton Gardens SW3 2DB. *Tel* (020) 7584 5533, *fax* (020) 7584 5449, *e-mail* bookings@franklinhotel.co.uk. Quiet, traditional hotel ("thick carpets, flowers, flounces") round corner from Knightsbridge. Overlooks large garden at rear. No restaurant, but room-service meals, breakfast room, sitting room. 50 bedrooms. B&B: single £155, double £180–£210. Breakfast: continental £9, English £14. (Underground: South Kensington.)

La Gaffe, 107–111 Heath Street NW3 6SS. *Tel* (020) 7435 8965, *fax* (020) 7794 7592, *e-mail* la-gaffe@msn.com. Italian restaurant-with-rooms in Hampstead village, near heath and underground. Friendly proprietor (for 38 years) Bernard Stella. Roof garden for tea; breakfast in coffee bar. 16 small, no-smoking bedrooms, most with shower (three 4-poster rooms have bath); quietest (rear) ones overlook garden square. B&B: single £65–£80, double £90–£125. (Underground: Hampstead.)

The Gate, 6 Portobello Road, W11 3DG. *Tel* (020) 7221 0707, *fax* (020) 7221 9128, *e-mail* gatehotel:thegate.globalnet.co.uk. In trendy Notting Hill Gate: Brian Watkins's pretty converted Georgian terrace house: cottage-like exterior. 6 small bedrooms, with fridge (continental breakfast delivered at bedtime). B&B £50–£85. (Underground: Notting Hill Gate.)

The Gore, 189 Queen's Gate SW7 5EX. *Tel* (020) 7584 6601, *fax* (020) 7589 8127, *e-mail* reservations@gorehotel.co.uk. Peter McKay's idiosyncratic hotel, run in laid-back style: 2 large Victorian houses in tree-lined terrace, near Albert Hall, South Kensington museums. Attractive decor: antiques, Oriental rugs, open fires, potted palms, over 5,000 paintings and prints. 54 bedrooms, varying greatly; best have a sitting room; some overlook adjacent Bulgarian Embassy; some no-smoking; some noisy (traffic, TV, etc). Popular bistro, *Bistrot 190* and *Fish Restaurant at One Ninety*. Public carpark nearby. Rooms: single £115–£150, double £170–£275. Breakfast: continental £7, English £9. Set dinner: bistro £12–£16, restaurant £22.50. (Underground: Gloucester Rd.)

Knightsbridge Hotel, 12 Beaufort Gardens SW3 1PT. *Tel* (020) 7589 9271, *fax* (020) 7823 9692. Conversion of stucco Victorian terrace houses in quiet street off Brompton Rd, near Harrods, Hyde Pk. Unfussy modern decor. Helpful staff. Bar, lounge; mini-health centre. No restaurant. 40 rooms, 10 apartments. B&B: single £110–£130, double £150–£195, suite £165–£315. (Underground: Knightsbridge.)

Lime Tree Hotel, 135–137 Ebury Street SW1W 9RA. *Tel* (020) 7730 8191, *fax* (020) 7730 7865. Family-run B&B near Victoria. Recently renovated with swanky bathrooms. Dining room, garden. B&B: single £75, double £100–£110. (Underground: Sloane Sq.)

London Elizabeth, Lancaster Terrace W2 3PF. *Tel* (020) 7402 6641, *fax* (020) 7224 8900. Large white building overlooking Hyde Park. Traditional decor. Restaurant, bar, boardroom, garden terrace. Parking. 55 bedrooms. B&B: single £110, double £125–£160, suite £150–£250. (Underground: Lancaster Gate.)

La Reserve, 422–428 Fulham Road SW6 1DU. *Tel* (020) 7385 8561, *fax* (020) 7385 7662. On Chelsea/Fulham border, by Chelsea Football Club. Public rooms with modern decor; restaurant open all day. 41 smallish bedrooms. B&B: single £95, double £110–£135. (Underground: Fulham Broadway.)

The Rookery, Peter's Lane, Cowcross Street EC1M 6DS. *Tel* (020) 7336 0931, *fax* (020) 7336 0932, *e-mail* reservations@ rookery.co.uk. Near St Paul's Cathedral and City. Run by Peter McKay (see *Gore*, above, and *Hazlitt's*, London, main entry). Smart decor: much panelling, antiques, Victorian bathroom fittings. Library (suitable for meetings), conservatory overlooking tiny garden. 33 bedrooms: single £160–£180, double £195, suite from £250. Continental breakfast £7.25. (Underground: Barbican, Farringdon.)

Searcy's Roof Garden Bedrooms, 30 Pavilion Road SW1X 0HJ. *Tel* (020) 7584 4921, *fax* (020) 7823 8694. In small side street off Sloane St, near Knightsbridge. No public rooms, no extras. 13 good-sized, well-equipped bedrooms; good bathrooms; access to fully equipped kitchen. Single £90–£120, double £130–£160. Continental breakfast £6. (Underground: Knightsbridge, Sloane Sq.)

The Stafford, 16–18 St James's Place SW1A 1NJ. *Tel* (020) 7493 0111, *fax* (020) 7493 7121, *e-mail* info@ thestaffordhotel.co.uk. In quiet backwater off St James's St. Sedate, pricey hotel with 81 conventional, comfortable bedrooms and suites, 13 in converted carriage house. Traditional restaurant; trophy-filled American bar. Room: single £209, double £230–£295, suite from £345. (Underground: Green Pk.)

Thanet Hotel, 8 Bedford Place WC1B 5JA. *Tel* (020) 7636 2869, *fax* (020) 7580 3377, *e-mail* thanetlon@aol.com. Bloomsbury B&B, 1 block from British Museum; Covent Garden nearby. Owned and run by Richard and Lynwen Orchard, 3rd-generation hoteliers. Pleasant Grade II listed Georgian terrace house. Plain decor. 16 bedrooms (back ones quietest), with shower/WC. B&B: single £65, double £85. (Underground: Holborn, Russell Sq.)

LOUGHBOROUGH Leicestershire   Map 2
The Old Manor, 11–14 Sparrow Hill LE11 1BT. *Tel* (01509) 211228, *fax* (01509) 211128, *e-mail* bookings@oldmanor. com. Roger Burdell's restaurant-with-rooms overlooking churchyard, adjacent to Ferrari garage. 5 mins' walk to Market Sq. Quirky Mediterranean-style decor; lounge with painted floral motif; many beams. Carpark. No smoking. Short Italian-influenced dinner menu. 6 bedrooms: single £70–£87.50, double £85–£115, suite £105–£140. Breakfast: continental £6, English £10.50.

LYME REGIS Dorset   Map 1
Alexandra Hotel, Pound Street DT7 3HZ. *Tel* (01297) 442010, *fax* (01297) 443229, *e-mail* enquiries@hotelalexandra.co.uk. In superb hillside position near The Cobb, Mr and Mrs Haskins's large Georgian hotel: old-fashioned style; welcoming to families and dogs. Lounge, conservatory; restaurant serving traditional English cooking; well-kept garden for afternoon teas. Beach 300 yds. 27 bedrooms (variable; best ones overlook sea). Parking in forecourt (sometimes a squeeze). B&B: single from £50, double £85–£122.

MANCHESTER   **Map 4**
Crescent Gate, Park Crescent, Victoria Park, Rusholme M14 5RE.
Tel (0161) 224 0672, *fax* (0161) 257 2822. Friendly guest house, run
for many years by Terry Hughes, in quiet crescent 2 miles S of city
centre, just off busy Wilmslow Rd, handy for university, airport.
Dining room. Carpark. 25 bedrooms, most with facilities *en suite*.
B&B: single £30–£38.50, double £52. Evening meal available.
Le Meridien Victoria and Albert, Water Street M3 4JQ. *Tel*
(0161) 832 1188, *fax* (0161) 834 2484, *e-mail* gm1452@forte.hotels.
com. Conversion of two riverside warehouses, full of Mancunian
character – decor themed to productions by Granada TV studios next
door. Restaurant, café, pub; conference room; health club. Wing for
lone female guests (with CCTV, windows impossible to open from
outside, special toiletries, etc). 156 rooms: single/double £165–£195,
suite £350–£450.

Further afield
Alderley Edge Hotel, Macclesfield Road, Alderley Edge SK9 7BJ.
Tel (01625) 583033, *fax* (01625) 586343, *e-mail* sales@
alderley-edge-hotel.co.uk. 14 miles S of Manchester; 7 miles from
airport; city centre 20 mins by car/taxi. Red sandstone house (former
home of wealthy cotton merchant), much extended. Classic French
cooking in popular restaurant. Close to famous beauty spot, The
Edge (stunning views of Cheshire Plain); 7 National Trust properties
nearby. 46 bedrooms (deluxe ones have whirlpool bath): single
£99.50–£115, double £115–£135, suite from £135. Breakfast: continental £7.50, English £8.50.
Etrop Grange, Thorley Lane, Manchester Airport, Greater
Manchester M90 4EG. *Tel* (0161) 499 0500, *fax* (0161) 499 0790.
Georgian Grade II listed country house, much extended, 12 miles
from city centre (airport and road noise). Edwardian decor; antique
and repro furniture; some original architectural features. Extensive
function facilities. Friendly staff. Light meals and snacks all day;
restaurant specialises in fish dishes. 40 bedrooms. B&B: single £121,
double £142–£152, suite £162.
Hazeldean, 467 Bury New Road, Kersal, Salford, Greater
Manchester M7 3NE. *Tel* (0161) 792 6667, *fax* (0161) 792 6668.
Graham Chadwick's guest house in Victorian house in residential
area of industrial city (painted by LS Lowry), 2½ miles W of central
Manchester. Pretty garden; carpark. 21 rooms. B&B: single
£35–£42, double £47–£53.
Springfield, 99 Station Road, Marple, Greater Manchester SK6 6PA.
Tel (0161) 449 0721, *fax* (0161) 449 0766. In attractive dormitory
town, 11 miles SE of Manchester. Mr and Mrs Giannecchini's small,
friendly Victorian hotel, 5 mins' walk from station (regular services
to city); 25 mins' drive from airport, 10 mins from Stockport.
Carpark. 7 bedrooms. B&B: single £40, double £55.
Stanneylands, Stanneylands Road, Wilmslow SK9 4EY. *Tel*
(01625) 525225, *fax* (01625) 537282, *e-mail* gordon.beech@
the-stanneylands-hotel.co.uk. Beech family's Edwardian country
house. Central Manchester 12 miles, airport 3 miles. Smart country

house decor. Sophisticated Franco-British cooking in panelled restaurant. Beautiful gardens. Much business trade during week. 32 rooms: single £88, double £98–£118. Breakfast: continental £7.50, English £10.50.

MARLBOROUGH Wiltshire   Map 2
Ivy House, High Street, SN8 1HJ. *Tel* (01672) 515333, *fax* (01672) 515338, *e-mail* ivy.house@btconnet.com. Formerly Marlborough Academy (built as boys' school by Earl of Aylesbury in 1707), creeper-covered Grade II listed Georgian building, owned and run by Josephine Scott and David Ball (the chef) for 11 years. "Kind reception; excellent service." Bar, lounge; conference facilities. Conventional decor and furnishings. English cooking in *Garden* restaurant; *Options* restaurant serves light meals/snacks. Courtyard; sun terrace. 29 bedrooms: smartest in main house, some in purpose-built wing, simplest in guest house annexe; 8 no-smoking. B&B: single £47.50–£85, double £60–£110.

MIDHURST West Sussex   Map 2
Spread Eagle, South Street GU29 9NH. *Tel* (01730) 816911, *fax* (01730) 815668. Famous 15th-century coaching inn, whitewashed, pantiled, with exposed brickwork, beams, antiques. Flower-filled conservatory lounge (light meals served). Good modern cooking in restaurant with inglenook fireplace, popular locally for Sun lunch. Serious health spa: swimming pool, sauna, steam room, gym, massage, etc. Landscaped garden with roses. 36 bedrooms, some beamed, some panelled. B&B: single from £95, double from £125. Set dinner £35; full alc £38–£46. *The Angel* (28 bedrooms), close by, is under same ownership.

MILTON KEYNES Buckinghamshire   Map 2
Different Drummer, 94 High Street, Stony Stratford MK11 1AH. *Tel* (01908) 564733, *fax* (01908) 260646. NW of centre, in old village absorbed into the new town, 15th-century coaching inn with Georgian façade, refurbished interior. Italian/English cooking in panelled restaurant, *Al Tamborista*; fish in *Umbrellas* restaurant, adjacent. 14 bedrooms. B&B: single £67, double £77.

NANTWICH Cheshire   Map 3
Rookery Hall, Worleston, Nantwich CW5 6DQ. *Tel* (01270) 610016, *fax* (01270) 626027. Georgian mansion, later transformed into small continental-style château. 38-acre grounds on Weaver River, with lake, fountain, tennis, croquet, fishing. Sumptuous decor. Modern European cooking in mahogany-panelled restaurant with open fire. Conference suite in former stables. Crewe 5 miles, M6 8 miles. 45 bedrooms, many large. B&B: single £95, double from £110. Set dinner £27.50.

NORWICH Norfolk   Map 2
Norfolk Mead, Church Lane, Coltishall NR12 7DN. *Tel* (01603) 737531, *fax* (01603) 737521. Don and Jill Fleming's

Georgian manor house, ½ mile from conservation village 7 miles N of Norwich, 12 miles from coast. In 12-acre grounds on River Bure (with garden, large swimming pool, pasture, fishing, yacht basin). Modern British cooking, sometimes with Oriental accent, much use of local fish and produce. Lounge, bar. 9 bedrooms. B&B: single £65–£90, double £75–£110.

NOTTINGHAM Nottinghamshire   Map 2
Hotel des Clos, Old Lenton Lane NG7 2SA. *Tel* (0115) 986 6566, *fax* (0115) 986 0343. Conversion of Victorian farm buildings on the banks of the River Trent. Peaceful surroundings, although 5 mins from city centre and close to M1. 3 miles from station. New owners since May 1999, the Ralley family, have extensively refurbished. New chef, Satwant Bains, has worked at *Michelin*-starred *Jardin des Sens,* Montpellier. 8 bedrooms: single/double £75–£80, suite £100–£125.

OXFORD Oxfordshire   Map 2
Galaxie, 180 Banbury Road OX2 7BT. *Tel* (01865) 515688, *fax* (01865) 556824, *e-mail* oxlink.couk/oxford/hotels/galaxie.html. Gwyn and Mair Harries-Jones's ivy-clad red brick B&B hotel, recently refurbished. "Bright and cheerful." In Summertown (residential area). Pleasant breakfast in large conservatory. Garden. Parking. 30 bedrooms (some small). B&B: single £42–£52, double £66–£99.
Marlborough House, 321 Woodstock Road, OX2 7NY. *Tel* (01865) 311321, *fax* (01865) 515329, *e-mail* enquiries@ marlbhouse.win-uk.net. Purpose-built small hotel in north Oxford. 1½ miles (an easy bus ride) from centre. No dining room, but all rooms have kitchenette. 10 mins' walk to good choice of restaurants. No garden. Parking in side street. 16 bedrooms. B&B: single £65, double £73.
Old Bank Hotel, 92–94 High Street OX1 4BN. *Tel* (01865) 799599, *fax* (01865) 799598, *e-mail* info@oldbank-hotel.co.uk. Central, with stylish public rooms (contemporary feel), newly converted by Jeremy Mogford of *Old Parsonage*, Oxford (see main entry). Collection of 20th-century British art. Large bar/grill, *Quod*; 2 reading rooms, terrace for summer eating, roof terrace with fine views. Parking. Service thought variable this year. 44 bedrooms (some small): single £135, double £155–£225, suite £300.

Further afield:
Studley Priory, Horton-cum-Studley OX33 1AZ. *Tel* (01865) 351203, *fax* (01865) 351613, *e-mail* res@studley-priory. co.uk. Large Elizabethan house, owned by Parke family, in 13-acre wooded grounds in village 7 miles NE of Oxford. Good views to W of Cotswolds, to E of Chilterns and Vale of Aylesbury. Elegant drawing room, restaurant, oak-panelled bar. 17 large, comfortable bedrooms. Grass tennis court, croquet. B&B: single £105–£175, double £140–£250, suite £275 (English breakfast £8 extra).
The Feathers, Market Street, Woodstock OX20 1SX. *Tel* (01993) 812291, *fax* (01993) 813158, *e-mail* enquiries@feathers.

co.uk. With new owners (Empire Ventures) this year: old coaching inn and neighbouring Georgian houses, close to Blenheim Palace (15 mins' drive from Oxford). Charming, rambling interior: antiques, paintings, fresh flowers; corridors, lots of steps. Drawing room, study, bar, restaurant; function facilities; courtyard. 22 bedrooms. B&B: single £105–£170, double £130–£185, suite £235–£290. Lunch £17.50–£21. Set dinner £48.

PLYMOUTH Devon   Map 1
Bowling Green Hotel, 9–10 Osborne Place, Lockyer Street PL1 2PU. *Tel* (01752) 209090, *fax* (01752) 209092. David and Paddy Dawkins' budget B&B, opposite Drake's bowling green on the Hoe, handy for Barbican area (with restaurants). Small front and rear gardens. Seafront 100 yds; ferry 5 mins' drive. 12 simple bedrooms. B&B: single £52, double £62–£78.
Invicta, 11–12 Osborne Place, Lockyer Street, The Hoe PL1 2PU. *Tel* (01752) 664997, *fax* (01752) 664994. Family-run budget guest house opposite the Hoe; 5 mins' walk from centre, Barbican. Secure carpark. Plain decor. "Attentive but unobtrusive service. Good value." Good, fresh, Mediterranean-style cooking. 23 bedrooms (3 family), most with facilities *en suite*. B&B: single £52, double £62.

Further afield:
Kitley House, Kitley Estate, Yealmpton PL8 2NN. *Tel* (01752) 881555, *fax* (01752) 881667, *e-mail* reservations@ kitleyhousehotel.com. Large old grey stone house in 30-acre estate, 7 miles E of Plymouth. Lounge, restaurant, bar (piped music). Function facilities. "Good dinner; breakfast less good." 20 bedrooms (some large). B&B: single £45–£110, double £60–£120, suite £90–£150. Set lunch £12.50, dinner £22.50.

PORTSMOUTH Hampshire   Map 2
The Beaufort, 71 Festing Road, Southsea PO4 0NQ. *Tel* (023) 9282 3707, *fax* (023) 9287 0270, *e-mail* enquiries@ beauforthotel.co.uk. Small hotel in residential area, 1-min walk from sea, owned by Penny and Tony Freemantle for 12 years. Lounge, bar; restaurant, serving "good home-cooked fare". Garden, carpark. 20 bedrooms (8 no-smoking). B&B: single £48–£55, double £65–£75.
Seacrest 12 South Parade, Southsea PO5 2JB. *Tel* (023) 9273 3192, *fax* (023) 9283 2523. Seafront hotel (good views) opposite D-Day museum. Resident proprietress, Antoinette Stretton. Simple decor. Comfortable lounge with leather seats. Bar, restaurant (traditional dishes, eg, roast lamb, game pie). 28 bedrooms. B&B: double £60–£72.

READING Berkshire   Map 2
The Upcross, 68 Berkeley Avenue RG1 6HY. *Tel* (0118) 9590796, *fax* (0118) 9576517, *e-mail* mrscecil@upcrosshotel.co.uk. Mrs Cecil's red brick house in large garden (ample parking), 10 mins from centre. "Lifestyle cuisine", using organic and low-fat

ingredients, in restaurant with open fire. Light lunches. Conference suite. 20 bedrooms. B&B: single £72.50–£77.50, double £82.50.

REIGATE Surrey   **Map 2**
The Cranleigh, 41 West Street RH2 9BL. *Tel* (01737) 223417, *fax* (01737) 223734. Carol and Pino Bussandri's pleasant hotel at end of high street, in lovely garden with swimming pool, tennis. *Garden Room* restaurant (weekday dinners only) serves Italian cooking; atmospheric conservatory for functions. Friendly feel. 10 neat bedrooms. B&B: single £45–£75, double £90.

SALISBURY Wiltshire   **Map 2**
Leena's, 50 Castle Road SP1 3RL. *Tel/fax* (01722) 335419. Finnish-born Leena Street's budget B&B in Edwardian house, all pine and white lace. Lounge with books, board games. Good breakfasts. Pretty garden. Parking. On busy Amesbury road. Double glazing. Pleasant 15 mins' walk along river to centre; park, leisure centre nearby. 6 simple bedrooms, most no-smoking. B&B: double £44–£46.
Milford Hall 206 Castle Street SP1 3TE. *Tel* (01722) 417411, *fax* (01722) 419444, *e-mail* milfordhallhotel@cs.com. At uninteresting north end of town, close to A30, 10 mins' walk from centre. Georgian house in landscaped gardens. 31 bedrooms, most (plain but comfortable) in modern extension. Parking easy. B&B: single £85–£98, double £95–£108; D,B&B: single £100–£113, double £125–£145.
Red Lion, Milford Street SP1 2AN. *Tel* (01722) 323334, *fax* (01722) 325756, *e-mail* reception@the-redlion.co.uk. Michael Maidment's historic coaching inn (Best Western), in city centre, with creepered courtyard, clock collection. Popular restaurant, "cooked breakfast particularly good". 54 bedrooms, "comfortable and clean", along rambling corridors. Parking awkward. Room: single £84, double £120. Breakfast: continental £5, English £9.
Rose and Crown, Harnham Road SP2 8JQ. *Tel* (01722) 399955, *fax* (01722) 339816. 13th-century half-timbered inn on River Avon, short walk from centre. 28 bedrooms, some in Tudor wing (old beams), modern ones in garden wing (cathedral views). No-frills cooking in riverside restaurant. Room: single £105, double £145. Breakfast £9.50.

Further afield:
Little Langford Farmhouse, Little Langford SP3 4NP. *Tel* (01722) 790205, *fax* (01722) 790086. Patricia Helyer's B&B in spacious Victorian farmhouse; 8 miles N of Salisbury, 2 miles from A36. Commanding position in Wylye valley, on Earl of Salisbury's estate. Farm includes pedigree herd of Friesian cows. Relaxed atmosphere; children welcomed. Billiard room, lounge. 3 simple bedrooms. B&B: £40–£50.

SCARBOROUGH North Yorkshire   **Map 4**
Interludes, 32 Princess Street YO11 1QR. *Tel* (01723) 360513, *fax* (01723) 368597, *e-mail* interludes@cwcom.net. Grade II listed

Georgian house, near castle, harbour: now a guest house with theatrical memorabilia, run by theatre aficionados Ian Grundy and Bob Harris. Discount at nearby NCP carpark. Continental, light or English breakfast. 4-course evening meal at 6 pm (£12 limited choice, communally served). 5 no-smoking bedrooms. B&B: single £27–£32, double £47–£55.

Tall Storeys, 131 Longwestgate, Old Town YO11 1RQ. *Tel/fax* (01723) 373696. Colin Milne's Grade II listed Regency house, overlooking castle, harbour. Somewhat cramped and "over-furnished". Dining room, bar and conservatory; light meals can be provided. 7 no-smoking bedrooms, some with sea views. B&B: £28–£32. Evening meal, by arrangement, £16.

SHEFFIELD South Yorkshire   **Map 4**
Hotel Bristol, Blonk Street S1 2AU. *Tel* (0114) 220 4000, *fax* (0114) 220 3900, *e-mail* sheffield@bhg.co.uk. "Inexpensive, unpretentious", near station: unprepossessing exterior; cheerful, colourful modern interior. *Picasso* restaurant liked – "someone in the kitchen cares about food". NCP carpark adjacent, free to residents. 112 bedrooms from £59.50. Breakfast: continental £5.95, English £7.95.

Westbourne House, 25 Westbourne Road S10 2QQ. *Tel* (0114) 266 0109, *fax* (0114) 266 7778. Michael and Christine Ratcliffe's B&B hotel in Broomhill conservation area, near universities, botanical gardens; city centre 1¼ miles. Victorian/Edwardian decor. Good breakfasts, cooked to order. Pleasant terraced garden; off-street parking. 9 bedrooms (some themed, Chinese, etc). B&B: single £38–£58, double £70–£78.

Whitley Hall, Elliott Lane, Grenoside S35 3NR. *Tel* (0114) 245 4444, *fax* (0114) 245 5414. 4½ miles N of centre. Fearn family's part Elizabethan house: mullioned windows, flagstone floors, balustraded gallery, oak panelling, country house decor. In 30-acre landscaped grounds: gardens, 2 lakes, croquet, putting, peacocks. English cooking in large restaurant. 19 bedrooms. B&B: single £70–£80, double £90–£100.

SIDMOUTH Devon   **Map 1**
The Belmont, The Esplanade EX10 8RX. *Tel* (01395) 512555, *fax* (01395) 579101, *e-mail* info@belmont-hotel.co.uk. Brend family's traditional seafront hotel, attracting mature clientele in winter, families in summer. Large public rooms. Formal dress required in no-smoking restaurant (pianist, dancing Sat). Garden, putting green. Access to indoor/outdoor swimming pools, tennis, gym, etc, at adjacent sister hotel, *The Victoria*. 51 bedrooms; best have balcony, sea view. D,B&B £66–£119.

Hotel Riviera, The Esplanade EX10 8AY. *Tel* (01395) 515201, *fax* (01395) 577775, *e-mail* enquiries@hotelriviera.co.uk. White bow-windowed Regency hotel, owned by Wharton family for 21 years. Terrace with tables, parasols, plants in urns, overlooking seafront road and beach. Large lounge, piano bar, smart restaurant. 27 well-appointed bedrooms. B&B £67–£103, D,B&B £77–£113.

The Victoria, The Esplanade EX10 8RY. *Tel* (01395) 512651, *fax* (01395) 579154. Prominent purpose-built (in 1903) holiday hotel on seafront. 5-acre grounds: swimming pool complex, tennis, putting green. Also indoor swimming pool, sauna, billiards, gym, table tennis, beauty salon. Traditional hotel decor. "Good value, warm welcome, good comfort; excellent food with affordable wine list." 40 bedrooms; most have view, some have French windows on to private balcony. D,B&B £75–£128.

SOUTHAMPTON Hampshire   Map 2
Highfield House, Highfield Lane, Portswood SO17 1AQ. *Tel* (023) 8035 9955, *fax* (023) 8058 3910, *e-mail* highfield@ zoffanyhotels.co.uk. Purpose-built hotel on outskirts of city, a short drive from Ocean Village. Restaurant, conference rooms, mini-gym. Parking. Newly refurbished. 66 bedrooms. B&B: single £85, double £90–£97.50.

STAMFORD Lincolnshire   Map 2
Garden House, St Martin's PE9 2LP. *Tel* (01780) 763359, *fax* (01780) 763339, *e-mail* gardenhousehotel@stamford60.freeserve. co.uk. 18th-century family house, now a 20-bedroom hotel close to centre, owned and run by Chris and Irene Quinn. Home cooking in dining room hung with Belgian tapestries. Bar and conservatory overlook large garden. Function/wedding facilities. B&B: single £60–£75, double £85–£95.

STOKE-ON-TRENT Staffordshire   Map 3
Haydon House, Haydon Street, Basford ST4 6JD. *Tel* (01782) 711311, *fax* (01782) 717470. Red brick Victorian mansion (with original features, collection of antique clocks), run by Machin family for over 40 years, offering good value. In quiet residential street close to centre, but overlooking countryside. Conference/function/wedding facilities. *Townhouse* restaurant serves "adequate, unfussy" cooking. 30 bedrooms (some in 2 adjacent houses): single £55–£70, double £65–£80. Breakfast £6. Set meals £15.90.

TRESCO Isles of Scilly   Map 1
New Inn, Isles of Scilly TR24 0QQ. *Tel* (01720) 422844, *fax* (01720) 423200, *e-mail* newinn@tresco.co.uk. Run by Graham and Sue Shone: small inn on beautiful, car-free island in Gulf Stream. Restaurant, bar (focal point for islanders). Children welcomed. Swimming pool. 14 bedrooms. D,B&B £60–£92.

WELWYN GARDEN CITY Hertfordshire   Map 2
Tewin Bury Farm, nr Welwyn AL6 0JB. *Tel* (01438) 717793/ 840793, *fax* (01438) 840440, *e-mail* hotel@tewinbury.co.uk. On 400-acre working farm on River Mimram: Angela and Vaughan Williams's hotel with "very good food, helpful staff, good value", much business/function/outside meal trade. 25 bedrooms in smartly converted barns and chicken sheds, around gravelled courtyard/ carpark. Attractive lounge with inglenook fireplace. Large restaurant in converted stables; small dining room. Landscaping of grounds in progress. B&B: single £70–£99, double £84–£99.

WHITBY North Yorkshire   **Map 4**
Dunsley Hall, Dunsley YO21 3TL. *Tel* (01947) 893437, *fax*
(01947) 893505. Carol and Bill Ward's stone, mullion-windowed
early 20th-century house (built by shipping magnate) in hamlet
3 miles NW of Whitby. "Very quiet; delicious breakfasts." Original
oak panelling; some original furnishings. 18 bedrooms, some large,
with antiques and views of garden and fields. Lounge, bistro/bar, no-
smoking restaurant (background music evenings), traditional cooking. Indoor swimming pool, sauna, mini-gym. 4-acre gardens:
putting green, croquet, tennis. Sea 1 mile. B&B £54.85–£94.85.
Saxonville, Ladysmith Avenue YO21 3HX. *Tel* (01947) 602631, *fax*
(01947) 820523, *e-mail* saxonville@onyxnet.co.uk. On West Cliff,
400 yards back from seafront, near cliff lift: converted red brick
terrace houses, run since 1946 by Newton family owners. Efficient
staff, friendly feel, good conventional food. Bar, lounge, spacious
restaurant. 24 bedrooms (plain modern decor). B&B: single £37.50,
double £75.

WINDSOR Berkshire   **Map 2**
Castle Hotel, High Street, Windsor SL4 1LJ. *Tel* (0870) 400 8300,
fax (01753) 830244, *e-mail* heritagehotels_windsor.castle@
forte-hotels.com. White Georgian building (a Forte heritage hotel) in
centre. Comfortable public rooms "well provided with sofas, chairs,
quiet corners". Restaurant, café, bar. "Good dinners; exceptional
breakfasts." Carpark. 90 bedrooms: single £150–£170, double
£175–£215, suite £235–£265.

WOLVERHAMPTON West Midlands   **Map 3**
Ely House, 53 Tettenhall Road WV3 9NB. *Tel* (01902) 311311, *fax*
(01902) 421098. Dark brick 18th-century former private school, with
new owners this year, June and Catherine Sanders. On A41, just off
town centre ring road, near shopping centre. 18 bedrooms. B&B:
single £44, double £54.

WORCESTER Worcestershire   **Map 3**
Diglis House, Severn Street WR1 2NF. *Tel* (01905) 353518, *fax*
(01905) 767772. Georgian house by River Severn, near cathedral.
Conservatory dining room; lounge with open fire. Terraced garden.
"Helpful staff." Parking. 26 bedrooms (some have "superb view").
B&B: single £60–£95, double £75–£105, suite £140–£160.

YORK North Yorkshire   **Map 4**
Dean Court, Duncombe Place YO1 2EF. *Tel* (01904) 625082, *fax*
(01904) 620305, *e-mail* deancourt@btconnect.com. Best Western
member, recently refurbished, opposite minster. Friendly staff, good
facilities for children. Traditional restaurant serving adequate meals;
conservatory tea room. Free valet parking. 40 bedrooms (12 no-
smoking). B&B: single £80, double £100–£140, suite £155–£170.
Hobbits, 9 St Peter's Grove, Clifton YO3 6AQ. *Tel* (01904) 624538,
fax (01904) 651765. In quiet cul-de-sac, B&B run by Rosemary
Miller in her Edwardian family home. Short walk to centre. 6

spacious bedrooms. Excellent breakfast. Off-street parking. B&B: single £35, double £70.

Holmwood House, 114 Holgate Road YO24 4BB. *Tel* (01904) 626183, *fax* (01904) 670899, *e-mail* holmwood.house@ dial.pipex.com. Owned by Rosie Blanksby and Bill Pitt: 10 mins' walk from Micklegate entrance to city walls, on busy A59, but backing on to pretty square. 2 listed houses, converted to no-smoking B&B. Parking. 14 bedrooms (rear ones have view of minster). B&B single/double £50–£90.

The Judges' Lodging, 9 Lendal YO2 2AQ. *Tel* (01904) 638733, *fax* (01904) 679947. 18th-century Grade I listed building in pedestrianised area (close to minster), with new owners this year, Mr and Mrs Mason. Traditional decor. Residents' lounge, bar; simple meals in brasserie. 14 no-smoking bedrooms, 1 reputedly once occupied by Prince Albert. Secure carpark. B&B: single £75–£85, double £100–£115, suite £130–£150.

WALES

ABERYSTWYTH Ceredigion   Map 3
Belle Vue Royal, The Promenade SY23 2BA. *Tel* (01970) 617558, *fax* (01970) 612190. Two-storey seafront hotel owned and very personally run by Alan and Marilyn Davies. Dining room, 3 bars, conference room. "High standard of service; good food." Carpark. 37 bedrooms (34 with facilities *en suite*, some with sea view). B&B: single £58, double £87–£98.

CARDIFF   Map 3
Churchills, Cardiff Road, Llandaff CF5 2AD. *Tel* (029) 2056 2372, *fax* (029) 2056 8347, *e-mail* reservations@churchillshotel.co.uk. In W area, near Llandaff Fields and cathedral, large white stuccoed house owned by Brains, the family brewery. Bar meals; traditional/modern cooking in restaurant. Function facilities. 22 bedrooms; 13 mews apartments. B&B: single £75, double £115.

The Town House, 70 Cathedral Road, CF1 9LL. *Tel* (029) 2023 9399, *fax* (029) 2022 3214, *e-mail* thetownhouse@msn.com. B&B in Victorian Gothic town house in conservation area by castle, with American owners, Iris and Bart Zuzik. "High standard of housekeeping; good breakfast." Secure parking. 7 simple bedrooms. B&B: single from £39.50, double from £49.50.

Walton House, 37 Victoria Road, Penarth, CF64 3HY. *Tel* (029) 2070 7782, *fax* (029) 2071 1012. Vanessa and Gino Damiani's spacious Edwardian guest house in residential area. 10 mins' walk from seafront; 4 miles from centre. Plain decor. Home-cooked evening meal. 12 bedrooms. B&B: single £30, double £45.

ST DAVID'S Pembrokeshire   Map 3
Warpool Court, St David's SA62 6BN. *Tel* (01437) 720300, *fax* (01437) 720676, *e-mail* warpool@enterprise.net. Peter Trier's large grey stone hotel in magnificent setting above St Bride's Bay. Decorated throughout with unique hand-painted tiles. Sunny lounge,

gloomy bar. 7-acre grounds: covered swimming pool (not always open); tennis, croquet, table-tennis, gym, sauna; beaches nearby. 25 bedrooms. B&B £56–£83

SWANSEA   Map 3
Hillcrest House, 1 Higher Lane, Mumbles SA3 4NS. *Tel* (01792) 363700, *fax* (01792) 363768. On edge of town (15 mins to centre). With new owners this year, Liz and David Bowen, and 7 themed bedrooms (Welsh, Scottish, African, Canadian, etc), some on busy road (effective double glazing). Terrace, small garden. Refurbished restaurant, *The Wall*, serves eclectic food. B&B: single £48, double £60–£80.

Windsor Lodge, Mount Pleasant, SA1 6EG. *Tel* (01792) 642158/65 2744, *fax* (01792) 648996. Ron and Pam Rumble's Grade II listed sky-blue 18th-century house close to centre, now in 27th year. Modern decor. "Very pleasant; helpful staff, good bedrooms and public rooms." Simple modern cooking; vegetarians welcomed. 19 bedrooms. B&B: single £55, double £65.

SCOTLAND

ABERDEEN   Map 5
Ardoe House, South Deeside Road, Blairs AB12 5YP. *Tel* (01224) 867355, *fax* (01224) 861283, *e-mail* info@ardoe. macdonald-hotels.co.uk. 4 miles E of centre. Baronial granite mansion, much extended, with original features (impressive hall, much panelling); mature grounds, views of River Dee. 108 bedrooms (40 no-smoking). *À la carte* restaurant; less formal meals in *Soapies Lounge*. New leisure club (swimming pool, beauty treatments, etc). B&B: single £115, double £155.

Atholl, 54 King's Gate AB15 4YN. *Tel* (01224) 323505, *fax* (01224) 321555, *e-mail* info@atholl-aberdeen.co.uk. In West End, 5 miles S of airport, granite house, managed by co-owner Gordon Sinclair. Bay-windowed lounge with views of city; varied menu in restaurant; function/conference facilities. Carpark. 35 no-smoking bedrooms. B&B: single £71–£81, double £89.

Craiglynn, 36 Fonthill Road AB11 6UJ. *Tel* (01224) 584050, *fax* (01224) 212225, *e-mail* craiglynn@compuserve.com. Chris and Hazel Mann's Victorian granite guest house, in residential area between Duthie Park and Union Street. Smoking in lounges only. 9 neat bedrooms. Home-cooked evening meal (£15.95) in panelled, parquet-floored, former billiard room. B&B: single £38–£49.50; double £62.50–£78.

The Marcliffe at Pitfodels, North Deeside Road, Pitfodels AB15 9YA. *Tel* (01224) 861000, *fax* (01224) 868860, *e-mail* reservations@marcliffe.com. In 8-acre landscaped grounds in West End, off A93 Deeside road. Stewart and Sheila Spence's large, white "country house in the city". Good food in smart restaurant and less formal conservatory. Large function facilities. 42 bedrooms (1 adapted for &). B&B: single £145–£165, double £155–£175.

ANNAN Dumfries and Galloway   **Map 5**
Warmanbie, Annan DG12 5LL. *Tel/fax* (01461) 204015, *e-mail*
warmanbiehotel@annan.fsnet.co.uk. Handsome stone Georgian
house, 4 miles E of M74 on B722 towards Annan. Home of Duncan
family since 1953, a hotel and restaurant since 1984; River Annan
(with fishing) flows through 45-acre wooded grounds; old roses in
walled garden. Old-fashioned decor; "friendly service; informal
atmosphere; good meals"; log fires in lounge and dining room. 7 bedrooms. B&B £34–£41.

DUNDEE   **Map 5**
Errolbank, 9 Dalgleish Road DD4 7JN. *Tel/fax* (01382) 462118.
Mike and Agnes Wilson's budget B&B: Victorian villa in quiet area
near river, convenient for centre, colleges, Tay Bridge. Off-
street parking. No smoking. 6 bedrooms. B&B: single £26–£30,
double £44.
Invercarse, 371 Perth Road DD2 1PG. *Tel* (01382) 669231, *fax*
(01382) 644112. On W side of city, near university. Extended
Victorian silk mercer's mansion in large grounds on hill, overlooking
River Tay (Best Western). Large function facilities. 35 bedrooms
(17 no-smoking). B&B: single £68–£78, double £90–£99, suite
£100.
Shaftesbury, 1 Hyndford Street, off Perth Road DD2 1HQ. *Tel*
(01382) 669216, *fax* (01382) 641598, *e-mail* reservations@
shaftesbury-hotel.co.uk. Dennis Smith's former 19th-century jute
baron's mansion on a corner in West End, 5 mins' drive from centre.
Rachel's restaurant; garden room for light meals. Good breakfasts.
12 bedrooms. B&B: single £47–£54, double £58–£68.
Strathdon, 277 Perth Road DD2 1JS. *Tel/fax* (01382) 665648. John
and Mo Melville's Edwardian terrace house, close to university, 1
mile from centre (unlimited parking). 8 bedrooms, some with river
view. B&B: single £25, double £40.

EDINBURGH   **Map 5**
Acer Lodge, 425 Queensferry Road EH4 7NB. *Tel* (0131) 336 2554,
fax (0131) 336 1112, *e-mail* ejohn81068@aol.com. Mr and Mrs
John's no-smoking guest house 10 mins' bus journey from centre.
"Excellent accommodation; guests are well looked after." Carpark. 4
bedrooms with fresh fruit, biscuits, etc. B&B £22.50–£27.50.
Channings, South Learmonth Gardens EH4 1EZ. *Tel*
(0131) 315 2225, *fax* (0131) 332 9631, *e-mail* reserve@channings.
co.uk. On comparatively peaceful cobbled street minutes from
centre: hotel composed of 5 Edwardian town houses; recently
extensively refurbished (owned by Town House Company; see
Bonham, Howard, full entries). Lounge with log fire, panelled
library, stylish bar (light meals all day), conservatory. Contemporary
Scottish cooking in restaurant. 46 bedrooms. B&B: single/double
£125–£198, suite £255.
The Grange, 8 Whitehouse Terrace EH9 2EU. *Tel* (0131) 667 5681,
fax (0131) 668 3300, *e-mail* grange-hotel@edinburgh.net.uk. Large
grey stone baronial house with garden, putting green, 1½ miles from

city centre. Smart country house decor. Hall, library, bar, conservatory/restaurant, small conference room. 15 bedrooms. B&B: single £80, double £100–£160.

Malmaison, 1 Tower Place, Leith EH6 7DB. *Tel* (0131) 468 5000, *fax* (0131) 468 5002, *e-mail* edinburgh@malmaison.com. Converted 19th-century seamen's mission on waterfront at Leith, 1¼ miles from centre. Part of well-established group of contemporary city hotels, with new manager and chef this year. French-style brasserie, café/bar, meeting/private dining room, health suite, "friendly staff". 60 bedrooms (not all have view): double £105–£110, suite £150–£165. Breakfast: continental £8.50, English £10.50. Full alc £30–£35.

Parliament House, 15 Calton Hill EH1 3BJ. *Tel* (0131) 478 4000, *fax* (0131) 478 4001, *e-mail* phhadams@aol.com. A few mins' walk from castle and Princes Street. Georgian façade; smart interior. Spacious lounge/entrance lobby; *MP's Bistro,* serving Scottish breakfast, evening meal. 53 bedrooms: single £90, double £130. Breakfast: continental £6.50, English £9.50.

17 Abercromby Place, 17 Abercromby Place EH3 6LB. *Tel* (0131) 557 8036, *fax* (0131) 558 3453, *e-mail* eirlys.lloyd@ virgin.net. Elegant New Town terrace house, overlooking large tree-filled garden square, 5 mins' walk from Princes Street. Run as Wolsey Lodge by barrister Mrs Eirlys Lloyd. Lounge/library, dining room. No smoking. "Great breakfast." 9 bedrooms. B&B: single £45–£50, double £90–£100. Evening meal by arrangement, £25.

GLASGOW   Map 5
Cathedral House, 28/32 Cathedral Square G4 0XA. *Tel* (0141) 552 3519, *fax* (0141) 552 2444. Just off M8, Scottish baronial house, built 1896 (view of cathedral and Provands Lordship). Restaurant (Scottish traditional/Icelandic "Hot Rocks" cuisine); café/bar; regular live music; function facilities. 8 bedrooms. B&B: single £49, double £69.

INVERNESS Highland   Map 5
Moyness House, 6 Bruce Crescent IV3 5EN. *Tel/fax* (01463) 233836, *e-mail* kayjonesmoyness@msn.com. Jenny and Richard Jones's "meticulously kept" guest house built 1880, in large, attractive garden. 10 mins' walk to centre. Near River Ness and loch. Old-fashioned decor. Sitting room, dining room. 7 bedrooms. B&B £31–£35.

MARYCULTER Aberdeenshire   Map 5
Maryculter House, South Deeside Road AB12 5GB. *Tel* (01224) 732124, *fax* (01224) 733510, *e-mail* maryculter.house. hotel@dial.pipex. Former Templar priory in 5-acre grounds on River Dee, 9 miles W of Aberdeen. Ample public rooms, efficient management. Somewhat functional decor, business-oriented clientele. 23 bedrooms, some on river, with pine furniture, flowery fabrics. Good bar meals, traditional French cuisine in restaurant. B&B: single £70–£115, double £85–£120. Set dinner £29.50.

MELROSE Scottish Borders   **Map 5**
Burts, Market Square, TD6 9PN. *Tel* (01896) 822285, *fax*
(01896) 822870, *e-mail* burtshotel@aol.com. Black-and-white 18th-
century dignitary's home in centre of ancient Border town (some
traffic noise). Personally run by Henderson family for over 25 years.
Formal restaurant; bar (with log fire) popular for meals. Residents'
lounge. Garden. Fishing on Tweed; golf locally. 20 no-smoking bedrooms (some small). B&B: single £50, double £88. Set lunch £20.75,
dinner £27.75.

MOFFAT Dumfries and Galloway   **Map 5**
Auchen Castle, Beattock DG10 9QZ. *Tel* (01683) 300407, *fax*
(01683) 300667, *e-mail* reservations@auchen-castle-hotel.co.uk.
Owned by Keith Parr: imposing grey stone building (Best Western)
in 30-acre grounds, 1 mile from Victorian spa town. Recently extensively refurbished. 15 bedrooms in main house; 11 in Cedar lodge.
B&B £50–£110. Set dinner £21.20.

OBAN Argyll and Bute   **Map 5**
Dungallan House, Gallanach Road PA34 4PD. *Tel* (01631) 563799,
fax (01631) 566711, *e-mail* welcome@dungallanhotel-oban.co.uk.
Half mile from centre: substantial cliff-top Victorian villa, owned by
George and Janice Stewart, in 5-acre grounds with views over Oban
Bay and beyond. Mrs Stewart is chef, using only Scottish ingredients.
Lounge bar, reading room, handsome dining room, 14 bedrooms.
B&B £33–£48. Set meal £19.50–£25.

OLDMELDRUM Aberdeenshire   **Map 5**
Cromlet Hill, South Road AB51 0AB. *Tel* (01651) 872315, *fax*
(01651) 872164. In historic old town, 16 miles (*c.* 30 mins' drive)
NW of Aberdeen, 15 mins from airport. John Page's guest house:
listed neo-classical Georgian mansion (*c.* 1805) in conservation area.
Quiet garden; fine views. 3 bedrooms. B&B £27.50–£32.50.
Communal evening meal by arrangement.
Meldrum House AB51 0AE. *Tel* (01651) 872294, *fax*
(01651) 872464. In 15-acre park and garden, 1½ miles from centre
on A947. Douglas and Eileen Pearson's part 13th-century baronial
house, with antiques, *objets d'art*, ancestral portraits. In large park
with woods and golf course. Conference facilities. Traditional
Scottish cooking. 9 bedrooms. B&B: single £85, double £110–£120.
Set dinner £26.50–£29.

PEEBLES Scottish Borders   **Map 5**
Cringletie House EH45 8PL. *Tel* (01721) 730233, *fax*
(01721) 730244, *e-mail* cringletie@bestloved.com. Pink stone
Victorian baronial mansion, turreted, gabled, recently refurbished. In
28-acre estate in lovely Border countryside 2 miles N of Peebles.
Wonderful views; tennis, putting, croquet, children's play area.
Traditional decor, panelled lounge, restaurant. 13 bedrooms, some up
3 flights (no lift). B&B: single £75–£95, double £150–£180.
Park Hotel, Innerleithen Road EH45 8BA. *Tel* (01721) 720451, *fax*
(01721) 723510. Just outside town, white turreted and gabled house

with views over Border hills. Oak-panelled restaurant (sometimes with "maddening background music"); tartan bar. Guests may use pool, sauna, squash, tennis, and riding facilities at large sister hotel, *Peebles Hotel Hydro*, 700 yds away. No lift. 24 bedrooms. D,B&B £63–£75.

ST ANDREWS Fife Map 5
The Peat Inn, Peat Inn, by Cupar KY15 5LH. *Tel* (01334) 840206, *fax* (01334) 840530. Owned by Patricia and David Wilson, famed for his modern Scottish cooking: old coaching inn with modern residence at crossroads in village 6 miles SW of St Andrews. ½-acre grounds. 8 smart split-level suites. B&B: single £95, double £145.
Rufflets, Strathkinness Low Road KY16 9TX. *Tel* (01334) 472594, *fax* (01334) 478703, *e-mail* reservations@rufflets.co.uk. Built in 1924 and set in 10-acre grounds, Ann Russell's well-established hotel, 1½ miles from famous golf course. Paintings by Sir William Russell Flint. Wedding facilities. Library, meeting room, dining room, informal brasserie. Recently refurbished. 22 bedrooms. B&B: single £95, double £180–£200, suite £220.

THURSO Highland Map 5
Pentland Hotel, Princes Street KW14 7AA. *Tel* (01847) 893202, *fax* (01847) 892761. In centre of most northerly town on British mainland, 5 mins' walk from railway station, 21 miles from Wick airport, 2 miles from ferry to Orkney. Near sea fishing, golf and empty beaches. Half modern, half old building with plain decor; recently refurbished. "Very helpful staff: pleasant restaurant; good bar meals." 42 bedrooms. B&B: single £35, double £60.

NORTHERN IRELAND

BELFAST Map 6
Dukes, 65–67 University Street BT7 1LH. *Tel* (028) 9023 6666, *fax* (028) 9023 7177, *e-mail* info@dukes-hotel.com. 1 mile S of centre, just behind Queen's University. Victorian residence in tree-lined street, well modernised, popular meeting point for business and university people. Refurbished restaurant, 2 bars, gymnasium, function facilities. 21 bedrooms. B&B: single £85, double £110.

Further afield:
The Dunadry, 2 Islandreagh Drive, Dunadry, Co. Antrim BT41 2HA. *Tel* (028) 9443 2474, *fax* (028) 9443 3767, *e-mail* mooneyhotelgroup@talk21.com. 15 miles NW of Belfast, 4 miles SE of Antrim, just off M2 motorway; 5 miles NE of Belfast airport. Set amid quiet countryside, unusual modern white building, now fairly swish hotel, much used for functions. Impressive public rooms; bedrooms with Scandinavian feel; good restaurant (vast breakfast). 10-acre grounds with country club, free to residents (indoor pool, spa bath, solarium, beauty salon); croquet, cycling, trout-fishing. 67 bedrooms: single £95–£120, double £120–£140. Full Irish breakfast £8.95.

The Old Inn, 15 Main Street, Crawfordsburn, Co. Down BT19 lJH. *Tel* (028) 9185 3255, *fax* (028) 9185 2775, *e-mail* info@ theoldinn.com. In village 10 miles E of Belfast, 3 miles W of Bangor, 1 mile from sea. Historic inn renovated in fancy style: much wood panelling, chintz, pastels; canopied 4-posters; quaint honeymoon cottage. Bistro; conservatory-style restaurant, *1614*, serving seafood (set dinner £23). Function facilities. 32 bedrooms. B&B: single/double £70–£90; cottage £150.

THE REPUBLIC OF IRELAND

DUBLIN   **Map 6**
Aberdeen Lodge, 53–55 Park Avenue, Ailesbury Road, Dublin 4. *Tel* (01) 283 8155, *fax* (01) 283 7877, *e-mail* aberdeen@iol.ie. In exclusive Ballsbridge neighbourhood: B&B (Relais du Silence) in 3-storey house with spacious lounge, garden, carpark. DART to city centre in 7 mins. Stylish modern interior; spacious lounge, dining room. 20 bedrooms (some large). B&B: single IR£70–£85, double IR£90–£119. Associated hotel, *Merrion Hall*, is close by.

Albany House, 84 Harcourt Street, Dublin 2. *Tel* (01) 475 1092, *fax* (01) 475 1093, *e-mail* albany@indigo.ie. Central, off St Stephen's Green, Richard Byrne's Georgian house. Traditional decor, good breakfasts, pleasant staff. 33 bedrooms (quietest ones at rear; some are small). B&B: single IR£60, double IR£100.

Brooks, 59–62 Drury Street, Dublin 2. *Tel* (01) 670 4000, *fax* (01) 670 4455, *e-mail* reservations@brookshotel.ie. Comfortable, classy and central. Club-style decor, glass lifts. 75 well-equipped bedrooms: single IR£125–£145, double IR£165–£185, suite IR£220. Breakfast: continental IR£8.50, Irish IR£10.95.

Butlers Town House, 44 Lansdowne Road, Dublin 4. *Tel* (01) 667 4022, *fax* (01) 667 3960, *e-mail* info@butlers-hotel.com. Manager Chris Vos runs this B&B in Victorian house in Ballsbridge "embassy belt". Smart drawing room, conservatory for breakfast. No restaurant, but room-service meals or transport to restaurant of sister hotel, *Longfield's* (see below). Small walled garden. Carpark. 19 bedrooms, some on ground floor. B&B: single £86–£99, double £123–£148.

Kilronan House 70 Adelaide Road, Dublin 2. *Tel* (01) 475 5266, *fax* (01) 478 2841. More than 30 years as a guest house, near St Stephen's Green, Trinity College, etc. "Spotless, quiet, friendly; great breakfast." TV lounge, wine licence. 12 bedrooms. B&B: single IR£55, double IR£90.

Longfield's, Fitzwilliam Street Lower, Dublin 2. *Tel* (01) 676 1367, *fax* (01) 676 1542. Select hotel formed from 2 Georgian houses. Elegant furnishings, attractive lounge. Good food in basement restaurant, *Number Ten*. 26 bedrooms. B&B: single IR£80–£95, double IR£110–£140, suite IR£150–£160.

The Morgan, 10 Fleet Street, Temple Bar, Dublin 2. *Tel* (01) 679 3939, *fax* (01) 679 3946, *e-mail* morganhtl@iol.ie. Stylishly minimalist, modern hotel in lively area. Beechwood furniture, contemporary Irish paintings. Restaurant/bar, *All Sports Café* (pasta, salads, etc). 65 bedrooms (with CD-player, state-of-the-art telecommunications): single IR£105, double IR£130. Breakfast £7.

Number 31, Leeson Close, Dublin 2. *Tel* (01) 676 5011, *fax* (01) 676 2929, *e-mail* number31@iol.ie. Owners Noel and Deirdre Comer run this B&B in 2 buildings in leafy mews (lots of steps) in Georgian Dublin, near St Stephen's Green. Former home of architect Sam Stephenson. French antiques, Oriental rugs. Huge conservatory for breakfast (communally served). 20 bedrooms (some large): single IR£85, double IR£110–£130.

Raglan Lodge, 10 Raglan Road (off Pembroke Road), Dublin 4. *Tel* (01) 660 6697, *fax* (01) 660 6781. In tree-lined street in residential Ballsbridge, 1 mile SE of centre: Helen Moran's above-average guest house in restored Victorian mansion. Attractive decor, some antiques. Award-winning breakfasts. Small garden. Secure carpark. 7 bedrooms. B&B IR£40–£65.

Trinity Lodge, 12 South Frederick Street, Dublin 2. *Tel* (01) 679 5044/5182/5184, *fax* (01) 679 5223, *e-mail* trinitylodge@tinet.ie. Georgian town house in quiet street adjacent to Trinity College. Bright colours, modern pictures. 13 bedrooms. B&B: single IR£60–£87.50, double IR£95–£120, suite IR£160.

Further afield:

Ashbrook House, River Road, Ashtown, Castleknock, Dublin 15. *Tel* (01) 838 5660, *fax* (01) 838 5660. Eve and Stan Mitchell's comfortable, quiet Georgian house. 10 mins' drive from centre (4 miles), airport. Large grounds: walled garden, grass tennis court. 6 no-smoking bedrooms. B&B: single IR£40, double IR£60.

KILLARNEY Co. Kerry   **Map 6**
Lake Hotel, Muckross Road, Killarney. *Tel* (064) 31035, *fax* (064) 31902, *e-mail* lakehotel@tinet.ie. 1 mile NW of town, large white building on shore of Lough Leane; family run, with cheerful atmosphere. Views of mountains, floodlit 12th-century castle. Spacious public rooms: lounge with open fires, traditional Irish entertainment in bar. Tennis, golf, fishing; scenic trips in horse-drawn carriage. 82 bedrooms. B&B IR£33–£50.

Alphabetical list of hotels

(S) indicates a Shortlist entry

A

Abbey Penzance 214
Abbey Court London (S) 516
Abbey House Abbotsbury 1
Abbey House London (S) 516
Aberdeen Lodge Dublin (S) 534
Academy London (S) 516
Acer Lodge Edinburgh (S) 530
Adelaide Brighton (S) 507
Aherne's Youghal 503
Ainsley House Brighton (S) 507
Airds Port Appin 412
Albannach Lochinver 399
Albany House Dublin (S) 534
Alderley Edge Manchester (S) 520
Alexander House Gatwick (S) 513
Alexandra Lyme Regis (S) 519
Altnaharrie Ullapool 427
Amberley Castle Amberley 4
Amerdale House Arncliffe 10
Angel Bury St Edmunds (S) 508
Angel Guildford (S) 514
Anglesea Town House Dublin 468
Apple Lodge Lochranza 400
Appletree Holme Farm Blawith 38
Apsley House Bath 21
Archway Windermere 308
Ardanaiseig Kilchrenan 394
Ardnamona House Lough Eske 487
Ardoe House Aberdeen (S) 529
Ardsheal House Kentallen 393
Ardvourlie Castle Ardvourlie 353
Arisaig Hotel Arisaig 354
Arisaig House Arisaig 354
Ark Erpingham 91
Arkleside Reeth 224
Arundel House Cambridge (S) 508
Arundell Arms Lifton 156

Ascot House Harrogate 117
Ashbrook House nr Dublin (S) 535
Ashburn House Fort William 381
Ashelford East Down 88
Ashfield House Grassington 109
Ash-Rowan Belfast 442
Ashwick House Dulverton 87
Asquith House Birmingham (S) 505
Assolas Country House Kanturk 480
At the Sign of the Angel Lacock 143
Atholl Aberdeen (S) 529
Atlantic St Brelade 435
Auchen Castle Moffat (S) 532
Auchendean Lodge Dulnain Bridge 371
Avondale Carlisle 60
Aynsome Manor Cartmel 61

B

Baile-na-Cille Timsgarry 424
Bales Mead West Porlock 299
Balgonie Country House Ballater 358
Ballycormac House Aglish 449
Ballymakeigh House Killeagh 483
Ballymaloe House Shanagarry 498
Ballyrafter House Lismore 486
Ballyvolane House Castlelyons 460
Bank House Oakamoor 209
Bantry House Bantry 455
Bark House Bampton 15
Barton's Cross Exeter (S) 513
Basil Street London 162
Bath Priory Bath 21
Bay Horse Ulverston 284
Bayview Ballycotton 452
Bear Crickhowell 327
Beaufort London 163

Molesworth Manor Little Petherick 159
Monachyle Mhor Balquhidder 360
Moonfleet Manor Fleet 98
Morgan Dublin (S) 534
Morgans Nottingham 208
Morston Hall Morston 194
Mount Juliet Thomastown 500
Mount Royale York 318
Mount Somerset Lower Henlade 181
Moyglare Manor Maynooth 488
Moyness House Inverness (S) 531
Mr Underhill's Ludlow 182
Muckrach Lodge Dulnain Bridge 372
Mulberry House Torquay 277
Mullardoch House Glen Cannich 387
Mustard Seed at Echo Lodge Ballingarry 451
Mynd House Little Stretton 160

N

Nailcote Hall Coventry (S) 511
Nairns Glasgow 385
Nanscawen House St Blazey 238
Nansloe Manor Helston 130
Nare Veryan 286
Narrows Portaferry 445
Netherfield Place Battle 28
New Hall Sutton Coldfield 264
New House Farm Lorton 179
New Inn Tresco (S) 526
New Inn at Coln Coln St Aldwyns 72
Newport House Newport 492
Nobody Inn Doddiscombsleigh 84
Nonsuch House Dartmouth 80
Norfolk Mead Norwich (S) 521
Norman Villa Galway 473
North Euston Fleetwood (S) 513
Northcote Manor Burrington 54
Northcote Manor Langho 146

Northleigh House Hatton 123
Number Sixteen London 174
Number Thirty One Carlisle 60
Number 31 Dublin (S) 535
Number Twenty Eight Ludlow 183
Nuthurst Grange Hockley Heath 133

O

Oak Tree Farm Hopwas 136
Oaks Porlock 217
Ockenden Manor Cuckfield 78
Old Bakery Blockley 39
Old Bank Oxford (S) 522
Old Beams Waterhouses 291
Old Bell Malmesbury 185
Old Bridge Huntingdon 138
Old Church Watermillock 293
Old Hall nr Liverpool (S) 516
Old Inn nr Belfast (S) 534
Old Library Lodge Arisaig 355
Old Manor Loughborough (S) 519
Old Mansion House Auchterhouse 356
Old Millfloor Trebarwith Strand 277
Old Parsonage Frant 100
Old Parsonage Oxford 211
Old Parsonage Westdean 298
Old Pines Spean Bridge 418
Old Presbytery Kinsale 484
Old Rectory Bettws Gwerfyl Goch 321
Old Rectory Boduan 322
Old Rectory Campsea Ashe 57
Old Rectory Great Snoring 111
Old Rectory Hopesay 135
Old Rectory Country House Llansanffraid Glan Conwy 338
Old Store Halnaker 115
Old Vicarage Dover (S) 512
Old Vicarage Milborne Port 194
Old Vicarage Rye 237
Old Vicarage Worfield 314
One Aldwych London 175

Maps

British Isles maps

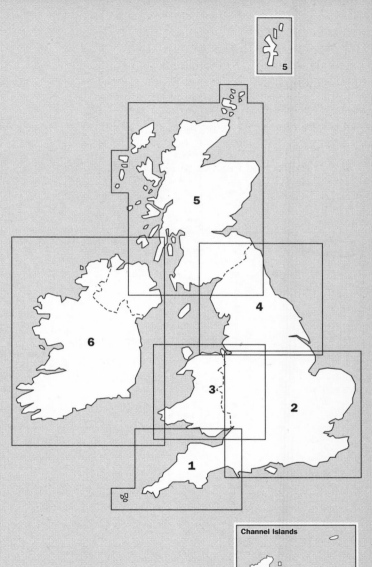

Channel Islands

1

Not to scale

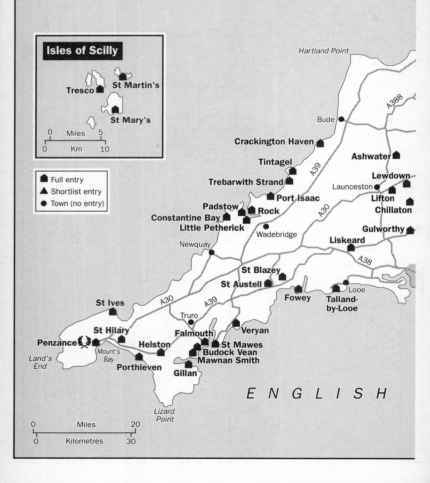

Isles of Scilly

Tresco

St Martin's

St Mary's

0 Miles 5

0 Km 10

■ Full entry

▲ Shortlist entry

● Town (no entry)

BRISTOL

Pembroke

Tenby

Hartland Point

Bude

A388

Crackington Haven

Ashwater

Tintagel

Lewdown

Trebarwith Strand

Launceston

Lifton

A39

Port Isaac

Chillaton

Padstow

Rock

Constantine Bay

Gulworthy

Little Petherick

Wadebridge

Liskeard

Newquay

A30

A38

St Blazey

St Austell

Looe

Fowey

Talland-by-Looe

St Ives

A30

Truro

A39

Veryan

St Hilary

Falmouth

Penzance

St Mawes

Land's End

Helston

Budock Vean

Mount's Bay

Mawnan Smith

Porthleven

Gillan

Lizard Point

ENGLISH

0 Miles 20

0 Kilometres 30

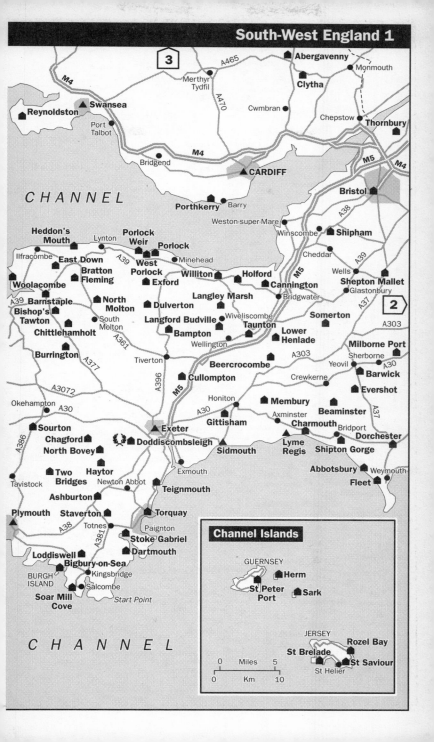

3

Abergavenny
Monmouth
Clytha
Merthyr Tydfil
Cwmbran
Chepstow
Thornbury

M4
Reynoldston
Swansea
Port Talbot
Bridgend
M4
M5
M4

CARDIFF
Bristol
A38

CHANNEL
Porthkerry Barry
Weston-super-Mare
Winscombe
Shipham
A39
M5
Cheddar
Wells
Shepton Mallet
Glastonbury
2

Heddon's Mouth
Lynton
Porlock Weir
Porlock
Minehead
Ilfracombe
East Down
West Porlock
Williton
Holford
Cannington
A39
Woolacombe
Bratton Fleming
Exford
Langley Marsh
Bridgwater
Somerton
A37
A303
Barnstaple
North Molton
Dulverton
Wiveliscombe
Bishop's Tawton
South Molton
Langford Budville
Taunton
Lower Henlade
Milborne Port
Sherborne
Chittlehamholt
Bampton
Wellington
A303
Yeovil
A30
Barwick
Burrington
A361
Tiverton
Beercrocombe
Crewkerne
Evershot
A3072
A396
Cullompton
A37
Okehampton
A30
Honiton
Membury
Beaminster
Sourton
A30
Gittisham
Axminster
Charmouth
Bridport
Dorchester
Chagford
Exeter
Doddiscombsleigh
Sidmouth
Lyme Regis
Shipton Gorge
North Bovey
A386
Haytor
Exmouth
Abbotsbury
Weymouth
Two Bridges
Newton Abbot
Teignmouth
Fleet
Tavistock
Ashburton
Staverton
Torquay
Plymouth
A38
Paignton
A381
Totnes
Stoke Gabriel
Loddiswell
Dartmouth
Bigbury-on-Sea
Kingsbridge
BURGH ISLAND
Salcombe
Soar Mill Cove
Start Point

CHANNEL

Channel Islands

GUERNSEY
Herm
St Peter Port
Sark

JERSEY
Rozel Bay
St Brelade
St Saviour
St Helier

0 Miles 5
0 Km 10

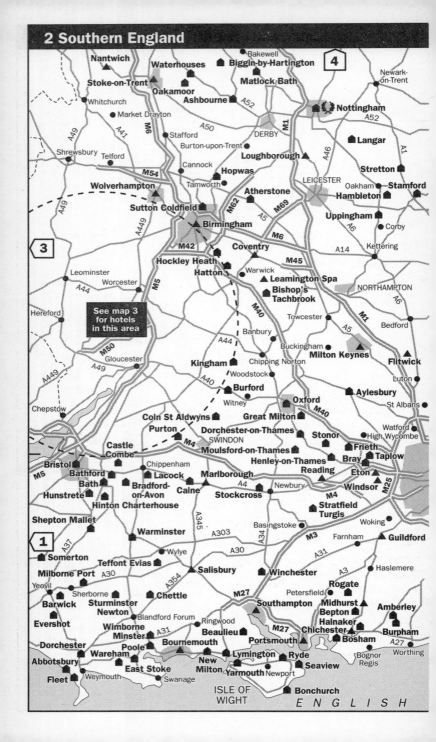

4

Nantwich
Waterhouses
Bakewell
Biggin-by-Hartington
Stoke-on-Trent
Oakamoor
Matlock Bath
Whitchurch
Ashbourne
A52
Newark-on-Trent
Market Drayton
A50
Nottingham
Shrewsbury
Telford
A41
Stafford
DERBY
M1
A52
Langar
A6
A1
M6
Burton-upon-Trent
Loughborough
A46
Stretton
Cannock
Hopwas
LEICESTER
Oakham
Stamford
Wolverhampton
Tamworth
Atherstone
Hambleton
M54
A449
Sutton Coldfield
M62
A5
M69
Uppingham
Corby
3
Birmingham
M6
Kettering
A14
Leominster
Worcester
M42
Coventry
A5
A449
Hockley Heath
Warwick
M45
NORTHAMPTON
A44
Hatton
Leamington Spa
A6
Hereford
M5
Bishop's
Tachbrook
M50
Gloucester
A49
Towcester
M1
Bedford
A44
Banbury
A5
See map 3
for hotels
in this area
Kingham
Chipping Norton
Buckingham
Milton Keynes
Flitwick
Chepstow
A449
Burford
Woodstock
Luton
A40
Witney
Oxford
Aylesbury
St Albans
Coln St Aldwyns
Great Milton
M40
Purton
Dorchester-on-Thames
Stonor
Watford
High Wycombe
Castle
Combe
M4
SWINDON
Moulsford-on-Thames
Frieth
Taplow
Bristol
Chippenham
Henley-on-Thames
Bray
Eton
Bathford
Lacock
Marlborough
Reading
Windsor
M25
Bath
Calne
A4
Newbury
M5
Bradford-on-Avon
Stockcross
M4
Hunstrete
Hinton Charterhouse
A345
Stratfield
Turgis
Woking
Shepton Mallet
Basingstoke
M3
Farnham
A31
Guildford
1
Warminster
A303
A34
A37
Wylye
Somerton
A30
Haslemere
Teffont Evias
Salisbury
Winchester
A3
Milborne Port
A30
Rogate
Yeovil
Sherborne
A354
Petersfield
Midhurst
Barwick
Chettle
Southampton
Bepton
Amberley
Sturminster
Newton
Blandford Forum
M27
Halnaker
Chichester
Burpham
Evershot
Wimborne
Minster
Ringwood
Beaulieu
M27
Bosham
A27
Worthing
Dorchester
A31
Bournemouth
Portsmouth
Bognor
Regis
Abbotsbury
Wareham
Poole
Lymington
Ryde
Fleet
East Stoke
Weymouth
New
Milton
Yarmouth
Newport
Seaview
Swanage
ISLE OF
WIGHT
Bonchurch
E N G L I S H

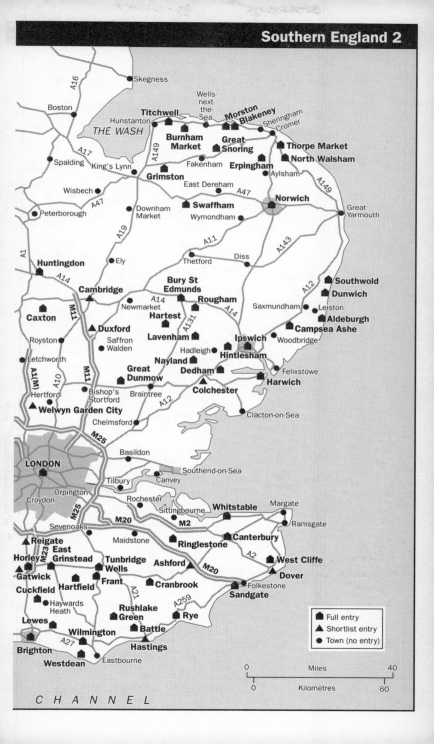

Skegness

Boston

A16

Wells-
next-
the-
Sea

Titchwell

Morston
Blakeney

Sheringham
Cromer

Hunstanton

THE WASH

Burnham
Market

Great
Snoring

Thorpe Market

North Walsham

A149

Spalding

King's Lynn

A17

Fakenham

Erpingham

Aylsham

A149

Wisbech

A47

Grimston

East Dereham

A47

Norwich

Peterborough

A1

Downham
Market

Swaffham

Wymondham

Great
Yarmouth

A19

Ely

Thetford

A11

Diss

A143

A12

Huntingdon

A14

Cambridge

Bury St
Edmunds

Rougham

Southwold

Dunwich

Newmarket

A14

Saxmundham

Leiston

A14

Aldeburgh

Caxton

A1

M11

Hartest

A131

Campsea Ashe

Royston

Duxford

Lavenham

Ipswich

Saffron
Walden

Woodbridge

Letchworth

A1(M)

A10

M11

Hadleigh

Hintlesham

Nayland

Dedham

Felixstowe

Harwich

Hertford

Great
Dunmow

Welwyn Garden City

Bishop's
Stortford

Braintree

Colchester

A12

Clacton-on-Sea

Chelmsford

M25

LONDON

Basildon

Southend-on-Sea

Tilbury

Canvey

Orpington

Rochester

Croydon

M25

Sittingbourne

Whitstable

Margate

M2

Ramsgate

Sevenoaks

M20

Canterbury

M2

Maidstone

Ringlestone

Reigate

East
Grinstead

Tunbridge
Wells

Ashford

A2

West Cliffe

Horley

M23

Frant

Cranbrook

M20

Dover

Gatwick

Hartfield

A21

Folkestone

Cuckfield

Sandgate

Haywards
Heath

A259

Rushlake
Green

Rye

Lewes

Battle

Wilmington

A27

Hastings

Brighton

Eastbourne

Westdean

CHANNEL

■	Full entry
▲	Shortlist entry
●	Town (no entry)

0 Miles 40

0 Kilometres 60

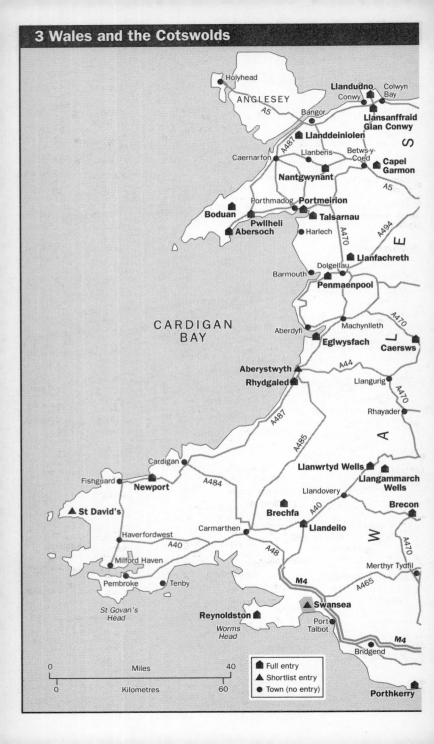

3 Wales and the Cotswolds

Holyhead

ANGLESEY

A5

Bangor

Conwy

Llandudno

Colwyn Bay

Llansanffraid Glan Conwy

Llanddeiniolen

Llanberis

Caernarfon

Betws-y-Coed

Capel Garmon

A5

Nantgwynant

Porthmadog

Portmeirion

Boduan

Talsarnau

A494

Pwllheli

Abersoch

Harlech

A470

Llanfachreth

Dolgellau

Barmouth

Penmaenpool

A470

CARDIGAN BAY

Aberdyfi

Machynlleth

Eglwysfach

Caersws

Aberystwyth

Rhydgaled

A44

Llangurig

A470

Rhayader

A487

A485

Llanwrtyd Wells

Llangammarch Wells

Cardigan

Llandovery

Brecon

Fishguard

Newport

A484

Llandovery

St David's

Brechfa

A40

Haverfordwest

Carmarthen

Llandeilo

A470

A48

Milford Haven

Merthyr Tydfil

Pembroke

Tenby

M4

A465

St Govan's Head

Reynoldston

Swansea

Port Talbot

M4

Worms Head

Bridgend

M4

| | Miles | 40 |

| | Kilometres | 60 |

Porthkerry

Full entry
Shortlist entry
Town (no entry)

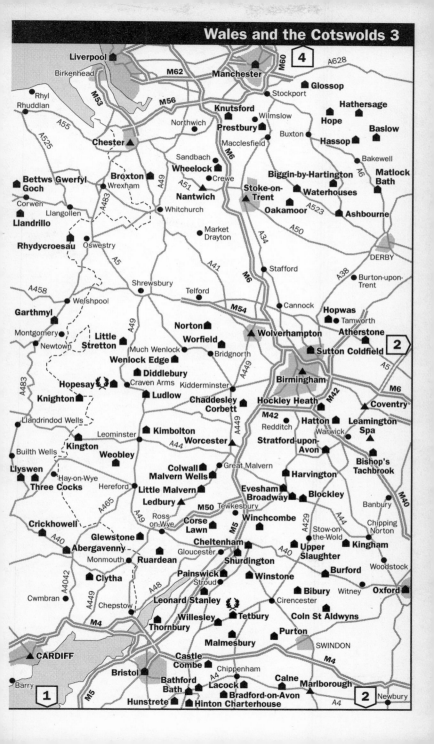

4

Liverpool
Birkenhead
Rhyl
Rhuddlan
M53
M62
Manchester
Stockport
M60
A628
Glossop
Hathersage
M56
Knutsford
Wilmslow
Hope
Baslow
Northwich
Prestbury
Buxton
Hassop
Chester
Macclesfield
Bakewell
A6
Matlock
Bath
Sandbach
M6
Broxton
Wheelock
Stoke-on-
Biggin-by-Hartington
Wrexham
Crewe
Trent
Waterhouses
Bettws Gwerfyl
Goch
A49
A51
Nantwich
Ashbourne
Corwen
Whitchurch
Oakamoor
A523
Llangollen
A50
Llandrillo
Market
Drayton
A34
DERBY
Rhydycroesau
Oswestry
A5
Stafford
A38
Burton-upon-
Trent
A458
Welshpool
Shrewsbury
Telford
M6
Cannock
Hopwas
Garthmyl
M54
Tamworth
Montgomery
Norton
Wolverhampton
Atherstone
Newtown
Little
Stretton
Worfield
A49
Much Wenlock
Bridgnorth
Sutton Coldfield
A5
Wenlock Edge
A41
M6
A483
Diddlebury
Kidderminster
Birmingham
Coventry
Hopesay
Craven Arms
Ludlow
Chaddesley
Corbett
Hockley Heath
M42
Knighton
Leamington
Spa
Llandrindod Wells
Leominster
A449
M42
Hatton
Redditch
Warwick
Kimbolton
Bishop's
Tachbrook
Kington
A44
Worcester
Stratford-upon-
Avon
Builth Wells
Weobley
Colwall
Malvern Wells
Great Malvern
Harvington
M40
Llyswen
Hay-on-Wye
Hereford
Evesham
Blockley
Banbury
Three Cocks
Little Malvern
Broadway
Chipping
Norton
Crickhowell
Ledbury
M50
Tewkesbury
Stow-on-
the-Wold
A44
Glewstone
Ross-
on-Wye
Corse
Lawn
Winchcombe
A429
Kingham
Abergavenny
Cheltenham
Upper
Slaughter
Woodstock
Monmouth
Ruardean
Gloucester
A40
Burford
Clytha
Painswick
Shurdington
Winstone
Cwmbran
A4042
Stroud
Bibury
Witney
Oxford
A449
Chepstow
Leonard Stanley
Cirencester
Coln St Aldwyns
M4
Willesley
Tetbury
Thornbury
Purton
SWINDON
CARDIFF
Malmesbury
M4
Barry
Castle
Combe
Chippenham
M5
Bristol
Bathford
Calne
Marlborough
A4
Bath
Lacock
Newbury
Hunstrete
Bradford-on-Avon
Hinton Charterhouse

1
2

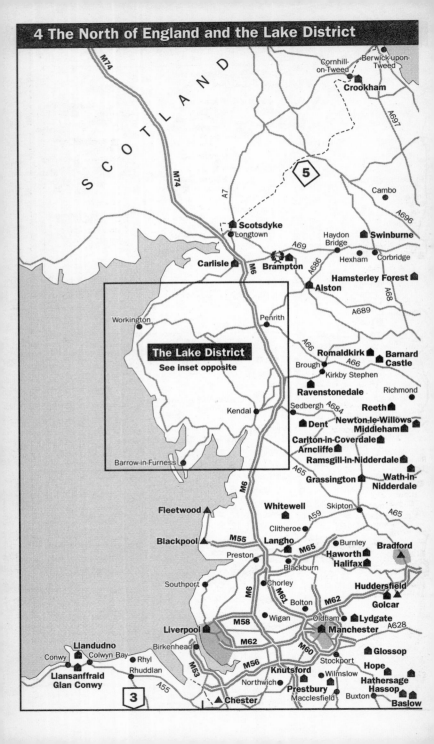

4 The North of England and the Lake District

SCOTLAND

M74

Cornhill-on-Tweed

Berwick-upon-Tweed

Crookham

5

Cambo

A696

Scotsdyke
Longtown

Haydon Bridge

Swinburne

A7

A69

Carlisle

M6

Brampton

A686

Hexham

Corbridge

Hamsterley Forest

Alston

A68

A689

Workington

Penrith

A66

Romaldkirk

Barnard Castle

The Lake District
See inset opposite

Brough

A66

Kirkby Stephen

Ravenstonedale

Richmond

Kendal

Sedbergh

A684

Reeth

Dent

Newton-le-Willows

Middleham

Carlton-in-Coverdale

Arncliffe

Ramsgill-in-Nidderdale

Barrow-in-Furness

A65

Grassington

Wath-in-Nidderdale

M6

Fleetwood

Whitewell

Skipton

A65

A59

Clitheroe

Blackpool

M55

Langho

M65

Burnley

Bradford

Preston

Blackburn

Haworth

Halifax

Southport

Chorley

Huddersfield

M6

M61

Bolton

M62

Golcar

Wigan

Oldham

Lydgate

Liverpool

M58

Birkenhead

M62

Manchester

A628

Llandudno

Conwy

Colwyn Bay

Rhyl

M53

M60

Stockport

Glossop

Rhuddlan

Wilmslow

Hope

Llansanffraid Glan Conwy

A55

3

Chester

Northwich

Knutsford

Prestbury

Macclesfield

Buxton

Hathersage

Hassop

Baslow

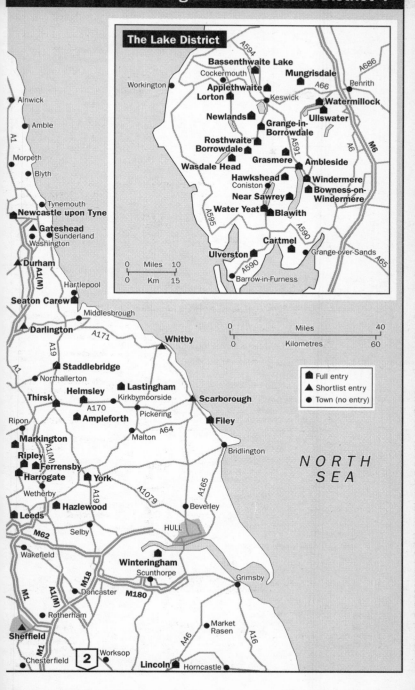

The Lake District

Workington
Cockermouth
Bassenthwaite Lake
Mungrisdale
Penrith
Applethwaite
Keswick
Lorton
Watermillock
Newlands
Ullswater
Grange-in-Borrowdale
Rosthwaite
Borrowdale
Grasmere
Ambleside
Wasdale Head
Hawkshead
Coniston
Windermere
Near Sawrey
Bowness-on-Windermere
Water Yeat
Blawith
Cartmel
Ulverston
Grange-over-Sands
Barrow-in-Furness

A594 · A66 · A686 · A6 · M6 · A591 · A595 · A590 · A65

Miles 10
Km 15

Alnwick
Amble
Morpeth
Blyth
Tynemouth
Newcastle upon Tyne
Gateshead
Sunderland
Washington
Durham
A1(M)
Hartlepool
Seaton Carew
Middlesbrough
Darlington
A171
Whitby
A19
Staddlebridge
Northallerton
Lastingham
Helmsley
Kirkbymoorside
Scarborough
Thirsk
A170
Pickering
Filey
Ripon
Ampleforth
Malton
A64
Bridlington
Markington
A1(M)
Ripley
Ferrensby
Harrogate
York
Wetherby
A19
A1079
A165
Hazlewood
Beverley
Leeds
M62
Selby
HULL
Wakefield
M18
Winteringham
Scunthorpe
M180
Grimsby
Doncaster
Rotherham
Market Rasen
A46
A16
Sheffield
M1
Chesterfield
Worksop
Lincoln
Horncastle

NORTH SEA

Miles 40
Kilometres 60

■ Full entry
▲ Shortlist entry
● Town (no entry)

2

5 Scotland

The Uists & Barra

HARRIS
Lochmaddy
NORTH UIST
SOUTH UIST
Lochboisdale
Tangasdale
BARRA
Castlebay

YELL
UNST
MAINLAND
Walls
Lerwick
Shetland Islands

Miles 0 — 40
Kilometres 0 — 60

Orkney Islands
Westray
SANDAY
Kirkwall
MAINLAND
St Margaret's Hope
HOY

Thurso
Forss
Scourie
A836
Wick
Timsgarry
Ardvourlie
Tarbert
HARRIS
Stornoway
Lochinver
Achiltibuie
Ullapool
A838
Lairg
A99
Lybster
Dornoch
Outer Hebrides
LEWIS

MORAY FIRTH

Gairloch
A835
Dingwall
Colbost
Shieldaig
Nairn
Elgin
A98
Dunvegan
Portree
Muir of Ord
Beauly
Inverness
A96
Oldmeldrum
Talisker
Plockton
Bunchrew
SKYE
Kyle of Lochalsh
Glen Cannich
Grantown-on-Spey
A90
Isle Ornsay
Glenelg
A82
A9
Dulnain Bridge
Kildrummy
Aberdeen
RUM
Mallaig
Fort Augustus
Whitebridge
Aviemore
A830
A86
Kingussie
Maryculter
Arisaig
Spean Bridge
Braemar
A93
Ballater
Strontian
Fort William
A9
Tobermory
Onich
Pitlochry
A90
Dervaig
Kentallen
A923
Blairgowrie
Tiroran
Port Appin
Dunkeld
Auchterhouse
MULL
Eriska
Tyndrum
Dundee
Pennyghael
Oban
Kilchrenan
Perth
St Andrews
Balquhidder
Strathyre
Callander
Cupar
Dairsie
Crinan
Doune
Kinross
Glenrothes
Lochgilphead
Stirling
Kirkaldy
FIRTH OF FORTH
JURA
Dunoon
M90
Cardross
Falkirk
Gullane
Tighnabruaich
Greenock
Dunbar
ISLAY
BUTE
Glasgow
M8
EDINBURGH
A1
Berwick-upon-Tweed
Lochranza
Kilmarnock
Peebles
Campbeltown
Brodick
Melrose
Swinton
ARRAN
Darvel
Skirling
Biggar
Selkirk
Kelso
Ayr
M74
Maybole
Moffat
Hawick
Jedburgh
A1
FIRTH OF CLYDE
A76
4
Ballantrae
Newton Stewart
Canonbie
A7
ENGLAND
Stranraer
Gatehouse of Fleet
Dumfries
Annan
Portpatrick
A75
Kirkcudbright
Carlisle
M6

■ Full entry
▲ Shortlist entry
● Town (no entry)

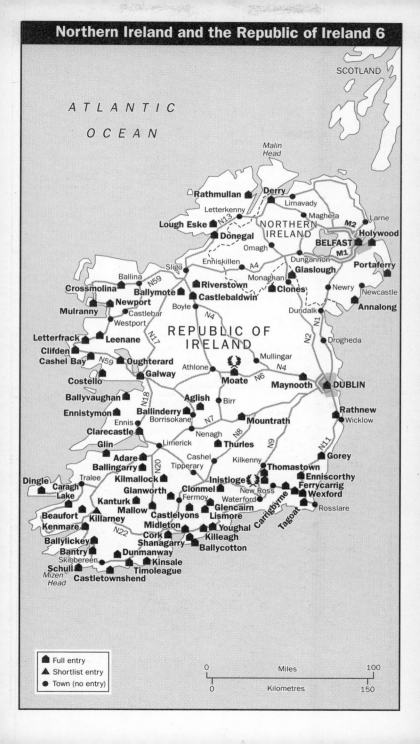

SCOTLAND

ATLANTIC

OCEAN

Malin
Head

Rathmullan

Derry

Limavady

Letterkenny

Maghera

Larne

M2

Lough Eske

N13

NORTHERN
IRELAND

Donegal

Omagh

Dungannon

BELFAST

Holywood

Enniskillen

N4

Monaghan

Glaslough

M1

Portaferry

Sligo

Clones

Newry

Newcastle

Ballina

N59

Riverstown

Crossmolina

Ballymote

Castlebaldwin

Dundalk

N1

Annalong

Newport

Castlebar

Boyle

N4

Mulranny

Westport

N2

Drogheda

REPUBLIC OF
IRELAND

Letterfrack

Leenane

N7

Mullingar

Clifden

Cashel Bay

N59

Oughterard

Athlone

Moate

N6

N4

Maynooth

DUBLIN

Costello

Galway

Ballyvaughan

N18

Aglish

Birr

Rathnew

Ennistymon

Ballinderry

Wicklow

Clarecastle

Ennis

Borrisokane

N7

Mountrath

Glin

Limerick

Nenagh

N8

Thurles

N9

Gorey

Adare

Cashel

Kilkenny

Thomastown

Ballingarry

N20

Tipperary

N11

Enniscorthy

Tralee

Kilmallock

Inistioge

Ferrycarrig

Caragh
Lake

Glanworth

Clonmel

New Ross

Wexford

Dingle

Kanturk

Fermoy

Waterford

Rosslare

Beaufort

Mallow

Castlelyons

Glencairn

Killarney

Midleton

Lismore

Youghal

Tagoat

Kenmare

Cork

Killeagh

N22

Shanagarry

Ballycotton

Ballylickey

Dunmanway

Kinsale

Bantry

Skibbereen

Timoleague

Schull

Castletownshend

Mizen
Head

▮	Full entry
▲	Shortlist entry
●	Town (no entry)

0	Miles	100
0	Kilometres	150

Champagne winners: Report of the Year competition

As usual we have awarded a dozen bottles of champagne for the best reports of the year. A bottle apiece, and a free copy of the *Guide*, will go to the following generous and eloquent readers for their contributions to this volume.

Mr PE Carter, of West Lavington, Sussex
Mr TW Child, of Swindon, Wiltshire
Patricia Darby, of Alcester, Warwickshire
Sue Davies, of Isfield, Sussex
Katherine Galligan, of St Paul's, Minnesota, USA
Colin Hendrie, of Brympton, Somerset
Susan Hill, of Ebrington, Gloucestershire
Peter Jones, of Edinburgh
Colin Pearson, of London
Professor N Craig Sharp, of Birmingham
Charlotte Stradtman, of Irvine, California
Janet Winslow, of Cleobury Mortimer

A further dozen bottles will be awarded to readers who write to us about hotels on the Continent when the 2001 guide to Continental Europe is published, and another case will be on offer for reports to the 2002 edition of this volume. No special entry form is required; everything we receive in the course of the year will qualify. A winner may be someone who nominates a new hotel or comments on an existing one. We award champagne to those whose reports are consistently useful, as well as to individually brilliant examples of the art of hotel criticism.

Hotel reports

The report forms on the following pages may be used to endorse or criticise an existing entry or to nominate a hotel that you feel deserves inclusion in the *Guide*. But it is not essential that you use our forms or restrict yourself to the space available.

All reports (*each on a separate piece of paper, please*) should include your name and address, the name and location of the hotel, and the date and length of your stay. Please nominate only places that you have visited in the past 12 months, unless you are sure from friends that standards have been maintained. And please be as specific as possible, and critical where appropriate, about the character of the building, the public rooms and the bedrooms, the meals, the service, the night-life, the grounds.

If you can give some impression of the location as well as of the hotel, particularly in less familiar regions, that is very helpful. Comments about worthwhile places to visit in the neighbourhood and, in the case of B&B hotels, recommendable restaurants, would also be much appreciated.

Do not feel embarrassed about writing at length. We want the *Guide* to convey the special flavour of its hotels, and any small details that you give will help to make a description come alive. Many nominations just don't tell us enough. We mind having to pass up a potentially attractive place because the report is too brief. You need not bother with prices and routine information about the number of rooms and facilities; we obtain such details direct from the hotels. We want readers to supply information that is not accessible elsewhere. And we should be extremely grateful, particularly in the case of new nominations and foreign hotels, if you would include brochures whenever possible.

Please never tell a hotel that you intend to file a report. Anonymity is essential to objectivity.

The 2002 edition of this volume will be written between mid-March and the end of May 2001, and published in early September 2001. Nominations should reach us not later than 25 May 2001. The latest date for comments on existing entries is 1 June 2001.

Please let us know if you would like us to send you more report forms. Our address for UK correspondents (no stamp needed) is: *The Good Hotel Guide*, Freepost PAM 2931, London W11 4BR.

Reports can also be faxed to us on (020) 7602 4182, or sent by e-mail to Goodhotel@aol.com. Reports posted outside the UK should be stamped normally and addressed to: *The Good Hotel Guide*, 50 Addison Avenue, London W11 4QP, England.

[2001]

To: *The Good Hotel Guide*, Freepost PAM 2931, London W11 4BR

NOTE: No stamps needed in UK, but letters posted outside the UK should be addressed to 50 Addison Avenue, London W11 4QP and stamped normally. Unless asked not to, we shall assume that we may publish your name if you are recommending a new hotel or supporting an existing entry. If you would like more report forms please tick ☐

Name of Hotel _____

Address _____

_____

Date of most recent visit   Duration of visit
☐ New recommendation   ☐ Comment on existing entry
Report:

Please continue overleaf

I am not connected directly or indirectly with the management or proprietors

Signed _____

Name (CAPITALS PLEASE)_____

Address _____

_____

[2001]

To: *The Good Hotel Guide*, Freepost PAM 2931, London W11 4BR

NOTE: No stamps needed in UK, but letters posted outside the UK should be addressed to 50 Addison Avenue, London W11 4QP and stamped normally. Unless asked not to, we shall assume that we may publish your name if you are recommending a new hotel or supporting an existing entry. If you would like more report forms please tick ☐

Name of Hotel _____

Address _____

_____

Date of most recent visit
☐ New recommendation
Report:

Duration of visit
☐ Comment on existing entry

Please continue overleaf

I am not connected directly or indirectly with the management or proprietors

Signed _____

Name (CAPITALS PLEASE)_____

Address _____

_____

[2001]

To: *The Good Hotel Guide*, Freepost PAM 2931, London W11 4BR

NOTE: No stamps needed in UK, but letters posted outside the UK should be addressed to 50 Addison Avenue, London W11 4QP and stamped normally. Unless asked not to, we shall assume that we may publish your name if you are recommending a new hotel or supporting an existing entry. If you would like more report forms please tick ☐

Name of Hotel _____

Address _____

_____

Date of most recent visit   Duration of visit
☐ New recommendation   ☐ Comment on existing entry
Report:

Please continue overleaf

I am not connected directly or indirectly with the management or proprietors

Signed _____

Name (CAPITALS PLEASE)_____

Address _____

_____

To: *The Good Hotel Guide*, Freepost PAM 2931, London W11 4BR

NOTE: No stamps needed in UK, but letters posted outside the UK should be addressed to 50 Addison Avenue, London W11 4QP and stamped normally. Unless asked not to, we shall assume that we may publish your name if you are recommending a new hotel or supporting an existing entry. If you would like more report forms please tick ☐

Name of Hotel _____

Address _____

_____

Date of most recent visit   Duration of visit
☐ New recommendation   ☐ Comment on existing entry
Report:

Please continue overleaf

I am not connected directly or indirectly with the management or proprietors

Signed _____

Name (CAPITALS PLEASE)_____

Address _____

_____

[2001]

To: *The Good Hotel Guide*, Freepost PAM 2931, London W11 4BR

NOTE: No stamps needed in UK, but letters posted outside the UK should be addressed to 50 Addison Avenue, London W11 4QP and stamped normally. Unless asked not to, we shall assume that we may publish your name if you are recommending a new hotel or supporting an existing entry. If you would like more report forms please tick ☐

Name of Hotel _____

Address _____

_____

Date of most recent visit   Duration of visit
☐ New recommendation   ☐ Comment on existing entry
Report:

Please continue overleaf

I am not connected directly or indirectly with the management or proprietors

Signed _____

Name (CAPITALS PLEASE)_____

Address _____

_____

[2001]

To: *The Good Hotel Guide*, Freepost PAM 2931, London W11 4BR

NOTE: No stamps needed in UK, but letters posted outside the UK should be addressed to 50 Addison Avenue, London W11 4QP and stamped normally. Unless asked not to, we shall assume that we may publish your name if you are recommending a new hotel or supporting an existing entry. If you would like more report forms please tick ☐

Name of Hotel _____

Address _____

_____

Date of most recent visit   Duration of visit
☐ New recommendation   ☐ Comment on existing entry
Report:

Please continue overleaf

I am not connected directly or indirectly with the management or proprietors

Signed _____

Name (CAPITALS PLEASE)_____

Address _____

_____

[2001]

To: *The Good Hotel Guide*, Freepost PAM 2931, London W11 4BR

NOTE: No stamps needed in UK, but letters posted outside the UK should be addressed to 50 Addison Avenue, London W11 4QP and stamped normally. Unless asked not to, we shall assume that we may publish your name if you are recommending a new hotel or supporting an existing entry. If you would like more report forms please tick □

Name of Hotel _____

Address _____

_____

Date of most recent visit   Duration of visit
□ New recommendation   □ Comment on existing entry
Report:

Please continue overleaf

I am not connected directly or indirectly with the management or proprietors

Signed _____

Name (CAPITALS PLEASE)_____

Address _____

_____

[2001]

To: *The Good Hotel Guide*, Freepost PAM 2931, London W11 4BR

NOTE: No stamps needed in UK, but letters posted outside the UK should be addressed to 50 Addison Avenue, London W11 4QP and stamped normally. Unless asked not to, we shall assume that we may publish your name if you are recommending a new hotel or supporting an existing entry. If you would like more report forms please tick ☐

Name of Hotel _____

Address _____

_____

Date of most recent visit
☐ New recommendation
Report:

Duration of visit
☐ Comment on existing entry

Please continue overleaf

I am not connected directly or indirectly with the management or proprietors

Signed _____

Name (CAPITALS PLEASE)_____

Address _____

_____

To: *The Good Hotel Guide*, Freepost PAM 2931, London W11 4BR

NOTE: No stamps needed in UK, but letters posted outside the UK should be addressed to 50 Addison Avenue, London W11 4QP and stamped normally. Unless asked not to, we shall assume that we may publish your name if you are recommending a new hotel or supporting an existing entry. If you would like more report forms please tick ☐

Name of Hotel _____

Address _____

_____

Date of most recent visit   Duration of visit
☐ New recommendation   ☐ Comment on existing entry
Report:

Please continue overleaf

I am not connected directly or indirectly with the management or proprietors

Signed _____

Name (CAPITALS PLEASE)_____

Address _____

_____

To: *The Good Hotel Guide*, Freepost PAM 2931, London W11 4BR

NOTE: No stamps needed in UK, but letters posted outside the UK should be addressed to 50 Addison Avenue, London W11 4QP and stamped normally. Unless asked not to, we shall assume that we may publish your name if you are recommending a new hotel or supporting an existing entry. If you would like more report forms please tick ☐

Name of Hotel _____

Address _____

_____

Date of most recent visit   Duration of visit
☐ New recommendation   ☐ Comment on existing entry
Report:

Please continue overleaf

I am not connected directly or indirectly with the management or proprietors

Signed _____

Name (CAPITALS PLEASE)_____

Address _____

_____

The Good Hotel Guide 2001 Continental Europe 24th Edition
Edited by Adam and Caroline Raphael

'Quite simply indispensable. You don't need any other hotel guide.'
– Susan Hill

'Invaluable and unique' – David Lodge

'It has never given me wrong advice.' – Claire Bloom

In its 24 years of selecting the best hotels in Europe, the *Good Hotel Guide* has gathered more praise than any other hotel guide. The original market leader, it provides independent and reliable information on a wide range of accommodation to suit every pocket, from budget-priced B&Bs to grand hotels. Particular attention is paid to value for money. Specialising in owner-managed hotels of unusual appeal in wonderful locations, the *Good Hotel Guide* is the passport to a successful continental holiday.

✳ Includes discount vouchers worth £150

✳ Over 900 selected hotels, guest houses and B&Bs

✳ Cross-referenced maps plus available facilities and suitability for the disabled and children

The Good Hotel Guide 2001 Continental Europe is available from February 2000. To order your copy direct from Ebury Press (p&p free), use the form below or call our credit card hotlines on (01206) 255800.

Please send me ..... copies of **The Good Hotel Guide 2001 Continental Europe** @ £16.99 each.

I enclose a cheque/postal order for £................. made payable to The Book Services Ltd.

Please debit my Access/Visa/Switch/Delta card (delete where appropriate) to

the amount of £.................

Card No: Expiry date:

Signature

Name

Address

                                                              Postcode

Delivery address (if different from above)

                                                              Postcode

Post order to TBS DIRECT, Colchester Road, Frating Green, Colchester, Essex CO7 7DW

POSTAGE AND PACKING ARE FREE
Offer open in Great Britain including Northern Ireland. Books should arrive less than 28 days after we receive your order; they are subject to availability at the time of ordering. If not entirely satisfied return in the same packaging and condition as received with a covering letter within 7 days. Ebury Press books are available from all good booksellers.